D1554601

ADVANCES IN THE BIOSCIENCES

Volume 57

ADAPTIVE PROCESSES IN VISUAL AND OCULOMOTOR SYSTEMS

ADVANCES IN THE BIOSCIENCES

Latest volumes in the series:

Participants in the International Symposium on
"Adaptive Processes in Visual and Oculomotor Systems",
Asilomar Conference Center, California,
September 16-20, 1985

ADAPTIVE PROCESSES IN VISUAL AND OCULOMOTOR SYSTEMS

Proceedings of a conference held in Asolimar, California, USA
16–20 June 1985

Editors:

E. L. KELLER and D. S. ZEE

PERGAMON PRESS

OXFORD · NEW YORK · TORONTO · SYDNEY
FRANKFURT · TOKYO · SAO PAULO · BEIJING

U.K.	Pergamon Press, Headington Hill Hall, Oxford OX3 0BW, England
U.S.A.	Pergamon Press Inc., Maxwell House, Fairview Park, Elmsford, New York 10523, U.S.A.
CANADA	Pergamon Press Canada, Suite 104, 150 Consumers Road, Willowdale, Ontario M2J 1P9, Canada
AUSTRALIA	Pergamon Press (Aust.) Pty. Ltd., P.O. Box 544, Potts Point, N.S.W. 2011, Australia
FEDERAL REPUBLIC OF GERMANY	Pergamon Press GmbH, Hammerweg 6, D-6242 Kronberg, Federal Republic of Germany
JAPAN	Pergamon Press, 8th Floor, Matsuoka Central Building, 1-7-1 Nishishinjuku, Shinjuku-ku, Tokyo 160, Japan
BRAZIL	Pergamon Editora Ltda., Rua Eça de Queiros, 346, CEP 04011, São Paulo, Brazil
PEOPLE'S REPUBLIC OF CHINA	Pergamon Press, Qianmen Hotel, Beijing, People's Republic of China

Copyright © 1986 Pergamon Books Ltd.

All Rights Reserved. No part of this publication may be reproduced, stored in a retrieval system or transmitted in any form or by any means: electronic, electrostatic, magnetic tape, mechanical, photocopying, recording or otherwise, without permission in writing from the publishers.

First edition 1986

British Library Cataloguing in Publication Data

Adaptive processes in visual and oculomotor systems.
—(Advances in the biosciences; 57)
1. Vision   2. Adaption (Biology)
I. Keller, Edward L.   II. Zee, David S.
III. Series
591.1'823   QP475
ISBN 0 08 032012 0

In order to make this volume available as economically and as rapidly as possible the authors' typescripts have been reproduced in their original forms. This method unfortunately has its typographical limitations but it is hoped that they in no way distract the reader.

QP
474
.A33   66271
1986
Vol.57

Printed in Great Britain by A. Wheaton & Co. Ltd., Exeter

Preface

The conference, ADAPTIVE PROCESSES IN VISUAL AND OCULOMOTOR SYSTEMS, was held in Asilomar, California, on September 16-20, 1985. This conference was the latest in a series of symposia specifically designed to bring together basic research scientists in ocular motility, neurophysiology and anatomy, and clinical scientists in the fields of strabismus, amblyopia, and neuro-ophthalmology. Previous symposia in this series were held in Stockholm in 1974 and 1981 and the idea for the Asilomar meeting was conceived in Stockholm in 1981 during Professor Granit's opening presentation in which he stated his abiding interest in adaptive plasticity in sensory and motor systems. As that former conference proceeded, it became clear that the majority of the presentations addressed in one manner or another the theme of adaptative control in health and disease. The present editors therefore organized the Asilomar Conference around this topic. It was attended by 112 scientists from 16 different countries, facts which attest to the world wide interest in this subject. To highlight the symposium Geoffrey Melvill Jones from Montreal's McGill University was invited to give the keynote lecture. His seminal observations in the early 1970's on visual modification of vestibular reflexes have laid the groundwork for much of the present day interest in adaptive control. He delivered the Horrow lecture which was a stimulating and imaginative discussion of the mechanisms underlying descending cortical control of basic reflex operation. Included in his presentation were examples of short-term intrusion of cognitive influences into on-going reflex activity and longer-term remodelling of sensory-motor correspondence at the levels of both reflex and cognitive function.

The symposium itself was organized around clinically related topics to which both basic and clinical scientists were asked to address themselves. The symposium organizers turned to their colleagues Alan Scott, Takuji Kasamatsu, Laurence Young, Clifton Schor, Michael Goldberg, Bernard Cohen, Robert Baloh, Rober Baker, and Thomas Brandt for expert advice in selecting pertinent topics

CAMROSE LUTHERAN COLLEGE
LIBRARY

and stimulating speakers for the nine sessions comprising the symposium and this
volume. These scientists deserve the majority of the credit for the excellent
scientific caliber of the meeting. The editors are deeply appreciative of the
time and effort these individuals put into insuring the success of the meeting.

Early organizing efforts on the session devoted to reviewing recent
progress in the field of compensation to vestibular lesions was carried out by
Wolfgang Precht before his unexpected death during the planning stages of the
conference. In view of his long-term and unique scientific prominence in the
field of vestibular neurophysiology and his close association with previous, as
well as the present symposia in this series, the editors are privileged to be
able to dedicate this publication to his memory.

The symposium was made possible by generous financial support from The
Smith-Kettlewell Eye Research Foundation and by a conference grant from the
National Institutes of Health (1 R13EY06430-01). The editors also wish to thank
Susan Ovington and Jona Countie, who served as secretarial assistants for the
conference and this volume, Chris Cushman for photography, and Carole Lynne
Keller for conference planning and execution of the social program for the
meeting.

Edward L. Keller
David S. Zee

WOLFGANG PRECHT
(1938 - 1985)

These proceedings of a symposium in visual and oculomotor science held at Asilomar, California, are dedicated to the memory of Wolfgang Precht who helped plan this meeting before his death on March 12, 1985. He died in Zurich, Switzerland, at the age of 46 years.

He received a degree as a medical doctor in 1963 following training at the Universities of Tubingen, Munster, Basel and Freiburg. Soon thereafter he joined Professor Rolf Hassler, Director of the Max Planck Institute for Brain Research in Frankfurt, to study the neuronal organization of the vestibular system and its plasticity. Following an invitation by Sir John Eccles he spent three scientifically successful years in Chicago, where he worked together with Rudolfo Llinas on the functional organization of vestibulo-cerebellar projections and their comparative aspects. Back in Frankfurt he became Privatdozent in 1971 and Professor in 1976. During this time, as Adjunct Professor of Physiology and Biophysics at the University of Iowa, he regularly continued his collaboration with colleagues in the United States. In 1980 he became Professor and Co-director of the Brain Research Institute at the University of Zurich.

Within the field of neurobiology, he was particularly interested in the analysis of the neuronal control of compensatory eye movements. More than 250 publications on the synaptic organization, pharmacology, morphology and plasticity of vestibular and optokinetic reflex systems, on their control by the cerebellum and on the performance of these systems in different species indicate how comprehensive his approach and how inspiring and successful was his work. His scientific excellence without a trace of vanity and his warm personality attracted within his short lifespan more than 50 colleagues from Japan, the United States and Europe to work with him. He enjoyed these collaborations and this joy was characteristic of the spirit present in his laboratories. Exemplary in his dedication to science, in his readiness to help and in his encouragement of younger scientists: this was Wolfgang Precht.

Contents

x   Contents

Contents

RECOVERY IN VISUO-OCULOMOTOR CONTROL FOLLOWING CORTICAL INJURY

Contents

BRAINSTEM AND CEREBELLAR MECHANISMS IN OCULOMOTOR CONTROL

ADAPTATION TO VESTIBULAR LESIONS

Contents

NEURONAL MECHANISMS OF ADAPTATION

OSCILLOPSIA AND CONGENITAL NYSTAGMUS

Conference Participants

Lawrence A. Abel
Veterans Administration Med. Ctr.
10701 East Boulevard
Cleveland, OH 44106

Chiye Aoki
Laboratory of Neurobiology
Cornell University Medical College
1300 York Avenue
New York, NY 10021

Constance Atwell
National Institutes of Health
Bldg. 31, Room 6A49
Bethesda, MD 20205

Bruno Bagolini
Clinica Oculistica
Universita Cattolica
Policlinico Gemelli
Largo A. Gemelli, 8
00168 Rome, ITALY

Robert G. Baker
Department of Physiology
New York University Med. Ctr.
550 First Avenue
New York, NY 10016

Robert W. Baloh
Department of Neurology
Reed Neurological Center
University of California, L.A.
Los Angeles, CA 90024

Alain Berthoz
Lab de Physiologie
Neurosensorielle, CNRS
15 rue de l'Ecole de Medicine
75270 Paris, Cedex 06, FRANCE

Willem Bles
E.N.T. Dept., Akademisch Ziekenhuis
Free University of Amsterdam
De Boelelaan 1117, Amsterdam 1011
THE NETHERLANDS

Thomas Brandt
Klinikum Grosshadern
University of Munich
Marchioninistr. 15
8000 Munchen, F.R.G.

Stephen C. Cannon
The Wilmer Institute
The Johns Hopkins Hospital
601 N. Broadway
Baltimore, MD 21205

James R. Carl
Laboratory of Sensorimotor Research
National Eye Institute
Bldg. 10, Room 10B09
Bethesda, MD 20892

Charles Chase
CNC Engineering
P.O. Box 75567
Seattle, WA 98125

Alberto O. Ciancia
Instituto de Oftalmologia Pediatrica
Callao 1395
Buenos Aires 1023, ARGENTINA

Alexander L. Cogan
Smith-Kettlewell Inst. Vis. Sci.
2232 Webster Street
San Francisco, CA 94115

Bernard Cohen
Department of Neurology
The Mount Sinai Medical Center
1 Gustave Levy Place
New York, NY 10029

Han Collewijn
Department of Physiology I
Erasmus University
3000DR Rotterdam, THE NETHERLANDS

Carter C. Collins
Smith-Kettlewell Inst. Vis. Sci.
2232 Webster Street
San Francisco, CA 94115

Jon N. Currie
Neuro-Ophthalmology Section
NEI, NIH
Bldg. 10, Room 10C205
Bethesda, MD 20205

Max Cynader
Department of Psychology
Dalhousie University
Halifax, N.S., CANADA B3H 4J1

Robert B. Daroff
Department of Neurology
Case Western Reserve University
University Hospital
Cleveland, OH 44106

Louis F. Dell'Osso
Department of Neurology
Case Western Reserve University
University Hospital
Cleveland, OH 44106

Shu-yi Deng
Laboratory of Sensorimotor Research
National Eye Institute
Bethesda, MD 20892

Norbert Dieringer
Institut fur Hirnforschung
University of Zurich
August Forel-Strasse 1
CH-8029 Zurich, SWITZERLAND

Rolf Eckmiller
Department of Biophysics
Division of Biocybernetics
University of Dusseldorf
Universitatsstrasse 1
D4000 Dusseldorf 1, F.R.G.

Stephen R. Ellis
NASA
Ames Research Center
Moffett Field, CA 94035

Michael Fetter
3301 St. Paul Street
Apt. 212
Baltimore, MD 21218

Anthony Fisher
Sir Charles Gairdner Hospital
The Queen Elizabeth II Med. Ctr.
Verdun Street
Nedlands, WEST AUSTRALIA

Edmond J. Fitzgibbon
Laboratory of Sensorimotor Research
NEI, NIH
Bldg. 10, Room 10B09
Bethesda, MD 20892

William Fletcher
Dept. of Neurological Surgery
Neuro-Ophthalmology Department
876 Moffitt Hospital
San Francisco, CA 94143

Hans Flohr
Department of Neurobiology
University of Bremen
2800 Bremen 33, F.R.G.

Merton C. Flom
College of Optometry
University of Houston-Univ. Park
4800 Calhoun Road
Houston, TX 77004

H. L. Galiana
McGill University
Aerospace Medical Research Unit
Department of Physiology
3655 Drummond Street
Montreal, P.Q., CANADA H36 1Y6

James A. Gammon
Ophthalmology Section
2889 Wendland Drive
Atlanta, GA 30345

Gabriel Gauthier
Laboratoire de Psychophysiologie
University of Provence
rue Henri-Poincare-St. Jerome
13397 Marseille, Cedex 13, FRANCE

Michael E. Goldberg
Laboratory of Sensorimotor Research
NEI, NIH
Bldg. 10, Room 10B09
Bethesda, MD 20892

Michael Gresty
MRC Neuro-Otology Unit
Institute of Neurology

National Hospital, Queen Square
London WC1N 3B6, U.K.

R.A. Grigoryan
I.M. Sechenov Institute of
Developmental Physiology
and Biochemistry
USSR Academy of Sciences
Leningrad, USSR

Stephen Grossberg
Center for Adaptive Systems
Department of Mathematics
Boston University
111 Cummington Street
Boston, MA 02215

Gerald Grossman
Department of Neurology
University Hospitals
2074 Abington Road
Cleveland, OH 44106

G. Michael Halmagyi
Royal Prince Alfred Hospital
Department of Neurology
Missinden Road
Camperdown, N.S.W. 2050, AUSTRALIA

Mohamed A. Hamid
Vestibular Laboratory
The Cleveland Clinic Foundation
9500 Euclid Avenue
Cleveland, OH 44106

Marlene Hayman
NEI, NIH
Bldg. 10, Room 10B09
Bethesda, MD 20892

Volker Henn
Univeritatsspital Zurich
Neurologische Klinik und Poliklikik
Ramistrasse 100, 8091 Zurich
SWITZERLAND

Richard W. Hertle
1930 Coltman
Cleveland, OH 44106

Peter Hoffmann
Department of Neurobiology
University of Ulm
D-7900 Ulm, F.R.G.

John Hotson
Department of Neurology
Santa Clara Valley Med. Ctr.
751 S. Bascom Avenue
San Jose, CA 95128

William F. Hoyt
Dept. of Neurological Surgery
Neuro-Ophthalmology Unit
876 Moffitt Hospital
San Francisco, CA 94143

Michael Hyson
1155 N. Verdugo Rd., #C
Glendale, CA 91206

Lea Hyvarinen
Harmasaparrankuja 3
SF-02200 Espoo
FINLAND

Makoto Igarashi
Baylor College of Medicine
Houston, TX 77030

Kazuyuki Imamura
Smith-Kettlewell Inst. Vis. Sci.
2232 Webster Street
San Francisco, CA 94115

Richard Imes
217 San Diego Court
Danville, CA 94526

Arthur Jampolsky
Smith-Kettlewell Inst. Vis. Sci.
2232 Webster Street
San Francisco, CA 94115

Geoffrey Melvill Jones
Aerospace Medical, Dept. Physiology
McGill University
McIntyre Med. Sci. Bldg., Rm. 1223
3655 Drummond Street
Montreal, Que. CANADA H3G 1Y6

Takuji Kasamatsu
Smith-Kettlewell Inst. Vis. Sci.
2232 Webster Street
San Francisco, CA 94115

Kenji Kawano
Bionics Section
Electrotechnical Laboratory
1-1-4 Umezono, Sakura-mura
Nuhari-gun, Ibaraki 305 JAPAN

Edward L. Keller
Smith-Kettlewell Inst. Vis. Sci.
2232 Webster Street
San Francisco, CA 94115

W. Michael King
Department of Physiology
University of Rochester Med. Ctr.
Rochester, N.Y. 14642

Guntram Kommerell
Department of Ophthalmology
University of Freiburg
Killianstr. 5
7800 Freiburg, F.R.G.

R. John Leigh
Department of Neurology
Case Western Reserve University
University Hospital
Cleveland, OH 44106

Stephen Lisberger
Dept. of Physiology, 762-S
University of California, S.F.
San Francisco, CA 94143

James McElligott
Department of Pharmacology
Temple University Sch. of Med.
Philadelphia, PA 19140

Keith McNeer
West End Eye Center Inc.
5700 W. Grace Street, Suite 110
Richmond, VA 23226

Leonard Matin
Department of Psychology
Columbia University
New York, NY 10027

Jack May
Smith-Kettlewell Inst. Vis. Sci.
2232 Webster Street
San Francisco, CA 94115

Lawrence E. Mays
Neuroscience Program
University of Alabama
Birmingham, AL 35294

Joel Miller
Smith-Kettlewell Inst. Vis. Sci.
2232 Webster Street
San Francisco, CA 94115

Donald E. Mitchell
Department of Psychology
Dalhousie University
Halifax, N.S., CANADA B3H 4J1

Yasushi Miyashita
Department of Physiology
Faculty of Medicine
University of Tokyo
Bunkyoku, Tokyo
JAPAN

Michael Mustari
Regional Primate Research Center

University of Washington
1-421 Health Science Bldg. SJ-50
Seattle, WA 98195

William Newsome
Dept. of Neurobiology & Behavior
SUNY, Graduate Biology Bldg.
Stony Brook, NY 11794

Martin O'Connor
Smith-Kettlewell Inst. Vis. Sci.
2232 Webster Street
San Francisco, CA 94115

Lance Optican
Laboratory of Sensorimotor Research
N.I.H., Bldg. 10, Rm. 10B09
Bethesda, MD 20892

Gary D. Paige
University of California Service
San Francisco General Hospital
San Francisco, CA 94110

Donald E. Parker
Department of Psychology
Miami University
Oxford, Ohio 45056

Misha Pavel
Dept. of Psychology, Bldg. 420
Stanford University
Stanford, CA 94305

Barry W. Peterson
Department of Physiology
Northwestern University Med. Sch.
Chicago, IL 60611

Nathaniel Pitts
Neurobiology Program
National Science Foundation
1800 G Street, NW
Washington, D.C. 20550

Ottavio Pompeiano
University of Pisa Med. Sch.
Istituto di Fisiologia Umana
Via S. Zeno 31
56100 Pisa, ITALY

Nagbhushan S. Rao
Department of Neurology
District of Columbia Gen. Hosp.
19th St. & Massachusetts Ave., SE
Washington, D.C. 20003

Theodore Raphan
Dept. of Computer & Info. Sci.
Brooklyn College
Bedford Ave. & Ave. H
Brooklyn, NY 11210

Robert R. Reinecke
Wills Eye Hospital
9th and Walnut Streets
Philadelphia, PA 19107

David A. Robinson
The Wilmer Institute
The Johns Hopkins Hospital
601 N. Broadway
Baltimore, MD 21205

Paul Romano
Department of Ophthalmology
College of Medicine
University of Florida
Gainesville, FL 32610

Mark S. Ruttum
2055 Mount Kisco Drive
Elm Grove, WI 53122

John T. Schmidt
Dept. Biological Sciences
State University of New York
1400 Washington Avenue
Albany, NY 12222

Clifton Schor
School of Optometry
University of California
Berkeley, CA 94720

Alan B. Scott
Smith-Kettlewell Inst. Vis. Sci.
2232 Webster Street
San Francisco, CA 94115

Steven H. Scott
6020 Ridgemont Drive
Oakland, CA 94619

Mark A. Segraves
Laboratory of Sensorimotor Research
NEI, NIH
Bldg. 10, Room 10B09
Bethesda, MD 20892

James A. Sharpe
Department of Neurology
University of Toronto
399 Bathurst Street
Toronto, Ont. CANADA M5T 2S8

Keith Sherman
Smith-Kettlewell Inst. Vis. Sci.
2232 Webster Street
San Francisco, CA 94115

John I. Simpson
Dept. of Physiology & Biophysics
New York University
School of Medicine

550 First Avenue
New York, NY 10016

David L. Sparks
Dept. of Physiology & Biophysics
University of Alabama
P.O. Box 190
Birmingham, AL 35294

Robert Spencer
Department of Anatomy
Medical College of Virginia
P.O. Box 906
Richmond, VA 23298

Stephen E. Thurston
Department of Neurology
University Hospitals of Cleveland
2074 Abington Road
Cleveland, OH 44106

Rodolfo Trevino
Smith-Kettlewell Inst. Vis. Sci.
2232 Webster Street
San Francisco, CA 94115

Ronald Tusa
Department of Neurology
The Johns Hopkins University
Baltimore, MD 21205

Christopher W. Tyler
Smith-Kettlewell Inst. Vis. Sci.
2232 Webster Street
San Francisco, CA 94115

Guillermo Velez
Calle 49-B-No. 64-B-37
Centro Suramericana
Medellin, COLOMBIA

David M. Waitzman
627 Bainbridge Street
Foster City, CA 94404

Barbara M. Weissman
Rainbow Babies & Children's Hosp.
University Hospitals of Cleveland
2074 Abington Road
Cleveland, OH 44106

Isla M. Williams
15 Collins Street
Melbourne 3000, AUSTRALIA

Shirley H. Wray
Neuro-Visual Unit
Ambulatory Care Center
Massachusetts General Hospital
15 Parkman Street
Boston, MA 02114

Robert D. Yee
Department of Ophthalmology
Jules Stein Eye Institute
University of California, L.A.
Los Angeles, CA 90024

Laurence R. Young
Dept. Aeronautics/Astronautics
Massachusetts Inst. of Tech.
77 Massachusetts Avenue
Cambridge, MA 02139

Wolfgang Zangemeister
Neurological University Clinic
University of Hamburg
Martinstr. 52
D2000 Hamburg 20, F.R.G.

David S. Zee
Department of Neurology
The Johns Hopkins University
601 N. Broadway, Rm. 1422
Baltimore, MD 21205

THE HARRY R. HORROW LECTURE

Cognitive Management of Sensory-Motor Correspondence in Visual, Vestibular and Oculomotor Systems

G. Melvill Jones

Aerospace Medical Research Unit, Department of Physiology,
McGill University, Montréal, Québec, Canada H3G 1Y6

Introduction

I would like to begin by saying how deeply I appreciate the honour of having been invited to deliver this address, named for Mr. Harry R. Horrow, who has done so much to foster both basic and clinical research in the Smith Kettlewell Institute for Visual Sciences. It is a pleasure and privilege to have our honoured guests with us today and I shall try to make my talk of interest to them as well as the scientist delegates of the meeting.

Let me begin by looking back over the shoulder of time to glance at the historical evolution of that concept of subcortical neurophysiological function, the automated sensory-motor reflex. Its emergence as a viable entity rests on the fact that contemporary experimentalists learned how to separate lower elements of the nervous system from the complicating influence of cognitive "interference". But now with introduction of the alert, behaving, animal preparation, a veritable "Pandora's Box" has been opened for the neuroscientist. By so doing we have released those teaming, yet mysterious, cognitive activities whose descending influences transform the subcortical automaton into a vital living organism capable of purposeful behaviour. As a result, reflexes previously labelled "involuntary", spring to life as highly maleable entities, nicely matched in their performance characteristics to the extenuating demands of purposeful behaviour. The following text falls into two main sections focussing respectively on (a) short-term intrusion of cognitive influences into on-going reflex activity, and (b) the longer-term phenomenon of adaptive remodelling of sensory-motor correspondence at the levels of both reflex and cognitive function.

Cognitive "Steering" of Brainstem Reflexes

The Saccadic System. Consider first those brainstem mechanisms which participate in generating oculomotor saccades. Briefly they comprise visuo-motor pathways passing through superior colliculus and premotor cell assemblies in the brainstem, to deliver a "packaged" burst of oculomotor neural discharge suitable for "flicking" the foveal line of sight onto a specified visual target (reviewed e.g. by Robinson, 1981). If a novel target suddenly appears in an otherwise darkened room, this saccadic "flick" may be driven by an automated "Visual Grasp Reflex", operating through subcortical pathways (Akert, 1949). However, turn on the lights in a visually rich environment, and the sensory input to the reflex arc becomes flooded with a virtually infinite variety of potential targets. A cognitive choice must then determine to which target the substrate system will turn the eyes: Which raises the interesting question, how does the relevant cognitive drive intrude itself into the automated "grasp reflex" elements of the brainstem?

This question has recently attracted considerable interest amongst neurophysioligsts (Goldberg & Wurtz, 1972; Wurtz & Mohler, 1976; Guitton & Mandl, 1978; Hikosaka & Wurtz, 1983a; Bruce & Goldberg, 1985; Munoz & Guitton,

G. Melvill Jones

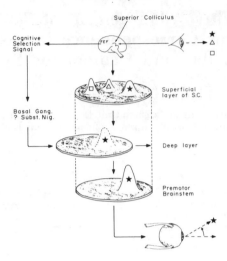

Fig. 1. Cognitive selection of the "visual grasp reflex": A
schematic outline of emerging ideas (see text).

1985).   In overview we may turn to Fig. 1 for a simplified sketch of emerging
ideas.   At top right the eye is presented with three different points of visual
interest, one of which (the star) is to be consciously selected for driving the
appropriate saccadic shift of gaze direction.   The retinotopic
(i.e. place-on-the-retina) locations of all three targets are faithfully
represented by corresponding spatial concentrations, or "hillocks", of neural
activity in the superficial layer of the superior colliculus, which receives
afferent input from the retina (e.g. Schiller, 1972).   In deeper regions, where
formulation of the appropriate oculomotor discharge takes place (Robinson, 1972;
·Stryker & Schiller, 1975; Guitton and co-workers, 1980) a single "hillock" of
premotor activity must be selected, as illustrated somewhat fancifully in the
lowest "surface" of the sketch.   Presumably the cognitive selection process must
operate between these two locations, by as it were "sliding in" the middle
template (i.e. "disc") of spatially coded neural information after the fashion
suggested in Fig. 1.

What evidence is available concerning the physiological nature of this selection
process?   Fig. 2 from Munoz & Guitton (1985) exemplifies the kind of neural
correlate which may be at play.   An alert head-free cat is trained to play a
"cat-and-mouse" game with the experimenter, who "jumps" an interesting target
(food) from side to side behind an opaque screen.   On unexpected occasions (as
in this instance) the target becomes invisible as it jumps behind the screen
(trace T_h) and does not emerge on the other side.   On this occasion the cat did
not immediately move its gaze from the original target location (middle picture
of cat).   However, during this period the previously silent tectospinal unit
shown in the figure, (presumed also to project to oculomotor brainstem regions;
Rose & Abrahams, 1978; Grantyn & Grantyn, 1982), sprang into a state of active
discharge despite the absence of any eye or head movement.   The discharge ceased
with execution of the required gaze shift (G_h), but was not itself necessary for
driving the saccade since it remained silent during arbitrary saccades of
similar size and direction, performed for example by chance in the dark.
Rather, this neural signal appears to be associated with the intention to move

to a known (remembered) location in space. Significantly saccade
"memory-contingent" and other cognitively contingent saccade neural activity has

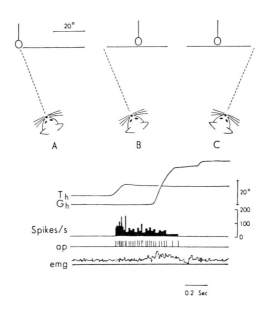

Fig. 2. Pre-saccadic tecto-spinal activity associated with
the intention to make a predetermined gaze shift. T_h,
horizontal target position; G_h, horizontal gaze position;
EMG recorded from right splenius neck msucle (modified from
Fig. 2 of Munoz & Guitton, 1985).

been noted in colliculus-related areas of the basal ganglia. Thus selective
suppression of spontaneous unit activity in substantia nigra (pars reticulata)
has been reported in the monkey, when it makes a saccade to a remembered, but
invisible, target (Hikosaka & Wurtz, 1983a). Bearing in mind that collicular
projections of substantia nigra appear to be inhibitory (Chevalier and
colleagues, 1981; Hikosaka & Wurtz, 1983b), such an effect could lead to
disinhibition of units of similar genre to that of Fig. 2. The question
then arises, how does increased activity in the selected "hillock" ensure that
the appropriate saccade is triggered? A possible mechanism has recently been
proposed by R. Douglas (unpublished), who has shown that a putative collateral
inhibitory network within the colliculus could leave the highest hillock
untouched meanwhile suppressing all other activity. Whilst by itself such a
network can produce reflex-like saccades to single unexpected visual stimuli,
the advantage of this model is that cognitive and attentional inputs could
readily change the selection order by making one hillock slightly higher than
the rest.

Where is the origin of the cognitively driven discharge? A good candidate is
the frontal eye field (FEF) of the frontal cortex, which not only projects via
basal ganglia to superior colliculus but also exhibits neural activity keyed to
similar cognitive correlates (reviewed by Bruce & Goldberg, 1984). Thus in
summary we can envisage an automated subcortical substrate, itself properly

calibrated to produce strict sensory-motor correspondence for prevailing environmental conditions, but which yet can be accessed by cognitively initiated inputs to allow the vital element of choice to determine which stimulus-response pattern shall be activated.

The Vestibulo-Collic System. Next we briefly glance at cognitive correlates in the vestibulo-collic system, responsible for autostabilization of the head relative to space during body movement. Previous human experiments demonstrated that during body rotation in the dark, a head-free subject may generate marked nystagmoid head stabilizing movements. When present, this response tended to combine nicely with concurrent nystagmoid eye movements to produce more or less effective stabilization of gaze (eye + head movement) (Outerbridge & Melvill Jones, 1971). However, in those experiments there was great variability between subjects in the extent of their head movements, some individuals producing no such movement at all. A recent study by Guitton and co-workers (1985) has demonstrated a commanding cognitive input to the reflex which could well account for this variability. Subjects with head free were rotated stochastically using white noise stimuli under three different conditions. First, they tried to maintain the collimated beam of a head-fixed lamp on an earth-fixed target seen in front of them. Second, they tried to perform the same task by imagining the beam and target in complete darkness; that is with a mental set focussed on the functional goal of head stabilization. Third, the mental state was divorced from the task by performing mental arithmetic.

TABLE 1 Effects of Mental set on Gain of Head Stabilization ("VCR", Vestibulo-Collic Response; L.D., Labyrinthine Deficient; brackets contain S.D.s) (Guitton, Kearney, Wereley & Peterson, 1985, Exp. Brain Res. in Press)

	"VCR" gain	
	Normals (n=10)	LD Patients (n=3)
Real Target	0.81 (.05)	0.54 (.23)
Imagined Target	0.61 (.15)	0.08 (.01)
Mental Arithmetic	0.12 (.10)	0.09 (.07)

The outcome was clear. Whilst best achievement was with vision, a good stabilizing response was induced in normal subjects simply by "thinking" of performing the target-holding task in the dark. On the contrary, when cognitive activity was dissociated from the task by performing mental arithmetic, head movement relative to the body was virtually abolished. We may ask, to what extent was the induced head movement of vestibular reflex origin? The answer is seen in the summary data of Table 1, which compares calculated "reflex" gain (head/body movement) in comparable sets of normal and labyrinthine-deficient (L.D.) subjects. Note particularly the consistent absence of response in the latter subjects when they tried to perform the task without vision. Taken together, these findings indicate that a vigorous head-stabilizing reflex of vestibular origin is available to normal humans, but that it is only brought into action when intentionally called for. Presumably in natural life it is important to permit voluntary head movements unimpeded by the vestibular stabilizing mechanism, until such time as the cognitive choice is made to stabilize the head platform during body perturbations of natural locomotion.

The Vestibulo-Ocular System. The vestibulo-ocular reflex (VOR) is also subject to effective volitional influences (e.g. Barr, and co-workers, 1976; Baloh and co-workers, 1984). Extreme examples are illustrated in Fig. 3, which shows simultaneous records of horizontal head and eye rotations in four different conditions. Those on the left were obtained in the light; those on the right in complete darkness. In the upper records the volitional goal was ocular fixation on an earth-fixed target (calling for compensatory eye movement); in the lower records the goal was fixation on a target moving exactly with the head (calling for abolition of the VOR). It is quite clear from these and similar records that the reflex can be invoked or suppressed at will, even in the absence of visual feedback. Here again we see the effects of an all-powerful influence of willfull origin which is capable of radically altering the performance of an otherwise automated brainstem reflex. However, in this instance the ability to do so allows us to raise an intriguing question addressed in the next section.

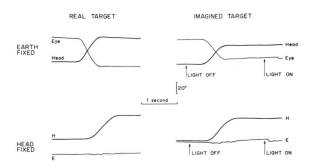

Fig. 3. The cognitive choice of behavioural goal determines sensory-motor relations in the "VOR". Eye and head movements recorded during passive head rotation. Left column, the subject views a real earth-fixed (upper) or head-fixed (lower) target. Right column, the same targets are imagined in the dark.

Cognitive Correlates of Long-Term Adaptive Phenomena

As evidenced in the proceedings of this conference, it is now a well established fact that suitable behavioural paradigms can produce long-term plastic (Barlow & Gaze, 1977) changes in the prevailing state of a subcortical reflex and notably without the provocation of an internal lesion (reviewed in Berthoz & Melvill Jones, 1985). For example, the response of the goal-directed VOR as tested in the dark can be made to increase, decrease or even change direction by appropriate optical alteration of vision. The question arises, might not adaptive remodelling within the brainstem reflex itself, serve the functionally useful rôle of off-loading the cerebrally "expensive" mental effort needed to produce cognitive "steering" of the kind discussed in the above sections?

To address this question we asked human subjects to suppress their VOR during active horizontal head rotations by trying to "look" at a head-fixed target in the dark over a total period of 3 hours (Melvill Jones and co-workers, 1984). We used a real dentally-fixed target to aid its imagined fixation in the dark. The VOR was tested before and after this period by asking subjects to imagine they were fixating on an earth-fixed target (i.e. a test which calls for perfect compensatory eye movement) during transient rotations in the dark, as in the top right hand quadrant of Fig. 3. Figure 4 illustrates an example of the results obtained. On the left we see normal patterns of response, in which head

8   G. Melvill Jones

movement was well compensated by reflex eye movement. However, on the right we
see that after the 3 hr period of willful VOR suppression in the dark, the
reflex response was systematically reduced, even though the subject was trying
as hard as possible to restore VOR gain to unity by "fixating" the (imagined)
earth-fixed target. When lights were turned on (end of shaded areas) the
resulting under-compensation was seen by the subject, who then made a visually
triggered corrective saccade. Evidently maintained willful effort was
sufficient to produce an inherent change of VOR gain. Furthermore, the gain
change did occur in a sense suitable for offloading the mental effort needed to
produce voluntary suppression of the reflex.

Perceptual Correlates. A further question arises: If persistent voluntary motor
effort can lead to recalibration of the subcortical reflex, would there be
corresponding recalibration of the cortical correlate of sensory perception of
rotation? Certainly the findings of Gauthier & Robinson (1975) indicate that

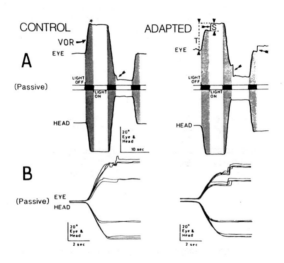

Fig. 4. Maintaining volitional suppression of VOR in
darkness leads to adaptive attenuation of the reflex after
3 hr of mental suppression (from Fig. 2 of Melvill Jones,
Berthoz & Segal, 1984).

this does occur after visually induced adaptive augmentation of the VOR. Using
a psychophysical method similar to their's, we also found significant
correlation between alteration of consciously perceived movement and the
measured alteration of reflex gain. It seems that not only can the steady
application of volitional effort produce an altered state of sensory-motor
correspondence in the relevant brainstem reflex but, perhaps more significantly,
it can also change in a correlated way, our conscious interpretation of the
common vestibular afferent signal representing the physical event of head
rotation relative to inertial space.

Concluding Remarks

In the first part of this address we saw how the working substrates of certain brainstem reflexes can be brought under the compelling influence of cognitively generated directives. Indeed the extent of such influence on reflex performance surely implies that without the working cerebral link, the behavioural significance of a given reflex pathway can never be properly understood. In turn we may guess that pathological interference with this vital link might be responsible for as yet unrecognized neurological disorders of "reflex" function. Pointing this way is the interesting recent finding that patients with frontal cortical lobe lesions are disabled from making "antisaccades" _away_ _from_ a visible target; yet they are quite capable of making the normal saccadic jump onto that target (Guitton and co-workers, 1985). Again, although a Parkinsonian patient (with basal ganglia lesions, refer to Fig. 1) may be quite capable of executing the normal visual grasp reflex onto a new target, he may nevertheless exhibit marked akinesia in the voluntary execution of a saccadic jump from one stationary target to another (DeJong & Melvill Jones, 1971).

In the second part we saw that persistent _mentally_ produced rearrangement of sensory-motor relations in a reflex, can gradually alter key controlling parameters (e.g. gain) within the reflex, in apparently the same way as that produced by real sensory stimuli. Furthermore, such alteration as we observed in the VOR was of a kind which would tend to off-load cognitive levels of the brain from the need to generate that mental effort. Perhaps amongst other things the adaptive process serves to automatically preserve higher cerebral mechansims from long-term involvement in the task of meeting persistently changed behavioural criteria.

Finally it appears that adaptive recalibration of the reflex response to the vestibular input may be associated with matching alteration of the allied perceptual sensory experience of rotation. Moreover, it transpires that this alteration in our cognitive interpretation of sensory events can apparently be induced by the exercise of _internally_ generated thought processes. Does this imply that without adaptive "homeostasis" through persistent contact with the real physical world, the veridical nature of its cognitive perception would be jeopardized? If so, we are left with a further teasing question: Could it be that pathological interference with these self-adjusting adaptive mechanisms might underly the etiological origins of illusionary sensory perception in specific forms of psychiatric illness? The possibility adds a certain impetus to the urge for further understanding of the neurophysiological, perhaps neurochemical, basis of the adaptive processes with which this conference is concerned.

References

Akert, K. (1949). Der visuelle greifreflex. Helv. Physiol. Pharmacol. Acta, 7, 112-134.
Baloh, R.W., K. Lyerly, and R.D. Yee (1984). Voluntary control of the human vestibulo-ocular reflex. Acta Oto-laryngol., 97, 1-6.
Barlow, H.B., and R.M. Gaze (1977). A discussion on the structural and functional aspects of plasticity in the nervous system. Phil. Trans. R. Soc. (B) Lond., 278, 243-244.
Barr, C.C., L.W. Schultheis, and D.A. Robinson (1976). Voluntary, non-visual control of the human vestibulo-ocular reflex. Acta Oto-laryngol. 81, 365-375.
Berthoz, A., and G. Melvill Jones (1985). Adaptive Mechanisms in Gaze Control, Elsevier Press, Amsterdam, New York, Oxford.
Bruce, C.J., and M.E. Goldberg (1984). Physiology of the frontal eye fields. Trends in Neurosci., 7, 436-441.
Bruce, C.J., and M.E. Goldberg (1985). Primate frontal eye fields. I. Single neurons discharging before saccades. J. Neurophysiol., 53, 603-635.

Chevalier, G., A.M. Thierry, T. Shibazaki, J. Feger (1981). Evidence for a GABAergic inhibitory nigrotectal pathway in the rat. Neurosci. Lett. 21, 67-70.
DeJong, J.D., and G. Melvill Jones. (1971). Akinesia, hypokinesia and bradykinesia in the oculomotor system of patients with Parkinson's Disease. Exp. Neurol., 32, 58-68.
Gauthier, G.M., and D.A. Robinson (1975). Adaptation of the human vestibulo-ocular reflex to magnifying lenses. Brain Res., 92, 331-335.
Goldberg, M.E., and R.H. Wurtz (1972). Activity of superior colliculus in behaving monkey. II. Effect of attention on neuronal responses. J. Neurophysiol., 35, 560-574.
Grantyn, A., and R. Grantyn (1982). Axonal patterns and sites of termination of cat superior colliculus neurons projecting in the tecto-bulbo-spinal tract. Exp. Brain Res., 46, 243-256.
Guitton, D., and G. Mandl (1978). Frontal "oculomotor" area in alert cat. II. Unit discharges associated with eye movements and neck muscle activity. Brain Res., 149, 313-327.
Guitton, D., M. Crommelinck, and A. Roucoux (1980). Stimulation of suprior colliculus in the alert cat. I. Eye movements and neck EMG activity evoked when the head is restrained. Exp. Brain Res., 39, 63-73.
Guitton, D., H.A. Buchtel, and R.M. Douglas (1985). Frontal lobe lesions in man cause difficulties in suppressing reflexive glances and in generating goal-directed saccades. Exp. Brain Res., 58, 455-472.
Guitton, D., R.E. Kearney, N. Wereley, and B.W. Peterson (1985). Visual, vestibular and voluntary contributions to human head stabilization. Exp. Brain Res. In Press.
Hikosaka, O., and R.H. Wurtz (1983a). Visual and oculomotor functions of monkey subtantia nigra pars reticulata. III. Memory-contingent visual and saccade responses. J. Neurophysiol., 49, 1268-1284.
Hikosaka, O., and R.H. Wurtz (1983b). Visual and oculomotor functions of monkey substantia nigra pars reticulata. IV. Relation of substantia nigra to superior colliculus. J. Neurophysiol., 49 1285-1301.
Munoz, D.D., and D. Guitton (1985). Tectospinal neurons in the cat have discharges coding gaze position error. Brain Res., 341, 184-188.
Melvill Jones, G., A. Berthoz, and B.N. Segal (1984). Adaptive modification of the vestibulo-ocular reflex by mental effort in darkness. Exp. Brain Res. 56, 149-153.
Outerbridge, J.S., and G. Melvill Jones (1971). Reflex control of head movement. Aerospace Med., 42, 935-940.
Robinson, D.A. (1972). Eye movements evoked by collicular stimulation in the alert monkey. Vision Res., 12, 1795-1808.
Robinson, D.A. (1981). Control of eye movements. In V.B. Brooks, American Physiological Society (Ed.), The Nervous System, Handbook of Physiology, Vol. II, Part 2, Williams & Wilkins, Baltimore, pp. 1275-1320.
Rose, P.K., and V.C. Abrahams (1978). Tectospinal and tectoreticular cells: their distribution and afferent connections. Can. J. Physiol. Pharmacol., 56 650-658.
Schiller, P.M. (1972). The rôle of the monkey superior colliculus in eye movement and vision. Invest. Ophthalmol., 11, 451-460.
Stryker, P., and P.M. Schiller (1975). Eye and head movements evoked by electrical stimulation of monkey superior colliculus. Exp. Brain Res., 23, 103-112.
Wurtz, R.H., and C.W. Mohler (1976). Enhancement of visual responses in monkey striate cortex and frontal eye fields. J. Neurophysiol., 39, 766-772.

Supported by Canadian Medical Research Council, Natural Sciences and Engineering Research Council of Canada and Fonds de la Recherche en Santé du Québec.

NEUROMUSCULAR ADAPTATIONS

Morphological Basis of Junctional or Muscle Adaptation in Pharmacological Denervation of Monkey Extraocular Muscles

R. F. Spencer and K. W. McNeer

Departments of Anatomy and Ophthalmology, Medical College of
Virginia, Richmond, VA 23298, USA

The use of botulinum toxin (BTX) is an effective pharmacological alternative to the surgical management of strabismus (Magoon, 1984; Scott, 1980). Injection of the toxin into a clinically overacting muscle produces a temporary reversible paralysis of that muscle, the duration of which is dose dependent. The result of this paralysis is a change in the force dynamics of the paired antagonistic muscles that allows the weaker opposing muscle to gain mechanical strength.

The mechanism of action of BTX is blockade of neuromuscular synaptic transmission by interference with the calcium-dependent neurogenic quantal and spontaneous non-quantal release of the neurotransmitter acetylcholine (Sellin, 1981; Simpson, 1981; Thesleff, 1984). This presynaptic action of the toxin induces denervation-like alterations in the motor innervation of skeletal muscle fibers, including axonal sprouting (Brown and Ironton, 1978; Brown and colleagues, 1980; Duchen and Strich, 1968; Duchen, 1970a, 1971a) and the extrajunctional spread of acetylcholine receptors on the postsynaptic membrane (Mathers and Thesleff, 1978; Pestronk and Drachman, 1976; Pestronk and colleagues, 1978). Physiological (Brown and colleagues, 1982; Drachman and Houk, 1969; Drachman and Johnston, 1975; Tonge, 1974), histochemical (Drachman and Romanul,1970; Duchen, 1970b), and ultrastructural (Duchen, 1971b) changes in muscle fibers also have been observed as a consequence of BTX paralysis. Differential long-term effects furthermore have been noted between fast versus slow skeletal muscles in the severity and duration of, and subsequent recovery from, these changes.

Morphological changes in the extraocular muscles of the monkey have been examined following intramuscular injection of BTX. Data have been obtained from 13 Rhesus monkeys, including 6 adults (>4 years) in which the medial rectus muscles were injected bilaterally, and 3 juveniles (1-2 years) and 4 infants (4-6 months) in which the lateral rectus muscles were injected bilaterally. Muscles were injected under Ketamine anaesthesia with 10 units (7.28 x 10^{-3} μg) of BTX type A (Oculinum, Inc.) using a hypodermic needle with which the EMG activity of the muscle could be monitored through an amplifier (Scott and colleagues, 1973). All monkeys developed exotropia or esotropia, and ptosis, within 72 hours after injection, the onset of which was more rapid and the duration longer in the younger animals than in the adults. Postinjection survival periods ranged from 3 days to 8 weeks in adults and 1 to 10 weeks in infants, after which animals were sacrificed under Nembutal anaesthesia by transcardial perfusion of aldehyde fixative solution and muscles were processed for light and electron microscopy (Spencer and Porter, 1981).

13

The rectus muscles of the monkey, like those of most mammals including humans, are organized into orbital, intermediate, and global regions. Six basic morphological types of muscle fibers are differentially located within these regions. The orbital layer contains one type of singly-innervated and one type of multiply-innervated fiber, while the intermediate and global layers contain 3 types of singly-innervated fibers and another type of multiply-innervated fiber (Pachter, 1982; Spencer and Porter, 1981). Differences in the capillary vascular network also are apparent in the different regions of the muscle, the orbital layer exhibiting the most extensive microvasculature as demonstrated by alkaline phosphatase histochemistry (Ringel and colleagues, 1978). By electron microscopy, the most apparent difference between the singly-innervated muscle fiber types is in relation to the number, size, and disposition of mitochondria. These differences correlate well with the different oxidative and/or glycolytic enzyme activities of the various fiber types (Durston, 1974; Ringel and colleagues, 1978). In particular, the singly-innervated fiber in the orbital layer is characterized by prominent central and subsarcolemmal aggregations of mitochondria in the end-plate region, and a moderate internal membrane system comprised of T-tubules and sarcoplasmic reticulum that delineate the myofibrils. The muscle fiber is focally innervated by synaptic endings that literally encircle the fiber, but that exhibit little subjunctional folding. Yet another characteristic feature of this fiber type that is further indicative of its high oxidative capacity is the extensive capillary vascular network with which it is associated (Fig. 1A).

The orbital singly-innervated muscle fiber type and its associated microvasculature demonstrate the most profound adaptive changes as a consequence of BTX paralysis of neuromuscular transmission. In the adult medial rectus muscles, the most apparent change in the morphology of this fiber type is in the disposition of the central and subsarcolemmal aggregations of mitochondria (Fig. 1B). Specifically, there is a dispersion of the central mitochondria toward the periphery of the muscle fiber (Fig. 2A), with the formation of massive aggregates that distort the surface profile of the fibers (Fig. 2B). With longer times, there also appears to be a decrease in the amount of peripheral mitochondria. By 6 weeks, however, at which time recovery of function clearly had returned as indicated by adduction of the eye during vergence and conjugate horizontal eye movements, despite the persistence of exotropia during fixation in the primary position, the morphology of this muscle fiber type appears relatively normal (cf., Figs. 1A and 1C). Another change that occurs, and that is particularly apparent in comparing Figs. 1A and 1B, is a decrease in the capillary vascular network with which this muscle fiber type is associated. Correlated with the restoration of the morphology of this fiber type is the proliferation of the microvasculature (Fig. 1C). An intimate relationship thus exists between neuromuscular activity, metabolic capacity, and microvascular supply (Appell, 1984; Hudlicka and colleagues, 1984). Microvascular changes also recently have been observed in skeletal muscle as a consequence of denervation (Large and Tyler, 1985).

The most extreme change that has been observed, albeit only rarely in the adult and juvenile muscles, is a regression of the ultrastructural profile of the muscle fiber to an undifferentiated state. Yet, as with all other fiber types, the neural innervation is intact as indicated by the presence of apparently normal neuromuscular synaptic endings that innervate the fiber (Fig. 2C). Another change that is particularly prominent at more advanced stages is the appearence of large pale subsarcolemmal areas (Fig. 1B) that correspond to tubular aggregates, the early formation of which can be seen in Fig. 2C. Recent findings in autosomal-dominant neuromuscular disease have attributed the appearance of similar tubular aggregates to hypertrophied terminal cisternae of sarcoplasmic reticulum, suggesting that their formation may be a compensatory phenomenon to an increased intracellular level of calcium (Salviati and colleagues, 1985). Consistent with this postulated origin, when observed in BTX-paralyzed extraocular muscle, as also noted in skeletal muscle (Duchen, 1971b),

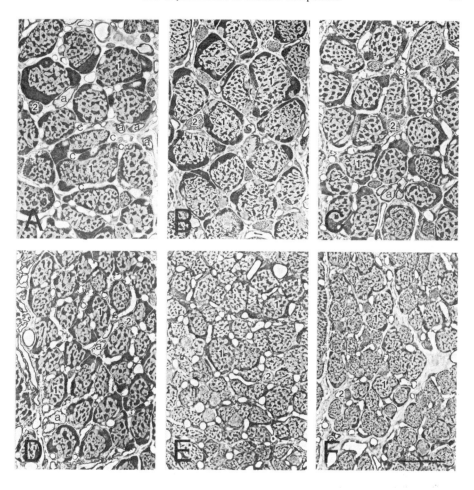

Fig. 1. Phase contrast light micrographs; orbital innervated muscle fibers (1) in normal adult medial rectus muscle (A) compared to 3 weeks (B) and 8 weeks following BTX paralysis; orbital singly-innervated muscle fibers in normal 4 month infant lateral rectus muscle (D) compared to 1 week (E) and 8 weeks (F) after BTX paralysis. c = capillary. Scale = 50 μm.

the tubular aggregates accompany disruption of the myofibrillar organization and internal membrane system. Other abnormal sarcoplasmic inclusions include aggregates of large lysosome-like organelles and numerous large lipid droplets. It is particularly significant that these organelle abnormalities are in the vicinity of the end-plate region of the muscle fiber, like other alterations in mitochondria and lipids observed by Davidowitz and colleagues (1984), who suggest an association of the increased metabolic capacity in this region of the fiber

with events related to neuromuscular activity.   Alterations in the distribution
and/or morphology of mitochondria may be indicative of deficits in oxidative
metabolism (Shah and colleagues, 1982).

With longer survival periods, the process of restoration of function is suggested
by the appearence of activated satellite cells (Fig. 2D). Axonal sprouting, as
noted in toxin-paralyzed skeletal muscle and indicated by enlarged presynaptic
endings that form superficial en passant contacts (Fig. 2D), also has been
observed. Neuromuscular transmission at these sites is suggested by the
accumulation of synaptic vesicles and the activity of endocytotic vesicles along
the presynaptic membrane.   Degenerative changes in presynaptic endings following
axonal denervation (Cheng-Minoda and colleagues, 1968) have not been observed in
BTX-paralyzed extraocular muscle.

Findings similar to these demonstrated in the adult medial rectus muscle have
been observed in the juvenile monkeys with injection of the toxin into the
lateral rectus muscles. In infant monkeys, however, the findings are more
dramatic.   In comparison to the normal adult lateral rectus muscle, the orbital
singly-innervated muscle fibers in the normal infant monkey, although
differentiated, are not mature. Quantitatively, the cross-sectional area of this
fiber type in the infant is, on the average, approximately 40% less than that in
the adult (cf., Figs. 1A and 1D). The morphological changes in this fiber type
are more rapid, as seen by the dispersion of central mitochondrial aggregates
already after 1 week (Fig. 1E). Furthermore, the toxin produces more of a true
denervation effect, as evidenced by the nearly complete regression of this muscle
fiber type to an undifferentiated state (Fig. 1F).   The more rapid onset and
prolonged duration of the effects of BTX in infants when compared to adults,
therefore, may be related to the developmental status of this muscle fiber at the
time of injection.

Injection of BTX into the medial rectus or lateral rectus muscles invariably
resulted in ptosis.   The uninjected levator palpebrae muscle, whose function
could be assessed more easily in the unrestrained animal, thus served as an
excellant control in these experiments.   The levator muscle contains essentially
the same 3 types of singly-innervated muscle fibers as are found in the
intermediate and global layers of the rectus muscles, though the microvascular
supply is greater. The changes in the adult levator muscle, like those in the
injected rectus muscles, are most apparent in the mitochondria-rich muscle fibers
and their associated capillary vascular supply.   With the return of apparently
normal eyelid elevation, the morphology of this singly-innervated muscle fiber
type and its associated microvasculature are comparable to the normal muscle. As
was the case for the injected rectus muscles, the other singly-innervated muscle
fiber types show few, if any, obvious changes as a result of BTX paralysis.

The interpretation of the structural alterations that have been observed as a
consequence of BTX paralysis of monkey extraocular muscles is based upon current
concepts regarding the mechanism of action of the toxin.   Botulinum toxin
abolishes both quantal and non-quantal Ca++-dependent release of acetylcholine
(reviewed in Thesleff, 1984; Thesleff and Molgo, 1983). The quantal release is
related to nerve impulse-evoked neuromuscular transmission, while the spontaneous
non-quantal release is largely responsible for the production of miniature end-
plate potentials.   BTX induces a third type of transmitter release that is
insensitive to either transmembrane Ca++ fluxes or nerve terminal membrane
depolarization.   This toxin-induced abnormal "secretory" release of acetylcholine
furthermore may have a trophic function on the muscle fibers, thus preventing the
spread of extrajunctional acetylcholine receptors on the muscle fiber surface
membrane to the same extent as that produced by axonal denervation.

The effect of BTX in blocking evoked neuromuscular transmission in extraocular
muscles, therefore, probably is disuse of all muscle fiber types, thus resulting
in paralysis of the muscle.   The specific morphological changes in the orbital

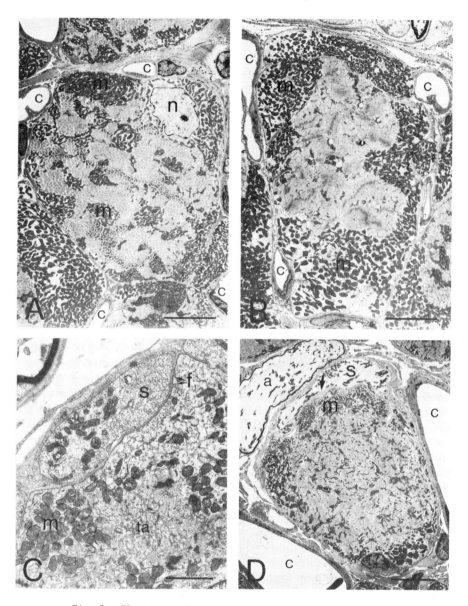

Fig. 2. Electron micrographs of orbital singly-innervated muscle fibers in adult medial rectus muscle 1 (A), 2 (B), 3 (C), and 5 (D) weeks after BTX paralysis. m = mitochondria; n = myonucleus; s = neuromuscular synaptic ending; f = subjunctional folds; ta = tubular aggregates. Scale = 10 μm (A,B,D), 2 μm (C).

singly-innervated muscle fibers presumably are the consequence of withdrawal of the capillary microvascular supply upon which this fiber type is dependent for oxidative metabolism. Other fiber types are less affected since they rely more upon glycolytic pathways. The integrity of the muscle fibers in BTX-paralyzed muscles may be maintained by the neurotrophic influence of acetylcholine released from intact neuromuscular synaptic endings.

In conclusion, factors that may influence the complete recovery of function of BTX-paralyzed muscle include: (a.) the complete restoration of the biochemical, physiological, and morphological properties of the muscle fibers; (b.) the ability of the microvasculature to respond to the increased demand for oxidative metabolism related to muscle activity following the return of neuromuscular transmission, and (c.) the developmental status of the muscle fibers and the neural innervation. Although the short-term adaptive response to BTX paralysis occurs primarily at the cellular and subcellular levels, these alterations affect the behaviour of the entire muscle. Similarly, the long-term consequences of BTX paralysis in affecting ocular motility may involve other aspects of muscle fiber architecture (e.g., sarcomere) that relate to the length and extent of muscle contraction.

ACKNOWLEDGEMENTS

This study was supported by U.S. Public Health Service Research Grant EY02191, and Biomedical Research Support Grants RR05430, RR05697, and RR05724.

REFERENCES

Appell, H.-J. (1984). Variability in microvascular pattern dependent upon muscle fiber composition. Prog. appl. Microcirc., 5, 15-29.

Brown, M.C., and R. Ironton (1978). Sprouting and regression of neuromuscular synapses in partially denervated mammalian muscles. J. Physiol. (Lond.), 278, 325-348.

Brown, M.C., R.L. Holland, and R. Ironton (1980). Nodal and terminal sprouting from motor nerves in fast and slow muscles of the mouse. J. Physiol. (Lond.), 306, 493-510.

Brown, M.C., W.G. Hopkins, and R.J. Keynes (1982). Short- and long-term effects of paralysis on the motor innervation of two different neonatal mouse muscles. J. Physiol. (Lond.), 329, 439-450.

Cheng-Minoda, K., T. Ozawa, and G.M. Breinin (1968). Ultrastructural changes in rabbit extraocular muscles after oculomotor nerve section. Invest. Ophthalmol., 7, 599-616.

Davidowitz, J., G. Philips, D.J. Chiarandini, and G.M. Breinin (1984). Distribution of mitochondrial and lipidic alterations in abnormal extraocular muscle of rat. Graefes Arch. Clin. Exp. Ophthalmol., 221, 153-156.

Drachman, D.B., and J. Houk (1969). Effect of botulinum toxin on speed of skeletal muscle contraction. Amer. J. Physiol., 216, 1453-1455.

Drachman, D.B., and D.M. Johnston (1976). Neurotrophic regulation of dynamic properties of skeletal muscle: effects of botulinum toxin and denervation. J. Physiol. (Lond.), 252, 657-667.

Drachman, D.B., and F.C.A. Romanul (1970). Effect of neuromuscular blockade on enzymatic activities of muscles. Arch. Neurol., 23, 85-89.

Duchen, L.W. (1970a). Changes in motor innervation and cholinesterase localization induced by botulinum toxin in skeletal muscle of the mouse: differences between fast and slow muscles. J. Neurol. Neurosurg. Psychiat., 33, 40-54.

Duchen, L.W. (1970b). Effects of botulinum toxin on the distribution of succinate dehydrogenase and phosphorylase in fast and slow skeletal muscles of the mouse. J. Neurol. Neurosurg. Psychiat., 33, 580-585.

Duchen, L.W. (1971a). An electron microscopic study of the changes induced by botulinum toxin in the motor end-plates of slow and fast skeletal muscle fibres of the mouse. J. Neurol. Sci., 14, 47-60.

Duchen, L.W. (1971b). Changes in the electron microscopic structure of slow and fast skeletal muscle fibres of the mouse after the local injection of botulinum toxin. J. Neurol. Sci., 14, 61-74.

Duchen, L.W., and S.J. Strich (1968). The effects of botulinum toxin on the pattern of innervation of skeletal muscle in the mouse. Quart. J. Exp. Physiol., 53, 84-89.

Durston, J.H.J. (1974). Histochemistry of primate extraocular muscles and the changes of denervation. Brit. J. Ophthalmol., 58, 193-331.

Hirokawa, N., and J.E. Heuser (1981). Structural evidence that botulinum toxin blocks neuromuscular transmission by impairing the calcium influx that normally accompanies nerve depolarization. J. Cell Biol., 88, 160-171.

Hudlicka, O., K.R. Tyler, A.J.A. Wright, and A.M.A.R. Ziada (1984). Growth of capillaries in skeletal muscles. Prog. appl. Microcirc., 5, 44-61.

Large, J., and K.R. Tyler (1985). Changes in capillary distribution in rat fast muscles following nerve crush and reinnervation. J. Physiol. (Lond.), 362, 13-21.

Magoon, E.H. (1984). Botulinum toxin chemo-denervation for strabismus in infants and children. J. Pediat. Ophthalmol. Strabismus, 21, 110-112.

Mathers, D.A., and S. Thesleff (1978). Studies on neurotrophic regulation of murine skeletal muscle. J. Physiol. (Lond.), 282, 105-114.

Pachter, B.R. (1982). Fiber composition of the superior rectus extraocular muscle of the Rhesus monkey. J. Morphol., 174, 237-250.

Pestronk, A., and D.B. Drachman (1978). Motor nerve sprouting and acetylcholine receptors. Science, 199, 1223-1225.

Pestronk, A., D.B. Drachman, and J.W. Griffin (1976). Effect of botulinum toxin on trophic regulation of acetylcholine receptors. Nature (Lond.), 264, 787-788.

Pumplin, D.W., and T.S. Reese (1977). Action of brown widow spider venom and botulinum toxin on the frog neuromuscular junction examined with the freeze-fracture technique. J. Physiol. (Lond.), 273, 443-457.

Ringel, S.P., W.K. Engel, A.N. Bender, N.D. Peters, and R.D. Yee (1978). Histochemistry and acetylcholine receptor distribution in normal and denervated monkey extraocular muscles. Neurology, 28, 55-63.

Salviati, G., S. Pierobon-Bormioli, R. Betto, E. Damiani, C. Angelini, S.P. Ringel, S. Salvatori, and A. Margreth (1985). Tubular aggregates: sarcoplasmic reticulum origin, calcium storage ability, and functional implications. Muscle Nerve, 8, 299-306.

Scott, A.B. (1980).   Botulinum toxin injection into extraocular muscles as an alternative to strabismus surgery. Arch. Ophthalmol., 87, 1044-1049.

Scott, A.B., A. Rosenbaum, and C.C. Collins (1973). Pharmacologic weakening of extraocular muscles. Invest. Ophthalmol., 12, 924-927.

Sellin, L.C. (1981). The action of botulinum toxin at the neuromuscular junction. Med. Biol., 59, 11-20.

Shah, A.J., V. Sahgal, G. Muscchler, V. Subramani, and H. Singh (1982). Morphogenesis of the mitochondrial alterations in muscle diseases. J. Neurol. Sci., 55, 25-37.

Simpson, L.L. (1981). The origin, structure, and pharmacological activity of botulinum toxin. Pharmacol. Rev., 33, 155-188.

Spencer, R.F., and J.D. Porter (1981). Innervation and structure of monkey extraocular muscles in comparison to those of the cat. J. Comp. Neurol., 198, 649-665.

Thesleff, S. (1984). Transmitter release in botulinum-poisoned muscles. J. Physiol. (Paris), 79, 192-195.

Thesleff, S., and J. Molgo (1983). A new type of transmitter release at the neuromuscular junction. Neuroscience, 9, 1-8.

Tonge, D.A. (1974). Chronic effects of botulinum toxin on neuromuscular transmission and sensitivity to acetylcholine in slow and fast skeletal muscle of the mouse. J. Physiol. (Lond.), 241, 127-139.

Orbital Stiffness Changes Induced by Injection of Botulinum Toxin into Simian Extraocular Muscles

W. M. King, R. N. Yeaple and H. Metz

Departments of Physiology and Ophthalmology, University of
Rochester Medical Center, Rochester, NY 14642, USA

Intramuscular injections of botulinum A toxin (BTX) were first introduced by
A.B. Scott and co-workers (1973) as a surgical alternative to correct strabismus
in selected cases. Clinical experience to date shows that BTX is especially
effective in treating third and sixth nerve palsy (Scott 1980; Scott and Kraft
1985) and early endocrine ophthalmopathy (Scott 1984), but is less effective in
treating chronic sixth nerve palsy or longstanding endocrine ophthalmopathy
(Scott 1985). Clinical use of BTX has not, however, revealed the mechanism by
which BTX injections exert a long lasting effect on ocular alignment. Magoon
(1984) has suggested that the injected muscle elongates with time, thus allowing
a permanent position change. This assumption was not based upon actual measurements of muscle length, but was an inference based upon the change in ocular
position. Alternatively, a change in passive muscle stiffness could also alter
ocular alignment. Scott and Kraft (1985) have shown that medial rectus contractures secondary to chronic lateral rectus palsy can be released by BTX injections. The release of these contractures was associated with a complete limitation of adduction in the first three weeks after the injection. In addition,
these investigators demonstrated that the occurrence of medial rectus contracture in cases of total sixth nerve palsy can be prevented by BTX injection.
However, BTX treatment has had little effect on the tightness of muscles encountered in endocrine ophthalmopathy (Scott 1985), possibly because of the associated fibrotic changes in these muscles.

These data suggest that ocular re-alignment may result from structural changes
in extraocular muscle that alter muscle length, passive stiffness, and/or active
force generation. We have begun a series of experiments to examine these
suggestions, and to reveal the mechanisms by which BTX treatment can produce
permanent ocular re-alignment. In a series of preliminary experiments, we measured passive orbital stiffness of the intact globe-muscle system in three rhesus
monkeys (macacca mulatta) before and after injection of 1-2 U of botulinum toxin
into the medial rectus muscle of the left eye. During these measurements,
active stiffness caused by neural excitation was eliminated by anesthetizing the
monkeys with 2% halothane. The effectiveness of the anesthesia was confirmed by
comparing data collected when the monkey was pharmacologically paralyzed and
anesthetized with data collected under anesthesia alone. Orbital stiffness was
measured by pulling tangentially against the globe and rotating it in temporal
or nasal directions by means of fine vicryl sutures sewn into the sclera at the
limbus. While the eye was slowly rotated over a time course of several minutes,
changes in length and tension were measured simultaneously with a sensitivity
of 10 microns (length) or 1 mg (tension) using an opto-electronic transducer

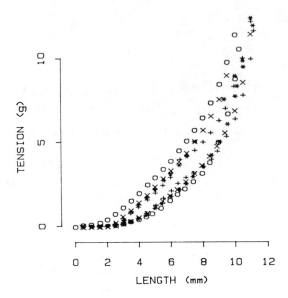

Fig. 1. Length- tension characteristics of left
eye during a temporal rotation. Data are
from four consecutive runs.

specifically developed for these experiments by R.N. Yeaple. The collected data
were entered into a computer and displayed as length-tension plots. Orbital
stiffness was calculated as the slope of the increasing length-tension characteristic, either over the first 6.0 mm of stretch or over the range of 0.5 to
4.5 grams of force. Both methods produced similar results. For these values of
length or tension, the length-tension characteristics were almost linear, and
could be fit by linear regressions with coefficients of determination (r-
squared) exceeding 0.98.

The length-tension characteristics for four consecutive temporal rotations of
the left eye during a representative experiment are shown in Fig. 1. For
changes in length up to 12 mm (ca. 50 deg rotations), the maximum change in tension was about 12 grams. Fig. 1 shows that the data were highly repeatable from
run to run, and always exhibited a marked hysteresis between pulling and releasing the globe. For these data, the stiffness was calculated to be 0.961 g/mm
with a coefficient of determination of 0.99.

Figure 2 shows the stiffness of the left eye as a function of time before and
after BTX injection into the left medial rectus muscle, and a subsequent tenotomy of the left lateral rectus muscle. Figure 2A shows the time course of
orbital stiffness changes for temporal rotations that stretched the injected
medial rectus muscle. Prior to the injection, stiffness was 1.00 g/mm. Injection of 2 units of BTX into this muscle with a hypodermic syringe did not significantly alter orbital stiffness measured 1 hour after the injection. However,
stiffness increased 22% 5 days after the injection, and did not return to its
control value until 19 days after the injection. This transient increase in
stiffness was not accompanied by a noticible strabismus in this monkey. Similar
increases in passive orbital stiffness were observed in two other monkeys
injected with BTX. In one of these animals, a control injection of an identical

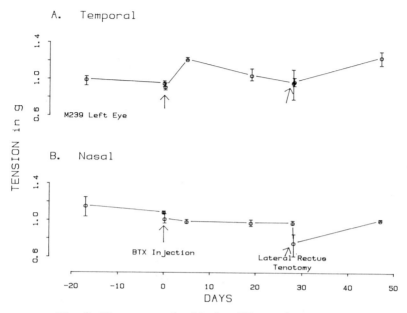

Fig. 2. Time course of orbital stiffness changes in
the left eye. At day zero, BTX was injected
into the left medial rectus. At day 28, a
tenotomy was performed on the left lateral
rectus muscle. A. Temporal rotations stretch
the medial rectus muscle. B. Nasal rotations
stretch the lateral rectus muscle. All data
in this figure and in Fig. 3 are from monkey 239.

volume of saline was made into the medial rectus of the right eye on the same
day as the BTX injection into the medial rectus of the left eye. An increase in
stiffness of the right eye was detected shortly after the saline injection, but
4 days later stiffness had returned to its control value. The results of this
experiment suggest that the increase in stiffness of BTX injected eyes was
induced by the toxin itself, and was not an irritative effect or edema caused by
the injection procedure. Figure 2B shows that there were no consistent changes
in passive stiffness for nasal rotations of the injected eye.

The time course of the BTX induced stiffness change was about three weeks, similar to the time course of adductive paralysis noted by Scott and Kraft (1985) in
their patients, and similar to the time course of morphological changes observed
in monkey extraocular muscles after BTX injection (Spencer and McNeer, this
volume). The increase in passive stiffness in the injected eye was an unanticipated finding, since BTX injections in contractured (stiff) muscle decrease passive stiffness (Scott and Kraft 1985). To provide a better comparison of our
data with that of Scott and Kraft, we weakened the left lateral rectus muscle by
performing a tenotomy on it 28 days after the medial rectus injection. By that
time, orbital stiffness had stabilized at pre-injection control values. Our
plan was to induce a contracture of the medial rectus muscle, that we could
relieve with BTX injections. Immediately after the tenotomy, we detected a
sharp drop in orbital stiffness for nasal rotations, that were previously
opposed by an intact lateral rectus muscle (Fig. 2B). There was no immediate
post-operative change in orbital stiffness for temporal rotations of the

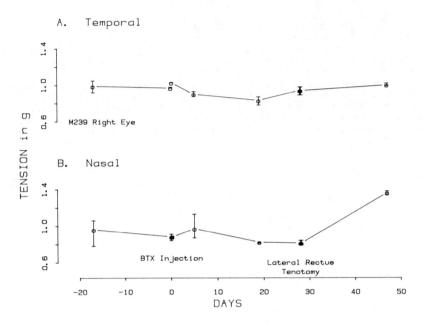

Fig. 3. Time course of orbital stiffness changes in
the unoperated right eye. A. Temporal
rotations. B. Nasal rotations.

tenotomized eye (Fig. 2A). However, three weeks after the tenotomy, orbital
stiffness for nasal rotation returned to its control value (Fig. 2B), suggesting
an effective re-attachment of the lateral rectus muscle to the globe. We also
recorded an expected increase in orbital stiffness for temporal rotations (Fig.
2A), presumably caused by partial contracture of the medial rectus muscle. However, Fig. 3B shows an unexpected finding of sharply increased stiffness for
nasal rotations of the unoperated control eye. There was no corresponding
change in stiffness of the control eye for temporal rotations (Fig. 3A), suggesting a selective stiffening of the right lateral rectus muscle. Since we did
not operate at all on this eye, the stiffness change must have been induced by a
behavioral strategy adopted by the monkey. For example, the monkey may have
attempted to fixate with his tenotomized left eye. To compensate for the weakened lateral rectus, innervation to the unopposed medial rectus muscle would
have to be reduced. According to Hering's Law, this strategy would result in
reduced innervation to the yoked lateral rectus muscle of the right eye. Alternatively, the monkey may have attempted to fuse by rotating his head to the
left, toward the weakened left lateral rectus muscle. This strategy would produce a rightward shift in eye position, resulting in an increased innervation to
the yoked lateral rectus. Either strategy implies a change in tonic innervation
to the lateral rectus muscle of the opposite eye that may have produced the
change in stiffness we detected. These ideas must, however, be regarded as
speculative, until they can be confirmed by direct measurements of eye position
and eye movement that are correlated with stiffness changes. Because of this
unexpected finding, we are continuing to follow this animal's recovery without
further BTX treatment of the partially contractured medial rectus muscle.

Our preliminary data demonstrate that passive stiffness changes are produced by
BTX injections or by tenotomy. The time course of these changes in BTX injected
eyes is consistent with their being produced by the toxin, and not by a nonspecific effect of the injection procedure. In normal muscle, stiffness
increases after BTX injection, an unanticipated finding that cannot be explained
at this time. We also find that lateral rectus tenotomy may induce stiffness
changes in the unoperated eye, that may be caused by a behavioral strategy
adopted by the monkey to compensate for the ocular misalignment or muscle weakness induced by the tenotomy. These findings suggest that orbital stiffness is
a sensitive indicator of altered orbital morphology or muscle coordination. In
future experiments we will examine the functional significance of these findings
by correlating stiffness changes with changes in muscle morphology and oculomotor performance.

ACKNOWLEDGEMENTS

This research was supported by PHS grants EY-05862 to R.N. Yeaple, and EY-04045
and BRSG RR05403 to W.M. King. It is a pleasure to acknowledge the invaluable
technical assistance of Kathy Frenz and Cindy Smith. Jeff Wyatt, DVM and Frank
Colgan, MD provided expert advice on the use of inhalation anesthesia.

REFERENCES

1. Magoon, E.H. (1984). Botulinum toxin chemo-denervation for strabismus in
infants and children. J. Pediat. Ophthalmol. Strabismus, 21, 110-112.

2. Scott, A.B. (1984). Injection treatment of endocrine orbital myopathy. Doc.
Ophthalmol., 58, 141-145.

3. Scott, A.B. and Kraft, S.P. (1985). Botulinum toxin injection in the management of lateral rectus paresis. Ophthalmology, 92, 676-683.

4. Scott, A.B., Rosenbaum, A. and Collins, C.C. (1973). Pharmacologic weakening
of extraocular muscles. Invest. Ophthalmol., 12, 924-927.

5. Spencer, R.F. and McNeer, K.W. Morphological basis of junctional or muscle
adaptation in pharmacological denervation of monkey extraocular muscles. (This
Volume).

Mechanical Correlates of Extraocular Muscle Contracture

C. C. Collins and A. Jampolsky

The Smith-Kettlewell Eye Research Foundation, San Francisco,
California, USA

INTRODUCTION

In this paper we will discuss muscle motor adaptations, comparing normal, contractured (sometimes called contracted) and "stretched" muscles. We will emphasize contractures that occur in strabismus problems, comparing the muscle characteristics of unoperated patients with those of operated esotropic and exotropic patients with recessed muscles, having large and small deviations. We will show that all of these cases exhibit a wide variation of motor adaptations which can lead to a wide variation of passive mechanical characteristics of the muscles.

Extraocular muscles can become contractured (shortened) in three different ways:

1) Naturally, e.g., 6th nerve palsy, lateral incomitancy, etc.
2) By surgery, e.g., a recessed muscle which later took up its slack.
3) Through maintained eye position, e.g., a large strabismic deviation in which the slack muscle took up the slack and consequently became shorter (by a mechanism of contracture discussed later). Generally this short muscle subsequently stretches its antagonist which becomes permanently longer (by the inverse of the contracture mechanism).

We will address a number of clinical problems resulting from the contracture of an extraocular muscle. Two particular problems are: 1) the rapid recurrence of a contracture due to the tonic, shortening force of a muscle which is unopposed by a stretched, weakened antagonist, and 2) the magnitude of strabismus surgery depends upon the **balancing** of the force between the operated muscle and its antagonist. The first problem is illustrated by a large eso deviation from a previous medial rectus muscle recession. The medial rectus became contractured and subsequently stretched out the lateral rectus muscle which is now slack while the eye is in the primary position. In this case, the esotropia recurs because the shorter medial rectus takes up its slack sooner than the now longer lateral rectus muscle. In such cases it is also necessary to resect the lateral rectus muscle so that the muscles are more nearly the same length and the slack will be taken up equally. Then the mechanical characteristics of each muscle will remain balanced around the primary position as required for stable orthophoria.

The second problem is illustrated by the fact that the muscle opposing the contractured muscle has an effect on the necessary amount of surgery. Recessing a muscle of a normal eye produces a certain angle of deviation determined by the opposing spring return forces of the opposite muscle (the "pullover" effect).

27

Less deviation or effect is produced if the opposite muscle is weak or has been recessed since in this case there is not as much "pullover" force. On the other hand, if the other muscle is contractured, exerting a stronger force, one observes a greater effect from the same recession. All this depends upon whether the opposite muscle forces are normal, weak or strong. So the opposite muscle must be taken into consideration.

The major motor adaptation we will describe is the process of contracture, a muscle taking up its slack. One piece of evidence for muscles taking up their slack is the patient with exotropia whose inferior obliques are overacting, which is typical in large degree exotropia. How can this happen? One hypothesis is that in an exotropic eye both obliques are on the slack. By the process of contracture they subsequently take up their slack, becoming shorter and thereby overacting (Jampolsky, 1957).

All clinicians are aware that if they recess a muscle it takes up its slack. No matter whether they recess it a little or a lot, it takes up the slack appropriately. If the surgeon attempts to put such a muscle back from whence it came, he will find that it will now be restrictive.

In order to study the nature of contracture in human eye muscles, we have made physical length-tension measurements of the passive mechanical properties of eye muscles in consenting patients undergoing corrective surgery for strabismus. These measurements have been compared with, and found to validate simpler clinical assessments of muscle mechanics. These measurements have permitted descriptions of the salient mechanical characteristics of contractured muscles and some of their clinical sequelae which are reported here.

METHODS

Selection of cases was made on the basis of a diagnosis of at least one short, contractured (clinically so-called "tight") muscle detected at the time of surgery.

We have measured 56 muscles from 32 patients who met these criteria. Fifteen of these measured muscles were from strabismus patients not previously operated upon (i.e., with strabismus of natural origin). The remaining 41 muscles were from patients previously operated upon. Twenty two of these latter muscles had been previously recessed (12 medial rectus and 10 lateral rectus muscles). Eleven of these had deviations of 30 prism diopters or greater (9 exo, 2 eso).

In the method of measurement of the length-tension characteristics of the individual medial and lateral rectus muscles of strabismus surgical patients, we have utilized specially instrumented eye forceps which have been previously described (Collins, 1978). The protocol and methods for collecting patient data have also been described earlier (Collins and Jampolsky, 1981).

In all cases the following measurement protocol was observed:

1) After full surgical anesthesia, the length-tension forceps were utilized to grasp the muscle suture and the forceps were maintained perpendicular to the muscle suture (within $\pm$ 10°) at all times to avoid cosine angle artifacts. 2) The globe was held accurately in primary position with surgical forceps by the assisting surgeon. 3) The severed muscle tendon stump was then held in apposition to its original insertion point on the globe. 4) This primary muscle length was recorded for subsequent length reference as the zero point on the length axis of the length-tension curve. 5) By means of the length-tension forceps the muscle was slowly extended (not exceeding 2 mm/sec to avoid adding artifactual viscous forces). 6) The muscle was then slowly permitted to become shorter, to some 4 mm shorter than the slack condition of the muscle in order to establish the zero force calibration.

The length-tension curves were subsequently compared with a number of clinical assessments including the limitations of eye rotations measured preoperatively in the office to determine their correlations with the "presumptive diagnosis" of deficient movement.

Of crucial diagnostic importance is the exact resting position of the eye and the relative values of the passive spring forces of the extraocular muscles which determine this resting eye position. Clinical methods of assessing these mechanical entities comprise intraoperative tests including forced ductions, the amount of "spring-over" of the eye when one muscle is detached, and the "springback test". In the springback test the globe is moved rapidly back and forth to free it up, i.e. reducing sources of static friction such as fibrin clots or thixotropic hysteresis. The globe is then released from one side and the resting point to which it returns is noted. The globe is then released from the other side and the resting point to which it returns from this direction is also noted. The rationale of the springback test is discussed later.

The springback test and the amount of "spring-over" of the eye on detaching a muscle are useful correlative measurements permitting comparative clinical assessments of the relative stiffness of two opposed, passive extraocular muscles, while length-tension measurements provide an absolute measure of the pertinent mechanical characteristics of each muscle.

For baseline comparison four normal extraocular muscles were measured. Measurements of normal muscles were obtained from operations on the normal unaffected and previously unoperated eye of strabismus patients only when it was clinically indicated as the best planned procedure for the patient (such as bimedial recessions for a monocular sixth nerve palsy).

RESULTS

Our primary data is presented graphically as length-tension curves of selected representative, abnormal medial rectus muscles. Both contractured and stretched muscles are compared with the length-tension characteristics of a normal medial rectus muscle in Fig. 1. In all cases the horizontal axis is calibrated in millimeters change of muscle length relative to the primary length and in equivalent degrees of eye rotation nasally and temporally from the primary position (0 on the graph). Increasing length is to the right, extending the muscle. The vertical axis is calibrated with tick marks for every ten grams of tension applied to the muscle. The baseline is zero grams.

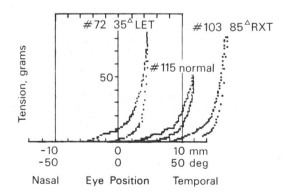

Fig. 1. From left to right: typical contractured, normal and stretched human medial rectus muscle length-tension characteristics (see text for details).

In Fig. 1 the length-tension characteristic of a normal passive medial rectus muscle is shown as the middle curve of the three. This record was obtained from the right eye of a 19 year old male patient (#115) who suffered a traumatic sixth nerve palsy of the left eye. This and other passive human eye muscles measured in this study and in previous investigations (Robinson and others, 1969; Collins, 1975) exhibited some 25 grams of tension when extended to the equivalent of extreme gaze length (10 mm beyond its primary length, or 50° of eye rotation).

A passive contractured medial rectus muscle length-tension curve (of patient #72, a 45 year old male with 35 prism diopters of left esotropia) is presented on the left in Fig. 1. In this case it will be noted that the 25 gram point occurs at about 12° of temporal rotation. This contractured muscle is some 7 mm shorter than normal. However, it will be noted that the shape of the length-tension curve rather closely duplicates that of the normal muscle (moved 7 mm horizontally). The passive contractured muscle appears as a normal muscle except for its length (measured to its slack point, or zero force starting point on the graph).

A limitation of rotation of this eye occurred at 20° (40 prism diopters) of abduction (temporal gaze) due to the restriction imposed by the tether of this short muscle (clinically diagnosed as a -2 abduction limitation on a scale of limitations from 0 to 4). This tether is shown in the length-tension diagram as the very stiff (steep) region at the temporal termination of the medial rectus muscle extension.

In comparing these two normal and contractured medial rectus muscles, the passive slack length of the normal muscle is one or two mm greater than its primary length, which is typical of measurements made under general anesthesia. The absolute resting or slack length of a normal medial rectus muscle is 38 mm. The contractured muscle is 7 mm or 18% shorter than this 38 mm absolute slack length in the passive state.

It may be noted that the stiffness of these passive muscles (the slope of the length-tension curve) below 10 grams shows that the normal muscle stiffness is approximately 1.5 grams per millimeter, while the contractured muscle shows a stiffness of about 1.75 grams per millimeter, or about 17% greater stiffness. This small stiffness increase is in accord with Young's modulus of elasticity, i.e., as for any elastic body, the stiffness of a muscle is inversely proportional to its length just due to physics. However, such a small stiffness increase is not generally clinically significant. But a doubling of stiffness could be of clinical importance.

The right-most curve in Fig. 1 is the passive length-tension characteristic curve of the medial rectus muscle of a 14 year old male patient (#103), a large angle (85 prism diopter) exotrope. This is a stretched muscle which has become extended some 5 mm beyond normal length as a consequence of being paired with a previously recessed and subsequently contractured (short) lateral rectus muscle. In this case there is no restriction of eye movement since the tether region of the muscle lies well beyond the normal range of extreme gaze. As expected, in the preoperative clinical assessment of eye rotations, it was noted that there was no limitation of rotation in temporal gaze caused by this stretched medial rectus muscle. The magnitude and shape of the length-tension characteristics of this stretched muscle appear quite normal (except for the 5 mm horizontal extension).

It was surprising to find that contractured short and stretched long muscles can show normal passive length-tension characteristics, that they can appear as normal muscles except for their adapted length. In these cases it appears that a normal passive length-tension curve has simply shifted toward or away from primary muscle length. But not all of the strabismic muscles we have measured have appeared normal.

In exotropia the lateral rectus muscle is generally contractured and short which results in the medial rectus muscle being stretched longer than normal (as shown in the right curve of Fig. 1). However, this situation does not always pertain. Figure 2 presents the length-tension characteristics of the right medial rectus muscle of a 35 prism diopter exotrope (patient #107, a 42 year old male). This medial rectus muscle has <u>not</u> been stretched, it is very stiff, displays an abrupt tether and has resisted stretching. (The surgical treatment for this type of muscle will be discussed later.)

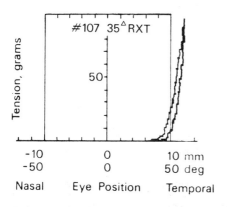

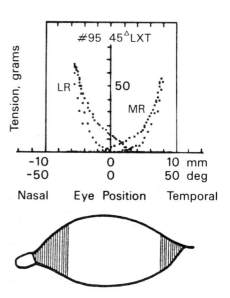

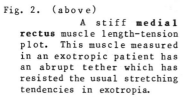

Fig. 2. (above)
     A stiff **medial**
rectus muscle length-tension
plot. This muscle measured
in an exotropic patient has
an abrupt tether which has
resisted the usual stretching
tendencies in exotropia.

Fig. 3. (above right; left curve) The stiff lateral rectus muscle and (right curve) the medial rectus muscle length-tension characteristics measured in an **exotropic** patient diagnosed as exhibiting lateral incomitance. (Below) In the sketch of the eye the shaded portions indicate the limitations of voluntary rotations, -1 1/2 adduction, -1 abduction.

The last case which we present in this brief paper is a 15 year old male patient (#95) with 45 prism diopters of left alternating exotropia who had two previous operations (originally for esotropia and subsequently for a resulting exotropia). This patient was diagnosed as exhibiting lateral incomitancy. The length-tension measurements of both the lateral rectus and medial rectus muscles are shown in Fig. 3. In this case each muscle was both short (contractured) <u>and</u> physically stiff which resulted in restrictions in both nasal and temporal gaze. In the sketch of the eye below, the shaded portions of the eye indicate the observed limitations of voluntary eye rotations (clinically diagnosed preoperatively in the office as a -1 1/2 adduction limitation and a -1 abduction limitation). These clinical assessments can be seen to correlate quite well with the tether locations in the length-tension measurements of Fig. 3.

DISCUSSION

From these clinically assessed and objectively measured findings it can be seen
that informed strabismus surgery must be guided by a knowledge of the mechanical
characteristics of the muscles involved. For instance, in considering the
exotropic case of the medial rectus muscle of Fig. 2 (patient #107) with a stiff
and abrupt tether, the surgeon should not treat such a muscle as he would the
stretched out medial rectus muscle normally occurring in exotropia. Much less
surgery is required on such a stiff muscle as this to bring the eye into
alignment. In this case the usual formula for strabismus surgery called for 6
mm resection of the medial rectus muscle (and 7 mm LR recession) which would
have resulted in a gross overcorrection and unnecessary limitation of eye
rotation. The successful surgery performed was only 3 mm resection of the
medial rectus muscle (and 9 mm LR recession).

Another example is the contractured lateral rectus muscle of the lateral
incomitancy case shown in Fig. 3 (patient #95). Any recession of this
physically stiff lateral rectus muscle would cause a large, more than normal
nasal shift, and surgery by formula would produce unexpected and undesirable
results. It is this kind of problem that produces difficulties for surgeons
using formulas.

The stiffness of this lateral rectus muscle could also be detected clinically by
detaching the medial rectus muscle and observing the resultant large temporal
"spring-over" such as would occur due to the strong lateral rectus "pullover"
force. If the lateral rectus muscle exerted only a weak force there would be
only a small temporal spring-over shift of the eye, and a length-tension
measurement in such a case would show that the lateral rectus muscle was not
stiff.

Not only must the surgeon deal with the agonist muscle, he must also deal with
the antagonist. Either or both of these may be abnormal, short and/or stiff or
short with normal stiffness. This is what can lead to untoward effects if the
surgeon is not familiar with the mechanical characteristics of each of the
muscles. The surgeon can measure these mechanical characteristics with the
springback test, the spring-over effect or lenth-tension measurements.

Now let us review the measurable elements which describe the mechanical
characteristics of a muscle. Figure 4 indicates that the length-tension
characteristics of passive extraocular muscles can be described in terms of a
few clinically significant measurable elements:

A) **Muscle slack length** (measured as the point of zero force and recorded with
    respect to the primary length of the muscle).
B) **Muscle primary length** (measured with the globe held accurately in the
    primary position). This is the reference or zero length from which all
    other lengths are generally measured. The absolute value of the primary
    length is 36 mm for the medial rectus muscle and 41 mm for the lateral
    rectus muscle.
C) **Tether or restriction length** (measured with respect to the primary length
    of the muscle and corresponding to the eye position at the locale of the
    tether stiffness which causes the restriction).
    This tether length is probably a better clinical measure of muscle length
    because it is more definite and easier to measure than the traditional
    slack length and it is in fact responsible for limitations of eye movement.
D) **Average muscle stiffness** measured in the transition region between muscle
    slack length and its restricted or tether length.
E) **Tether stiffness** (measured beyond the restricted or tether length). This
    is usually 20-30 times the average muscle stiffness. The tether stiffness
    is actually only of academic interest. As stated above, it is the tether
    length which is of clinical importance.

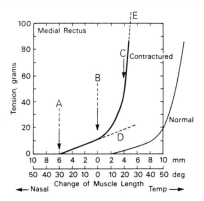

Fig. 4. The clinically significant measurable mechanical
elements of passive human extraocular muscles:
A. Slack length
B. Primary length
C. Tether length
D. Average muscle stiffness
E. Tether stiffness

These are the mechanical characteristics the surgeon should be aware of if he
wishes to minimize the number of operations. These characteristics can be
measured by intra-operative tests leading to successful surgical management.

One of these clinical intraoperative tests, the springback test, can perhaps be
better understood from Fig. 5 (left), a graphical depiction of the interaction
of tissue stiffness (solid inclined line) tending to pull the globe towards its
true resting position (primary position for a normal eye) and the impeding
frictional force (dashed horizontal lines) tending to stop this center-ward
movement short of the true resting position of the eye. In the springback test,
when released from one side or the other, the eye will stop at a springback
return point where the spring force becomes equal to, and is thus cancelled by,
the opposing static frictional force. This is not the true resting position of
the eye.

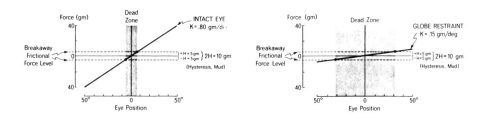

Fig. 5. (left diagram) An illustration of the springback
range (dead zone) resulting from the friction of
the ocular tissues preventing the intact eye from
returning all the way to its true resting position
(right curve). The springback range observed when
the muscles are detached from the globe.

The bisector (or average) of the springback return points from two different directions determines the true resting position of the eye. A valid passive resting position of the eye is otherwise generally difficult to establish because the eye stays wherever it is put within the "dead zone" existing between these springback return points.

In Fig. 5 (left diagram) it can be seen that stiffer tissues (the eye with muscles attached) result in a small dead zone. In the right diagram of Fig. 5, less stiff tissues (the globe with muscles detached) result in a large dead zone.

The angular difference between the two springback return points (the dead zone) is called the springback range. The magnitude of this springback range is an inverse measure of the spring return forces exerted by the passive muscles and globe tissues against the assumedly fixed restraining frictional (hysteresis) forces of the globe. This inverse relationship means that a high stiffness results in a very small springback range, and a low stiffness results in a large springback range. Normally the springback range is fairly small, indicating normal passive extraocular muscle elastic forces. If a muscle is abnormal, the range will generally be smaller or larger than this normal springback range. This simple observation can be used to great clinical advantage.

We here wish to point out again our surprise on finding that contractured short and stretched long muscles can show normal passive length-tension characteristics, that they can appear as **normal muscles** except for their adapted length. The results of our measurements of the mechanical characteristics of extraocular muscles tend to confirm the findings in the literature for skeletal muscles (Goldspink and others, 1974) that contracture is an adaptive mechanism resulting in a shortening of a muscle which does not usually appear to affect its contractile properties. Although a few contractured muscles exhibit a significant increase in passive stiffness, most contractured muscles do not. From observation of their passive length-tension relationships, except for their inappropriate length, most contractured muscles appear to be otherwise mechanically **normal**, healthy, and completely functional muscles which have taken up their slack (by a reduction in the number of series sarcomeres comprising the muscle) to adapt to a new, if inappropriate, length. This conclusion is also supported by further morphological studies (Martinez, Hay and McNeer , 1976; Spencer and McNeer, 1980).

The opposite effect, the adaptive stretching of a muscle to a new and longer length over a period of time, appears to be governed by the same physiological process, that is, the adjustment of (in this case adding to, rather than subtracting from) the number of sarcomeres in series making up the length of the muscle, as described by Goldspink and others.

Further evidence for the adaptability of extraocular muscles is the observation that relaxation by pharmacological denervation and consequent stretching of a contractured muscle results in release and elimination of the contracture (Scott and Kraft, 1985). In addition, Jampolsky (unpublished) has completely relieved a medial rectus muscle contracture (due to a sixth nerve palsy) by repeatedly performing a forcible temporal forceps duction of the eye, stretching out the contracture over a period of a few weeks.

In conclusion, the traditional assumption on which "formulas" for surgery have been predicated has been that all extraocular muscles are normal or average and perfectly uniform, as if the medial rectus and lateral rectus muscles were always the same and as predictable as rubber bands in parallel with pieces of leather, with equal mechanical properties such as their length-tension characteristics. Our measurements indicate that this assumption is quite incorrect and that this unwarranted assumption of muscle equality explains why there is such a large number of reoperations in strabismus surgery performed by traditional formulas. The millimeters of surgery cannot be based on the existing deviation alone as taught by past dogma. The stiffness and length of each muscle must be considered separately in a rational and objective approach to strabismus surgery.

One cannot always predict the mechanical characteristics of muscles. One can find normal length-tension characteristics of muscles in abnormal patients and one can find abnormal mechanical characteristics in relatively normal strabismus patients. And even in large degrees of strabismus one may find a stiff medial rectus muscle in exotropia which is not stretched as usual. These types of variations are what cause multiple reoperations.

To succeed with strabismus surgery in such cases, one should measure the length-tension characteristics of each muscle, or at least make relative comparisons of the stiffnesses of opposing muscles such as provided by the springback test and the spring-over of the eye on detaching one muscle. An increased incidence of successful surgery lies in using this type of information effectively.

REFERENCES

Collins, C.C. (1975). The human oculomotor control system. In G. Lennerstrand, P. Bach-y-Rita (Eds.), Basic Mechanisms of Ocular Motility and Their Clinical Implications. Permagon Press, Ltd., Oxford, England. pp. 145-180.

Collins, C.C. (1978). Length tension recording strabismus forceps. In C. Sousa-Dias (Ed.), Smith-Kettlewell Symposium on Basic Sciences in Strabismus: Mechanical and Tonic Factors on Strabismus Diagnosis and Surgery, Annex to the V Congress of the Conselho Latino-Americano de Estrabismo (C.L.A.D.E.), Oficinas das Edicoes Loyola, Sao Paolo. pp. 7-19.

Collins, C.C. and A. Jampolsky (1981). Objective calculation of strabismus surgery. In G. Lennerstrand, E. Keller and A. Scott (Eds.), Functional Basis of Ocular Motility Disorders. Permagon Press, Ltd., Oxford, England. pp. 185-194.

Goldspink, G., C. Tabarg, J.C. Tabary, C. Tardieu and G. Tardieu (1974). Effect of denervation on the adaptation of sarcomere number and muscle extensibility to the functional length of the muscle. J. Physiol., 236, 733-742.

Jampolsky, A. (1957). Bilateral anomalies of the oblique muscles. Trans. Am. Acad. Ophthalmol. Otolaryngol., 61, 689-698.

Martinez, A.J., S. Hay and K.W. McNeer (1976) Extraocular muscles light microscopy and ultrastructural features. Acta. Neuropath. (Berl.), 34, 237-253.

Robinson, D.A., D.O'Meara, A.B. Scott and C.C. Collins (1969) The mechanical components of human eye movements. J. Appl. Physiol., 26, 548-553.

Scott, A.B. (1985) Botulinum toxin injection in the management of lateral rectus paresis. Ophthalmology, 92, No. 5, 676-683.

Spencer, R.F. and K. McNeer (1980) Structural alterations in overacting inferior oblique muscles. Arch. Ophthalmol., 98, 128-133.

The Bielschowsky Head-tilt Phenomenon is Exacerbated by Vertical-recti Overaction — Why?

D. A. Robinson

Department of Ophthalmology, The Johns Hopkins University,
Baltimore, MD 21205, USA

Three issues concerning the Bielschowsky head-tilt phenomenon are examined. The first leads to the suggestion that a superior oblique (SO) palsy by itself is inadequate to produce the results usually seen on clinical examination and that leads to the proposal that other muscles are behaving abnormally. The second is which muscles are involved and how are they changed? Finally, is the net result beneficial or maladaptive?

Hofmann and Bielschowsky Were Only Partly Right

The first issue is raised by the observation that many patients with a SO palsy have elevations of that eye, with the head upright, of as much as 8-10 deg. From force measurements on human extra-ocular muscles (Robinson and co-workers, 1969) one can estimate that in the primary position, the SO exerts about 2.6 g on the eye of which only 1.5 g acts to depress it. Collins and colleagues (1981) showed that when a force is applied to the globe it rotates at a rate of 1.0 g/deg. Thus the loss of 1.5 g after a SO palsy might be expected, roughly, to cause the eye to elevate by 1.5 deg. There seems to be a serious conflict between theory and clinical findings.

When the patient's head is tilted ipsilaterally, many show an elevation in the palsied eye of 15-25 deg. Yet the otolith stimulus for this is quite weak. When the head tilts in roll, a vestigial otolith-ocular reflex, more vigorous in lower animals, counter-rolls the eye by only about 7 deg at most in humans. As suggested by Hofmann and Bielschowsky (1900) this is accomplished in the ipsilateral eye by simultaneous contractions of the superior rectus (SR) and SO - the former raises and intorts, the latter depresses and intorts. Normally the torsion forces add, the vertical forces cancel and the eye simply intorts. With a SO palsy, the SR is unopposed and the eye elevates. But if the eye is only to be intorted by 7 deg, each of the vertical recti and obliques need make an effort appropriate to only about 5 deg (considering vector summation) and since only about 70% of the SO action goes into depression (again due to vector summation) one could crudely estimate that the involved eye would further elevate by about 3.5 deg on head tilt to a total elevation of 5 deg (3.5 + 1.5). Again, our knowledge of eye muscle mechanics is incompatible with the quantitative attempt to predict the results of a SO palsy from the theory of Hofmann and Bielschowsky. Their ideas are correct for a starting point but they alone cannot explain quantitatively what is seen in the clinic.

To eliminate the rough estimations above, a model eye for strabismus was tested (Miller and Robinson, 1984; Robinson, 1975). This model utilizes the lengths, strengths, paths and force-innervation-length relationships of the six extra-ocular muscles to calculate the innervations needed to hold the eye in any position, the position that the eye will assume, normal or abnormal, given any innervation set and the corrections that would occur for any type of muscle surgery. The model is currently being tested clinically at the Smith-Kettlewell Institute of Visual Sciences in San Francisco by J.M. Miller and colleagues and the extent to which it can aid in diagnosis and guide planned surgery is being investigated. It has, however, one interesting virtue: it is a public eyeball. Anyone with an hypothesis about eye-muscle mechanics or strabismus surgery can, provided it can be translated into numbers, work their will upon it and test their hypothesis. The model is by no means perfect and several details need further clarification, but it does a rather good job in predicting the results of simple palsies and common types of surgery so that it forms a reasonable testing ground for trying out ideas. The Bielschowsky head-tilt phenomenon is a case in point.

This model was given a SO palsy with the head upright. The model eye elevated by only 2.4 deg. This is larger than the crude estimate of 1.5 deg above but that did not take into account the interactions of all of the remaining five muscles and passive tissues. Further, when an ipsilateral head tilt was simu-lated by asking the palsied eye to intort by 7 deg, it elevated to 4.1 deg. Again, this differs from the crude estimation above of 5 deg, probably for similar reasons. The point is that computer simulation confirms our suspicion that elevations seen in the clinic cannot be accounted for by the conventional explanation of Hofmann and Bielschowsky; they are much too large.

One may, of course, conclude that the model is wrong, but it simply could not be that wrong. Modest changes in estimates of muscle length or strength or the path each takes across the globe to its origin would make equally modest changes in the elevation upon head tilt but could never increase the predicted value of 4 deg to the range 15-25 deg. Thus, whether the model replicates the human eye in every detail or not, it confirms the suspicion that while Hofmann and Bielschowsky were certainly correct, other things must be happening as a consequence of a SO palsy.

The Vertical Recti Also Overact

To answer the second issue the parameters of the model were altered, muscle by muscle, to simulate contractures or overactions, see the effect on the head-tilt phenomenon and try to simulate clinical observations. The latter were drawn largely from a study by Simonsz and colleagues (1985). They discovered, in 23 cases, that patients with a SO palsy older than six months had a signi-ficantly exaggerated Bielschowsky head-tilt phenomenon compared with cases of shorter duration. In recent cases, with head upright, the average elevation of the involved eye for straight-ahead fixation was 3.8 deg; the average extorsion was 6.4 deg. Upon ipsilateral head tilt, the former value rose to 8.2, the latter fell to 2.0 deg. It is important to note the angles of torsion since many maneuvers with the model could easily increase the elevation but would create incorrect torsions. For example, increasing the passive force of the inferior oblique (IO) to simulate a contracture elevated the eye and increased the further elevation on ipsilateral head tilt but decreased the change in intorsion on head tilt which, in the model, was too small to start with.

Details of these manipulations are given in Robinson (1985) but the main read-justments that proved successful in simulating the clinical data were: 1) a contracture of the IO coupled with an underaction and 2) an overaction of both the SR and inferior rectus (IR). The latter was, not surprisingly, the most effective method of all since it is these muscles that largely create the

Bielschowsky head-tilt phenomenon in the first place and making them more sensitive to the otolith signal makes them exaggerate the phenomenon in both elevation and intorsion, just as is observed in patients.

What is perhaps equally important is what did not work. Manipulations of the
horizontal recti and the stiffnesses of the muscles relative to the passive
orbital tissue did little or nothing. Changes in the vertical recti and IO
opposite to those indicated made the phenomenon smaller, not larger. Thus,
there was not a great deal of ambiguity about the model, only a few things worked, most did not, so the model pointed fairly specifically to overaction of the
vertical recti. The conclusion to be drawn is that shortly after a SO palsy
(how soon is not known) a reaction occurs that creates overaction of at least
the SR and probably the IR as well. Obviously hypertrophy of these muscles
would make them overact but this seems less likely than a change in innervation
from the central nervous system.

In patients with SO palsies older than six months, the mean vertical deviation
with the head upright was 8.1 deg, rising to 15 deg on ipsilateral head tilt.
If there was any question before of the necessity of invoking overactions of the
vertical recti to explain the data, there is none here. It is impossible to
even approach these deviations in any other way except vertical-recti overactions. The conclusion is that what began as a mild overaction continues in
many patients to increase with time.

Is Overaction Adaptive?

Unfortunately the answer to this question remains unknown. Since overaction of
the vertical recti apparently makes the elevation of the involved eye worse it
is hard to see how any benefit comes of it, yet there are so many examples of
adaptation and compensation in motor behavior - the basis of this conference -
that it is difficult to accept the idea that these reactions are occurring without purpose.

Recently Kommerell and Klein (1985) proposed such a purpose. If the gain of the
otolith-ocular reflex were increased in roll, it would, of course, make the
Bielschowsky phenomenon worse for ipsilateral head tilt but, by the same token,
it would decrease the elevation of the involved eye more rapidly on contralateral tilt thus requiring patients to tilt their heads less to recapture
binocular vision. In support of this view they investigated a patient with a
SO palsy of 6 years duration whose involved eye elevated 28 deg as the head
tilted from contralateral to ipsilateral. They found that the normal eye ex-
torted by 18 deg for similar tilts but of only 30 deg, about twice normal. This
is clearly an increased gain for the otolith-ocular reflex. This reflex hyperactivity had disappeared upon examination one year after corrective surgery.

This hypothesis is supported in part by the study of Simonsz and colleagues
(1985). Three of their 23 patients, two old cases and one recent, had a counter-
rolling in the intact eye, as the head was tilted from 45 deg in one direction
to 45 in the other, of 15.8, 18.2 and 21 deg. Since 11 deg is normal, the
figures suggest an increase in the otolith-ocular response of from 50 to 100%.
On the other hand, the remaining 20 patients had normal or even hypometric
counter-rolling suggesting that this strategy is not adopted by most patients.
Further, in this study the group of patients with lesions older than six months
developed, on average, elevations of the involved eye that increased for all
head positions. Even with the head tilted contralaterally, an elevation of 4.0
deg persisted. Thus the tropias became worse regardless of head position. An
additional problem is why, in the patient of Kommerell and Klein, was an increase in the gain of the otolith-ocular reflex accompanied by a further elevation of the eye with the head upright since this acts to defeat the purpose of
the adaptation.

It has also been suggested that the increasing elevation of the palsied eye is
an attempt to increase the tropia and aid in suppression of vision in the
palsied eye. Unfortunately little is known about how this is dealt with by such
patients once contralateral head tilt no longer works. Even before that, they
have loss of fusion in cyclorotation and their central handling of this is unknown. Contralateral head tilt, which improves the vertical tropia, worsens
the torsional tropia. In short, little is known about the visual psychophysics
of these patients, vis a vis binocular vision, and without such knowledge it may
be difficult to understand the motor response.

ACKNOWLEDGEMENTS

The author's laboratory is supported by Grant EY00598 from the National Eye
Institute. Computer facilities were supported in part from Grant EY01765 from
the National Eye Institute.

REFERENCES

Collins, C. C., M. R. Carlson, A. B. Scott, and A. Jampolsky (1981). Extra-
    ocular muscle forces in normal human subjects. Invest. Ophthalmol. & Vis.
    Sci., 20, 652-664.
Hofmann, F. B., and A. Bielschowsky (1900). Die Verwertung der Kopfneigung zur
    Diagnostik von Augenmuskellähmungen aus der Heber- und Senkergruppe.
    Albrecht von Graefe's Arch. f. Ophthalmol., 51, 174-185.
Kommerell, G., and U. Klein (1985). Das ungelöste Problem des Bielschowsky-
    Kopfneigephänomens. Vortrag beim überregionalen Orthoptistinnentreffen,
    Freiburg.
Miller, J. M., and D. A. Robinson (1984). A model of the mechanics of binocular
    alignment. Comput. & Biomed. Res., 17, 436-470.
Robinson, D. A. (1975). A quantitative analysis of extraocular muscle coopera-
    tion and squint. Invest. Ophthalmol., 14, 801-825.
Robinson, D. A. (1985). Bielschowsky head-tilt test. II. Quantitative mechan-
    ics of the Bielschowsky head-tilt test. Vision Res., in press.
Robinson, D. A., D. M. O'Meara, A. B. Scott, and C. C. Collins (1969). Mechani-
    cal components of human eye movements. J. Appl. Physiol., 26, 548-553.
Simonsz, H. J., R. A. Crone, J. van der Meer, C. F. Merckel-Timmer, and A. M.
    van Mourik-Noordenbos (1985). Bielschowsky head-tilt test. I. Ocular
    counterrolling and Bielschowsky head-tilt test in 23 cases of superior
    oblique palsy. Vision Res., in press.

Comment on the Bielschowsky Head-tilt Phenomenon

G. Kommerell

Department of Ophthalmology, University of Freiburg, FRG

When we learned about Dr. Robinson's calculations that lack of the superior oblique torque would account for a Bielschowsky head-tilt phenomenon (BHP) of only 2.8°, we considered two possibilities to explain the much greater BHPs frequently encountered in the clinic: Firstly, in a fourth nerve palsy, degenerating motoneurons could influence brainstem circuitry. Secondly, visual feedback (double vision?) could be responsible. To sort out these two possibilities, we searched for a patient with a superior oblique palsy of mechanical, rather than neural origin. Fortunately, such a patient turned up (described in detail in: G. Kommerell and U. Klein: Adaptive changes of the otolith-ocular reflex after injury to the trochlea. Neuro-ophthalmology, in press).

The patient's right trochlea had been severed by a glass fragment six years previously. He showed a huge BHP of 28°. Myotomy of the right inferior oblique almost completely corrected his deviations in the various directions of gaze with the head upright, but left his BHP at 23°. In the following year, the BHP spontaneously decreased to 10° without further therapy. This led us to consider that we were dealing with an adaptive process. Increasing the gain of his otolith-ocular reflex (OOR) after injury might have allowed the patient to achieve binocular single vision using only a small head-tilt to his left (contralateral) shoulder.

Our examination findings supported this hypothesis. Before surgery, the patient had good stereopsis with a contralateral head-tilt of only 10° (using also his fusional capacity, a factor not recognized in Dr. Robinson's discussion of our patient; see previous article in this book). While taking advantage of the increased gain of the OOR on contralateral head-tilt, the patient had to put up with the large vertical deviation on ipsilateral head-tilt. He did this by avoiding ipsilateral head-tilt in everyday life. Surgery in the adapted condition corrected the vertical deviation for the head erect position making the increased gain of the OOR superfluous. Our hypothesis that gain changes of the OOR were indeed taking place was supported by the photographically documented fact that counterrolling of the unaffected left eye decreased from 18° to 5°, in parallel with the diminution of the BHP.

The changes described above look like a purposeful adaptation in the interest of binocular vision. However, we cannot yet explain why, when the gain of the OOR was increased, the exacerbated vertical deviation was not confined to ipsilateral head-tilt, but was also present, although to a lesser degree, in the head erect position. This fact requires to invoke an additional, yet unknown factor.

41

PATHOLOGY AND ADAPTATION IN
VISUAL PATHWAYS

Spatial Mechanisms for Visual Acuity Deficits in Strabismic and Anisometropic Amblyopia — Developmental Failure or Adaptation?

M. C. Flom, H. E. Bedell and R. Barbeito

College of Optometry, University of Houston, University Park,
Houston, TX 77004, USA

Amblyopia is a human anomaly, typically monocular, defined as substandard visual acuity even though any refractive error present has been optically neutralized and there is no ocular disease. It develops mainly in children who have significant interocular difference in refractive error (anisometropia) or have a manifest oculomotor deviation (strabismus). Associated with amblyopia are a number of other vision conditions commonly presumed to be a consequence or concomitant of the acuity deficit. Monocular nonfoveal (eccentric) fixation and spatial abnormalities are two examples. When amblyopes function with only the affected eye viewing, as occurs in therapeutic patching of the preferred eye, they are typically bothered more by difficulties in eye aiming and spatial localization than by problems of acuity or resolution.

About 25 years ago, Pugh (1958, 1962) reported the perceived distortions described by her amblyopic patients when they viewed acuity letter charts. These descriptions included abnormal spacing between letters, fragmenting of letters, and changes in the shapes of letters. Similar descriptions have been reported by Hess and colleagues (1978) for amblyopes viewing suprathreshold bar gratings. Quantification of this spatial distortion was probably first accomplished by Schor in 1972. He had an esotropic amblyope monocularly match nasal and temporal field spaces; with the amblyopic eye, whose acuity was 20/70, the subject underestimated distances in the temporal field by as much as a factor of three.

Fig. 1. Stimulus configuration used to evaluate relative directionalization.

In 1981, Bedell and Flom described two different methods for quantifying the spatial distortion of amblyopic eyes. We reported on thirteen strabismic amblyopes. Our first method measured monocular relative directionalization; the subjects specified the perceived horizontal location of a 0.5-degree luminous vertical line with respect to the vertical axis of two isosceles triangles whose apices were separated by about a degree and a half (Fig. 1). The locus of subjective alignment (the position of the flashed test line at which the percentages of "left" and "right" responses were equal) was less than 1.5 min arc for normal eyes. However, eleven of thirteen of our amblyopic eyes had a locus of subjective alignment between 10 and 40 min arc. This result suggests a "bending" of vertical lines of direction through the fixing point of strabismic

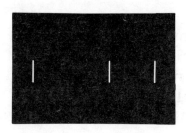

Fig. 2. Stimulus target used to match spaces in the horizontal meridian.

amblyopic eyes. Our second method involved monocular matching of spaces in the horizontal meridian. We always presented a standard (reference) space to the right of the fixation mark; the subject adjusted the left-hand target so that the space between it and the fixation mark was perceived as equal to the standard space (Fig. 2). A common response for the strabismic amblyopic eyes was a large under-estimation of the temporal-field space for standard nasal-field spaces less than 2 deg (illustrated for a left amblyopic eye in Fig. 2) and an overestimation for larger standard spaces out to 8 deg. Inside the region of transition between under- and overestimation of space in the temporal field, a single or tightly packed set of spatial settings corresponded to different spaces in the nasal field. We refer to this packing as "compression" of horizontal spatial values, and the contrary effect in the opposite field, and perhaps elsewhere, as "expansion." We have shown (Bedell and Flom, 1981) that these distortions for strabismic amblyopic eyes in the vertical and horizontal meridians are not a consequence of the unsteady and eccentric fixation of these eyes.

In the present paper, we describe a third method which provides a two-dimensional map of monocular space values and distortions. At the time of conceiving this experiment, we sought to determine whether the spatial distortions of strabismic amblyopic eyes are a feature of the amblyopia or the strabismus. And, we wanted to know whether spatial distortion occurs in anisometropic amblyopic eyes when there is no strabismus.

The experimental method consisted of having the subject monocularly fixate the central white button (12 min diam) on a black felt tangent screen at a distance of 3 meters. A yellow map pin (5 min diam) was positioned in the zero-degree meridian 8 deg to the right of the fixation mark. A 5-mm white disc, mounted on the end of a foot-long stiff black wire, was moved by the investigator on directions from the subject until it was perceived as lying equidistant from the fixation mark as the 8-deg reference spot and lying exactly in the 180-degree meridian. (A 100-watt desk lamp just behind the subject's head provided low photopic illumination so that the button, pins, and disc were easily seen, but not the stitched reference lines of the tangent screen.) The procedure was repeated for the 45, 90, 135, 225, 270, and 315 degree meridians, the reference always being the pin in the zero-degree meridian at 8 deg. The resulting eight locations were thus perceived as lying equally separated around the circumference of a circle, the center being at the fixation point. The subject then perceptionally bisected the space between the fixation point and the 8-deg reference spot, all other pins first being removed. The location of this bisection spot served as the reference for the subject to construct the "4-deg" circle. "Two-" and "6-deg" circles were similarly constructed, the references being obtained by bisection of, respectively, the zero to "4-deg" space and the "4" to 8-deg space. The aggregate of the physical settings that produced these perceived concentric circles constitutes a two-dimensional space map.

We obtained such maps from identical-twin brothers, age 24, both of whom had 4-8 prism diopters of constant esotropia of uncertain onset but believed to be present by age 3 years. Only one of the strabismic twins had amblyopia (20/80), and only the spatial map for this amblyopic eye exhibited marked distortions (Fig. 3) which were confined mainly to the central 4 deg. The map for the strabismic (20/20) eye of the other twin was approximately as regular as the maps for the preferred eyes, suggesting that strabismus itself is an insufficient condition for the presence of spatial distortion. It is tempting to ascribe the observed distortions to the amblyopia in the strabismic eye, which would be in accord with our previous study (Bedell and Flom, 1981) in which strabismic amblyopic eyes with 20/40 or worse acuity exhibited spatial distortions measured one dimensionally. However, our strabismic amblyopic twin also had significant anisometropia, which raises the possibility of the distortion being ascribed, at least in part, to the anisometropia. To address this issue, we compared spatial distortion in two strabismic amblyopic eyes, one with and one without

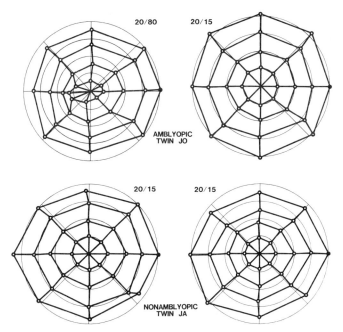

Fig. 3.   Two-dimensional maps of monocular space values and distortions for identical twin brothers with esotropia. The one with amblyopia showed marked central-field distortion.   The 8-deg reference spot is designated with a filled circle.

anisometropia; additional comparison was made with two nonstrabismic anisometropic amblyopic eyes. Figure 4 (next page) shows that both of the strabismic amblyopic eyes had substantial spatial distortion (on both the relative directionalization test and the nasal-temporal space-matching test) even though one strabismic had anisometropia and one did not. For both of the nonsquinting anisometropes (Fig. 4, lower four plots), there was little spatial distortion in the amblyopic eye. The nonsquinting anisometrope with 20/200 acuity in his amblyopic right eye (bottom-most plots in Fig. 4) exhibited spatial distortion only on the relative directionalization test (triangles and flashed line) in the amount of about 9 min.

To pursue this point of how much spatial distortion anisometropic amblyopes might have in the centralmost part of the field, we measured the errors of relative directionalization for eight nonsquinting anisometropes (seven were amblyopes with acuity of 20/40 or worse in the affected eye, and one was previously a 20/50 amblyope whose acuity had improved after therapy to slightly better than 20/20). The spatial distortions for these anisometropes were all less than 6 min in the affected eye and less than 3 min in the preferred eye. In a control group of thirteen normal eyes, the distortions were less than 2 min and increased to a maximum of only about 5 min when acuity was optically blurred to between 20/70 and 20/200. Recall that Bedell and Flom (1981) found that eleven of thirteen of their strabismic amblyopic eyes had spatial distortions between 10 and 40 min.

In sum, the evidence strongly indicates that strabismic amblyopic eyes tend to exhibit unique monocular spatial distortions: a "bending" in the vertical isodirection line through the fixation point, unequal space matches in the nasal and temporal fields, and irregularly located points being perceived as circles concentric with the fixation point. Such distortions were very much smaller in anisometropic amblyopic eyes where the constant errors were similar to a) the small errors observed for strabismic eyes without amblyopia, b) the preferred eyes of strabismic and anisometropic amblyopes, and c) normal eyes optically

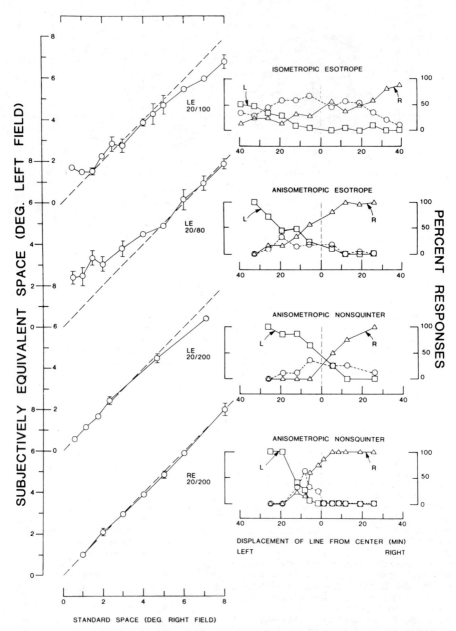

Fig. 4.   Left column: for standard spaces of several degrees in the right field, two strabismic amblyopes underestimated the perceived equivalent spaces in the left field (see Fig. 2).   Right column: with target illustrated in Fig. 1, the point of subjective equality of flashed line is decidedly to the left for strabismic amblyopic eyes and only somewhat off center for anisometropic amblyopic eyes.   Spatial uncertainty shown by the relatively shallow slope for the "left" and "right" responses (open circles = "aligned" responses).

blurred or optically corrected. Clearly, strabismic amblyopic eyes seem to be unique in the magnitude and type of spatial distortion they exhibit in the central several degrees of the visual field. These distortions are apparently not a direct result of the unsteady and eccentric fixation that are characteristic of strabismic amblyopic eyes. Indeed, argument has been presented (Bedell and Flom, 1981, 1983) that spatial distortion in strabismic amblyopic eyes may explain their abnormal, generally asymmetric, oculomotor behavior.

During the course of our initial experiments on strabismic amblyopic eyes, we were struck by their large and quantifiable constant errors which are interpreted as spatial distortions. When we subsequently investigated anisometropic amblyopes for spatial distortion and found little of it, we were nonetheless impressed by finding that the flashed vertical line could be positioned laterally over an abnormally large range before the subject was sure (consistent in his reports) that the line was to one side or the other of the apices of the vertically separated triangles (Fig. 1). This behavior of imprecision in responses indicates spatial uncertainty in anisometropic amblyopic eyes which seemed to be greater than in normal eyes and somewhat less than in strabismic amblyopic eyes. It was important to us to explore this other aspect of the space sense, spatial uncertainty, to see what it might additionally tell us about differences between strabismic and anisometropic amblyopia. The results obtained on spatial uncertainty are every bit as interesting as those obtained for spatial distortion. In fact, by combining the spatial distortion and spatial uncertainty results, we believe a coherent "explanation" emerges that strabismic and anisometropic amblyopia have different underlying mechanisms and are different clinical syndromes.

Returning to Fig. 4, we see that the two strabismic amblyopic eyes have larger ranges of uncertainty on both tests than the anisometropic amblyopic eyes, even though the strabismics had better acuity than the anisometropes. To elaborate on these initial findings, Bedell and colleagues (1985) reported on the spatial uncertainty measured for 120 eyes categorized in five groups. Twenty-three strabismic amblyopic eyes (acuity 20/40 or worse) had spatial uncertainty that was distributed fairly uniformly from about 4 to 24 min (actually min/probit from the probit fit of the psychometric function), with one extreme value at 32 min. For 22 other strabismics (acuity better than 20/40 in the deviating eye), spatial uncertainty occurred evenly from about 2 to 8 min, with one value at 12 min. Spatial uncertainty was essentially equivalent in the preferred eyes of both groups of strabismics and was never larger than 5 min. For 30 normal subjects, the maximum uncertainty was 2.5 min, with most of them having less than 2.0 min of spatial uncertainty. Thus, amblyopic eyes of strabismics have spatial uncertainty that is about three times that measured in their preferred eyes, and at least ten times as large as in normal eyes.

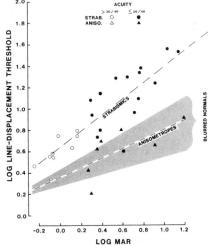

In the present paper we present, for comparison with strabismic eyes, new data on spatial uncertainty obtained in the central visual field of eight nonsquinting anisometropes, seven with acuity in the affected eye of 20/40 or worse, and one with better than 20/20 acuity after receiving amblyopia therapy. The differences in refractive errors in corresponding meridians ranged from 1.5 to 13.25 diopters for a 40-year-old amblyope (20/50) operated on for traumatic cataract at age 6. Although acuity in these anisometropic amblyopic eyes was reduced to as low as 20/160 and 20/300, as were the strabismic amblyopic eyes, the spatial uncertainty for the anisometropes never exceeded 8 min, but was as large as 35 min for the strabismic amblyopic eyes. The comparative spatial uncertainties for equivalent acuities in strabismic and anisometropic amblyopia are shown in Fig. 5. For each level of acuity in the amblyopic eyes, strabismic amblyopes had more spatial uncertainty than did anisometropes. For both the strabismics and the aniso-

Fig. 5. Spatial uncertainty (ordinate), in min/probit, vs. minimum angle of resolution (abscissa), in min. Target in Fig. 1.

metropes, the correlation between spatial uncertainty (in log min/probit) and visual acuity (expressed as log of the minimum angle of resolution) was statistically significant and quite high, being respectively +0.86 and +0.76. (Visual acuity for this analysis was determined using an array of eight 4-position Landolt C test letters imbedded in a background of seventeen 4-position E's and using the 50% threshold, corrected for guessing, obtained from the fitted psychometric function — as described by Flom and coworkers, 1963.) These correlations indicate, of course, that the measure of one variable is a good predictor of the other variable for these eyes. The actual predictions of uncertainty (U), in log min/probit, come from the linear regression equations of the fitted lines, which are quite different for strabismics (U = 0.74 log MAR + 0.65) and anisometropes (U = 0.44 log MAR + 0.36). The greater slope of the strabismics' fitted line (Fig. 5) indicates that as acuity worsens (MAR increases) by a certain amount, spatial uncertainty increases much more for strabismic eyes than for anisometropic eyes. The difference in ordinate intercepts is also noteworthy. The strabismics' curve indicates that spatial uncertainty reduced to 4.5 min (log = 0.65) when acuity in the deviating eye was 20/20 (log MAR = 0). The anisometropes' line, on the other hand, shows that for an acuity of 20/20 in the "amblyopic" eye, the spatial uncertainty would only be 2.3 min (log = 0.36), which approximates the 1.7 min median uncertainty obtained from 30 normal eyes having 20/20 or better acuity (Bedell and colleagues, 1985). Thus, even when acuity in a strabismic eye is "normal" (20/20 or better), spatial uncertainty is abnormally large — being about twice as large as the spatial uncertainty of normal eyes or the eyes of anisometropes with 20/20 acuity.

Comparing spatial uncertainty in anisometropes and normal eyes is revealing. For six normal subjects, we measured monocular visual acuity psychometrically (Flom and colleagues, 1963) with the optimal refractive correction in place and also with the addition of each of three convex fogging lenses (1.00, 1.50, and 2.50 diopters) that reduced acuity to about 20/30, 20/70, and 20/160. We also measured each subject's spatial uncertainty under each lens condition. The resulting 24 data points were used to define the shaded area in Fig. 5, which more or less symmetrically surrounds the anisometropes' regression line. The corresponding regression line for the normal subjects (U = 0.35 log MAR + 0.37) is remarkably similar to the anisometropes' line. This indicates that the spatial uncertainty of anisometropic amblyopic eyes (when optically corrected) approximately equals the uncertainty for normal eyes when they are blurred to equivalent acuity levels. In other words, even though the anisometropic amblyopic eyes were optically corrected (providing sharp retinal imagery), they exhibited spatial uncertainty as though the reduced acuity were artificially produced by optical blur.

In our present paper we have reviewed previous work and presented new results on the spatial abnormalities of strabismic and anisometropic amblyopic eyes. These two types of amblyopia have differences in spatial distortion and spatial uncertainty that suggest different underlying mechanisms for the amblyopia.

Strabismic amblyopic eyes exhibit both spatial distortion and spatial uncertainty, neither of which can be accounted for by the acuity deficit. We base this on the fact that blurring normal eyes a) does not introduce significant spatial distortion, and b) produces spatial uncertainty at a much lower rate per unit of acuity loss than for strabismic amblyopic eyes. Moreover, strabismic eyes with acuity of 20/20 or 20/15 have abnormally large spatial uncertainty. Finally, Levi and Klein (1982) have found that strabismic amblyopes have poorer vernier acuity than predicted from their bar grating resolution, even at low spatial frequencies. Rather than blur leading to acuity loss as a fundamental deficit in strabismic amblyopia (Ikeda and Wright, 1976), another explanation is more attractive. The malalignment of one eye in the everyday life of the young strabismic produces a cortical disregistration of the two retinal images onto loci that have different cortical magnifications and, at least in part, onto cortical loci in opposite hemispheres. Such cortical disregistration, particularly of the central ocular images, in a young plastic visual system may be sufficient to interfere with development, producing spatial distortions and spatial uncertainty — although accompanying suppression may contribute. (The role of suppression in effecting spatial abnormalities in amblyopic eyes is now under investigation in our laboratory.) On the other hand, spatial distortions and/or uncertainty may represent adaptive changes designed to facilitate some form of binocular vision, albeit rudimentary — anomalous retinal correspondence and/or uniquely shaped horopters may be examples. Whether the spatial abnormalities of strabismic amblyopic eyes result from incomplete development or loss of function or from neural adaptation, the combined effect of these abnormalities in producing reduced visual acuity (i.e., amblyopia) would be the same. If the parts of a test letter are uncertainly localized in space and some parts are also erroneously directionalized, a reduction in acuity is expected but resolution of repetitive bar gratings is not.

Since anisometropic amblyopic eyes have negligible spatial distortion and show spatial uncertainty that equals that obtained by blurring normal eyes, it is logical to suspect that the greater unilateral blur in one eye of an anisometropic child would lead to incomplete development or functional loss of neural structures responsible for fine resolution. Other evidence (Eggers and Blakemore, 1978; Levi and Klein, 1982) supports this hypothesis. It is appropriate to attribute the anisometrope's spatial uncertainty to a fundamental resolution deficit — which is consistent with their demonstrating equivalent reductions in performance for optotypes, bar gratings, and vernier targets (Levi and Klein, 1982).

Besides the different underlying bases for strabismic and anisometropic amblyopia, it is important to recognize that these two amblyopias present clinically as different syndromes (Flom and Bedell, 1985), one major difference being in oculomotor control (Ciuffreda and colleagues, 1979). Although the spatial distortion of strabismic amblyopes has been used as an explanation of their eccentric fixation and asymmetric tracking (Bedell and Flom, 1983), it is only a partial one; the full explanation must also include the centrally generated, high-velocity, nasal drifts (Bedell and Flom, 1985; Schor, 1975, 1983). Whether there is any connection between strabismic amblyopes' spatial distortion and their oculomotor drift bias is an intriguing and open question.

Supported by National Eye Institute Research Grant EY-03694 (to Merton C. Flom).

REFERENCES

Bedell, H. E., and M. C. Flom (1981). Monocular spatial distortion in strabismic amblyopia. Invest. Ophthal. Vis. Sci., 20, 263-268.

Bedell, H. E., and M. C. Flom (1983). Normal and abnormal space perception. Am. J. Optom. Physiol. Opt., 60, 426-435.

Bedell, H. E., and M. C. Flom (1985). Bilateral oculomotor abnormalities in strabismic amblyopes: evidence for a common central mechanism. Documenta Ophthalmologica, 59, 309-321.

Bedell, H. E., and M. C. Flom, and R. Barbeito (1985). Spatial aberrations and acuity in strabismus and amblyopia. Invest. Ophthal. Vis. Sci. 26, 909-916.

Ciuffreda, K. J., R. V. Kenyon, and L. Stark (1979). Fixational eye movements in amblyopia and strabismus. J. Am. Optom. Assoc., 50, 1251-1258.

Eggers, H. M., and C. Blakemore (1978). Physiological basis of anisometropic amblyopia. Science, 201, 264-267.

Flom, M. C., and H. E. Bedell (1985). Identifying amblyopia using associated conditions, acuity, and nonacuity features. Am. J. Optom. Physiol. Opt., 62, 153-160.

Flom, M. C., F. W. Weymouth, and D. Kahneman (1963). Visual resolution and contour interaction. J. Opt. Soc. Am., 53, 1026-1032.

Hess, R. F., F. W. Campbell, and T. Greenhalgh (1978). On the nature of the neural abnormality in human amblyopia: neural aberrations and neural sensitivity loss. Pflugers Arch., 377, 201-207.

Ikeda, H., and M. J. Wright (1976). Neurophysiological basis of squint amblyopia. Orthoptics, 1, 31-36.

Levi, D. M., and S. A. Klein (1982). Differences in vernier discrimination for gratings between strabismic and anisometropic amblyopes. Invest. Ophthal. Vis. Sci., 23, 398-407.

Pugh, M. (1958). Visual distortion in amblyopia. Br. J. Ophthal., 42, 449-460.

Pugh, M. (1962). Amblyopia and the retina. Br. J. Ophthal., 46, 193-211.

Schor, C. M. (1972). Neurosensory Analysis of Amblyopia. Doctoral Dissertation, University of California.

Schor, C. M. (1975). A directional impairment of eye movement control in strabismus amblyopia. Invest. Ophthal. Vis. Sci., 14, 692-697.

Schor, C. M. (1983). Subcortical binocular suppression affects the development of latent and optokinetic nystagmus. Am. J. Optom. Physiol. Opt., 60, 481-502.

Mechanisms Underlying
Developmental Alterations of
Cortical Ocular Dominance

M. Cynader and C. Shaw

Departments of Psychology, Physiology & Biophysics, Dalhousie
University, Halifax, NS B3H 4J1, Canada

By now it is well established that visual exposure during the early postnatal
period molds the future development of the visual system. While considerable
specificity can be observed in the visual responses of the neonatal visual system
(Hubel & Wiesel 1963, Imbert & Buisseret 1975), the final configuration of visual
processing mechanisms depends on what the organism sees (or does not see) during
early postnatal life. If cats are reared in the dark, for instance, many cortical neurons become visually unresponsive and those that remain so generally fail
to show the specific responses based on stimulus orientation, velocity, and disparity which characterise cortical units in normal cats. (Cynader, Berman &
Hein, 1976).

Binocular vision and its development appear especially sensitive to the postnatal
history of the animal. Wiesel & Hubel (1963a,b) showed that rearing kittens with
one eyelid sutured caused profound changes in the Lateral Geniculate Nucleus and
visual cortex. In the Lateral Geniculate Nucleus, (LGN) neurons connected to the
deprived eye were shrunken by over 40%. Moreover, examination of the terminal
field of these shrunken cells in the cortex showed that LGN inputs connected to
the deprived eye occupied less than 20% of the cortex, while the other, nonsutured eye had an expanded representation covering over 80% of the thalamic-
recipient zone in cortical layer 4. Single unit recording studies showed that
stimuli presented through the sutured eye failed to influence the vast majority
of cortical cells. Instead the nonsutured eye became the sole effective route
for visual stimuli. Finally, kittens were unable to use the deprived eye for
vision when the sutures were opened.

There is evidence that the loss of visual capacities and the associated alterations in the visual system are due to competitive interactions between the two
eyes rather than resulting simply from disuse. The behavioural effects of monocular eyelid suture are considerably less severe (for the deprived eye) if the
other eye is sutured as well. Furthermore, Guillery (1972) showed that a partial
lesion in the retina of the nondeprived eye prevented geniculate cell shrinkage
at the corresponding locus in the deprived LGN lamina.

The Site of Binocular Competition:

While there is evidence for changes in LGN cell size, in LGN terminals and in
cortical cell responses, the evidence indicates that the primary site of binocular competition is cortical, and LGN cell size and terminal field changes are
secondary to these cortical changes. We (Cynader and Mitchell, 1977) showed this

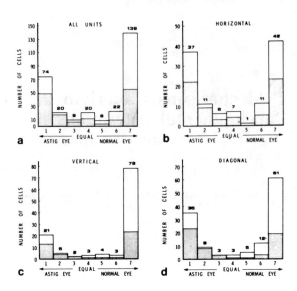

Fig. 1   The distribution of ocular dominance for units in the
visual cortex of cats reared with one eye viewing through a
cylindrical lens and the other eye viewing normally.   The
numbers from 1 to 7 represent a trend from the "astigmatic"
eye to the normal eye.   cells in group 1 are driven exclusively
by the astigmatic eye; cells in groups 4 are driven equally by
both eyes; cells in group 7 exclusively by the normal eye.   a
shows the distribution of ocular dominance for all cells in
these cats.   b–d show the distribution of ocular dominance as a
function of the orientation of the unit.   The vertical and
horizontal distributions represent cells which prefer orientations within 30° of vertical and horizontal.   The "diagonal"
distribution (d) represents cells preferring stimulus orientations
within 15° of either diagonal.   The hatched parts of the distribution represent cells in the hemisphere contralateral to the
astigmatic eye.

by raising kittens with goggles so that one eye viewed normally and the other
looked through a cylindrical lens which defocussed contours of vertical orientation.   The rationale for this experiment rested on the fact that cortical cells
show orientation selectivity, while LGN cells do not.   Thus, if the competition
between the two eyes occurs at the level of the LGN, or among LGN terminals, the
changes in cortical ocular dominance should be independent of the orientation
selectivity of the cortical cells, so that the deprived eye would lose control
equally of cortical cells of all orientations.   If, on the other hand, the primary deprivation effect occurs at orientation selective cortical cells, then the
deprived eye would be at a disadvantage only for vertically-oriented cells and
not for cells preferring horizontal orientations.   The results of this experiment
are shown in Fig. 1.   If one considers the total population of cortical cells,
the eye which wore the cylindrical lens controlled fewer neurons.   If one breaks
down the total cell population by orientation selectivity, it becomes apparent
that for the vertical cells there is a very large deprivation effect, with many
more cells being driven by the normal than by the defocussed eye, whereas for
horizontal cells there is essentially no effect; diagonal units shown an inter-

mediate effect. Thus, binocular competition must occur at the orientation-
selective striate cortical neurons, and the changes seen in the LGN are secondary
consequences of the primary cortical changes.

The preparation described above is of additional interest because the lens system
used simulates the common clinical condition of astigmatism. With astigmatism,
contours of one orientation are blurred during early development resulting in
permanently lowered visual acuity for stimuli of that orientation even after the
optical error is corrected (Mitchell et al. 1973). The experiments reported here,
in showing that vertically oriented neurons driven by the deprived eye are rarer
in these kittens than are horizontally oriented units, point toward a neural
mechanism underlying astigmatism. Goggle systems like the one described here,
but using ordinary negative lenses over one eye have also been used to produce a
kitten model for anisometropic amblyopia (Cynader 1976). In this case most cortical neurons can be driven only via stimulation of the eye which viewed normally,
rather than through the eye which was forced to view through the negative lens.

The Critical Period for Binocular Interactions

Competitive binocular interactions occur within a critical period (Hubel and
Wiesel 1970; Cynader et al. 1980) during early development. The critical period
for monocular deprivation in cats peaks at three to four weeks of age. At this
time, eyelid closure for as little as one day produces profound effects. Progressively smaller effects result as the animal ages. We have found that this
critical period is really not a fixed period at all; rather, the sensitivity of
the organism to monocular deprivation depends on the animal's rearing history
(Cynader and Mitchell 1980). By using an experimental paradigm in which cats
were reared in the dark until long after the normal end of the critical period
and only then brought into the light for monocular deprivation, we have found
that monocular deprivation can still produce marked effects on cortical ocular
dominance no matter how long an animal is kept in the dark (Fig. 2).

Further experiments (Cynader, 1983) have demonstrated that dark-reared cats
undergo a new critical period in the first few weeks after they are brought into
the light. This was shown by dark-rearing animals for four months and then
bringing them into the light for three months of monocular deprivation. If the
monocular deprivation is started after only three intervening weeks of light exposure, strong deprivation effects result. However, waiting six weeks to start
monocular deprivation gives a much smaller effect, and an 8-12 week wait gives
little or no effect. Therefore, when animals are brought out of the dark, they
seem to undergo a new critical period which lasts 6-8 weeks.

Cellular Mechanisms of Plasticity: Alterations of Receptors?

We remain ignorant of molecular mechanisms by which LGN inputs representing one
eye increase their influence on cortical cells at the expense of those representing the other eye. Yet there is reason to believe that neurotransmitter receptors may play an important role in this process. Receptors are proteins with
specific recognition sites which recognize and bind a particular neurotransmitter.
Once the receptor has bound the transmitter, a variety of changes, ranging from
local alterations in ionic permeability, to protein phosphorylation, to longer
term changes in gene expression, may result. Modifications of neurotransmitter
receptors have been implicated in plasticity mechanisms in a variety of different
situations. Examples include the development of tolerance to many drugs, the
phenomenon of denervation supersensitivity in muscles, plasticity associated with
long term potentiation in the hippocampus, and VOR modification. Figure 3 is a
schematic illustrating how changes in receptor distribution, and/or number might
be involved in cortical plasticity. In the initial stage, inputs from both eyes
(L and R of fig. 3) impinge on the postsynaptic cell. Receptors for two different neurotransmitters are shown (solid and open circles) distributed evenly
around the postsynaptic cell. If the right eye is sutured shut, preventing high-

3 MONTHS MONOCULAR SUTURE

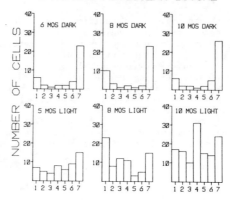

Fig. 2   The distribution of cortical ocular dominance in dark-
reared and light-reared cats of comparable ages subjected to
three months of monocular eyelid suture. The conventions for
this figure are similar to those of Fig. 1, with cells in group
1 driven via the previously-sutured eye and those of group 7
via the normal eye. In the dark-reared cats, most cells encountered prefer inputs presented via the normal eye regardless
of the animal's age at the onset of deprivation. In normal
cats the effects of deprivation become less pronounced as the
animal ages.

frequency impulse activity on the R input, receptors tend to aggregate toward the
L input, which carries high frequency activity. A similar process may occur for
other neurotransmitters or neuromodulators, denoted here in black, in association
with their own inputs. The presence and distribution of these modulatory inputs
may also influence the process by which the primary receptors are reorganised.
Migration of receptors eventually prevents responses to inputs mediated by the
right eye. The retraction of right eye axons and the shrinkage of LGN cells
connected to the right eye then occurs as a secondary consequence of the loss of
functional contact with the postsynaptic cell.

This model is speculative and schematic, but it encourages us to search for
changes in cortical receptor populations during the critical period and also in
dark-reared animals which retain prolonged plasticity. We used the method of
receptor autoradiography (Snyder, 1984, Young & Kuhar, 1979) which enables direct
visualisation of the location and concentration of specific neurotransmitter
receptors.

Thus far, we have examined nine different cortical receptor populations and their
ontogeny. We have found, in general, that the number of receptor binding sites
in the visual cortex increased from birth to a peak value during the critical
period and then declined somewhat into adulthood. Each receptor population displays a characteristic and striking laminar distribution within the cortex. Moreover, we have found that this laminar distribution frequently changes during the
critical period. Figure 4 illustrates the development and distribution of one
particular receptor binding site in the visual cortex, the muscarinic binding
site for acetylcholine. This receptor population is labelled with [3H] Quinucli-
dinyl Benzilate (QNB), a specific muscarinic antagonist (Walmsly et al, 1980,
Shaw et al. 1984). The figure shows coronal sections through the visual cortex

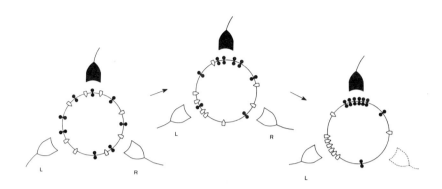

Fig. 3 A schematic diagram showing how receptor alterations
might be involved in binocular competition. Initially, inputs
from the Left (L) and Right (R) eyes converge on a single cell
and receptors for various neurotransmitters (two are shown) are
distributed equally across the postsynaptic cell surface. High
frequency impulse activity causes receptors to aggregate toward
the site of activation and to avoid areas of lowered input. An
"enabling input" represented by the shaded terminal may participate in this process by controlling the distribution of other
receptors which interact with those receiving L and R inputs.
With continued exposure, receptors have aggregated to the site
of activity and the deprived eye's input is removed.

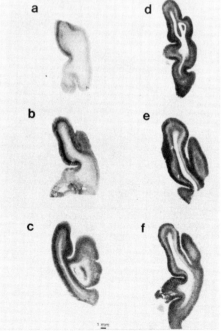

Fig. 4 Distribution of [^{3}H] QNB binding sites in the visual cortex of cats
of different ages. Autoradiograms are
from LKB Ultrofilm (a) 3 days; (b) 15
days; (c) 30 days; (d) 60 days; (e) 95
days; (f) adult. Ligand concentrations,
5nM; exposure, 24 days. Note the reversal of the pattern of [^{3}H] QNB binding during development. For each cat
the different laminae were identified
in alternate sections stained with
cresyl violet or cytochrome c. Calibration all panels: 1 mm. Dorsal is up,
medial is left for all panels.

of kittens of various ages. Each section shows an autoradiogram in which
increasing density reflects a greater number of neurotransmitter receptors. In
neonatal kittens (Panel A) the visual cortex is demarcated by a clear band of
dark label running through the grey matter. By examining adjacent sections with
nissl and cytochrome oxidase stains, we can localise the labelled binding sites
to cortical layer IV. The intense band of label ends with the cytoarchitectonic
border of the visual cortex. In more ventral and lateral parts of the section,
the labelling is much fainter and less distinct. Subsequent panels of fig. 4
show the binding site distributions in kittens of 15, 30, 60, 90 days of age,
and in adults. By 15 days (Panel B) binding sites have increased in number
(darker label) and have spread out from layer 4 into layers 2 and 3, closer to
the cortical surface. The process continues in Panel C (30 days of age) by which
time the receptors extend fully to the surface, occupying layers 1-4. Between 30
and 60 days of age (Panel D) the distribution of receptors changes again with
decreased binding in layer 4 and increased binding in layer 6, the deepest cortical layer. By this age, the original pattern of receptor concentration in the
middle of the cortex (layer 4) has entirely reversed in favour of a pattern in
which muscarinic receptors are distributed in the upper and lower cortical layers. The 95 day old (Panel E) and adult animals (Panel F) show a similar laminar
distribution to that of the 60 day old kittens, with some further decrease in
binding in layer 4.

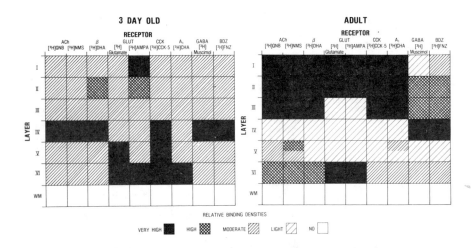

Fig. 5 Schematic representation of the laminar binding patterns
for nine receptor populations in 3 day old and adult cats. Note
that binding densities are given only in qualitative values: very
high, high, moderate, low and no binding. Using this scale it is
possible to compare the relative binding density for any receptor
population across the cortical laminae, but not to directly compare different receptors to each other. In young kittens, most
receptors concentrate in layer IV or in lower layers. In adults
the distribution for most receptors is very different with maximal concentrations in the superficial cortical layers.

This finding of redistribution of acetylcholine receptors with age is by no means unique. We have found that the majority of the receptor populations studied thus far show different laminar patterns at different stages of postnatal development. These receptor redistributions take place during the physiologically-defined critical period. Figure 5 summarises data for 9 different receptor populations, comparing the laminar distributions in neonatal animals with those of adult cats. The receptors examined include those for inhibitory and excitatory amino-acids, excitatory peptides, and various modulatory substances. In general, receptors tend to be most concentrated in layer 4 of young animals, and in upper and lower layers in adult animals, but each receptor displays an idiosyncratic binding progression with age. GABA receptors, for instance, are one of three receptors studied here which do not alter their laminar distribution during development. They are found in layer 4 of both neonatal and adult animals. Other receptors, including those for excitatory amino acids (labelled with ^{3}H-Glutamate and ^{3}H-AMPA) (see Greenamyre et al. 1984 for methods) appear to avoid layer 4 at all ages.

These findings, showing marked changes in both number and distribution of several receptor populations during the critical period, are intriguing and raise many questions for future research. However since alterations are the rule rather than the exception, these findings do not allow us to assign any particular neural system a special role in plasticity mechanisms like those outlined in fig. 3. To approach the plasticity issue more directly we have begun to examine receptor ontogeny in animals subjected to special rearing conditions. We have begun with dark-reared cats, asking whether the developmental alterations which we observe reflect passive maturational processes independant of visual experience, or whether vision is required. In general, these studies have shown that many of the developmental progressions in receptor number and distribution which we observe occur regardless of whether animals are allowed visual exposure. The laminar alterations in QNB binding, for instance, illustrated in fig. 4, are very similar in normal and dark-reared animals of the same age. While there is a transient increase in QNB binding in dark-reared animals relative to normals at 30 days of age, the adult distribution and number of receptors is largely unchanged by dark-rearing. Initial studies of the other receptors illustrated in fig. 5 (with one exception outlined below) reveal that the overall development of receptor number and the redistributions during development occur with or without visual exposure.

A striking exception to the general rule has appeared in our study of the A1-adenosine receptor (labelled with [^{3}H]-cyclohexyladenosine or CHA) (Bruns et al. 1980; Goodman & Synder, 1982). We included adenosine receptors in our early studies because of evidence that this purine dervative could control the release of several other neurotransmitters, because its application was known to inhibit the firing of cortical neurons, and because of its role in Cyclic AMP activation (see Synder, 1985 for a Review). Adenosine receptors are distributed in the lowest cortical layer (layer 6) in young animals, then become more homogenously distributed during the critical period and finally concentrate in the upper cortical layers in adulthood. In dark-reared animals we found a marked retardation of this developmental redistribution pattern. Receptors in a two month old dark-reared cat were still concentrated in layer 6, like those of neonatal kittens, and even with prolonged dark-rearing showed only an attenuated progression toward the superficial layers. Figure 6 compares the distribution of A1-adenosine receptors in a normal adult and in dark-reared cats. The normal cats show dense binding extending up to the outer surface of the cortex, with a small sublayer in layer 5. The dark-reared cats show a much fainter labelling pattern with the best defined binding in layer 3. Quantitative studies of receptor number (B_{max}) show that long-term dark-reared cats have less than half as many Adenosine receptors as do normal cats of comparable age. These data indicate that the A1-adenosine receptor is differentially affected by dark-rearing. While other receptors are relatively little influenced by dark-rearing, adenosine receptors are reduced in number and altered in their cortical distribution. The

CAMROSE LUTHERAN COLLEGE
LIBRARY

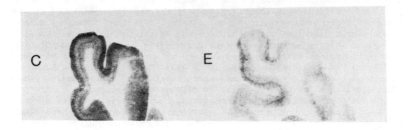

Fig. 6 Distribution of Al-adenosine binding sites in normal
(left hand side) and dark-reared (right hand side) cat visual
cortex. In normal cats receptors are most dense in layers
1-3 and the top of layer 5. In dark-reared animals only
layer 3 is heavily labelled and the overall number of receptors
is diminished by over 50%.

susceptibility of this receptor population suggests that it may play a role in
the extended plasticity shown by dark-reared cats.

Summary & Conclusions:

Unequal visual inputs from the two eyes during development results in permanently
reduced visual capabilities through the deprived eye. These behavioural deficits
are caused by a process of binocular competition which takes place in the visual
cortex. Normally this competition occurs only during a well-defined critical
period during the first few months of postnatal life. It is possible however to
extend this critical period, apparently indefinitely, by rearing animals in the
dark. The cellular mechanisms underlying binocular competition remain unknown.
Alterations in neurotransmitter receptors which have been shown to be involved
in several other forms of plasticity are however implicated in this process. We
have found that several different transmitter receptors show substantial alterations in number and cortical distribution during the critical period. At least
one of these, the Al-adenosine receptor is markedly affected by dark-rearing and
may play a special role in the extended plasticity of the dark-reared cat.

References:

Bruns, R.E., J.W. Daly and S.H. Synder (1980). Adenosine receptors in Brain
    Membranes: Binding of N^6-cyclohexyl-[^{3}H] Phenyl-xanthine. J. Neurochem.
    39, 647-52.
Cynader, M. April (1976). Some factors influencing the development of ocular
    dominance in the cat visual cortex. Presented at Association for Research
    in Vision and Ophthalmology. Sarasota, Fla.
Cynader, M. (1983). Prolonged Sensitivity to Monocular Deprivation in Dark-
    reared Cats: Effects of Age and Visual Exposure. Dev. Brain Res. 8,
    155-64.
Cynader, M., N. Berman and A. Hein (1976). Recovery of function in cat visual
    cortex following prolonged deprivation. Exp. Brain Res. 25, 139-156.
Cynader, M. and D.E. Mitchell (1977). Monocular astigmatism effects on kitten
    visual cortex development. Nature, 270, 177-178.
Cynader, M. and D.E. Mitchell (1980). Prolonged sensitivity to monocular
    deprivation in dark-reared cats. J. Neurophysiol. 43, 1026-1040.
Cynader, M., B.N. Timney and D.E. Mitchell (1980). Period of susceptibility of
    kitten visual cortex to the effects of monocular deprivation extends beyond
    six months of age. Brain Res. 91, 545-550.

Goodman, R.R. and S.H. Snyder (1982). Autoradiographic localisation of adenosine receptors in rat brain using [3H] Cyclohexyladenosine. J. Neurosci, 2, 1230-41.

Greenamyre, J.T., A.B. Young and J.B. Penney (1983). Quantitative autoradiography of L[3H] glutamate binding to rat brain. Neurosci. Lett. 37, 155-160.

Guillery, R.W. (1972). Binocular competition in the control of geniculate cell growth. J. Comp. Neurol. 144, 117-127.

Hubel, D.H. and T.N. Wiesel (1963). Receptive fields of cells in striate cortex of very young, visually inexperienced kittens. J. Neurophysiol. 26, 994-1002.

Hubel, D.H. and T.N. Wiesel (1970). The period of susceptibility to the physiological effects of unilateral eye closure in kittens. J. Physiol. 206, 419-436.

Imbert, M. and P. Buisseret (1975). Receptive field characteristics and plastic properties of visual cortical cells in kittens reared with or without visual experience. Exp. Brain Res. 22, 25-36.

Mitchell, D.E., R.D. Freeman, M. Millodot and G. Haegerstrom (1973). Meridional amblyopia: Evidence for modification of the human visual system by early visual experience. Vis. Res. 13, 535-558.

Shaw, C., M.C. Needler and M. Cynader (1984). Ontogenesis of muscarinic acetylcholine binding sites in cat visual cortex: reversal of specific laminar distribution during the critical period. Dev. Brain Res. 14, 295-299.

Snyder, S.H. (1984). Drug and neurotransmitter receptors in the brain. Science, 224, 22-31.

Snyder, S.H. (1985). Adenosine as a neuromodulator. Ann. Rev. Neurosci. 8, 103-124.

Wamsley, J.K., M.A. Zarbin, J.H. Nigel, N.J.M. Birdsall and M.J. Kuhar (1980). Muscarinic cholinergic receptors: autoradiographic localization of high and low affinity agonist binding sites. Brain Res. 200, 1-12.

Wiesel, T.N. and D.H. Hubel (1963a). Single cells responses in the striate cortex of kittens deprived of vision in one eye. J. Neurophysiol. 26, 1003-1017.

Wiesel, T.N. and D.H. Hubel (1963b). Effects of visual deprivation on morphology and physiology of cells in the cat's lateral geniculate body. J. Neurophysiol. 26, 978-993.

Young, W.S. and M.J. Kuhar (1979). A new method for receptor autoradiography: [3H] opioid receptors in rat brain. Brain Res. 179, 255-270.

Selective Stabilization of Retinotectal Synapses by Activity Dependent Mechanism

J. T. Schmidt, L. E. Eisele, J. C. Turcotte
and D. G. Tieman

Department of Biological Sciences and Neurobiology Research
Center, State University of New York at Albany,
1400 Washington Ave., Albany, NY 12222, USA

INTRODUCTION

Because much of the brain is taken up with maps of visual and auditory space and of body surfaces, topographic maps and the mechanism of their formation have been topics of general interest. The most intensively studied map, the direct retinotopic map on the optic tectum of fish and frogs, can be studied both during development in the embryo and during regeneration of the optic nerve in the adult. The central question is: 'How does each ingrowing retinal fiber select the correct termination site in the tectum?'

The major ideas about the mechanisms involved in the formation of maps have centered in three areas: 1) Differential chemospecific adhesion between retinal fibers and tectal cells (Sperry, 1943,1963), 2) Fiber self ordering and pathway interactions en route to the tectum (Horder and Martin, 1977; Schmidt, 1982; Stuermer and Easter, 1984), 3) Activity dependent stabilization of a retinotopic pattern after a diffuse early innervation (Keating, 1975; Changeux and Danchin, 1976; Willshaw and von der Malsburg, 1976; Meyer, 1983; Schmidt and Edwards, 1983). In this chapter, we will briefly review the evidence that the first two mechanisms are sufficient only to orient a crude map, then we will review in more detail the evidence that the third mechanism serves to sharpen both the retinotectal map and other topographic maps.

Chemoaffinity Mechanisms Have Limited Resolution.

The earliest suggested mechanism is a selective chemoaffinity between retinal fibers and tectal cells, based upon the position of the ganglion cell in the retina and the tectal cell in the tectum. Sperry (1943) initially postulated that fiber to tectum interactions were influenced by general biochemical gradients across the tectum, but later made his interpretation much more rigid, postulating unique surface markers for each cell (Sperry, 1963). This idea of unique markers appeared to be supported by the anatomical experiments of Attardi and Sperry (1963), who used a modified silver stain to study the pathways and termination sites of optic fibers that regenerated from a half retina. They reported that the optic fibers grew back selectively to the original sites, even if they had to bypass open sites en route. More modern methods have not upheld this finding (see below). Further evidence against the notion of unique markers came in experiments demonstrating dramatic plastic rearrangements made by the projection either following surgical intervention (reviewed by Schmidt, 1982) or during normal development (reviewed by Easter, 1983). Surgically induced reorganizations include the compression of the full projection onto a half tectum, and the expansion of a half retinal projection over the full tectum. In both cases, retinotopic order is maintained even though each retinal fiber terminates at a different tectal site. During development in fish and frogs, similar movements of optic arbors, with the continual changing of postsynaptic partners, occur because of the disparate geometric growth patterns of the retina and tectum (Easter, 1983). These movements, as well as the surgically induced rearrangements, are consistent with general chemoaffinity gradients (which may in fact be necessary to orient the projection), but they are not consistent with unique positional markers on the tectum.

Clearly factors other than chemospecific fiber–target interactions must contribute to the precision of these retinotopic maps. A second similar mechanism is selective fiber–fiber chemoaffinity which could maintain the relative ordering of retinal fibers in the presynaptic array (Horder and Martin, 1977; Schmidt, 1982). Postulation of this mechanism led to a careful study (Stuermer and Easter, 1984) of the degree of order in both the normal and the regenerated optic pathway using HRP staining. The normal pathway in goldfish was found to be highly ordered, and to undergo several reorganizations along the way to the tectum. For example, where the optic tract bifurcates, the fibers from dorsal retina normally all go ventrally and those from ventral retina all go dorsally. After regeneration, however, approximately one fiber in five enters through the wrong branch. This ratio of correct to incorrect pathways shows that pathway interactions may play some role in organizing the projection, but many mistakes are left to be corrected after entry into the tectum.

Early Diffuse Projections In Regeneration.

Anatomical studies. Many experiments demonstrate mistakes in the zone of tectal innervation. Meyer (1980) used radioautography, instead of the silver stain employed by Attardi and Sperry (1963), to trace the projection from a partial retina, and determined that at least half of the retina would have to be removed to create a denervated zone in the tectum. Both Stuermer and Easter (1984) and Cook and Rankin (1984) showed this same diffuseness by making punctate injections of HRP both in normal tecta and in tecta after regeneration. Normally the ganglion cells that are retrogradely labelled through their terminals are confined to a small retinal area. Early in regeneration, however, labelled cells were scattered over the entire retina with only a slight preponderance in the correct half. After two months or more, the labelled ganglion cells were once again compactly clustered, as in the normal (Cook and Rankin, 1984).

These diffuse projections could result from errors in targeting of individual regenerated arbors. In the newt, Fujisawa and coworkers (1982) were the first to stain regenerated optic arbors with HRP and view them in tectal whole mounts. The regenerated fibers often took aberrant paths into and through the tectum, and also made many branches in inappropriate tectal areas. We have used similar techniques in goldfish (Schmidt and coworkers, 1984). Normal optic arbors range in size from 100 to 400 um across, but early in regeneration many optic arbors make greatly enlarged arbors that are more than two millimeters across but sparsely branched (Fig. 1). As time progresses, the arbors shrink back to their normal size, but the paths of the regenerated fibers often remain abnormal. In parallel studies of development, there is some evidence that early projections also tend to be diffuse in Xenopus (Sakaguchi and Murphey, 1985), chick (McLoon, 1982), rat (Fawcett and O'Leary, 1985) and hamster (Schneider and coworkers, 1981).

Electrophysiology. In the case of the goldfish, electrophysiological recordings during this early diffuse phase are difficult because the responses fatigue extremely rapidly. The earliest recordings at 34 days postcrush show maps that are already normal in organization. In the frog, however, the sharpening of the map can be followed with the electrophysiological mapping technique (Adamson and

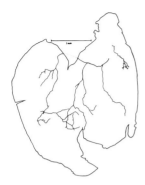

Figure 1: Camera lucida drawing of a regenerated optic arbor, stained with HRP at 21 days after nerve crush, showing the widespread branching. The heavy lines at the outside mark the boundaries of the tectum, which was split both rostrally and caudally to allow it to lie flat. A normal optic arbor is shown for comparison. Scale bar: 1 mm. (From Schmidt, 1985).

coworkers, 1984; Humphrey and Beazley, 1982). In the early weeks, recording at each tectal point yielded many units responding to stimulation of a wide area of the visual field. This area is called a multiunit receptive field. Its large size indicates that only a very crude level of retinotopic organization was present on the tectum. Over the next 20 to 30 days, these large responsive areas shrunk to the normal size. In addition to the direct retinotectal projection, frogs also have an intertectal relay through the Nucleus Isthmi that is easily recorded. This relay allowed Adamson and coworkers to assess the postsynaptic effects of the crude retinotopic projection. Early in regeneration, the receptive fields of single relay fibers in the normal tectum were grossly enlarged, reflecting the crude map on the opposite tectum. Thus the misdirected arbors or branches of arbors within the crude map appeared to have established effective synaptic connections. We will see below in the studies of goldfish regeneration that effective synaptic transmission appears to be necessary for the sharpening to occur.

DIFFUSE MAP SHARPENED BY ACTIVITY DURING REGENERATION

Effects of Blocking Activity.

Intraocular TTX studies. In adult goldfish, both anatomical (Meyer, 1983) and electrophysiological (Schmidt and Edwards, 1983) studies have demonstrated an activity-dependent sharpening of the initially diffuse regenerated projection. Meyer (1983) used radioautographic tracing and lesions to show that the regenerated projection does not sharpen but remains diffuse when activity is blocked with intraocular injections of tetrodotoxin (TTX). Blocking from 32 to 80 days postcrush prevented the return to a normal topography, but the map could still sharpen if the fish were allowed a further 24 days of activity after the TTX was discontinued. Thus, in small goldfish, activity could still sharpen the map several months after the fibers reached the tectum.

Schmidt and Edwards (1983) used electrophysiological recording to assess the sharpening of retinotectal maps in large goldfish. In control fish, maps recorded at 35 days postcrush were already normal both in organization and in the size of the multiunit receptive fields, which averaged 11 degrees. In projections blocked for the first 28 days, however, the multiunit receptive fields were greatly enlarged, averaging around 30 degrees (Fig. 2). The centers of these enlarged fields were in the retinotopically appropriate region of the visual field, indicating that the gross organization of the map was correct. The enlarged multiunit receptive fields reflect the convergence onto each tectal point of arbors from retinal ganglion cells distributed over a wide area of retina. This interpretation was supported by other evidence. First, the units persisted during a postsynaptic block with BTX demonstrating that the tectal recordings were of presynaptic origin. Second, the receptive fields of single

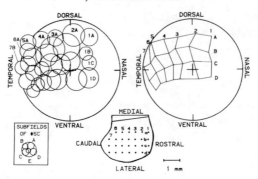

Figure 2: Retinotectal map recorded 63 days after optic
nerve crush in fish blocked intraocularly with TTX from 0
to 27 days. The two large circles are two representations
of the visual field that contain the outlines of the receptive fields and the positions of their centers. Below,
electrode penetrations are marked on the drawing of the
tectal surface. The receptive fields recorded at these
points fall into an orderly array in the visual field
similar to the array on the tectal surface and are numbered
accordingly. The inset at the lower left diagrams the relationship between a multiunit receptive field and several of its
single unit components, mapped separately with a spike height
discriminator. Normally multiunit receptive fields are the
size of single unit fields. (From Schmidt and Edwards, 1983).

ganglion cells recorded in the retina of these same fish were not enlarged.
Finally, the tectal recordings yielded many units at each site, which when
isolated by amplitude, were found to have receptive fields of normal size (Fig.
2). The simplest interpretation is that the enlarged multiunit receptive fields
reflect errors in the targeting of regenerated arbors that are usually corrected
with activity. This interpretation is consistent with the finding of many
enlarged arbors early in regeneration, and the presence of enlarged multiunit
receptive fields in the frog as a normal phase in regeneration. Preliminary
results from HRP stained optic fibers suggest that TTX prevents the arbors from
concentrating their branches, which remain scattered over a wider area than
normal.

Sensitive period. The period of sensitivity corresponds to the period of
synaptogenesis. The first synapses, as assessed by recording field potentials,
were detectable on day 20 (Schmidt and coworkers, 1983). Blocking before this
time (0-14 days) did not prevent the sharpening. Blocking from 14 to 34 days,
however, was extremely effective, producing enlarged fields averaging
approximately 40 degrees. Synaptogenesis continues at a declining rate until 80
to 100 days postcrush as determined by counts of total synaptic density (Murray
and Edwards, 1982). Eisele and Schmidt (1985) have now assessed the effects of
blocking activity for two weeks starting at later times (35, 50, 65, 80, 95 or
110 days postcrush). Blocks imposed at 35 days cause the receptive fields, which
had already sharpened, to become enlarged again. The size of this effect,
however, becomes progressively smaller at later times, and no effect is seen in
the mature projection, where synaptogenesis should be minimal. The results
suggest a parallel between the rate at which synapses are added and the degree of
disorder produced by blocking activity.

TTX does not appear to cause a decreased rate of synaptogenesis as judged by the
field potentials elicited by optic nerve shock. A similar lack of effect of TTX

was noted concerning neuromuscular synapse formation in vitro (Obata, 1977). In the fish tectum, the amplitude of the field potentials from eyes blocked during regeneration was not decreased when they were recorded just after the block wore off (Schmidt and coworkers, 1983). For the small field potentials in early regeneration, amplitude is likely to be a reasonably sensitive measure of the number of synapses formed. This result suggests that the block of activity may not affect the quantity of synapses made, but instead may interfere with the deployment of the synapses in the retinotopically correct order.

A Model Based on Correlated Activity.

The model. A proposed model for sharpening the map is based upon the correlated firing of neighboring ganglion cells and the resultant summation of their EPSP's in the postsynaptic tectal cells (Willshaw and von der Malsburg, 1976; Schmidt and Edwards, 1983). Neighboring ganglion cells, which view the same part of the visual world, are likely to fire with a high degree of correlation if they are of the same type (eg., ON or OFF; Ginsberg and coworkers, 1984). Both Arnett (1978) and Ginsberg and coworkers (1984) have in fact demonstrated such correlations even in absolute darkness when only spontaneous activity is present. The model also assumes that the arbors in the initial diffuse projection are large, and have a high degree of overlap. For neighboring ganglion cells having some overlap of their arbors and firing with a high degree of correlation, there would be a summation of the postsynaptic EPSP's. Finally, if the most effective synapses are differentially stabilized and retained (Hebb, 1949; Changeux and Danchin, 1976), then the correlated activity, resulting in larger EPSP's, would stabilize their synapses in the region of overlap. Of course, arbors from distant ganglion cells would also overlap, but without correlated firing there would be no summation and no stabilization of those synaptic connections. Such a cue for convergence would, therefore, be specific to the arbors of neighboring ganglion cells, because they would have correlated activity.

Testing the model. Recent experiments (Schmidt and Eisele, 1985) have upheld two of the major features of this model. First, the model proposes that the sharpening would still be disrupted even if the ganglion cells were allowed activity as long as the strictly local correlation in firing of neighboring ganglion cells is disrupted. Two methods were used : stroboscopic illumination and dark rearing. Stroboscopic illumination caused correlated firing in all ganglion cells, since single unit recordings from the retinas during regeneration showed that both 'OFF' cells and 'ON' cells fired one or two spikes at a constant latency after each flash. When all cells, not just near neighbors, fire in synchrony, correlated firing can no longer be a cue for finding neighbors from the retina. Projections regenerated under stroboscopic illumination, like those regenerated without activity, had enlarged multiunit receptive fields that averaged 33.2° in diameter. The period of sensitivity to strobe matches that for TTX (Eisele and Schmidt, 1985). In addition, preliminary anatomical studies suggest that strobe rearing may also prevent the arbors from concentrating their branches into one area.

Projections regenerated in total darkness also had enlarged multiunit receptive fields, averaging 28.7° in diameter. This is somewhat smaller than the average of 33.2° under strobelight illumination or the 40° with the equivalent TTX block, and may reflect a slight degree of sharpening due to the correlation in the low levels of spontaneous activity of neighboring ganglion cells (Arnett, 1978). The strobe and dark rearing experiments make unlikely the possibility that the TTX effect upon sharpening was caused by the deficit in axonal transport in regenerating optic fibers that was demonstrated by Edwards and Grafstein (1983). The high and low levels of activity in the strobe and dark reared fish are unlikely to be associated with similar decrements in axonal transport. The experiments also show that sharpening depends upon the pattern of activity, presumably the aforementioned correlation in firing between neighbors in the retina.

A second prediction from the model is that, in order for the synapses to be
stabilized, the correlated activity must be transmitted to the postsynaptic
tectal cell to allow summation of the EPSP's. To test this prediction, synaptic
transmission was blocked during the period of early synaptogenesis (Schmidt,
1985). An osmotic minipump was attached to the fish's head to deliver a
continuous infusion of   BTX, previously shown to decrement retinotectal
synaptic transmission (Freeman and coworkers, 1980). The resulting maps had
enlarged multiunit receptive fields similar to those seen in the TTX blocked,
strobe reared and dark reared fish, averaging 28.5^o in diameter. This experiment
suggested that fibers with correlated activity may not interact directly, but
through the transmission of their signals to the postsynaptic tectal cells,
probably through the summation of EPSP's. At the present time, we cannot
determine exactly what form of activity in the postsynaptic cell (whether EPSP's
or spike activity) may be important in the stabilization of synaptic contacts,
nor do we know the nature of the feedback to stabilize the presynaptic contact.
This feedback might be direct or through feedback circuits either within the
tectum or through Nucleus Isthmi.

In order to test the role of sharpening in development as well as in
regeneration, we recently reared newly hatched larval goldfish for more than a
year under alternate 12 hour periods of darkness and stroboscopic illumination.
The multiunit receptive fields of these year old fish were enlarged to the same
degree as in the regenerates, demonstrating the relevance of this mechanism in
development.

Activity and other projections.   Several other CNS maps are known to be
sharpened, organized or otherwise altered by activity dependent mechanisms. In
Xenopus, Keating (1975) has shown that the indirect retinotectal pathway, which
relays information from the ipsilateral eye, can adjust itself, following
rotation of one eye, to bring the maps from the two eyes into register. Archer
and coworkers (1982) have shown that the retinotopic map in the lateral
geniculate nucleus of the cat is also sharpened by activity. The segregation of
visual afferents into eye specific patches or stripes is activity dependent
(Meyer, 1982; Boss and Schmidt, 1984; Reh and Constantine-Paton, 1985; Stryker
and Harris, 1985), probably driven by the correlated activity of neighboring
ganglion cells within each eye but not between eyes. Also in visual cortex, the
selection of neurons participating in the callosal connections may depend upon
patterned visual activity, as a different subset remain connected when the animal
is reared in the dark (Innocenti, 1981). Finally, in the auditory system of the
owl, a tectal map of auditory space apparently aligns itself to the visual map
already in place on the tectum via activity cues (Knudsen, 1983).

The production and subsequent elimination of excess synaptic connections is also
a familiar pattern outside the CNS, occurring in the autonomic ganglia (Purves
and Lichtman, 1980) and at the neuromuscular junction, where the elimination of
polyneuronal innervation requires that presynaptic activity be transmitted to the
postsynaptic muscle fiber (Thompson, 1985).

Concluding remarks.   Activity dependent mechanisms for the selective
stabilization or elimination of the initially diffuse synaptic connections may
represent a widespread phenomenon, occurring at all levels from the neuromuscular
junction to the callosal connections between the cortices. Such mechanisms do
not act alone, but in concert with the differential cell adhesion mechanisms
commonly known as chemoaffinity. Activity dependent stabilization of totally
random synapses would not be able to generate the reproducibly oriented maps that
one finds in the nervous system. Instead, a random mix of retinal fibers would
result either in randomly oriented maps or in "mosaic" maps with occasional
discontinuities (Willshaw and von der Malsburg, 1976). Rather, the reproducible
polarity must stem from the ability of differential affinity mechanisms to bring
a greater number of temporal versus nasal retinal fibers to rostral tectum, and
nasal fibers to caudal tectum, etc. On the other hand, a completely rigid
developmental process (rigid chemoaffinity alone) might not be sufficiently

flexible to succeed. Factors such as the variable geometry of the head, the separation between the eyes, between the ears, etc., might demand flexibility in the process of aligning the visual maps from the two eyes or aligning the auditory map with the visual maps.

REFERENCES

Adamson, J. R., J. Burke and P.Grobstein (1984) Reestablishment of the ipsilateral oculotectal projection after optic nerve crush in the frog: evidence for synaptic remodelling during regeneration. J. Neurosci., 4, 2635-2649.

Archer, S. M., M. W. Dubin, and L. A. Stark (1982) Abnormal development of kitten retinogeniculate connectivity in the absence of action potentials. Science, 217, 743-745.

Arnett, D. W. (1978) Statistical dependence between neighboring retinal ganglion cells in goldfish. Exp. Brain Res., 32, 49-53.

Attardi, D.G. and R.W. Sperry (1963) Preferential selection of central pathways by regenerating optic fibers. Exp. Neurol., 7, 46-64.

Boss, V. and J. T. Schmidt (1984) Activity and the formation of ocular dominance patches in dually innervated tectum of goldfish. J. Neurosci., 4, 2891-2905.

Changeux, J. P. and A. Danchin (1976) Selective stabilization of developing synapses as a mechanism for the specification of neuronal networks. Nature, 264, 705-712.

Cook, J.E. and E.C.C. Rankin (1984) Use of a lectin-peroxidase conjugate (WGA-HRP) to assess the retiontopic precision of goldfish optic terminals. Neurosci. Lett., 48, 61-66.

Easter, S.S. (1983) Postnatal neurogenesis and changing neuronal connections. Trends in NeuroSci., 6, 53-56.

Edwards, D.L. and B. Grafstein (1983) Intraocular tetrodotoxin in goldfish hinders optic nerve regeneration. Brain Res., 269, 1-14.

Eisele, L.E. and J.T. Schmidt (1985) Activity sharpens the regenerated retinotectal projection: Sensitive period for strobe and TTX. Neurosci. Abstr., 11, 101.

Fawcett, J.W. and D.D.M. O'Leary (1985) The role of electrical activity in the formation of topographic maps in the nervous system. Trends in NeuroSci., 8, 201-206.

Freeman, J. A., J. T. Schmidt and R. E. Oswald (1980) Effect of -Bungarotoxin on retinotectal synaptic transmission in the goldfish and the toad. Neuroscience, 5, 929-942.

Fujisawa, H., N. Tani, K. Watanabe and Y. Ibata (1982) Branching of regenerating retinal axons and preferential selection of appropriate branches for specific neuronal connection in the newt. Developmental Biology, 90, 43-57.

Ginsberg, K.S., J.A. Johnsen and M.W. Levine (1984) Common noise in the firing of neighboring ganglion cells in goldfish retina. J. Physiol. (London), 351, 433-444.

Hebb, D.O. (1949) The organization of behavior. John Wiley and Sons, New York.

Horder, T.J. and K.A.C. Martin (1977) Morphogenetics as an alternative to chemospecificity in the formation of nerve connections. In A.S.G. Curtis (Ed.), Cell-Cell Recognition, 32 Symp. Soc. Exp. Biol., Cambridge Univ. Press, Cambridge, pp. 275-358.

Humphrey, M.F. and L.D. Beazley (1982) An electrophysiological study of early retinotectal projection patterns during optic nerve regeneration in Hyla moorei. Brain Res., 239, 595-602.

Innocenti, G.M. (1981) Growth and reshaping of axons in the establishment of visual callosal connections. Science, 212, 824-826.

Keating, M.J. (1975) The time course of experience dependent synaptic switching of visual connections in Xenopus laevis. Proc R. Soc. Edinburgh, B189, 603-610.

Knudsen, E.I. (1983) Early auditory experience aligns the auditory map of space in the optic tectum of the barn owl. Science, 222, 939-941.

McLoon, S. (1982) Alterations in precision of the crossed retinotectal projection during chick development. Science, 218, 1418-1420.

Meyer, R.L. (1980) Mapping the normal and regenerating retinotectal projection of goldfish with autoradiographic methods. J. Comp. Neurol., 189, 273-289.

Meyer, R. L. (1982) Tetrodotoxin blocks the formation of ocular dominance columns in goldfish. Science, 218, 589-591.

Meyer, R.L. (1983) Tetrodotoxin inhibits the formation of refined retinotopography in goldfish. Dev. Brain Res., 6, 293-298.

Murray, M. and M.A. Edwards (1982) A quantitative study of the reinnervation of the goldfish optic tectum following optic nerve crush. J. Comp. Neurol., 209, 363-373.

Obata, K. (1977) Development of neuromuscular transmission in culture with a variety of neurons and in the presence of cholinergic substances and tetrodotoxin. Brain Res., 119, 141-150.

Purves, D., J.W. Lichtman (1980) Elimination of synapses in the developing nervous system. Science, 210, 153-157.

Reh, T. and M. Constantine-Paton (1985) Eye specific segregation is dependent on neural activity in three eyed Rana pipiens. J. Neurosci., 5, 1132-1143.

Sakaguchi, D.S. and R.K. Murphey (1985) Initial development of the retinotectal projection in Xenopus: An examination of ganglion cell terminal arborizations. J. Neurosci., 5, (In press).

Schmidt, J.T. (1982) The formation of retinotectal projections. Trends in Neurosci., 5, 111-116.

Schmidt, J.T. (1985) Formation of retinotopic connections: Selective stabilization by an activity dependent mechanism. Cell. and Molec Neurobiol., 5, 65-84.

Schmidt, J.T., M. Buzzard and J. Turcotte (1984) Morphology of regenerated optic arbors in goldfish tectum. Neurosci. Abstr., 10, 667.

Schmidt, J. T. and D. L. Edwards (1983) Activity sharpens the map during regeneration of the retinotectal projection in goldfish. Brain Res., 269, 29-39.

Schmidt, J. T., D. L. Edwards and C. Stuermer (1983) The re-establishment of synaptic transmission by regenerating optic axons in goldfish: Time course and effects of blocking activity by intraocular injection of tetrodotoxin. Brain Res., 269, 15-27.

Schmidt, J.T. and L.E. Eisele (1985) Stroboscopic illumination and dark rearing block the sharpening of the regenerated retinotectal map in goldfish. Neuroscience, 14, 535-546.

Schneider, G., L. Rava, G.M. Sachs and S. Jhaveri (1981) Widespread branching of retinotectal axons: Transient in normal development and anomalous in adults with neonatal lesions. Neurosci. Abstr., 7, 732.

Sperry, R.W. (1943) Effect of 180 degree rotation of the retinal field on visuomotor coordination. J. Exptl. Zool., 92, 263-279.

Sperry, R.W. (1963) Chemoaffinity in the orderly growth of nerve fiber patterns and connections. P.N.A.S.U.S.A., 50, 703-709.

Stryker, M. P. and W. A. Harris (1985) Binocular impulse blockade prevents the formation of ocular dominance columns in cat visual cortex. J. Neurosci., 5, (In press).

Stuermer, C.A.O. and S.S. Easter (1984) A comparison of the normal and regenerated retinotectal pathways of goldfish. J. Comp. Neurol., 223, 57-76.

Thompson, W.J. (1985) Activity and synapse elimination at the neuromuscular junction. Cell. and Molec. Neurobiol., 5, 167-182.

Willshaw, D. J. and C. von der Malsburg (1976) How patterned neural connections can be set up by self-organization. Proc. Roy. Soc. Lond., B. 194, 431-445.

A Regulatory Mechanism of
Changes in Ocular Dominance

T. Kasamatsu

Smith-Kettlewell Institute of Visual Sciences, San Francisco,
CA 94115, USA

The nervous system can change its mode of action depending on a set of preceding responses or "experience". The age-dependent modification of neural connectivity in the mammalian brain is one of the adaptive processes in the brain. We have been studying roles of the central noradrenaline (NA)-containing pathway in the regulation of neuronal plasticity which is typically seen in the immature visual cortex of young kittens (e.g., Kasamatsu, 1983; Kasamatsu and co-workers, 1984). In this chapter, I would like to review briefly the recent development of the NA hypothesis for visuocortical plasticity.

General Consideration

Individual neurons in the kitten visual cortex quickly change their ocular dominance, when challenged with brief eyelid suture of one eye (Wiesel and Hubel, 1963). We used this change in ocular dominance to measure the extent of neuronal plasticity present in a given visual cortex. To describe numerically changes in ocular dominance, we usually calculate two indices based on a single ocular dominance histogram. The latter is compiled of 30 visually active cells recorded from a single microelectrode track placed near the center of projection of gaze in the primary visual cortex (area 17). The two indices are defined as follows:

Binocularity is the proportion of binocular cells (group 2-6 cells in the 7-group scheme of Hubel and Wiesel, 1962) to the total number of visually active cells.

Contra/ipsi ratio equals the number of group 1-3 cells divided by that of group 5-7 cells, excluding group 4 cells.

The former index is a measure of binocular overlap of visual afferent impinging on single cortical cells and the latter shows the extent of dominancy of the contralateral input over the ipsilateral input in a given ocular dominance distribution. We recently calculated the mean values of these indices and their statistical variabilities in the visual cortex of normal cats (Kasamatsu and co-workers, 1985). They are as follows:

	95% confidence limits	5% rejection limits
Binocularity=0.75	$0.81 \geq B \geq 0.69$	$0.98 \geq B \geq 0.53$
Contra/ipsi ratio=1.52	$1.94 \geq C/I > 1.10$	$3.19 > C/I > 0$

Usually, these two indices are thought to change concomitantly. However, under various conditions we obtained the W- or U-shaped distribution following monocular deprivation, as schematically shown in the middle of Fig. 1. In this unique distribution pattern binocularity decreases significantly, whereas contra/ipsi ratio does not change. Although it is conceptually hard to accept the presence of monocular cells which are exclusively driven through the deprived eye, this is consistent with the scattered but repeated observations by many investigators in the field. We would like to understand this W- or U-shaped distribution as a transition between normal and the totally shifted condition. As will be mentioned below, we in fact encountered this pattern often in the adult visual cortex to which visuocortical plasticity has been restored partly.

VISUOCORTICAL PLASTICITY

IN MONOCULAR DEPRIVATION PARADIGM

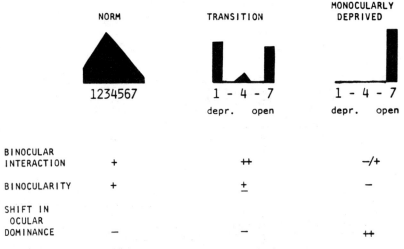

Fig. 1.   Schematic drawings of ocular dominance histograms in the normal cat visual cortex (left) and its changes after monocular eyelid suture (right). The numbers 1 through 7 refer to the 7-group classification of ocular dominance following the Hubel and Wiesel's scheme (1962). The U- or W-shaped distribution (middle) is often observed as a transition between the normal and the totally shifted distribution in monocular deprivation paradigm as well as during recovery from the total shift in ocular dominance. Author's interpretations of each of the three patterns are presented at the bottom in terms of three qualities. ++, more than normal; +, normal; ± less than normal; −, non; −/+, absence or presence depends on tests.

New evidence for necessity of NA terminals

Six pieces of evidence are summarized in Table 1, which are in support of the idea that NA is necessary, though not necessarily sufficient by itself, for maintaining visuocortical plasticity. We are primarily concerned here with the topic No. 5.

TABLE 1. Evidence in Support of the Original Thesis and its Extension

1) Restoration of visuocortical plasticity (shift in ocular dominance) with direct NA perfusion in the 6-hydroxydopamine (6-OHDA)-treated cortex (kitten).

2) Decrease in binocularity following monocular deprivation in the NA-perfused cortex (adult cat).

3) Recovery from the shift in ocular dominance following monocular deprivation: Acceleration by cortical perfusion with exogenous NA and suppression with 6-OHDA (kitten).

4) Changes in ocular dominance in the NA-perfused, otherwise normal cortex (kitten and adult cat).

5) Decrease in binocularity upon brief monocular exposure combined with electrical stimulation of the locus coeruleus (adult cat).

6) Decrease in binocularity in the NA-perfused, otherwise normal visual cortex during acute paralysis by Flaxedil (adult cat).

We recently showed the partial restoration of visuocortical plasticity to the mature and necessarily aplastic cortex by direct activation of the NA-containing cells in the locus coeruleus (LC) area in the cat brainstem. Cats which had been raised normally until the ages of 17 weeks to over 3 years were monocularly exposed for 2 hrs daily to the lit laboratory environment, during which period the LC was electrically stimulated by recurring, low-frequency pulse trains. The animals were kept in the dark for the remaining 22 hrs. The combined treatment continued for 6 consecutive days. On the 7th day, single-unit recordings were extracellularly carried out following the standard method of receptive field plotting. Control animals had the similar visual experience of brief monocular exposure followed by dark-rearing but without accompanying LC stimulation. No change whatsoever was obtained, as expected, in the control animals. However, the ocular dominance distribution in the LC-stimulated animals was very different from control, showing the W-shaped pattern with a significant decrease in binocularity (Kasamatsu and co-workers, 1985). These results are summarized in Fig. 2. In the same study, however, we found that the change in ocular dominance as expressed by a significant decrease in binocularity was not obtained if the visual cortex had been pretreated with 6-hydroxydopamine, an NA-related neurotoxin, for the preceding week.

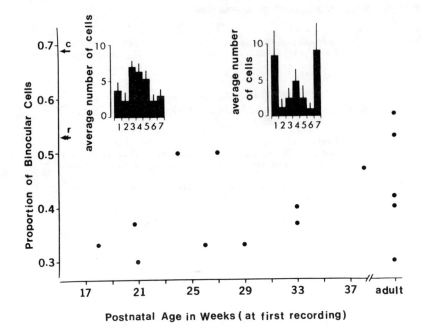

Postnatal Age in Weeks (at first recording)

Fig. 2. Significant decrease in proportion of binocular
cells (binocularity) caused by direct
activation of the locus coeruleus in
combination with brief monocular exposure.
Binocularity values (filled circles) are based
on respective ocular dominance histograms
obtained from 15 experimental animals.
Composite ocular dominance histograms from 15
experimental (right inset) and 3 control
animals (left inset) are also shown following
the convention used for Fig. 1, top. In both
groups of animals only the ipsilateral eye was
exposed to the lit environment. A vertical bar
on the top of each column is a standard
deviation. Number of original histograms; 15
experimental and 3 control, respectively.
Number of cells, 444 and 90. Binocularity is
0.41 and 0.78, respectively. The ratio of the
number of cells receiving dominant input from
the deprived eye (groups 1-3) to that from the
nondeprived eye (groups 5-7) is 1.38 and 1.26,
respectively. Group 4 cells which receive
balanced excitatory input from the two eyes are
excluded from the calculation of the
deprived/nondeprived ratio. c and r on the
ordinate indicate the lower ends of the 95%
confidence limits and the 5% rejection limits
of binocularity mentioned in the text,
respectively (reproduced with minimum
alteration from Kasamatsu and co-workers,
Neurosci. Res. 1985).

Thus, these results, taken together with the previous ones which showed release of endogenous NA within the neocortex in response to LC stimulation (e.g., Korf and co-workers, 1973; Tanaka and co-workers, 1976) strongly suggest that the observed loss of binocularity in the experimental animals was due most likely to endogenous NA released within the visual cortex by LC stimulation in combination with monocular exposure. We then interpreted the present result as suggesting that visuocortical plasticity was restored, at least in part, to the mature, usually aplastic cortex by the higher than normal availability of endogenous NA within the visual cortex.

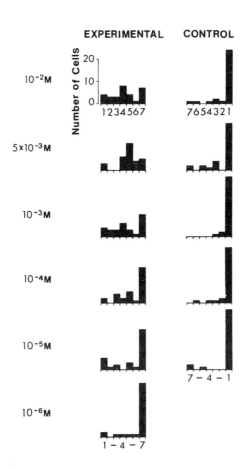

Fig. 3. A family of 5 paired and one single ocular dominance histograms obtained from the propranolol-perfused left and control right hemispheres of the same six kittens. The concentration of D,L-propranolol in an osmotic minipump varied from 10^{-2} M top to 10^{-6} M bottom. For the lowest concentration (10^{-6} M), only the propranolol-perfused hemisphere was

recorded. The conventions as in Fig. 1. Note
the propranolol-perfused, experimental left
hemisphere was contralateral to the monocularly
deprived, right eye (unpublished material).

Involvement of β adrenoreceptors

Our interpretation of the effects of LC stimulation a priori assumes the
involvement of NA-related receptors in the regulation of visuocortical
plasticity. A few years ago, G. Jonsson and I studied normal ontogeny of β
adrenoreceptor binding in the cat visual cortex, using ^{3}H-dihydroalprenolol as a
radioligand. We showed that the number of specific β receptor binding sites
rapidly increases after birth, attaining the value larger than the adult value
during the 5th and 11th postnatal week (Jonsson and Kasamatsu, 1983). On the
other hand, endogenous NA increased more or less continually to adulthood.
These results are essentially consistent with those previously reported for the
rat neocortex. We then suggested that changes in the number of NA-activated β
adrenoreceptors may be a more direct measure of visuocortical plasticity than
the absolute level of endogenous NA itself.

We decided, therefore, to test this premise more directly, perfusing the kitten
visual cortex with propranolol, a β adrenoreceptor antagonist, to see whether
such treatments block the expected shift in ocular dominance following brief
monocular lid suture. As exemplified by a family of paired ocular dominance
histograms in Fig. 3, we were able to decrease the extent of the shift in the
hemisphere which had been perfused with propranolol (Kasamatsu, 1979; Shirokawa
and Kasamatsu, 1984; Kasamatsu and Shirokawa, 1985). In the opposite, control
hemisphere of the same animals, however, the shift in ocular dominance took
place as expected, suggesting that the effect of propranolol was confined to
only the drug-perfused hemisphere. We soon learned that the blocking effect is
concentration-dependent (Fig. 3; see also Shirokawa and Kasamatsu, 1984) The
maximal extent of the blockade was obtained at 10^{-2} M propranolol in an osmotic
minipump, being the average binocularity 0.67. We could not use the propranolol
solution higher than 10^{-2} M in this study. When used, the drug's nonspecific
and toxic effects became discernible on visual responsiveness as well as
receptive field properties in general. The half-maximal effect was obtained at
about 10^{-4} M propranol, changing its concentration between 10^{-6} M and 10^{-2} M. We
estimated that in the present paradigm locally perfused propranolol is at least
170 times diluted at the recording site. This calculation was based on the
intracortical spread of the radioactivity within the visual cortex which had
been perfused with ^{3}H-propranolol. Applying the dilution factor of 1/170, it
was thus concluded that the necessary concentration of propranolol for the half-
maximal effect on visuocortical plasticity was at about 5.8 x 10^{-7} M or even
lower at the recording site (Shirokawa and Kasamatsu, 1984, 1985).

Essentially the same results were obtained with sotalol, another type of
common β adrenoreceptor antagonist (Shirokawa and Kasamatsu, 1984; Kasamatsu
and Shirokawa, 1985). Using the same paradigm of the localized and continual
perfusion in combination with or without monocular deprivation, we studied the
effects of α adrenoreceptor antagonists such as phenoxybenzamine and
piperoxane, and an authentic local anesthetic such as carbocaine. Results
obtained from these control studies were uniformally negative, at least at the
concentrations of the drugs which were higher than those used for β antagonists,
suggesting that the blockade of the shift in ocular dominance observed in the
experimental kittens was tightly related with specific blockade of β adrenoreceptors by selective β antagonists (Kasamatsu and Shirokawa, 1985;
Shirokawa and Kasamatsu, 1985).

Conclusion

The two studies reviewed above clearly made a factual link between the original NA hypothesis for visuocortical plasticity and β adrenoreceptors within the visual cortex. Therefore, we are in a position to extend the link further to the second messenger system such as cyclic AMP. We have already presented preliminary evidence in favor of the idea (Kasamatsu 1980, 1982).

Recently, several negative reports became available regarding the effects of significant decrease of endogenous NA in the kitten visual cortex on visuocortical plasticity (Adrien and co-workers, 1982; Bear and Daniels, 1983; Bear and co-workers, 1983; Daw and co-workers, 1983, 1984, 1985a, 1985b). Potentially serious shortcomings in the studies which produced these negative results have been already discussed elsewhere (e.g., Kasamatsu, 1983; Kasamatsu and co-workers, 1984; Kasamatsu and Shirokawa, 1985). Nevertheless, we should acknowledge that the negative results contributed decisively to shift our research strategy from quantitation of endogenous NA as a useful measure of visuocortical plasticity. As we have repeatedly stated elsewhere, however, it remains to be tested whether the NA- β adrenoreceptor-cyclic nucleotide sytem is only one of many factors that contribute to the regulatory mechanisms of visuocortical plasticity which is especially notable in the immature neocortex.

ACKNOWLEDGEMENTS

I am grateful to my colleagues, Drs. T. Shirokawa and K. Imamura, who are devoted neuroscientists in our laboratory. I am also thankful to Ms. C. Dang for improving the English in the text, Ms. M. King for typing the manuscript and Mr. C. Cushman for photographic reproduction. Supported by USPHS grant EY-05549 and the Smith-Kettlewell Eye Research Foundation.

REFERENCES

Adrien, J., P. Buisseret, Y. Fregnac, E. Gary-Bobo, M. Imbert, J.-P. Tassin, and Y. Trotter (1982). Noradrenaline et plasticite du cortex visuel du chaton: un reexamen. C.R. Acad. Sci. Paris, 295,745-750.
Bear, M.F., and J.D. Daniels (1983). The plastic response to monocular deprivation persists in kitten visual cortex after chronic depletion of norepinephrine. J. Neurosci., 3, 407-416.
Bear, M.F., M.A. Paradiso, M. Schwartz, S.B. Nelson, K.M. Carnes, and J.D. Daniels (1983). Two methods of catecholamine depletion in kitten visual cortex yield different effects on plasticity. Nature, 302, 245-247.
Daw, N.W., R.K. Rader,. T.W. Robertson, and T.O. Videen (1983). Do short term and long term depletion of noradrenaline have different effects on visual deprivation in the kitten visual cortex? Soc. Neurosci. Abstr. 9, 1217.
Daw, N.W., T.W. Robertson, R.K. Rader, T.O. Videen, and C.J. Coscia (1984). Substantial reduction of cortical noradrenaline by lesions of adrenergic pathways does not prevent effects of monocular deprivation. J. Neurosci. 4, 1354-1360.
Daw, N.W., T.O. Videen, D. Parkinson and R.K. Rader (1985a). DSP-4(N-(2-chloroethyl)-N-ethyl-2-bromobenzylamine) depletes noradrenaline in kitten visual cortex without altering the effects of monocular deprivation. J. Neurosci. 5, 1925-1933.
Daw. N.W., T.O. Videen, R.K. Rader, and T.W. Robertson (1985b). Substantial reduction of noradrenaline in kitten visual cortex by intraventricular injections of 6-hydroxydopamine does not always prevent ocular dominance shifts after monocular deprivation. Exp. Brain Res. 59, 30-35.

Hubel, D.H., and T.N. Wiesel (1962). Receptive fields, binocular interactions and functional architecture in the cat's visual cortex. J. Physiol. (Lond.) 160, 106-154.

Jonsson, G., and T. Kasamatsu (1983). Maturation of monoamine neuro-transmitters and receptors in cat occipital cortex during postnatal critical period. Exp. Brain Res. 50, 449-458.

Kasamatsu, T. (1979). Involvement of the β-adrenergic receptor in cortical plasticity. ARVO Abstr. Suppl. Invest. Ophthal. Vis. Sci., 18, 135.

Kasamatsu, T. (1980). A possible role for cyclic nucleotides in plasticity of visual cortex. Soc. Neurosci. Abstr. 6, 494.

Kasamatsu, T. (1982) A role of the central norepinephrine system in regulation of neuronal plasticity in cat visual cortex. In A. Kaneko, N. Tsukahara. and K. Uchizono (Eds.), Neurotransmitters in the Retina and Visual Centers. Biomed. Res. Suppl., 3, Biomed. Res. Foundation, Tokyo, pp. 87-93.

Kasamatsu, T. (1983). Neuronal plasticity maintained by the central norepinephrine system in the cat visual cortex. In J.M. Sprague and A.N. Epstein (Eds.), Progress in Psychobiology and Physiological Psychology, Vol. 10, Academic Press, New York, pp. 1-112.

Kasamatsu, T., T. Itakura, G. Jonsson, P. Heggelund, J.D. Pettigrew, K. Nakai, K. Watabe, B.D. Kuppermann, and M. Ary (1984). Neuronal plasticity in cat visual cortex: A proposed role for the central noradrenaline system. In L. Descarries, T.R. Reader, and H.H. Jasper (Eds.), Monoamine Innervation of Cerebral Cortex, Neurology and Neurobiology, Vol. 10, Alan R. Liss, New York, pp. 301-309.

Kasamatsu, T., K. Watabe, P. Heggelund, and E. Schöller (1985). Plasticity in cat visual cortex restored by electrical stimulation of the locus coeruleus. Neurosci. Res. 2, 365-386.

Kasamatsu, T., and T. Shirokawa (1985). Involvement of β adrenoreceptors in the shift of ocular dominance after monocular deprivation. Exp. Brain. Res. 59, 507-514.

Korf, J., R.H. Roth, and G.K. Aghajanian (1973). Alterations in turnover and endogenous levels of norepinephrine in cerebral cortex following electrical stimulation and acute axotomy of cerebral noradrenergic pathways. Eur. J. Pharmacol. 23, 276-282.

Shirokawa, T. and, T. Kasamatsu (1984). β-Adrenergic receptor mediates neuronal plasticity in visual cortex. ARVO Abstr. Suppl. Invest. Ophth. Vis. Sci. 25, 214.

Shirokawa. T. and, T. Kasamatsu (1985). Concentration-dependent suppression by β-adrenergic antagonists of the shift in ocular dominance following monocular deprivation in kitten visual cortex (submitted for publication).

Tanaka, C., C. Inagaki, and H. Fujiwara (1976). Labeled noradrenaline release from rat cerebral cortex following electrical stimulation of locus coeruleus. Brain Res., 106, 384-389.

Wiesel, T.N., and D.H. Hubel (1963). Single-cell response in striate cortex of kittens deprived of vision in one eye. J. Neurophysiol., 26, 1003-1017.

Experience-dependent Modification of MAP2, a Cytoskeletal Protein, in the Visual Cortex of Cats

C. Aoki

Department of Neurobiology, Cornell University Medical College,
411 E. 69 St., New York, NY 10021, USA

INTRODUCTION

From the time of birth and up to an age genetically predetermined, neurons in the visual cortex of mammals are involved in active, stimulus-dependent synaptogenesis (reviewed in Riesen, 1975). Abnormal visual experience during this critical period (CP) can cause life-long abnormal vision, indicating that the development of visual neural function is also stimulus-dependent (reviewed in Movshon & Van Sluyters, 1981). Thus, the visual cortex is said to be plastic during the CP. The aim of the studies reported here was to investigate the biochemical basis of this developmental plasticity.

Realizing that many events could be responsible for determining the state of cortical plasticity, the study was begun by examining the possible role of hormone-stimulated metabolism of cAMP in determining the beginning and the end of the CP. The reason for examining this was two-fold: 1)cAMP has been implicated in the control of many developmental events, such as the induction of the presumptive amphibian epidermis into derivatives of neural ectoderm and neural crest, and the stimulation of neurite outgrowth in neuroblastoma cell lines (reviewed in Nathanson, 1977); 2) it has been hypothesized by Kasamatsu and his colleagues that the maintenance of visual cortical plasticity in cats requires an increase in the release of cortical norepinephrine (NE) and as a consequence, a rise in intracellular cAMP (Kasamatsu, 1985; see also the preceding chapter).

In the cat visual cortex, the timing of the CP for ocular dominance shift following monocular deprivation can be altered by manipulating the visual environment. The onset of the CP can be postponed by dark rearing (DR) kittens from the time of eye-opening (Cynader & Mitchell, 1980; Mower et al., 1981). The length of postponement is determined by the length of the DR period. Thus, it is possible to trigger the CP at any time during the DR period by exposing the DR cats to light. This is the dark-light (DR+Lt) paradigm employed by Cynader and Mitchell (1980), Timney et al. (1980) and Mower et al. (1983). Since other aspects of growth of the animal continue uninterrupted by the DR procedure, the biochemical changes responsible for determining the state of plasticity during the CP can be temporally separated from other events relating to the general growth of the animal. It was reasoned that if the NE-stimulated cAMP metabolism plays a role in determining the state of plasticity, then the proteins involved in cAMP metabolism would be expected to exhibit temporal shifts in their ontogeny when the cat is raised by the DR+Lt procedure. For this reason, whole homogenates (unfractionated) of visual cortices were collected from the following three groups of cats: (1) normally reared cats (NR) of ages 3-days to adults, for the characterization of the normal biochemical events of ontogeny; (2) cats dark reared for 1-5 months (DR), for the characterization of biochemical events that are postponed as the onset of the CP is postponed; (3) cats dark reared, then exposed to a few hours of light (DR+Lt), so as to be able to identify the biochemical events that first occur as the CP is triggered for its onset.

In order to examine the proteins involved in cAMP-metabolism (Fig.1) and their ontogeny, the following assays were performed: (1) visualization of the laminar distribution of the neurohormone receptors involved in triggering adenylate cyclase, the enzyme that converts ATP into 3',5'-cyclic AMP (cAMP); (2) determination of the ability of the neurohormone, norepinephrine (NE), to stimulate adenylate cyclase; (3) measurement of the activity of phosphodiesterase (PDE), the enzyme that terminates the cAMP-cascade by hydrolyzing cAMP; (4) <u>in vitro</u> phosphorylation from observing the cAMP-activation of cAMP-dependent protein kinase (cAMPdPK), the effector enzyme within the cascade; and (5) identification of the substrate proteins phosphorylated by cAMPdPK and determination of their states of phosphorylation <u>in vivo</u>. The focus of this chapter will be the results from assay (5), which exhibited the strongest dependence on the rearing condition of the animal.

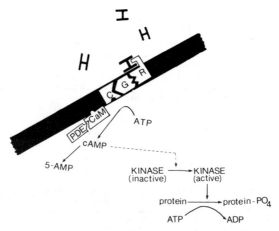

Fig. 1 The cascade of events involving cAMP. Abbreviations are: H=hormone in the extracellular fluid, such as NE; R, G and C=receptor, GTP-binding and catalytic subunits of adenylate cyclase; PDE=phosphodiesterase, localized intracellularly; CaM=calmodulin; KINASE=cAMP-dependent protein kinase; protein-PO$_4$=phosphorylated protein.

cAMP-DEPENDENT PHOSPHORYLATION OF PROTEINS

Current evidence indicates that in eukaryotes, every biological function modulated by cAMP involves the activation of cAMPdPK to phosphorylate specific proteins. (Nestler et al, 1984). Thus, cAMP-dependent phosphorylation can be viewed as the final effector system in the cAMP cascade. The proteins in the visual cortex of cats whose phosphorylations are cAMP-dependent were identified by carrying out <u>in vitro</u> phosphorylations of whole homogenates in the presence of i) an exogenous supply of cAMPdPK; ii) $-^{32}$P-ATP; and iii) with or without cAMP. The radioactive phosphate groups transferred from $-^{32}$P-ATP onto proteins were then identified autoradiographically by first separating protein species according to size via SDS-gel electrophoresis, then exposing the gels to x-ray films (Aoki & Siekevitz, 1985).

When the visual cortex of DR and NR cats were compared in this way (Fig.2), the in vitro phosphorylation of microtubule-associated protein 2 (MAP2), a dendritic cytoskeletal protein (Bernhardt & Matus, 1984), was found to exhibit a strong dependence on the animal's rearing condition. Following 2 to 3 months of DR from the time of eye-opening, the in vitro phosphorylation of MAP2 was diminished (Fig.2), while in tissues of DR+Lt littermates, in vitro phosphorylation of MAP2 concomitantly increased (Fig.3, right).[1] Altogether, the enhanced in vitro phosphorylation of MAP2 following light exposures was seen among cats from three litters DR for 2 months, two litters DR for 3 months and one litter DR for 5 months (Aoki & Siekevitz, 1985).

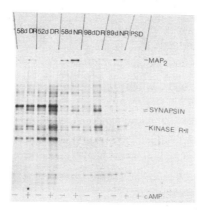

Fig. 2. Identification of the phosphoproteins in homogenates of the visual cortex of cats normally reared (NR) and dark reared (DR). Homogenates from each source was phosphorylated with or without cAMP, as indicated at the bottom (+/- cAMP), so as to test for the cAMP-dependence in their phosphorylation. MAP2, synapsin and the regulatory subunit of cAMPdPK (kinase R II) are three of the known phosphoproteins identified in this system (Aoki & Siekevitz, 1985). PSD=phosphorylated postsynaptic density fraction, run in parallel to serve as internal standards of molecular size in gels.

Might the enhanced in vitro phosphorylation in the DR+Lt animals simply reflect the effect of dark-adaptation followed by exposures to light, or does this effect reflect a change underlying the onset of the CP? This question was addressed by examining the in vitro phosphorylation of MAP2 in the visual cortex of animals that had been NR beyond the CP (7 months) to allow for normal development of visual function, then DR for 1 month, followed by re-exposure to light. The results (Fig.4) indicated no change in the in vitro phosphorylation of MAP2, suggesting that this was an event that occurred with the onset of the CP.

----

1. For the case of the 2-month DR+Lt, this enhanced level was equivalent to that of age-matched NR, while for the case of the 3-month DR+Lt, the enhanced level surpassed that of the 3-month normally reared.

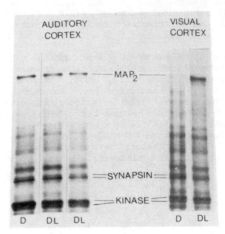

Fig. 3. A comparison of the effect of exposure to light following dark rearing
on phosphorylation of MAP2 in the auditory cortex and visual cortex.   All
samples were whole homogenates from the 52d DR litter. Whole homogenates were
phosphorylated in the presence of 1 uM cAMP and cAMPdPK.   D=dark reared for 52
days; DL=dark reared for 52 days, followed by 6 hr of light.   The "DL" of
auditory cortex lanes are from two different animals; the "D" and "DL" lanes of
visual cortex are from the same animals as the "D" and one of the "DL" lanes of
auditory cortex. (From Aoki & Siekevitz, 1985)

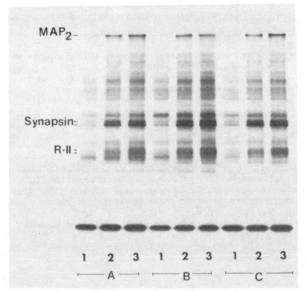

Fig. 4. The effect of dark rearing during adulthood upon the phosphorylation of
MAP2 in visual cortex. A litter, all 7 months old, were dark reared for 1
month, followed by exposures to light for 0 hr (A), 3.5 hr (B) or 4 hr (C), then
sacrificed. The following were added during the incubation for phosphorylation:
lane 1 - nothing; lane 2 - 1 uM cAMP; lane 3 - 1 uM cAMP and cAMPdPK.
(From Aoki & Siekevitz, 1985)

To further examine the specificity of the effect of environmental light upon plasticity, whole homogenates of two other brain structures were examined. Lateral geniculate nucleus (LGN), the thalamic relay nucleus of the visual system, is known not to exhibit a postnatal CP (reviewed in Movshon & Van Sluyters, 1981). Results indicated no change in MAP2 phosphorylation here, supporting the idea that the enhanced MAP2 phosphorylation reflects an event occurring at the onset of the CP. The auditory cortices of the same animals also did not exhibit any dependence on the environmental light (Fig.3, left), confirming the specificity of the effect of sensory deprivation.

There was no measurable difference in the concentration of MAP2 or of cAMPdPK between the three groups of animals (Aoki & Siekevitz, 1985), suggesting that the change in the in vitro phosphorylation is caused by a change in the in vivo state of phosphorylation of MAP2.[2] This notion is corroborated by the observation that the cAMP-stimulated phosphorylation of the other major phosphoprotein in the brain, synapsin, is not influenced by light (Figs.1-4). This finding also indicates that besides the cAMPdPK, both the ATPase and the phosphatase (if they act generally on all phosphoproteins) also are probably not affected by the rearing condition. These data suggest that MAP2 is relatively more phosphorylated under the DR condition in vivo, and becomes dephosphorylated with the onset of the CP. Since MAP2, when phosphorylated, induces microtubule depolymerization (Jameson & Caplow, 1981; Murthy & Flavin, 1983) and the relaxation of the cross-linking of cytoskeletal proteins in dendrites (Nishida et al, 1981; Selden & Pollard, 1983) the dendritic shape would be expected to remain more maleable under the DR condition. Taken together, the results suggest that visual cortical plasticity may be maintained at a high level by the DR procedure, at least in part, by the maintenance of a maleable cell shape, which is in turn dependent upon the maintenance of MAP2 in a highly phosphorylated state. The consequence of the maleable cell shape may be that the visual cortical microcircuitry may be allowed to become rewired in response to biased visual experiences (=biased neuronal activity); conversely, plasticity may begin to decline following the exposure of animals to light, partly due to the dephosphorylation of MAP2 that results in an increased rigidity of cell shape. How might the in vivo state of phosphorylation of MAP2 be altered by the DR procedure? The results summarized above suggest that the changes may occur at some step within the cAMP cascade that precedes the activation of the kinase system.

ADENYLATE CYCLASE SYSTEM

The specific activity of the enzyme, adenylate cyclase (ACase), in homogenated tissues from the three groups of animals was determined. Among the NR cats, there was observed a concerted 10-fold increase of the basal, the NE-stimulated and the maximal catalytic activities during the period from postnatal day 3 up to 1 month of age, and a plateau in its activities beyond (Aoki, 1985a). The results also indicated that while the basal activities were not dependent upon the rearing condition at any age, the NE-stimulatable ACase activity was. More specifically, the NE-stimulated ACase was enhanced among the tissues obtained from DR and the DR+Lt animals more than that in the age-matched NR animals (Aoki, 1985a). This enhancement was accounted for by the enhanced ability to stimulate ACase by GTP. This result, in turn, indicates that the coupling of the receptor subunit to the catalytic subunit that is controlled by the

----

2. This is because the sites that can be phosphorylated in vitro are the sites that are left unphosphorylated in vivo.

GTP-binding subunit and GTP (Schramm & Selinger, 1984) is increased in its efficiency (Aoki, 1985a). Thus, if the NE content within the visual cortex of DR cats is comparable to the content in NR cats, then it may be that MAP2 remains more phosphorylated in vivo due to the higher concentration of cAMP resulting from the enhanced activity of NE-stimuled ACase.

CYCLIC NUCLEOTIDE PHOSPHODIESTERASE ACTIVITY (PDE)

The postnatal ontogeny of PDE is more modest compared to that of ACase: there is an approximately two-fold increase in its specific activity from postnatal day 3 up to 1 month of age, and a plateau in its activity beyond (Aoki, 1985a). This enzyme's specific activity was enhanced among DR+Lt animals compared to the DR littermates, while the values in tissues of the NR and the DR animals were not significantly different (Aoki, 1985a). Combining this data with that of the ACase, it can be concluded that the concentration of cAMP within the cells of the visual cortex of DR animals remains relatively higher than the level in NR animals: once light evokes neuronal activities, the rate of turnover of cAMP (including the rate of its breakdown) accelerates. The increased intracellular level of cAMP may induce a stronger activation of cAMPdPK. On the other hand, how the rate of turnover of cAMP may relate to the chronic intracellular concentration of cAMP or to its ability to activate cAMPdPK is not known.

THE LAMINAR DISTRIBUTION OF RECEPTORS COUPLED TO ADENYLATE CYCLASE

As already noted above, MAP2 is exclusively localized within dendrites. However, beyond this knowledge, it is not known where the changes in the state of phosphorylation of MAP2 may occur. An attempt to localize the site of this event was made by examining the laminar distribution of the receptors known to be coupled to ACase. For this purpose, brain-sections mounted on slides were incubated with radioactive ligands so that the ligand-binding sites (=receptor sites) could be visualized autoradiographically. The receptors examined so far are the beta-1 and beta-2 adrenergic receptors (Aoki et al, 1985) and the adenosine A1 receptors (Aoki, 1985).

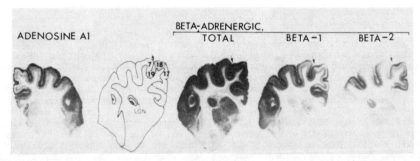

Fig. 5. Comparison of the laminar distribution patterns of adenosine A1, beta-1 adrenergic and beta-2 adrenergic receptor sites. Coronal sections from adult brains were incubated with radioactive ligands for the identification of the sites of the three receptors. Shown here are the autoradiograms obtained from exposing such sections to LKB Ultrofilms. The nonspecific labeling was undetectable in every experiment, indicating that the radioactivity reflected

specific binding. Total = labeling of beta-1 + beta-2 + nonspecific binding sites.

As shown in Fig.5, the laminar distribution in adulthood is strikingly similar for all of the receptors, being the highest density within laminae I through III, much less in lamina IV, and reappearing in laminae V and VI. However, the ontogenetic time courses for these receptors are different: while the adenosine Al (Aoki, 1985) and the beta-2 adrenergic (Aoki et al., 1985) receptor systems become adult-like at around the third postnatal month, the beta-1 adrenergic receptor system appears adult-like by the first postnatal month, or the beginning of the CP. Upon DR, none of these receptors exhibited any perturbation detectable in their ontogeny of the laminar distribution. Thus, the changes appear not to occur at the level of the spatial distribution of these receptors. There are other receptors known to be coupled to the enzyme, ACase, which would be interesting to examine in the future.

SUMMARY

Upon examination of the neurohormone-stimulated cAMP cascade, it was observed that the state of the in vivo phosphorylation of MAP2 is enhanced in visual cortices that are plastic, and begin to become dephosphorylated as the decline in plasticity is triggered by light. Thus, visual cortical plasticity may depend, in part, on the cytoskeletal structure within dendrites that is maintained relatively maleable, due to the phosphorylation of MAP2. This, in turn, may allow for the restructuring of the visual cortical microcircuitry in response to biased visual experience. This change in the state of phosphorylation may be due to the change in the chronic intracellular concentration of cAMP or the rate of turnover of cAMP. The sites of action of this event are most likely confined to dendrites, since MAP2 is found exclusively in dendrites. Further, this event may be more active within laminae I through III than in other laminae, since this is where the beta-1 adrenergic, beta-2 adrenergic and adenosine Al receptors are most concentrated.

ACKNOWLEDGEMENTS

I thank Dr. Philip Siekevitz, my thesis advisor, for his advice and support during the past six years and Keith Purpura for his critical reading of the manuscript. The research was funded by USPHS NEI 1RO3 EY 04812 01 to C.A. and USPHS Institutional Training Grant 5 T32 GM07524.

REFERENCES

Aoki, C. (1985). Development of the Al adenosine receptors in the visual cortex of cats, dark reared and normally reared, Dev. Brain Res., in press

Aoki, C. (1985a). The role of hormone-stimulated cAMP metabolism in visual cortical plasticity. Thesis, The Rockefeller University.

Aoki, C., D. Kaufman and T.C. Rainbow (1985). The ontogeny of the laminar distribution of beta-adrenergic receptors in the visual cortex of cats, normally reared and visually deprived. Dev. Brain Res., submitted.

Aoki, C. & P. Siekevitz (1985). Ontogenetic changes in the cAMP-stimulatable
     phosphorylation   of   cat   visual   cortex   proteins,   particularly   of
     microtubule-associated protein 2 (MAP2): Effects of normal and dark rearing
     and of the exposure to light. J. Neurosci., in press.

Bernhardt, R. and A. Matus (1984). Light and electron microscopic studies of
     the distribution of microtubule-associated protein 2 in rat brain: A
     difference between dendritic and axonal cytoskeletons. J. Comp. Neurol.
     226: 203-221.

Cynader, M. and D.E. Mitchell (1980). Prolonged sensitivity to molocular
     deprivation in dark-reared cats. J. Neurophysiol. 43: 1026-1040.

Jameson, L. and M. Caplow (1981). Modification of microtubule steady-state
     dynamics by phosphorylation of microtubule-associated proteins. Proc. Nat.
     Acad. Sci. (USA) 78: 3413-3417.

Kasamatsu, T. (1985). Norepinephrine hypothesis for visual cortical plasticity:
     Thesis, antithesis and recent development. In R.K.Hunt, A.A.Moscona and A.
     Monroy (Eds), Current Topics in Developmental Biology, Academic Press, New
     York, In press.

Movshon, J.A. and R.C. Van Sluyters (1981). Visual neural development. Ann.
     Rev. Psychol. 32: 477-522.

Mower, G.D., D. Berry, J.L. Burchfiel and F.H. Duffy (1981). Comparison of the
     effects of dark-rearing and binocular suture on development and plasticity
     of cat visual cortex. Brain Res. 220: 225-267.

Mower, G.D., W.G. Christen and C.J. Caplan (1983). Very brief visual experience
     eliminates plasticity in the cat visual cortex. Science 221: 178-180.

Murthy, A.S.N. and M. Flavin (1983). Microtubule assembly using the
     microtubule-associated protein MAP2 prepared in defined states of
     phosphorylation with protein kinase and phosphatase. Eur. J. Biochem. 137:
     37-46.

Nathanson, J.A. (1977). Cyclic nucleotides and nervous system function,
     Physiological Reviews 57: 157-256.

Nestler, E.J., S.I.Walaas & P.Greengard (1984) Neuronal phosphoproteins:
     Physiological and clinical implications. Science 225: 1357-1364.

Nishida, E., T. Kuwaki and H. Sakai (1981). Phosphorylation of
     microtubule-associated proteins (MAPs) and pH of the medium control
     interaction between MAPs and actin filaments. J. Biochem. 90: 575-578.

Riesen, A., ed. (1975) Developmental Neuropsychology of Sensory Deprivation,
     Academic Press, New York

Schramm, M. & Z. Selinger (1984)Message transmission: receptor-controlled
     adenylate cyclase system. Science 225: 1350-1356.

Seldon, S.C. and T.D. Pollard (1983). Phosphorylation of microtubule-associated
     proteins regulates their interaction with actin filaments. J. Biol. Chem.
     258: 7064-7071. brain regions. J. Neurosci., 4: 84-98.

An Experimental Analysis of Procedures that Promote Behavioral Recovery from the Effects of Monocular Deprivation in Kittens: a Search for an Optimum Occlusion Regimen for Treatment of Amblyopia

D. E. Mitchell

Psychology Department, Dalhousie University, Halifax,
NS B3H 4J1, Canada

It is now well known that a period of monocular deprivation in early postnatal
life can exert profound effects on the anatomical and physiological development
of the mammalian visual pathways (Movshon and Van Sluyters, 1981; Mitchell and
Timney, 1984). These changes are accompanied by severe deficits in the vision
of the deprived eye of both kittens (Giffin and Mitchell, 1978) and monkeys
(Boothe, Dobson and Teller, 1985) which are reminiscent of those observed in
various forms of human amblyopia (Hess, Campbell and Zimmern, 1980; Hess, France
and Tulunay-Keesey, 1981). As a consequence, this deprivation procedure has
been utilized widely in animals as a means for exploring the neural basis of
this common developmental visual disorder as well as for the study of the nature
and duration of certain sensitive periods in visual development (Mitchell, 1981).

Although the effects of monocular deprivation can be very severe, substantial
recovery is possible if normal visual input is restored to the deprived eye
sufficiently early. The extent of the behavioral and physiological recovery is
particularly pronounced in situations where the formerly nondeprived eye is
occluded once normal visual input is restored to the formerly deprived eye, a
procedure referred to as reverse occlusion (Blakemore and Van Sluyters, 1974;
Mitchell, Cynader and Movshon, 1977; Blakemore, Garey and Vital-Durand, 1981).
Just as with conventional patching therapy for human amblyopia, this procedure
forces the use of the deprived or amblyopic eye. Although this procedure can
produce substantial and sometimes complete recovery of visual acuity in the
formerly deprived eye of kittens during the period that the formerly nondeprived
eye is occluded (Giffin and Mitchell, 1978), it has been shown recently that
this recovery is not usually maintained afterwards once normal visual input is
restored to both eyes (Mitchell, Murphy and Kaye, 1984a, 1984b). Much of the
improvement in the vision of the formerly deprived eye is typically lost within
3 weeks, during which time the vision of the formerly nondeprived eye improves
from the depressed levels to which it had fallen during the period of reverse
occlusion. Systematic investigation of the long-term effects of periods of
reverse occlusion of different durations imposed on monocularly deprived kittens
at various ages (Murphy and Mitchell, in preparation) reveal that such reciprocal
changes in the visual acuities of the two eyes occur under a wide variety of
different conditions. In addition, in a variety of circumstances including
situations where reverse occlusion is imposed for either long periods (5 weeks
or more) or for shorter periods early in life, the vision of the formerly
nondeprived eye may never recover to normal levels (Mitchell, Murphy and Kaye,
1984b), a situation that may be analogous to the clinical condition of occlusion
amblyopia that is observed occasionally following prolonged full-time patching

therapy for amblyopia.

Another interesting outcome is observed when reverse occlusion is imposed at an
early age for brief periods of time that are nevertheless sufficiently long to
allow for virtually a complete shift of ocular dominance among cells in area 17
of the visual cortex (Movshon, 1976). Substantial reversal of cortical ocular
dominance can be induced in 4 week-old monocularly deprived kittens by only 9
to 12 days of reverse occlusion, and in 5 week old deprived kittens a similar
switch of ocular dominance can be induced in only 18 days (Movshon, 1976).
Despite the fact that reverse occlusion is terminated very early in such cases,
when the animals are only 6 to 8 weeks old, the visual acuity of the formerly
deprived eye fails to improve much beyond the level it attains during the short
period of reverse occlusion while that of the other eye improves to approximately
the same low level. Thus the end result of such regimens of reverse occlusion
is a condition of bilateral amblyopia.

In addition to the obvious implications for the nature of the processes that
underlie the behavioral and physiological events that occur during reverse
occlusion, these findings also invite a re-evaluation of certain patching
regimens for treatment of human amblyopia. The latter concern is reinforced by
observations of similar reciprocal changes in the visual acuity of the two eyes
following termination of full-time patching therapy of amblyopic human infants
(e.g. Odom, Hoyt and Marg, 1981; Jacobson, Mohindra and Held, 1981; 1983). In
an effort to find a procedure that promotes permanent recovery of vision in the
formerly deprived eye of monocularly deprived kittens, we (Mitchell, Murphy,
Dzioba and West, in preparation) have initiated a systematic investigation of
the effectiveness of various regimens of part-time occlusion, where the formerly
nondeprived eye is occluded for only part of each day. Surprisingly, this
procedure can be amazingly effective in certain circumstances.

The initial experiments were performed on 10 kittens that were monocularly
deprived by eyelid closure from near birth until 6 weeks of age at which time
the eyelids of the deprived eye were opened. Thereafter the kittens were
permitted only 7 hours visual experience each day during which time the formerly
nondeprived eye was occluded by means of a flexible neoprene rubber mask for
either 0, 1, 2, 3.5, 5, 6, or all 7 hours of daily visual exposure for 6 weeks.
Measurements of the visual acuity of each eye for square-wave gratings were
made on a jumping stand (Mitchell, Giffin and Timney, 1977; Giffin and Mitchell,
1978) at regular intervals throughout the period of patching and in the weeks
that followed. Once visual acuity had stabilized, measurements were made of the
contrast sensitivity functions for the two eyes using procedures described
earlier (Mitchell, Murphy and Kaye, 1984b). In selected animals, measurements
were also made of depth perception and dynamic vernier acuity by use of stimuli
similar to those developed by Shimojo, Birch, Gwiazda and Held (1984) for
evaluating the vernier acuity of human infants.

In agreement with earlier findings (Giffin and Mitchell, 1978), the two kittens
that were not patched at all showed only limited recovery of vision in the
deprived eye. The contrast sensitivity of the deprived eye was about 10 times
worse than that of the other eye at all spatial frequencies (Fig. 3). The
kittens from the opposite extreme condition that were patched for all 7 hours
(full-time patching) exhibited the same reciprocal changes in the visual acuity
of the two eyes that were observed earlier in animals that were reverse occluded
by eyelid suture (Mitchell, Murphy and Kaye, 1984a). The improvement in the
vision of the formerly deprived eye during patching and the changes that occurred
afterwards are shown in Fig. 1. Although the acuity of the formerly deprived
eye recovered to normal levels during the period of patching, it was not
maintained afterwards. Note also that the vision of the formerly nondeprived
eye did not recover to normal levels (6 to 8 cycles/degree) following termination
of patching. These points can also be observed from the contrast sensitivity
functions (Fig. 3). Comparison with the data from the nondeprived eye of the

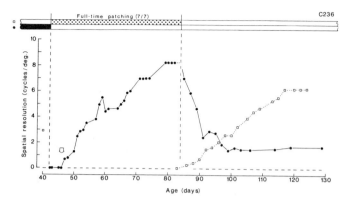

Fig. 1. Changes in the visual acuity of the two eyes of a
monocularly deprived kitten during and following
full-time patching (all 7 hours of daily visual
exposure) of the formerly nondeprived eye for 6
weeks. Filled and open symbols depict the acuities
of the formerly deprived and nondeprived eyes,
respectively.

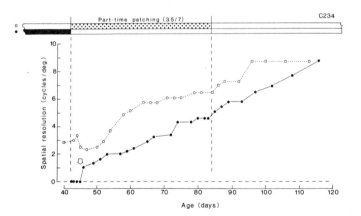

Fig. 2. Changes in the visual acuity of each eye of a
monocularly deprived kitten during and following
part-time patching (3.5 hours of a 7 hour period
of daily visual exposure) of the formerly
nondeprived eye for 6 weeks. Symbols are as
defined for Fig. 1.

animal that was not patched indicates that the contrast sensitivity of the
formerly nondeprived eye was reduced from normal levels at all spatial
frequencies. Moreover, the contrast sensitivities of the formerly deprived
eye of the animal that had been patched full-time were if anything worse than
those of the deprived eye of the animal that received no patching therapy at
all!

The recovery of vision by the formerly deprived eye of the 2 kittens that received either one or two hours of patching each day was not very different from that observed in the kittens that were not subjected to any patching. This was not only the case during the 6 week period of patching but also in the weeks that followed. On the other hand, the kittens that were patched for 3.5 hours each day (50% of the daily period of visual exposure) showed substantially greater improvement of acuity in their formerly deprived eyes during the period of patching. The gradual improvement in the vision of the formerly deprived eye of one of these two kittens (C234) both during and following the 6 week period of patching as well as the concurrent changes in the visual acuity of the other eye are shown in Fig. 2. As with Fig. 1., the arrow indicates the first day on which the animal showed signs of vision (the ability to distinguish an open from a closed door on the jumping stand) with its formerly deprived eye. The vision of this eye improved gradually to a value in excess of 4 cycles/degree during the period of patching while that of the formerly nondeprived eye also improved to about 6 cycles/degree. By comparison, the animal that was patched for all 7 hours of daily visual exposure (Fig. 1.) achieved a visual acuity of just over 8 cycles/degree with its formerly deprived eye during the period of patching while at the same time the vision of the other eye was reduced to blindness. In the case of C234, the 3.5 hours of patching each day was sufficiently long to cause the vision of the formerly deprived eye to improve beyond the level achieved by the kittens that received no patching, but at the same time was brief enough so that the vision of the other eye was not impaired. Following the period of patching, the vision of both eyes improved to normal levels within a month.

A similar final outcome was observed in the two kittens that were patched for 5 hours each day (equivalent to 70% of the daily period of visual exposure). As might have been anticipated, the acuity of the formerly deprived eye improved substantially during the 6 weeks of patching to 5.5 cycles/degree. However, at the same time the vision of the formerly nondeprived eye dropped to only 2 cycles/degree. Following termination of patching the acuity of both eyes (especially that of the formerly nondeprived eye) improved rapidly to normal levels within a month.

Contrast sensitivity functions for two animals that had the formerly nondeprived eye patched for 3.5 (C234) and 5 (C235) hours each day are shown in Fig. 3. (B and C). For both animals the contrast sensitivities of the two eyes were not only identical at all spatial frequencies but were also indistinguishable from those of normal animals. Although these results suggest complete recovery of vision in the formerly deprived eye, it is important to recall that the contrast sensitivity functions of human amblyopes can be virtually normal yet other measures of acuity, such as Snellen acuity or various hyperacuities like vernier acuity can be severely impaired. For this reason measurements were also made of dynamic vernier acuity which probes the ability to detect a region of a square-wave grating that has been horizontally offset from the rest of a vertical grating and which jumps vertically between various unpredictable positions within the background grating (see Fig. 1. of Shimojo and others, 1984). Under optimum conditions normal adult cats can detect a grating offset of only 1.2 minutes of arc (Murphy and Mitchell, in preparation). Both animals that received part-time patching for 3.5 or 5 hours each day recovered normal vernier acuities in both eyes, suggesting that the recovery of vision by the formerly deprived eye was indeed complete.

Although these measurements suggest an amazing degree of visual recovery by the formerly deprived eye, it is possible that binocular functions such as stereopsis may not have recovered. Measurements of the ability of these particular animals to employ purely disparity cues to depth have not yet been made. However, comparisons of the ability of these animals to perceive depth in patterns in which monocular cues to depth were severely reduced (but not entirely eliminated) under both binocular and monocular viewing conditions suggest that they possess

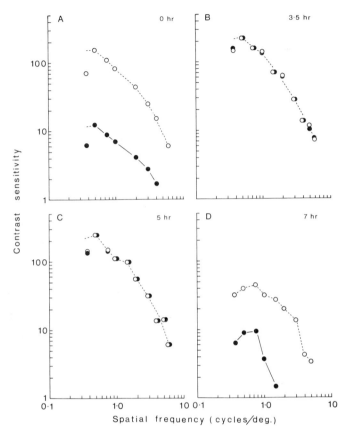

Fig. 3. Contrast sensitivity functions for the formerly
deprived (filled symbols) and nondeprived eyes
(open symbols) of 4 monocularly deprived cats that
received various regimens of patching of the formerly
nondeprived eye for 6 weeks as follows. A. No
patching; B. 3.5 hours of daily patching (C234) of
Fig. 2.); C. 5 hours of daily patching; D. full-time
patching (all 7 hours of daily visual exposure;
C 236 of Fig. 1.). In all cases the measurements
of contrast sensitivity were made between 2 and 3
months after termination of patching therapy and
introduction of visual input to both eyes.

a sensitive and uniquely binocular cue to depth such as stereopsis. The testing
procedure followed that described by Mitchell, Kaye and Timney (1979) in which
cats were trained to jump to the closer of two adjacent stimuli that appeared as
sheets of floating black dots of various sizes that could be seen through the
transparent top of the jumping stand. Masks placed just underneath the top of
the jumping stand obscured the edges of the surfaces on which the dots were
painted. Following training on the task, daily measurements were made of the
smallest separation of the two stimuli in depth that could be discriminated. On

each daily session a binocular measurement was made first followed immediately
by a measurement made with a contact lens occluder covering one eye. This same
procedure was followed for 10 consecutive daily sessions with monocular tests
alternated between the two eyes. Results from 3 monocularly deprived cats that
received either zero, 3.5, or 7 hours of daily patching therapy are shown in
Fig. 4. Depth thresholds are expressed as the ratio of Δ D, the threshold
separation of the two stimuli, to D, the distance to the farthest of the stimuli.
The retinal disparity corresponding to the threshold separation (Δ D) under
binocular viewing conditions can be read from the ordinate on the right.

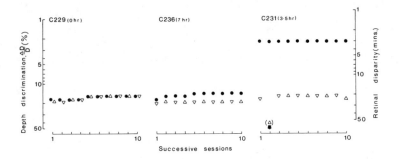

Fig. 4.   Depth discrimination on 10 successive testing
          sessions of 3 monocularly deprived cats that
          received either no patching therapy (C229, left),
          full-time patching (C236, middle), or part-time
          patching (C231, right) for 6 weeks. Depth
          thresholds (left-hand ordinate) are defined in
          text. Filled symbols show results obtained with
          both eyes open, while open symbols depict the
          results of monocular testing (upright triangles,
          right eye; inverted triangles, left eye). The
          ordinate on the right applies only to the binocular
          thresholds and represents the retinal disparity
          corresponding to the threshold separation of the
          two stimuli (ΔD).

The results obtained from the two animals (C229 and C236) that received either
zero or full-time (7 hours) patching were very similar; binocular and monocular
thresholds were both poor and also virtually identical. However the results
obtained from the animal (C321) that received part-time daily patching for 3.5
hours was typical of the behavior of normally reared animals. Binocular
thresholds were at least 8 times better than those achieved monocularly. This
binocular superiority was also very evident in the animals general behavior. In
contrast to the other two animals, who behaved exactly the same under monocular
testing conditions as they did just before with both eyes open, C231 behaved as
if confronted with an entirely new task when one eye was occluded. These
findings suggest that C231 possesses a uniquely binocular cue to depth that
provides an enormous advantage over those available monocularly. While this
suggests that C321 may possess stereopsis, this conclusion cannot strictly
be drawn until it has been demonstrated that the animal is capable of making
depth discriminations in situations where only disparity cues to depth are
available.

Although these findings apply only to one particular deprivation condition
(monocular deprivation to 6 weeks of age) and for a single period of patching
therapy, they nevertheless have important implications for patching therapy in

human amblyopia. In addition to reinforcing a long-held opinion that extensive patching is far more beneficial than short daily periods of occlusion, the findings also underscore concerns raised by earlier work on the long-term consequences of full-time occlusion. However the finding of most potential importance was that obtained from the animals that received part-time occlusion for between 50 and 70% of each day. The recovery of vision by the initially deprived eye of these animals was quite remarkable and also apparently permanent. While the optimum conditions of part-time occlusion will no doubt vary with both the length of initial deprivation and the duration of therapy, the successful outcome from certain of the part-time regimens of this study provide encouragement for the future elucidation of patching regimens that optimize recovery for a wide variety of deprivation conditions that in turn can lay the foundation for a successful and rational basis for occlusion therapy for human amblyopia.

This work was supported by a grant from the National Science Research Council (A7660) and by a Program grant (PG-29) from the Medical Research Council of Canada.

REFERENCES

Blakemore, C., and R.C. Van Sluyters (1974). Reversal of the physiological effects of monocular deprivation in kittens: further evidence for a sensitive period. J. Physiol. (London), 237, 195-216.
Blakemore, C., F. Vital-Durand, and L.J. Garey (1981). Recovery from monocular deprivation in the monkey. I. Reversal of physiological effects in the visual cortex. Proc. R. Soc. Lond. B., 213, 399-423.
Boothe, R.G., V. Dobson, and D.Y. Teller (1985). Postnatal development of vision in human and nonhuman primates. Ann. Rev. Neurosci., 8, 495-545.
Giffin, F., and D.E. Mitchell (1978). The rate of recovery of vision after early monocular deprivation in kittens. J. Physiol. (London), 274, 511-537.
Hess, R.F., F.W. Campbell, and R. Zimmern (1980). Differences in the neural basis of human amblyopias: the effect of mean luminance. Vision Res., 20, 295-305.
Hess, R.F., T. France, and U. Tulanay-Keesey (1981). Residual vision in humans who have been monocularly deprived of pattern stimulation in early life. Exp. Brain Res., 44, 295-311.
Jacobson, S.G., I. Mohindra, and R. Held (1981). Development of visual acuity in infants with congenital cataracts. Br. J. Ophthalmol., 65, 727-735.
Jacobson, S.G., I. Mohindra, and R. Held (1983). Monocular visual form deprivation in human infants. Doc. Ophthalmol., 55, 199-211.
Mitchell, D.E. (1981). Sensitive periods in visual development. In R.N. Aslin, J.R. Alberts, and M.R. Petersen (Eds.), The Development of Perception: Psychobiological Perspectives, Vol. 2, Academic Press, New York. pp. 3-43.
Mitchell, D.E., M. Cynader, and J.A. Movshon (1977). Recovery from the effects of monocular deprivation in kittens. J. Comp. Neurol., 176, 53-64.
Mitchell, D.E., F. Giffin, and B. Timney (1977). A behavioural technique for the rapid assessment of the visual capabilities of kittens. Perception, 6, 181-193.
Mitchell, D.E., M. Kaye, and B. Timney (1979). Assessment of depth perception in cats. Perception, 8, 389-396.
Mitchell, D.E., K.M. Murphy, and M.G. Kaye (1984a). Labile nature of the visual recovery promoted by reverse occlusion in monocularly deprived kittens. Proc. Natl. Acad. Sci. USA, 81, 286-288.
Mitchell, D.E., K.M. Murphy, and M.G. Kaye (1984b). The permanence of the visual recovery that follows reverse occlusion of monocularly deprived kittens. Invest. Ophthalmol. Vis. Sci., 25, 908-917.

Mitchell, D.E., and B. Timney (1984). Postnatal development of function in the
    mammalian visual system. In I. Darian-Smith (Ed.), Handbook of
    Physiology, Section I: The Nervous System, Vol. 3., Sensory Processes,
    Part 1., American Physiological Society, Bethesda. pp. 507-555.
Movshon, J.A. (1976). Reversal of the physiological effects of monocular
    deprivation in the kitten's visual cortex. J. Physiol. (London), 261,
    125-174.
Movshon, J.A., and R.C. Van Sluyters (1981).   Visual neuronal development.
    Ann. Rev. Psychol., 32, 477-522.
Odom, J.V., and C.S. Hoyt, and E. Marg (1981). Effect of natural deprivation
    and unilateral eye patching on visual acuity of infants and children.
    A.M.A. Arch. Ophthalmol., 99, 1412-1416.
Shimojo, S., E. Birch, J. Gwiazda, and R. Held. (1984). Development of vernier
    acuity in infants. Vision Res., 24, 721-728.

Plasticity of Human Acuity Development with Variations in Visual Experience

C. W. Tyler and A. M. Norcia

Smith-Kettlewell Institute of Visual Sciences, 2232 Webster St.,
San Francisco, CA 94115, USA

ABSTRACT

Visual acuity was measured in 202 infants by a rapid visual evoked potential
technique involving a swept spatial-frequency stimulus . The development of
acuity was consistent with the resolution limits of retinal receptor
development. Variation in time of birth up to ± 1 month relative to conceptional
term produced significant variations in the VEP acuity in the first four months
after birth. These results suggest that human acuity development is affected by
variations in visual experience.

INTRODUCTION

Perhaps one of the most basic questions regarding the development of the human
visual system is the role of experiential versus maturational control of visual
development. This question of "nature versus nurture" has a long history in the
neurophysiological literature dealing with animal experimental models and in the
literature of developmental psychology. In the case of human visual
development, the only feasible experimental paradigm available for studying the
role of visual experience comes from the natural variability of the time of
birth with respect to the normal gestation period.

Studies of the developing human visual system are hindered by the limited
response repertoire and attention span of the infant. We have been working with
a new visual evoked potential (VEP) technique for rapid measurement of sensory
thresholds (Norcia and Tyler, 1985a, b; Norcia et al., 1985) which requires a
minimum of cooperation on the part of the infant. VEP data provide a level of
analysis of the visual system intermediate between single unit neurophysiology
and behavioral studies. On the one hand, the VEP is known to arise in the
visual cortical areas which have been studied at the single unit level.
Furthermore, the surface VEP is correlated with the level of multi-unit field
activity in the different cortical layers (Kraut et al., 1985). On the other
hand, a number of studies have shown good agreement between psychophysically
derived thresholds and VEP derived thresholds (Campbell and Maffei, 1970;
Campbell and Kulikowski, 1972; Allen et al., submitted), at least in human
adults.

95

Anatomical Substrate of Human Visual Acuity Development

It is becoming clear that the fovea is anatomically quite immature at birth (Mann, 1964; Abramov et al., 1982; Hendrickson and Yuodelis, 1984). Foveal cones are quite sparse and poorly developed at birth (Abramov et al., 1982). They are separated by about 10 u with an outer segment length of about 1 u. Thus the resolution of the cone mosaic should be at least 5 times poorer than adults, who have a 2 u separation for foveal cones (Polyak, 1941). Studies of visual acuity can therefore be expected to reflect the development of foveal resolution and to be influenced by factors affecting this development.

Hendrickson and Yuodelis (1984) have shown that the development of the human foveola proceeds rapidly during the first year of life and reaches full maturity between one year and 45 months of age. Of primary significance is the rapid development of the foveal cones themselves and their migration towards the center, together with the migration of non-receptor cells away from the center, resulting in higher cone densities typical of the adult foveola. The morphology of the foveal cones is nearly adult-like around one year of age but migration continues up to 45 months. The retinal periphery, on the other hand, is adult-like at birth (Abramov et al., 1982).

De Courten and Garey (1982) have shown that the human LGN is morphologically and volumetrically indistinguishable from the adult by 9 months of age. Cell size continues to increase in the LGN up to about 2 years (Hickey, 1977). The developmental sequence for human visual cortex to an extent parallels that seen at the LGN. The growth in volume of both structures is rapid during the first few months; the LGN doubles in volume by six months and remains stable through adult life. The visual cortex increases 4-fold in volume between 28 weeks gestation and birth and again quadruples to reach adult size by 4 months (Huttenlocher et al., 1982; Sauer et al., 1983). Synaptogenesis reaches its peak in cortex at 8 months postnatally. A second period of synaptic development lasting until 11 years follows, during which the density of synapses declines to 60% of its maximum value (Garey and de Courten, 1983).

Electrophysiological Indices of Visual Development in Humans

The development of pattern resolution as indexed by the VEP is rapid during the first year of life (Marg et al., 1976; Pirchio et al., 1978; Sokol, 1978; de Vries-Khoe and Spekreijse, 1982; Norcia and Tyler, 1985). Starting from a level of about 5 c/deg near birth, our measure of grating acuity develops at a rate of 0.25 octaves/month until the eighth postnatal month when acuity has reached an asymptote of 20 c/deg (Fig. 1). Average adult acuity in our apparatus is about 25 c/deg or only one third octave higher. The rate of growth of VEP acuity is thus consistent with the initial constraints set by human retinal development and the known maturational sequence of the LGN. How then is its development affected by timing variations in the onset of visual experience?

METHODS

Apparatus

Details of the apparatus and analysis techniques can be found in Norcia and Tyler (1985,a) and in Norcia et al. (1985). Briefly, infants were presented with 80% contrast vertical sine-wave luminance gratings with space average luminance of 80 cd/^{2}. Gratings were square wave modulated at a rate of 12 contrast reversals per sec. Over a period of 10 sec, the spatial frequency of the reversing gratings was incremented linearly in 20 equally spaced steps, usually spanning a 30:1 range of spatial frequency.

The amplitude and phase of the second harmonic reversal response were calculated by a Discrete Fourier Transform. Acuity was determined by a linear extrapolation to zero-amplitude of the final portion of the VEP amplitude versus spatial frequency function, using the criteria for the occurrence of a significant signal described in full by Norcia et al., (1985).

RESULTS

The development of acuity as a function of natal age during the first year is shown for 202 full-term infants in Fig. 1 (open circles), with the log standard error of the mean estimates indicated by the lines above and below the data. All infants were born within +4 weeks of their expected due date. Sweep VEP acuity increased from about 5 c/deg in the first month to an asymptotic level close to the adult range by about 8 months of age. The newborn visual resolution is about a factor of 5 below adult levels measured in the same apparatus, which is close to the ratio predicted on the basis of foveal cone density in the newborn. Thus the VEP and the early cortical sources which generate it appear to be limited by the structural resolution of cone mosaic. At a functional level, VEP pattern resolution has been shown to have the same developmental sequence as does the simultaneously measured pattern ERG (Fiorentini et al., 1984), as expected if they were both limited by receptor density.

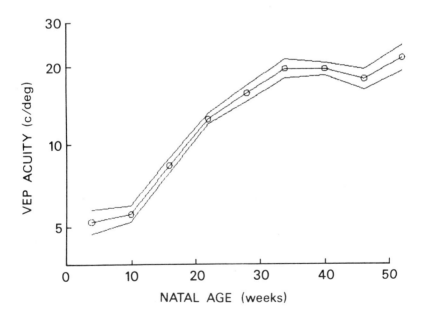

Fig. 1. Growth of VEP acuity at 12 rps for a sample of 202 infants (open circles) as a function of natal age.

Effects of Variations in Visual Experience

Norcia et al. (1985) found that the VEP acuity in infants more than one month
premature developed at the same rate as normals relative to the time of the
premature birth. The premature acuities were thus significantly advanced over
normal when considered in terms of a developmental schedule based on
conceptional age. To investigate further the effects of visual experience on
acuity developent, we separated the infants into 3 groups based on the predicted
due dates determined by their physician:
    PRETERM   - born from 4 to 1 weeks before due date (N = 44, mean
prematurity = 2 weeks)
    TERM   - born within ± 1 week of date (N = 87)
    POST-TERM - born from 1 to 4 weeks after due date (N = 71, mean
postmaturity = 2 weeks).

Based on the premature infant data, we would predict that when plotted in terms
of conceptional age, the effects of different amounts of visual experience
should tend to produce higher acuities in the preterm than the post-term
infants, with acuites for term infants falling between the two. The results are
shown in Fig. 2 over the 12 month age range. Up to the first 20 weeks of age
the points fall in the predicted order for all three birth groups. Fig. 4B
plots the growth functions for the pre- and post-term groups ±1 standard error
of the mean. The data are separated by more than 2 standard errors of the mean
for the first two age groups, or up to 4 months conceptional age. In the
youngest infants, acuities differ by 0.5 octave. Beyond about 16 weeks the
differences between the pre- and post-term groups are no longer significant. We
conclude that variations of less than 1 month in the time of birth relative to
conception have a significant effect on the development of visual acuity in the
first months of life. These effects appear to become insignificant by about 6
months of age.

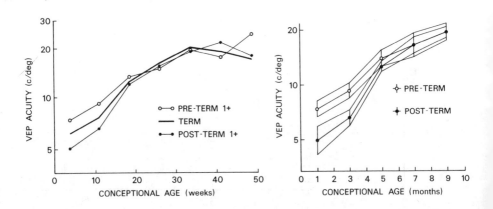

Fig. 2. A. Mean VEP acuities at 12 rps for the infants of Fig. 1. separated into
groups of term (full line), preterm (open circles) and post-term infants. Note
different developmental time courses.
        B. Pre- and post-term data from A. showing the standard errors of the
means (vertical bars).

DISCUSSION

The effects of variation of birth time relative to conception show early initiation of acuity development in infants born early relative to the gestational term. Similarly, development of acuity was delayed in post-term infants whose birth was delayed relative to the term age from conception. Thus the data are consistent with to the hypothesis that the initiation of acuity development controlled by the time of onset of visual experience. This effect may be analogous to the effect of delaying the onset of the critical period of visual development by dark rearing after birth in cats (Cynader and Mitchell, 1980). Only very brief exposure to light after dark rearing is sufficient to activate the critical period (Mower and Christen, 1985). However, the effects we have observed are small, and do not persist beyond six months of age.

It is possible that factors other than visual experience could have influenced the results. The postnatal environment differs from the prenatal environment in nutritional state, non-visual sensory stimulation, and activity level. However, these factors might also be expected to accelerate development of brain functions and behavioral indices of development. Most non-visual functions are considered to develop with a maturational time course and are not accelerated by premature birth. For example, body weight, sleeping time, and behavioral milestones of motor development all proceed on a corrected time course appropriate to conceptional age. It therefore seems likely that the modification of visual development is attributable more to the specific impact of visual experience on the development of the retina and its projections than to more generalized effects on the development of the rest of the brain.

Our thanks to Drs. Robert Piecuch and Ronald Clyman and the Mt. Zion Intensive Care Nursery for collaboration in this study. Supported by NIH grants #EY 3622, EY 1186, RR 5566, NIHR grant #6008005054 and The Smith-Kettlewell Eye Research Foundation.

REFERENCES

Abramov, I., Gordon, J., Hendrickson, A., Hainline, L., Dobson, V. and LaBossiere, E. (1982). The retina of the human newborn infant.Science, 217, 265-267.

Allen, D., Norcia, A.M. and Tyler, C.W. A comparative study of electrophysiological and psychophysical measurement of the contrast sensitivity function in humans. Am. J. Optom. Physiol. Opt. (submitted).

Campbell, F.W. and Kulikowski, J.J. (1972). The visual evoked potential as a function of contrast of a grating pattern. J. Physiol., 222, 345-356.

Campbell, F.W. and Maffei, L. (1970). Electrophysiological evidence for the existence of orientation and size detectors in the human visual system. J. Physiol., 207, 635-652.

Cynader, M. and Mitchell, D.E. (1980). Prolonged sensitivity to monocular deprivation in dark-reared cats. J. Neurophysiol., 43, 1026-1040.

De Courten, C. and Garey, L.J. (1982). Morphology of the neurons in the human lateral geniculate nucleus and their normal development. Exp. Brain Res., 47, 159-171.

De Vries-Khoe, L.H. and Spekreijse, H. (1982). Maturation of luminance and pattern EPs in man. Documenta Ophthal. Proc. Ser. (Edited by Neimeyer, G. and Huber, Ch.) vol. 31, pp. 461-475. The Hague, Junk.

100 C. W. Tyler and A. M. Norcia

Fiorentini, A., Pirchio, M. and Sandini, G. (1984). Development of retinal acuity in infants evaluated with pattern electro-retinogram. Human Neurobiol., 3, 93-96.

Garey, L.J. and de Courten, C. (1983). Structural development of the lateral geniculate nucleus and visual cortex in monkey and man. Behav. Brain Res., 10, 3-13.

Hendrickson, A.E. and Yuodelis, C. (1984). The morphological development of the human fovea. Ophthalmology, 91, 603-612.

Hickey, T.L. (1977). Postnatal development of the human lateral geniculate nucleus: Relationship to a critical period for the visual system. Science, 198, 836-838.

Huttenlocher, P.R., de Courten, C., Garey, L.J. and Van der Loos, H. (1982). Synaptogenesis in human visual cortex: evidence for synapse elimination during normal development. Neuroscience Lett., 33, 247-252.

Kraut, M.A., Arezzo, J.C. and Vaughan, H.G. (1985). Intracortical generators of the flash VEP. Encephalog. clin. Neurophysiol., 62, 300-312.

Mann, I. (1964). The Development of the Human Eye. 3rd Ed., London, British Medical Association.

Marg, E., Freeman, D.N., Peltzman, P. and Goldstein, P.J. (1976). Visual acuity development in human infants: evoked potential measurements. Invest. Ophthal. Vis. Sci., 15, 150-153.

Mower, G.D. and Christen, W.G. (1985). Role of visual experience in activating critical period in cat visual cortex. J.Neurophysiol., 53, 572-589.

Norcia, A.M., Clarke, M. and Tyler, C.W. (1985). Digital filtering and robust regression techniques for estimating sensory threshold from the evoked potential. IEEE Eng. Med. Biol. (in press).

Norcia, A.M. and Tyler, C.W. (1985). Spatial frequency sweep VEP: visual acuity during the first year of life. Vision Res. (in press).

Norcia, A.M. and Tyler, C.W. (1985). Infant VEP acuity measurements: Analysis of individual differences and measurement error. Electroenceph. Clin. Neurophysiol. (in press).

Norcia, A.M., Tyler, C.W., Piecuch, R. and Clyman, R. (1985). Visual acuity development in premature infants is controlled by experience. Invest. Ophthal. Vis. Sci., Suppl., 26, 136.

Pirchio, M., Spinelli, D., Fiorentini, A. and Maffei, L. (1978). Infant contrast sensitivity assessed by evoked potentials. Brain Res., 141, 179-184.

Sauer, B., Kammradt, G., Krauthausen, H.J., Kretchsmann, H.J., Lange, H.W. and Wingert, F. (1983). Qualitative and quantitative development of the visual cortex in man. J. Comp. Neurol., 214, 441-450.

Sokol, S. (1978). Measurement of infant visual acuity from pattern reversal evoked potentials. Vision Res., 18, 33-39.

ADAPTATIONS TO MICROGRAVITY

Vestibulo-ocular Reflex Changes Following Weightlessness and Preflight Adaptation Training

D. E. Parker*, M. F. Reschke**, L. Ouyang*,
A. P. Arrott* and B. K. Lichtenberg**

*Miami University, Oxford, OH 45056, USA
**Johnson Space Center, Houston, TX 77058, USA

INTRODUCTION

Several observations suggest that one important aspect of man's adaptation to weightlessness is the brain's reinterpretation of signals from the otolith receptors. Changes following prolonged weightlessness in eye movement reflexes, postural reflexes, and perception of self-motion provide the basis for this hypothesis. Based on the otolith reinterpretation hypothesis, a concept for preflight adaptation training has been developed and three prototype trainers have been constructed. Initial studies with the trainer prototypes indicate that exposure to the rearranged sensory environment produced by the trainers alters eye movement responses in ways consistent with the otolith reinterpretation hypothesis.

OTOLITH REINTERPRETATION

Results from several experiments support the hypothesis that after adaptation to weightlessness, otolith signals which result from head tilts during entry or on earth immediately postflight are interpreted by the brain as indicating translation (Parker and co-workers, 1985; Young and co-workers, 1984). This tilt-translation reinterpretation is reasonable in view of the normal function of the otolith receptors and analysis of how it must change during orbital flight. In weightlessness, slow head tilts (roll and pitch) produce no changes in otolith signals; only translations elicit responses from these receptors. Therefore, it is reasonable to expect that the adaptive brain learns to interpret all otolith signals as indicating translation and that eye movement reflexes, postural reflexes, and perception of self-motion would be altered accordingly.

Two new observations provide additional support for otolith reinterpretation. One of these relates to self-motion perception during entry when an astronaut experienced unexpected and strong sensations of translation associated with head pitch and roll following the onset of gravity. The second new observation concerns phase changes in the horizontal eye movements evoked by roll

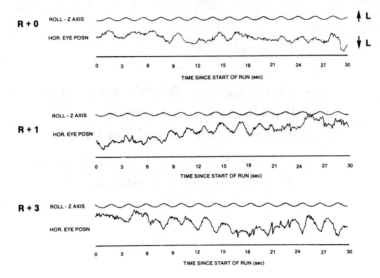

Fig. 1.   Horizontal eye movements recorded from
Astronaut 6 during roll stimulation at 0.5 Hz
2 hr (R+0), 1 day (R+1) and 3 days (R+3)
after landing. L = leftward roll (top
trace) or eye movement (middle trace).

stimulation immediately after landing relative to preflight and
later postflight recordings. The astronauts were placed in a roll
motion apparatus and horizontal eye movements were recorded as
described previously (Parker and co-workers, 1985). The results
from one subject are presented in Figs. 1 and 2. Figure 1
illustrates that immediately after landing (R+0) the phase angle of
the eye movements was shifted about 180 deg relative to other
observations obtained during the first (R+1) and third days (R+3)
after the landing. Figure 2 is a record of the eye movements
obtained from the same astronaut immediately after landing during
stimulation at a lower frequency of roll (0.25 Hz). Both figures
illustrate that, for the case 2 hr after landing (apparently with
the brain still partially adapted to weightlessness), roll toward
the left elicited rightward eye movement, whereas the normal reflex
for this subject was in the opposite direction.

The eye movement records are congruent with the astronaut's reports
of self-motion perception associated with roll and pitch head
motion during entry. Initially, forward pitch movement resulted in
the sensation of backward translation. Subsequently during entry,
pitch and roll elicited translation self-motion perception in the
same direction as the head movement; i.e., leftward head tilt
produced the sensation of leftward translation and so on. The eye
movement change exhibited by Astronaut 6 postflight is consistent
with this self-motion report. As illustrated in Figs. 1 and 2,
leftward head roll was associated with rightward horizontal eye
deviation. This direction of compensatory eye movement is
appropriate given the astronaut's reported self-motion preception.

The results obtained from Astronaut 6 suggest that the manner in
which otolith signals drive the horizontal eye movement system is
labile. It is reasonable that this should be the case. If a

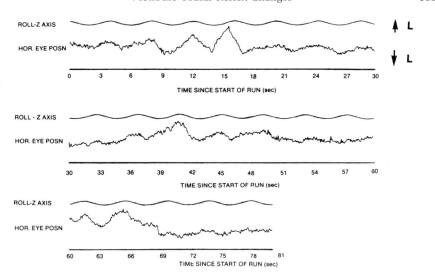

Fig. 2.   Horizontal eye movements recorded from
Astronaut 6 during roll stimulation at
0.25 Hz 2 hr after landing (R+0).

leftward displacement of the otoliths is produced by leftward head
roll, the appropriate direction of horizontal eye movement is to
the right. On the other hand, if the leftward otolith displacement
is produced by translation, the appropriate direction of horizontal
eye movement is to the left.

The report from Astronaut 6 is similar to previous reports from two
Spacelab I astronauts (Homick, 1983). They noted apparent
translation of the visual scene when they tilted their heads
during entry. In contrast to Astronaut 6, self-motion was not
experienced by the Spacelab I astronauts.

It would be inappropriate to place excessive reliance on one
self-motion report recorded 24 hr after the event. Nevertheless, we
view this report and the associated eye movement changes as
consistent with the otolith tilt-translation reinterpretation
hypothesis.

PREFLIGHT ADAPTATION TRAINER PROTOTYPES

Based on the otolith tilt-translation reinterpretation hypothesis,
we proposed a concept for preflight adaptation training (PAT)
apparatus and procedures (Parker and co-workers, 1985). In the PAT
trainer, relationships between otolith responses associated with
the subject's movements and the visual scene presented to him are
systematically altered. Normally, when the subject's head is rolled
toward his left shoulder, the visual scene rotates around the
corneal-retinal axis in the direction opposite to the head tilt. In
the trainer, a leftward head roll results in translation of the
visual scene toward the left without rotation; i.e., the vertical
axis of the scene remains aligned with the vertical retinal
meridian. Normally, when the subject's head is pitched backward,

the scene moves downward in the visual field. In the trainer, backward pitch is associated with apparent flow of the visual scene toward the subject, but the horizontal axis of the scene remains aligned with the horizontal retinal meridian.

Three PAT trainer prototypes have been developed. Two of these (the Miami University Seesaw and one that uses the Wright-Patterson Air Force Base Dynamic Environment Simulator) include a physical room that is moved relative to a restrained subject. The third trainer prototype employs a computer-generated scene and presents the image of a room to the subject. Apparent room motion is produced by the subject's voluntary head movements. This trainer uses the Wright-Patterson Air Force Base Visually Coupled Airborne Systems Simulator.

EYE MOVEMENT CHANGES PRODUCED BY PAT

Experiment MUS/PAT-1 addressed the following questions: can horizontal eye movement amplitude during roll stimulation be altered by exposure to the PAT sensory rearrangement? If so, what exposure conditions lead to the largest changes?

Apparatus and Procedure

The prototype trainer used to produce the sensory rearrangement consisted of a 75 by 100 by 100 cm styrofoam "room" that rolled on

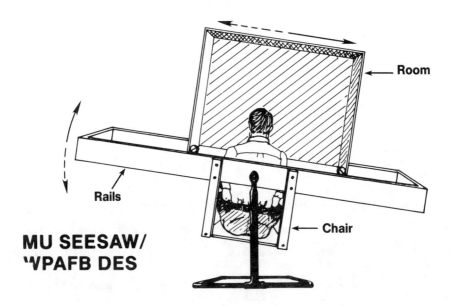

Fig. 3.   Prototype trainer. Seesaw device constructed at Miami University.

rails mounted on a seesaw (see Fig. 3). Colored lights were
attached to the inside walls of the room.

The subject was restrained in a chair attached to the center of the
seesaw. The axis of rotation was at the level of the subject's
larynx. A motor drive produced sinusoidal oscillation of the seesaw
(+/-12 deg). Room translation was produced by a pulley linkage when
the seesaw tilted. Twelve deg of tilt produced 36 cm of room
translation. When the subject was tilted to the left (rolled), the
room translated toward the subject's left and vice versa.

Electrodes for recording DC potentials were located at the outer
canthus of each eye. The resulting eye movement signals were
recorded on a strip chart and with a signal-averaging computer. Eye
movements were recorded in total darkness with the eyes open. The
subjects were asked to maintain "straight-ahead" gaze (defined
during calibration) and performed an alerting task during the eye
movement recording. Horizontal eye movements were recorded during
20 cycles of +/-12 deg roll at 0.33 Hz. After each recording, eye
movement amplitude was calibrated.

Eye movements were recorded following 5-min exposures to each of 6
types of sensory rearrangement. During exposure, the subject was
rolled +/-12 deg at 0.33 Hz. Three sensory modality conditions were
used: the subject (1) watched the room while he was rolled (visual
only), (2) lightly touched the side walls of the room with his eyes
closed (tactile only) or (3) both watched the room while lightly
touching the room walls (visual/tactile). Two room movement
conditions were used: the room either moved relative to the
subject, as described above, or the room remained fixed on the
rails and tilted with the subject.

Twelve subjects were exposed to each of the 6 exposure conditions.
Order of exposure condition across subjects was partially
counterbalanced.

Results

Samples of eye movement records are presented in Fig. 4. Amplitudes
of the horizontal eye movement signals at the frequency of the roll
stimulus were determined, and the average eye movement amplitudes
for the 6 conditions are presented in Fig. 5.

Eye movement amplitude was larger following exposure to a moving
room than following exposure to a fixed room (p < 0.003). For the
room-moving condition, combined visual-tactile stimulation produced
larger eye movements than visual or tactile stimulation alone (p <
0.02).

Discussion

The result that eye movement amplitude changes can be elicited by
relatively brief exposure to the PAT sensory rearrangement is
encouraging. Additional studies indicate that changes produced by
PAT exposure may persist for up to 10 min if the subject remains
stationary in darkness. Also, we have noted that phase
relationships between eye movements and the roll stimuli can be

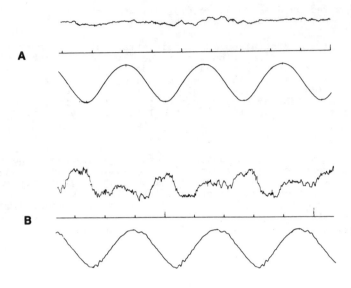

Fig. 4. Horizontal eye movement records recorded in
         darkness during roll stimulation. A--record
         following 5-min visual-tactile exposure to
         "fixed room". B--record following 5-min visual-
         tactile exposure to "moving" room.

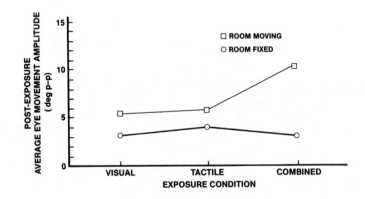

Fig. 5. Average amplitude of eye movements recorded
         in darkness as a function of previous sensory
         rearrangement condition.

altered by manipulation of the phase relationship between roll and room translation during training.

CONCLUSIONS

Astronauts adapt to weightlessness. One aspect of this adaptation appears to be central reinterpretation of otolith signals. New data from Shuttle Mission 51D provide additional support for an otolith tilt-translation reinterpretation hypothesis.

Based on this hypothesis preflight adaptation training procedures and apparatus have been developed.

Initial experiments to examine the effects of exposure to the sensory rearrangement associated with trainer prototypes suggest that vestibulo-ocular reflexes can be changed in appropriate ways.

While numerous problems need to be addressed, it does appear possible that apparatus and procedures to preadapt astronauts to the sensory rearrangement of weightless space flight can be developed.

ACKNOWLEDGMENTS

We thank J. Rock, H. von Gierke, D. Woodard, J. Sevier and the many others who helped with this effort. Funding was provided by Contract NAS 9-14538 between the National Aeronautics and Space Adminstration and Miami University.

REFERENCES

Homick, J. L. (1983). Spacelab I Science Payloads Crew Postflight Debriefing. Johnson Space Center, Houston.
Parker, D. E., M. F. Reschke, A. P. Arrott, J. L. Homick, and B. K. Lichtenberg (1985). Otolith tilt-translation reinterpretation following prolonged weighlessness: implications for preflight training. Aviat. Space Environ. Med., 56, 601-606.
Young L. R., C. M. Oman, D. G. D Watt, K. E. Money, and B. K. Lichtenberg (1984). Spatial orientation in weightlessness and readaptation to earth's gravity. Science, 225, 202-08.

Adaptive Modifications of the Optokinetic and Vestibulo-ocular Reflexes in Microgravity

T. Viéville, G. Clément, F. Lestienne
and A. Berthoz

Laboratoire de Physiologie Neurosensorielle du CNRS, 15, rue de
l'Ecole de Médecine, 75270 Paris Cedex 06, France

INTRODUCTION

The purpose of this work was to study the modifications of
the optokinetic and vestibulo-ocular reflexes induced by
suppression of gravity. Although it is known that vertical and
torsional (counterrolling) eye movements are induced by otolithic
stimulation (Woellner and Graybiel 1959, Diamond et al. 1979,
Young et al. 1981, Collewijn et al. 1985), the gain of the
otolith-ocular reflex (OOR) in darkness is very small. However,
it has been suggested that the central pathways relaying
otolithic information were involved in semicircular canal-otolith
interaction (Benson 1974, Goldberg and Fernandez 1982). A good
example of this property is the vestibulo-ocular reflex (VOR) in
the vertical plane. It is produced by the combined action of two
components whose exact contribution is not yet known. A semicircular canal dependent head velocity or acceleration component and
an otolithic dependent head position component due to the action
of gravity on the maculae during head tilt or pitch. The action
of the otolith is not, however, restricted to the vertical
plane. This is indicated by the strong horizontal nystagmus
observed during off vertical axis rotation (OVAR) which has been
proven, in the monkey, to be of otolithic origin (Cohen et al.
1983). Spaceflight is an elegant way to suppress selectively the
gravity vector and we have therefore attempted to measure
horizontal and vertical VOR during active head motion in microgravity.

Otolithic function can also be studied during visual-
vestibular interaction. Buizza et al. (1980) have demonstrated
that, although during linear acceleration no clear OOR could be
measured in darkness, if the subject was presented with a
constant velocty optokinetic stimulus, a large modulation of OKN
slow phase velocity was induced by the linear acceleration. Other
evidence for an action of otoliths on OKN stems from the fact
that surgical removal of the sacculus modifies in the monkey
horizontal and vertical OKN gain (Takahashi et al. 1977, Igarashi
et al. 1978), and selective removal of the uvula and nodulus
modifies optokinetic after nystagmus (OKAN) indicating an
otolithic control of optokinetic velocity storage mechanisms
(Matsuo and Cohen 1984). These facts, together with current ideas

concerning vertical OKN asymmetry (Matsuo et al. 1979, Die and
Collewijn 1982) have encouraged us to measure OKN during space
flight. All the experiments reported in this paper have been
performed with astronaut P. Baudry during the US Shuttle flight
51-G in June 1985. Only preliminary results will be given in this
paper. Complementary data have been obtained with astronaut S.
Al-Saud on flight days 2 and 4. Full results will be detailed in
a subsequent paper.

METHODS

Optokinetic stimulation. Monocular optokinetic stimulation was
made by a mechanically driven checkboard pattern moving in a
frontal plane inside a small box (10x9x8cm) attached to the head
of the subject by specially fitted goggles. This pattern could
move at 2 velocities (20 and 53 °/sec). The pattern motion
direction being in a plane, these velocities were calculated in
the middle of the pattern along the line of the primary eye
position. The pattern could be rotated in the frontal plane so as
to provide horizontal, vertical or oblique directions. Only the
first two were used in the present study. The pattern was viewed
by the subject through a double Fresnel lens. The image of the
pattern was therefore viewed at infinity. Each square of the
checkboard subtended an angle of 5°. The inside of the box was
illuminated with red light in order to reduce the changes in
electro-oculographic recording conditions. The light could be
turned off for the measurement of OKAN. The stimulus   was
triggered or stopped by the subject himself with a push button on
the side of the stimulator. The original set-up of this
stimulator was designed in our laboratory; it was constructed by
AETA (France).
Recording of eye and head movements. Vertical and horizontal
components of eye movements were recorded using DC electro-
oculography (EOG). Special amplifiers designed by F.X. Séné in
our laboratory allowed automatic DC compensation every 80 sec, or
when EOG reached saturation. The absence of any cross coupling
between the two components of EOG was checked during
calibrations. Each calibration was made in the light with the
subject fixating targets which were 10° apart. In the vertical
plane, 5 targets were fixated to check linearity. Measurements
made in darkness were always made eyes open and within less than
20 sec after extinction of the light in order to avoid any
artefact due to eyelid closure or changes in EOG gain. Head
angular motion during VOR measurements was always limited in
order to avoid, in the vertical plane, the eye lid artefact which
is known to occur. Head movement was measured by a potentiometer
connected to the wall by two universal joints. It allowed specific measurement of angular head position in one plane (horizontal
or vertical) depending upon where it was placed on the head of
the subject. Precision was less than 1°.
Experimental protocol and data processing. Experiments were
performed on one subject in 2 conditions of microgravity : a)
during parabolic flight which allowed for a 25 sec period of zero
gravity; and b) during a 7-day spaceflight aboard the US Shuttle
Discovery. Optokinetic stmulation lasted 40 sec followed by 20
sec of darkness. The subject was seated with the head still. VOR
was induced by active head oscillation in the horizontal and
vertical planes at two frequences 0.2 and 0.8 Hz. The subject
fixated a target on the wall in front of him. After performing a
calibration head still, he would oscillate the head while keeping
his gaze on the target. This combination of VOR and OKN at the

frequencies and head oscillation used yielded a gain of about 1
given the known performance of pursuit and VOR (Tomlinson et al.
1980, Jell et al. 1982) which was used as a control. Head
oscillation amplitude was about 25° peak to peak. The generation
of stable head oscillation frequency was helped by an
intermittent sound tone. For VOR gain measurement, the goggles
were occluded and the subject was asked to mentally keep his gaze
on the   target which was used for the previous control
experiment. Another reason for performing VOR measurement in
darkness withing 15 sec after closure of the goggles was to avoid
fading of the mental image and therefore maintain a constant
mental set. Suppression of VOR by vision was tested by attaching
to the goggle a small box which was about 30 cm long in order to
minimize vergence movements. This box was illuminated and the
inside covered by a checker board pattern. The subject was asked
to fixate a point at the far end of the box while oscillating the
head at the same frequencies as for VOR in measurement in darkness.
     Experiments were performed 30, 5 and 4 days before launch
(F-30, F-5 and F-4), every day during flight (FD1 to FD7) and
after landing, within one hour on the first day (R+0), and then 3
and 60 days after landing (R+3, R+60). The first inflight
experiment was made 6 hours after the shuttle was in orbit. Eye
velocity was calculated by a two channels analog Gould
differentiation circuit and OKN gain is expressed as the ratio of
average OKN slow phase velocity and pattern velocity. Measurements were made during the last 20 sec of OKN stimulation in
order to have a saturated OKN velocity. VOR gain and phases were
calculated by hand using the first 5 cycles of each experiment
except for the first five sec, in order to avoid any effect of
the transient induced by the very first head oscillation.

RESULTS

Modification of OKN gain. An example of the modification of OKN
gain for vertical direction is shown on Fig 1. The variations of
horizontal OKN gain are shown on Fig 2B. For the smaller velocity
(20 °/sec) the gain does not vary significantly between the
control (about 0.92) and the parabolic flight values indicated by
stars. On the first day of space flight however, gain dropped to
about 0.8 with a progressive return to control values after 7
days. The drop of gain is more marked at the higher stimulus
velocity (53 °/sec), it drops from about 0.8 (control value) to
about 0.6 in both the parabolic flight and during the first space
flight day (FD1). At this velocity the gain decreased during the
first three days and returned to control values with a small but
significant overshoot on FD7. For both velocities another drop of
gain is clearly seen within the first hour of return. However,
the control values 60 days after return are slightly smaller than
30 days before flight. The main finding concerning horizontal OKN
is therefore a small decrease of gain which immediately follows
suppression of gravity and possibly an increase of gain during
the adaptive period followed by a rapid return after landing.

     The modifications of **vertical OKN gain** are shown on Fig 2A.
For the smallest velocity (20 °/sec), the gain was not
significantly changed , either during parabolic flight or during
spaceflight. This stability is in contrast with striking changes
which occur for the highest stimulus velocity (53 °/sec). In this
case the control values gave an asymmetric gain which is

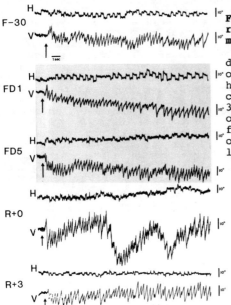

Fig 1 Optokinetic nystagmus in response to a vertical pattern motion

The visual pattern motion was directed upward with a velocity of 53°/sec. Records show the horizontal (H) and vertical (V) component of eye position taken 30 days before flight (F-30), on the first and fifth day of flight (FD1 and FD5), within one hour and 3 days after landing (R+0, R+3).

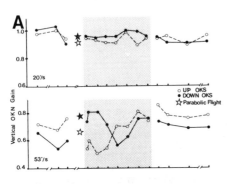

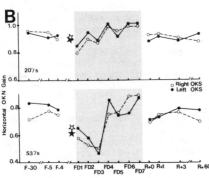

Fig 2 Gain of optokinetic nystagmus in the vertical (A) and horizontal (B) direction

OKN gain is expressed as the ratio between eye velocity and pattern velocity. Only the results for the direction of eye movement corresponding to pattern motion are given. 2 pattern velocities were used : 20 and 53 °/sec. Unfilled circles are data for OKN in response to upward (or rightward) moving pattern, filled circles to downward (or leftward) moving pattern. Unfilled and filled stars indicate the results obtained during parabolic flight for the upward (or rightward) and downward (leftward) moving patterns respectively.

consistent with the general observation of larger gain for upward
moving visual patterns. Average values of 0.73 and 0.58 were
found for respectively downward (slow phases up) and upward (slow
phases down) OKN gain. The remarkable result is the reversal of
this asymmetry both during parabolic flight and on the first day
of space flight. Downward OKN gain (slow phases up) shifts from a
mean value of 0.73 to 0.56 and return progressively to control
values during the 7 space flight days. This reversal of vertical
OKN gain asymmetry is immediately suppressed on return as shown
by the gain values obtained on R+0, R+1, R+3. They indicate a
small overshoot immediately after return. In summary, the
vertical OKN is drastically modified in microgravity and a clear
reversal of up-down asymmetry is observed.

Modification of optokinetic after nystagmus. For a reason which
is not clear at this time, OKAN time constant has shortened
during training. This constitutes in itself an interesting observation which is not directly relevant to the question asked in
this paper, but which would deserve an investigation on its own.
Control values indicate a time constant of about 1 sec for
horizontal and 1 to 2 sec for vertical OKAN for both velocities.
These values did not change significantly on the first flight day
in the **horizontal** direction. There was a small increase for low
velocity of leftward OKAN. However, a clear increase was seen on
R+0 for rightward OKAN at the highest OKN velocity.

In the **vertical** direction, a very large increase of OKAN
time constant following an optokinetic stimulation directed
upward (from 2 to 10 sec) was seen on the first flight day.
Interestingly, the time constant, which has returned to mean
control values on FD2 and FD3, increased at the end of the flight
to return to values which have been observed at the beginning of
the training session. The modifications of OKAN on return are
rather variable although some clear effect of return to normal
gravity can be seen for vertical OKN at 53 °/sec velocity.

Modification of optokinetic nystagmus beating field. The beating
field of OKN is generally shifted in opposite direction to visual
pattern motion. This is considered usually as related to an
anticipatory action of the oculomotor system in the direction
from which the visual pattern appears. Although the pathways
mediating this gaze regulatory signal are not known, we analyzed
its modification during space flight because we thought it could
be modified particularly in the vertical plane. No significant
change was seen in the horizontal plane. Fig 1 shows examples of
vertical nystagmus in the case of a pattern moving upward. The
control (F-30) recording was made 30 days before flight. As the
pattern moves upward, the beating field progressively shifts
downward and after 4 to 5 sec has a mean value of about 8°
downward. On the first day of flight, the beating field is
shifted downward. The remarkable finding is that on R+0, within
one hour after landing, there is a large drift of the beating
field upward followed by large reset downward (see Fig 1). This
upward drift is also accompanied by a drift of the eye movements
in the light during calibration. Three days after return to
normal gravity this effect is much weaker but present, the
beating field stays centered around the middle of the visual
pattern instead of being shifted downwards. Quantitative results

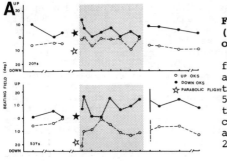

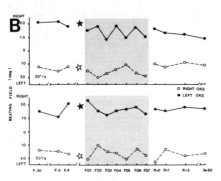

Fig 3 Beating field of vertical (A) and horizontal (B) optokinetic nystagmus
Average values of OKN beating field are given for horizontal and vertical pattern motion at two velocities (20 and 53°/sec). Only the results for the direction of eye movement corresponding to pattern motion are given. Same symbols as Fig 2.

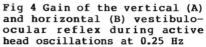

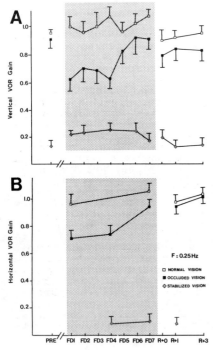

Fig 4 Gain of the vertical (A) and horizontal (B) vestibulo-ocular reflex during active head oscillations at 0.25 Hz
VOR gain is expressed as the ratio between peak to peak positions and head position. Average values and standard deviations for 5 cycles are shown for 3 situations : a) oscillations in the light, eyes open, with fixation of a target fixed in front of the subject on the wall of the Orbiter (unfilled squares), b) oscillations in the dark, eyes open, while imagining a target, as in the previous condition (black filled squares), and c) suppression of the VOR by fixating a target inside of a box fixed to the head of the subject (unfilled losanges). Experiments have been done before (PRE), during (FD1 to FD7) and after space flight (R+0, R+1, R+3).

are shown on Fig 4, where they are compared with measurements
made during short duration microgravity exposure during parabolic
flight. Note the coherence between space flight and parabolic
flight data.

Modification of horizontal and vertical vestibulo-ocular reflex.
The **horizontal VOR** was measured on FD1, FD4, FD7 and on R+0 and
R+3. Fig 4B shows a strong decrease of the VOR gain (from 1 to
0.7) at head oscillations of 0.25 Hz. The gain then returned to
values only slightly smaller than normal throughout the 7 days of
flight. The **vertical VOR** was also modified (Fig 4A). Control
values preflight showed gain of about 0.9 for 0.25 Hz head
oscillation frequencies. On FD1 the gain of pitch VOR dropped
from 0.9 to 0.6. At the fifth day only, VOR returned
progressively to normal values. Note the interesting changes in
the values measured in the light on the first day after landing
(R+0). This paradoxical decrease in what should be a control gain
of 1 has to be related to the drift in OKN which was shown on
Fig 1.

VOR suppression by vision. VOR suppression by vision is thought
to be due to the activity of the pursuit system in man (Benson
and Barnes 1978, review in Collewijn 1985), it was not modified
in the horizontal plane during exposure to microgravity. In the
vertical plane it was slightly impaired the first day of flight
but did not change significantly on consecutive days (Fig 4).

DISCUSSION

        These results show that both optokinetic nystagmus and
vestibulo-ocular reflex undergo modifications during both short
term (parabolic flight) and long term (space flight) exposure to
microgravity. Major changes are the gain and the beating field of
vertical OKN. The downward shift of beating field and the strong
decrease of downward (slow phase up) OKN gain (associated with an
increase in upward OKN gain), which are observed the first day of
flight and during parabolic flight, could be explained by the
occurrence of a downward drive on the oculomotor system. The
upward drift associated with a small increase in downward OKN
gain which is present one hour after return can be explained by
an upward drive. This upward drive on return was so strong that
the subject also had an upward drift during calibration in the
light. This may be due to a perception of motion of the visual
world. This type of perceptual effect due to adaptation has been
shown to occur by Gauthier and Robinson (1975) and Melvill Jones
and Berthoz (1985) after reversing prism adaptation in the
horizontal plane.

        How can this reversal of vertical OKN asymmetry be
interpretated ? In microgravity, the sacculus is released from
the constant pull of gravity. Its firing pattern must be the same
as if the head was accelerating downward. The fact that a
downward shift of beating field is observed as well as a decrease
in the velocity of slow phases directed upward means that the
effect is not a simple compensatory movement, because the eye is
not driven in a direction opposite to the acceleration. This is

actually in contrast with the results of Darlot et al. (1985) concerning OVAR who has shown that utricular stimulation by the rotating gravity vector induces vertical eye movements which are compensatory. The result of Igarashi et al. (1978) who observed an increase in slow phase velocity in both upward and downward directions after saccular ablation in the monkey does not either provide an explanation although they clearly suggest an inhibitory action of sacculus on OKN. Matsuo and Cohen (1984) also showed that the gain and time constant of downward OKAN is increased during lateral head tilt and suggested that downward OKN should be increased when the gravity is reduced. One possible explanation would be that in normal gravity the sacculus exerts a general activation of all extensor muscles of neck and limbs. It would also tend to elevate the eyes by an action on the superior rectus and inferior oblique thus exerting an inhibitory action on downward eye movements. In microgravity, this drive would be suppressed and the eye would therefore tend to move downward. It is particularly interesting to note that the reversal of vertical OKN asymmetry adapts after 3 days in weightlessness, that is also the time after which the strong reversal of flexor-extensor tonus in the lower limbs disappears (Clément et al. 1984). These two adaptive processes could be related.

Another result which is of interest is the decrease in slow phases velocity of OKN in the horizontal plane on the first days of flight. This decrease which is equal for both directions could reveal modifications occuring in the velocity storage mechanism of OKN (Cohen et al. 1977) because it is thought that horizontal nystagmus induced during OVAR for example is due to an action of the otoliths on this velocity storage.

A final point which deserves some comments is the strong drop of gain of both the horizontal and vertical VOR. This decrease had been predicted by the data of Lackner and Graybiel (1981) during parabolic flight. Here again, the interpretation is not easy. One possibility is, as mentioned in the Introduction, that in the vertical plane, the contribution of the otoliths to the vertical VOR would be important. In this case, the drop in gain would reveal the otolithic contribution. However, if this was the case, we should observe a phase shift which had actually been found in a previous experiment (Von Baumgarten et al. 1984). However, no phase shift greater than 5-10° is present in the data of P. Baudry. It is therefore possible that this subject suppresses the vestibular input in order to prevent any conflict which may cause space sickness. This suppression "strategy" would have been learned during the professional life of the subject who is a pilot. This hypothesis could in fact explain why he did not get sick. It would also account for the strong modifications in OKN because, having suppressed his VOR, the subject more heavily relies on vision for retinal stabilization. A last possibility is that this highly trained subject could not in space maintain fixation on a imagined target related to the spaceship. Rather than being an artefact, this default in "mental set" would actually be an interesting finding which would indicate a defect of the well-known non-visual control of VOR gain (Collins 1962, Barr et al. 1976, Baloh et al. 1984, Melvill Jones and Berthoz 1985) and therefore in the internal representation of space.

Acknowledgments

This research was supported by grants from Centre National
d'Etudes Spatiales, Paris. Engineering of the experimental
equipment was designed by F.X. Séné and M. Ehrette, with
collaboration of P. Simon. We would like to thank the Space
Biomedical Research Institute of NASA (JSC, Houston) and
particularly Dr. M.F. Reschke, S. Wood, and J. Hayes for their
support, and E. Michel from NASA for his help in accomodating the
experiment.

REFERENCES

Baloh RW, Lyerly K, Yee RD, Honrubia H (1984) Voluntary
control of the human vestibulo-ocular reflex arc. Acta Oto-
Laryngol 97: 1-6
Barr CC, Schultheis IW, Robinson DA (1976) Voluntary non-
visual control of the vestibulo-ocular reflex. Acta Otolaryngol
81: 365-375
Benson AJ (1974) Modification of the response to angular
acceleration by linear acceleration. In Handbook of Sensory
Physiology, Vol VI, 2, Springer Verlag, pp 281-320
Benson A, Barnes G (1978) Vision during angular oscillations
: the dynamic interaction of visual and vestibular mechanisms.
Aviat Space Env Med 49: 340-345
Buizza A, Leger A, Droulez J, Berthoz A, Schmid R (1980)
Influence of otolithic stimulation by horizontal linear
acceleration on optokinetic nystagmus and visual motion
perception. Exp Brain Res 39: 165-176
Clément G, Gurfinkel VS, Lestienne F, Lipshits MI, Popov KE
(1984) Adaptation of postural control to weightlessness. Exp
Brain Res 57: 61-72
Cohen B, Matsuo V, Raphan T (1977) Quantitative analysis of
the velocity characteristics of optokinetic nystagmus and
optokinetic afternystagmus. J Physiol (London) 270: 321-344
Cohen B, Suzuki J, Raphan T (1983) Role of the otolith
organs in generation of horizontal nystagmus: effect of selective
labyrinthine lesions. Brain Res 276: 159-164
Collewijn H (1985) Integration of adaptive changes of the
optokinetic reflex, pursuit and the vestibulo-ocular reflex. In :
A Berthoz and G melvill Jones (eds) Adaptive Mechanisms in Gaze
Control. Reviews in oculomotor research, vol 1, Elsevier,
Amsterdam, pp 51-69
Collins WE (1962) Effect of mental set upon vestibular
nystagmus. J Exp Psychol 63: 191-197
Darlot C, Cohen B, Berthoz A, Denise P (1985) Off vertical
axis rotation : perception effects and eye movements induced by
small angles of tilt. Neurosci Lett, suppl 22: S483
Diamond SG, Markham CH, Simpson NE, Curthoys IS (1979)
Binocular counterrolling in humans during dynamic rotation. Acta
Otolaryngol 87: 490-498
Die van GC, Collewijn H (1982) Optokinetic nystagmus in man.
Role of central and peripheral retina and occurence of
asymmetries. Human Neurobiol 1: 11-119
Fernandez C, Goldberg JM (1976) Physiology of peripheral
neurons innervating otolith organs of the squirrel monkey. I
Response to the static tilts and to long duration centrifugal
force. J Neurophysiol 39: 970-984

Gauthier GM, Robinson DA (1975) Adaptation of the human vestibulo-ocular reflex to magnifying lenses. Brain Res 92: 331-335

Goldberg JM, Fernandez C (1982) Eye movements and vestibular nerve responses produced in the squirrel monkey by rotation around an earth horizontal axis. Exp Brain Res 46: 393-402

Guedry FE (1965) Orientation of the rotation axis relative to gravity : its influence on nystagmus and the sense of rotation. Acta Oto-Laryngol 60: 30-48

Igarahi M, Takahashi M, Kubo T, Levy JK, Homick JL (1978) Effect of macular ablation on vertical optokinetic nystagmus in the squirrel monkey. Oto-Rhino Laryngol 40: 312-318

Jell RM, Guedry FE, Hixson WC (1982) The vestibulo-ocular reflex in man during voluntary head oscillations under three visual conditions. Aviat Space Env Med 53: 541-548

Lackner JR, Graybiel A (1981) Variations in gravito-inertial force level affect the gain of the vestibulo-ocular reflex : implications for the etiology of space motion sickness. Aviat Space Env Med 52: 154-158

Matsuo V, Cohen B (1984) Vertical optokinetic nystagmus and vestibular nystagmus in the monkey. Up-down asymmetry and effects of gravity. Exp Brain Res 53: 197-216

Matsuo V, Cohen B, Raphan T, de Jong V, Henn V (1979) Asymmetric velocity storage for upward and downward nystagmus. Brain Res 176: 159-164

Melvill Jones G, Berthoz A (1985) Mental control of the adaptive process. In : A Berthoz and G Melvill Jones (eds) Adaptive mechanisms in gaze control. Elsevier, Amsterdam, pp 203-208

Takahashi M, Igarashi M, Homick JL (1977) Effect of otolith end organ ablation on horizontal optokinetic nystagmus and optokinetic after nystagmus in the squirrel monkey. Oto-Rhino Laryngol 39: 74-81

Tomlinson RD, Saunders GE, Schwarz DW (1980) Analysis of human vestibulo-ocular reflex during active head movements. Acta Oto-Laryngol 90: 184-190

Von Baumgarten R, Benson A, Berthoz A, Brandt TH, Brand U, Bruzek W, Dichgans J, Kass J, Probst Th, Scherer H, Vieville T, Vogel H, Wetzig J (1984) Effects of rectilinear acceleration and optokinetic and caloric stimulations in space. Science 225: 208-211

Woellner RC, Graybiel A (1959) Counterrolling of the eyes and its dependence on the magnitude of gravitational or inertial force acting laterally on the body. J Appl Physiol 14: 632-634

Young LR, Lichtenberg BK, Arott AP, Cribes TA, Oman C, Edelman ER (1981) Ocular torsion on earth and in weightlessness . In : B. Cohen (ed) Vestibular and Oculomotor Physiology. Ann NY Acad Sci 374: 80-92

The Vestibulo-Cerebellar Regulation of Oculomotor Reactions in Microgravitational Conditions

R. A. Grigoryan*, O. G. Gazenko**,
I. B. Kozlovskaya**, V. A. Barmin**
and Yu. V. Kreidich**

*I. M. Sechenov Institute of Developmental Physiology and
Biochemistry, USSR Academy of Sciences, Leningrad, USSR
**Institute of Biomedical Problems, USSR Ministry of Health,
Moscow, USSR

INTRODUCTION

It is commonly accepted that body movements and orientation in space results
from mutual activity of vestibular, proprioceptive and visual afferent systems.
Findings obtained from acute and chronic animal experiments as well as clinical
observations on patients with organic lesions indicate the critical role of the
cerebellum. It provides for interaction of these systems during execution of
the motor acts (Dow and Moruzzi, 1958; Klinke and Schmidt, 1970; Kornhuber,
1979; Kozlovskaya, 1976) and for the mechanism of adaptation of the vestibulo-
ocular reflexes (Robinson, 1976; Ron and Robinson, 1973). The methodological
difficulties of direct evaluation of sensory interaction in man while executing
movements forced us to use the functional approach of a quantitative estimation
of the parameters of oculomotor reactions, the mechanisms of which have been
studied in considerable detail in animal experiments (Bizzi, 1975; Bizzi and
others, 1972; Kozlovskaya and colleagues, 1981; Melvill Jones, 1976; Morasso,
Bizzi and Dichgans, 1973). In this respect the gaze fixation reaction (GFR) to
a stationary visual object, suddenly appearing in the peripheral visual field,
was found to be very useful. The most complete data on the functional
organization of the GFR in primates are presented in the works of Bizzi and
others (1971, 1972). According to their data, the accuracy and quickness of
this biologically important orientative reaction in higher mammals (primates) is
provided by the reflex interaction of its three components: target—directed
saccade, head movement in the same direction and compensatory eye movement known
as counterrotation. Thereby rapid precise coordination of reflex reaction
occurs as a result of feedback systems including proprioceptive, visual and,
especially, vestibular afferentation. It was experimentally shown that the
cerebellum plays an important role in assuring close interaction of the above-
mentioned afferent systems (Robinson, 1974, 1976).

Based on the above, the purpose of this work was to study the pattern of interaction between the components of the GFR in normal individuals, in patients
having cerebellar disorders, as well as in healthy persons exposed to the long-
term effect of antiorthostatic hypokinesia (ANOH) or to microgravity.

METHODS AND MATERIALS

Functional organization of the GFR has been investigated in 28 healthy persons
and in 13 patients suffering from hereditary cerebellar ataxia. The effect of

microgravity on the vestibulo-oculomotor interaction patterns was studied on the basis of the components of the GFR observed in 14 cosmonauts flown on board the orbiting space station "Salyut-6" (before and after space flight). Similar studies are conducted during experiments which simulated the effects of long-term space flights during a 120-day ANOH.

Test subjects performed a motor task of fixing gaze on a 1 degree visual target presented on a white curved screen in six standard positions (20°, 40°, 60° to each side) located 30 cm from the eyes. The random order of switching on the target lights prevented position and temporal learning by subjects.

Gaze always began at the central target which served as a zero reference position. In some experiments, the thresholds of galvanic excitability of vestibular apparatus were determined using monaural anodic unipolar stimulation and eye movement recording. Excitation evoked eye shifts with an amplitude of 4-6 angular degrees toward the contralateral side. During experiments horizontal eye and head movements were recorded using EOG and by a precision potentiometer mounted on the subject's helmet. We analyzed the latent periods, durations, amplitudes and velocities of movements of eyes, head and gaze, quickness and accuracy of reactions, as well as relations between maximal velocities of compensatory movements of the eye and turning of the head.

RESULTS AND DISCUSSION

Healthy subjects executed the task accurately and quickly (Fig. 1). The saccade directed towards the target had a latency of 185-205 ms. Amplitude, velocity and duration of the saccades exhibited a distinct dependence upon initial gaze position with respect to the target. They covered the ranges of 18-30 deg, 300-259 deg/sec, and 60-149 ms, respectively. Following a delay of 20-60 ms after onset of this saccade, a second component of the reaction - a turn of the head - was recorded. Analysis indicates that normal subjects used two tactics of interaction of eye and head movements in solving this motor task (Fig. 1).

For the first tactic, turns of head were started earlier (within the range of 20-40 ms after saccade onset). Their amplitude and velocity were small. For the second tactic, head movements were delayed, starting 60 ms after saccade onset and had high velocity and amplitude. 20-60 ms after completion of the saccade, when gaze reached the end position and the head continued moving, a third component of reaction - counterrotation of eyes occurred, insuring an image stabilization on the retina. Maximal velocity of VOR was in line with the maximal speed of the head turn. Gain of the VOR was on the range of 0.96 - 1.00, remaining stable for movements of different velocities (Kozlovskaya and colleagues, 1981, 1984).

In patients with cerebellar disorders, the pattern of GFR was significantly changed regarding both eye and head movements. According to the pattern of disorders, the patients were divided in two groups (Fig. 2A). In the first group the execution of the motor task was characterized by the suppression of the oculomotor components of the GFR. This appeared as an amplitude decrease of 15-25% and a decline by a factor of 1.5 to 2.0 in mean velocities of the saccades. Duration of saccades was also increased. In brainstem and cerebellar patients, turn of the head began as normal, 20-60 ms after the onset of a saccade. However, its duration was longer - 445 to 590 ms. The compensatory movements of the eyes, relative to the velocity of the head, were inhibited (Fig. 2B).

In patients of the second group (pure cerebellar disorders), the oculomotor components of the GFR, on the contrary, were facilitated (Fig. 2A).

Compensatory eye movements were executed with velocity exceeding that of the head turn by more than 50 deg/sec. In these patients, the turn of head also started 20 ms later than in the control group, but with almost unchanged amplitude.

SCHEME OF EYE-HEAD COORDINATION

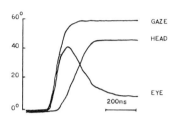

TWO TACTICS OF TASK PERFORMANCE

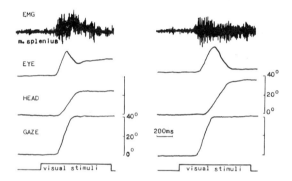

Fig. 1.   Gaze fixation reactions in man. Components of eye-head coordination and their tactic. Target spot at 60 and 40 degrees.

In general, in the 1st group, the gaze fixation was characterized by hypometry and in the 2nd group – by hypermetry[*]. However, the common sign for both groups was decay or disorder of interaction of reaction components and decrease in gaze accuracy. The amplitudes of errors in both groups reached 30 percent or more and the reaction time exceeded the control by more than 1.5 – 2.0 times.

An accepted model of microgravity is ANOH reproducing the effects of hypokinesthia, lack of support to the legs and redistribution of fluid volumes, which is typical of microgravity. A 120-day ANOH stay did not disturb the general pattern of the reaction, but significantly changed the parameters of its components and their interaction. As was done for the patients, the subjects were divided in two groups (Fig. 3). In the 1st group, latencies increased by 20-60 ms and the saccadic amplitude decreased after long-term hypokinesia, and

----

[*]According to the clinical data, the patients of the 2nd group were predominantly those having disorders of the cerebellar cortex, while in patients of the 1st group disorders covered brainstem and cerebellum.

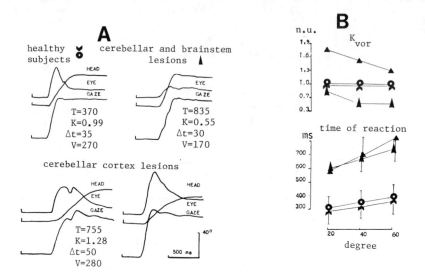

Fig. 2.   Patterns of gaze fixation (A) and parameters of eye
and head movements (B) in healthy subjects and
cerebellar patients. In A: T – latency of gaze
(ms); K – coefficient of gain vestibulo–ocular
reflex (velocity of eye counterrotation/velocity of
head movements); t – difference between the
latency of head and the latency of saccade (ms);
V – average velocity of saccade (deg/sec); in B: on
the abscissa is shown the location of the target
spots (deg).

the amplitudes and velocities of head movements also decreased. However, a
decline of the VOR velocity was even greater. Therefore, Kvor significantly
decreased to 0.7 for targets 40° and 60°.

In the 2nd group, as in the case of the cerebellar patients, the saccadic
amplitudes and velocities were slightly increased. The head movements, as with
the 1st group, were delayed. However, their amplitude and velocity were not
significantly changed. The velocity of ocular counterrotation exceeded that of
head turning, as reflected in an increase of Kvor in the range of 1.08 – 1.24.

The GFR in ANOH subjects of the 1st group was characterized by hypometry and in
those of the 2nd group – by hypermetry. However, as in the case of the
cerebellar patients in both groups there was a coordination of the reaction
components and a sharp decrease in gaze accuracy. The number of errors was
increase to more than 40%, and the time to completion of the GFR was raised to
100 ms.

The most pronounced changes in parameters of the GFR were immediately after
termination of ANOH (Fig. 3). However, on the 5th day after the end of ANOH
some traces of the GFR modification remained. By the 14th day after ANOH the
velocities and amplitudes of head turns were normal. Of particular interest

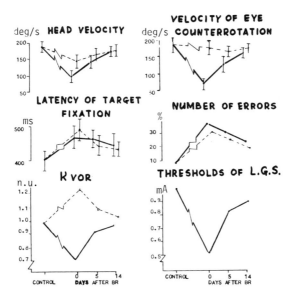

Fig. 3. Data of 120 day's bedrest. On the abscissa is
shown days of investigations. L.G.S. - labyrinthal
galvanic stimulation. Solid and dotted lines
present the 1st and 2nd groups of subjects. BR -
bedrest.

are the different direction of changes in the Kvor. The threshold of the
galvanic excitation of the vestibular apparatus after hypokinesia was decreased
for both groups, reaching 0.4 - 0.6 mA, as compared 0.9 - 1.2 mA control before
ANOH (Fig. 3).

Still greater disorders of the GFR were noted after prolonged exposure to
microgravity. As indicated in Fig. 4, the postflight saccadic amplitude in all
cosmonauts was elevated and overshot the target by 10-20°. In contrast, the
amplitudes and velocities of head movements were sharply decreased. The VOR
velocity was still further decreased, approaching 0 on the 3rd day postflight.
As a result, the magnitude of the Kvor was close to zero. Only in cosmonaut 3
(Fig. 4), in whom first testing was performed on the 5th day after the flight,
was the Kvor close to preflight. After the flight, in all cosmonauts, gaze
fixation showed great hypometry, considerable numbers of corrective ocular
saccades and even corrective saccades of the head. The time of the gaze
fixation was almost doubled.

Thus, as a whole, the pattern of disorders, which occurred after a prolonged
stay under the conditions of simulated and actual microgravity, resembles the
pattern situation observed in cerebellar patients. Rasumeev and Grigoryan
(1976) suggested that one of the main functions of the cerebellum is in an
adaptation of the sensorimotor systems to work in the earth gravitational field.
In turn, changes in the gravitational field must be accompanied by changes in
cerebellar functions. The present work is the first experimental demonstration
of this suggestion.

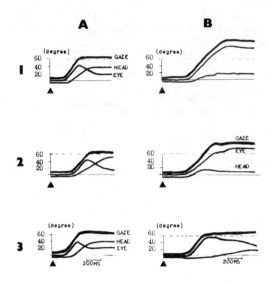

Fig. 4.   Patterns of gaze fixation before (A) and after (B)
237 day's spaceflight. Average diagram and
parameters of eye-head coordination on target spot
at 60 deg. 1-3 the cosmonauts of this expedition.

The neurophysiological mechanisms underlying these disorders still remain
unclear. It is known that the cerebellar cortex has an inhibitory effect on the
activity of vestibular nuclei (Eccles, Ito and Szenthagothai, 1967; Ito, 1972;
Ito, Kawai and Udo, 1968). It is natural to assume that normally a precise
agreement between velocities of eye and head movements is supplied by the
cerebellum by a mechanism of inhibition of an excessive vestibular signal into
the oculomotor motoneurons (Ritchie, 1976; Robinson, 1974; Ron and Robinson,
1973). This statement is supported by the studies on the effects of cerebellum
damage in animals (Fernandez and Frederickson, 1964; Robinson, 1976) and is in
good agreement our metric origin. In these persons the changes of performance
of gaze fixation resulted in facilitation of oculomotor reactions. However,
similar disorders of reaction accuracy were noted in the patients with the gaze
hypometry in whom the velocities and amplitudes of ocular movements were
distinctly lowered. It may be supposed that the hypometry observed in the other
groups of persons of this study resulted from compensatory processes of
inhibiting the transfer of the vestibular signals which are enhanced under
microgravity conditions (Kozlovskaya and colleagues, 1984). Indeed, a similar
inhibition of the oculomotor components of the GFR was previously observed by us
in patients with an increased labyrinthine excitability (Kozlovskaya and
colleagues, 1981).

REFERENCES

Bizzi, E. (1975). Central control of eye and head movements in monkey. In:
Basic mechanisms of ocular motility and their clinical application. Proc.
Int. Symp. Stockholm, 1974. Oxford, e.a., pp. 469-471.
Bizzi, E., R. Kalil, V. Tagliasso and P. Morasso (1971). Eye-head coordination
in monkey: the evidence of central patterned organization. Science, 173,
452-454.

Bizzi, E., R. Kalil, V. Tagliasso and P. Morasso (1972). Central programming and peripheral feedback during eye-head coordination in monkey. Bibl. Ophthal., 82, 220-232.

Dow, R.S. and G. Moruzzi (1958). The physiology and pathology of the cerebellum. University of Minnesota Press, Minneapolis.

Eccles, J.C., M. Ito and J. Szenthagothai (1967). The Cerebellum as a Neuronal Machine. New York, Springer-Verlag.

Fernandez, C., and J.M. Frederickson (1964). Experimental cerebellar lesions and their effects on vestibular functions. Acta Otolaryngol. (Suppl.), 192, 52-62.

Ito, M. (1972). Neural design of cerebellar motor control system. Brain Research, 40, 81-84.

Ito, M., N. Kawai and M. Udo (1968). The origin of cerebellar induced inhibition of Deiter's neurons. III. Localization of the inhibitory zone. Exp. Brain Res., 6, 247-264.

Klinke, R. and C.L. Schmidt (1970). Efferent influence on the vestibular organ during active movements of the body. Pflugers Arch., 318, 325-332.

Kornhuber, H.H. (1979). Cerebral cortex, cerebellum and basal ganglia: an introduction to their motor function. In: F.O. Schmidt and F.G. Worden (Eds.), Neuroscience 3rd program. MIT Press, Cambridge, 267-279.

Kozlovskaya, I.B. (1976). The afferent control of voluntary movements. Nauka, Moscow (in Russian).

Kozlovskaya, I.B., B.M. Babaev, V.A. Barmin, I.I. Belozerova, Yu.V. Kreidich and M.G. Sirota (1984). The effect of weightlessness on motor and vestibulo-motor reactions. Physiologist, 25, S111-S114.

Kozlovskaya, I.B., Yu.V. Kreidich, A.A. Repin and V.A. Barmin (1981). Eye and head movement coordination during gaze fixation in human subjects. J. Human Physiology, 7, 34-39 (in Russian).

Lisberger, S.G. and A.F. Fuchs (1978). The role of primate flocculus during rapid behavioural modification of vestibuloocular reflex. I. Purkinje cell activity during visually guided horizontal smooth-pursuit eye movements and passive head rotation. J. Neurophysiol., 41, 733-763.

Melvill Jones, G. (1976). The vestibular system for eye movement control. In: R.A. Monty and J.W.A. Sanders (Eds.). Eye movement and psychological processes. Hillsdale, New Jersey.

Morasso, P., E. Bizzi and J. Dichgans (1973). Adjustment of saccade characteristics during head movements. Exptl. Brain Res., 16, 492-500.

Rasumeev, A.N. and R.A. Grigoryan (1976). The Cerebellum and Gravitation. In: Problems of Cosmic Biology, vol. 29, Nauka, Moscow.

Ritchie, L. (1976) Effects of cerebellar lesions on saccadic eye movements. J. Neurophysiol., 39, 1246-1256.

Robinson, D.A. (1974) The effect of cerebellectomy on the cat's vestibulo-ocular integrator. Brain Res., 71, 195-207.

Robinson, D.A. (1976). Adaptive gain control of vestibuloocular reflex by cerebellum. J. Neurophysiol., 39, 954-969.

Ron, S. and D.A. Robinson (1973). Eye movements evoked by cerebellar stimulation in alert monkey. J. Neurophysiol., 36, 1004-1022.

Results of Tests on the Primate Vestibulo-Visualmotor Reactions in Biocosmos Experiments

A. A. Shipov, M. G. Sirota, I. N. Beloozerova,
B. M. Babaev and I. B. Kozlovskaya

Institute of Biomedical Problems, USSR Ministry of Health,
Moscow, USSR

The spectacular achievements of manned space programs have given an impetus to large-scale investigations of the vestibular structure and function performed during the last decades. The nature and mechanisms of vestibular disorders that are usually termed space motion sickness (SMS) occur in 60% space travellers upon insertion into orbit and therefore occupy an important place in space biology and medicine. A detailed study of SMS helped to describe the phenomenology of the disorders, their time-course variations and to identify the factors initiating its manifestations. Nevertheless, the pathogenesis of the disorders and mechanisms of SMS still remain obscure. Although the physiologists have been discussing the problem of over 20 years, they cannot answer the simple but cardinal question: does vestibular excitation vary in the weightless state and if it does then in what way?

The only investigation (Gualtierotti and co-workers, 1972) performed on the primary vestibular afferent of the frog was very important but statistically insignificant. Besides, the bioobject used did not allow direct extrapolation of the results obtained to highly organized living systems.

In this context, the purpose of the first primate study onboard the biosatellite was to investigate the excitation of the vestibular apparatus and to describe the process of vestibular adaptation to microgravity.

As an experimental model, we used the gaze fixation reaction (GFR) at a point target presented unexpectedly in the peripheral field of vision. This reaction in humans was described in detail at the end of the XIX century and was thoroughly investigated in primates in the 70s of this century.

According to Bizzi (1975), Bizzi and co-workers (1972), the velocity and accuracy of this biologically important orientation reaction in primates are provided by an automatic and well coordinated interaction of its three components, viz. saccade towards the target, head movement in the same direction, and compensatory eye movement. The coordination responsible for the formation of a single functional complex consisting of independent programs of rapid eye and head movements and compensatory eye movements works at the expense of a feedback system which includes proprioceptive, optic and, primarily, vestibular afferentation. The interaction of these afferent inputs is strongly dependent on the cerebellum.

In view of this, the gaze fixation reaction was assumed to be an adequate and informative method for studying the vestibular function in microgravity. The experiment was performed using one rhesus-monkey that was trained to carry out the GFR. The GFR parameters were recorded every day during the 5-day space flight and compared with those obtained 24 and 2 hours prelaunch. In parallel, human studies were conducted in order to understand in greater detail the GFR parameters and thus to identify the most informative parameters and to build a more realistic model of interaction of sensory signals, i.e. vestibular, visual, proprioceptive signals, involved in the control of the GFR.

Our findings have shown that the GFR is a highly informative test that provides quantitative data on the excitation of semicircular canals of the vestibular apparatus. In all the experiments the vestibular excitation changes were significantly and correctly reflected in the variations of oculomotor parameters, primarily K_{vor} and saccadic velocity and inhibition threshold. The latter is determined by the minimum velocity of head movements required to stop the saccade. As the excitation level increased, K_{vor} and saccadic velocities grew while the rate of saccadic inhibition decreased. As the excitation level decreased, all these changes were reversed. It is interesting to note that the threshold of galvanic excitation of the vestibulo-ocular reaction changes in the same manner.

Our investigations allowed us to detect two principal pathways along which the GFR can be compensated in the absence of adequate vestibular signals. These pathways can be designated as behavioural and neurophysiological. The behavioural pathway is the first to be triggered; it is regulated by the mechanisms of arbitrary movement control; it manifests as an increase in the latent periods of head movements and a drastic decrease of their velocity. Obviously, in this situation the interaction of GFR components is significantly facilitated.

The pathway of neurophysiological compensation develops in parallel but slightly behind the behavioural pathway. The neurophysiological processes include a strong inhibition of vestibulooculomotor transfer: in all experiments K_{vor} decreased continuously reaching 0.6 - 0.7 or less with increasing vestibular excitation. The only exception was the patients with lesions of the cerebellar cortex. The latter suggests that, if vestibular input signals are inadequate, the adaptive changes in K_{vor} are ensured by the cerebellum.

Throughout the five flight days the experimental monkey uneventfully performed 256 conditioned-reflex complexes. The basic portion of the complexes was a rapid gaze fixation at the targets that were randomly presented at a distance of 40 degrees of arc on the right and on the left from the center.

Exposure to microgravity significantly modified the amplitude and velocity characteristics of the GFR. These changes were greatly pronounced in the parameters of the oculomotor components of the GFR. On the first flight day (22 hours after launch) the saccadic amplitudes and velocities were noticeably increased (Fig.1). The increase persisted postflight. Simultaneously, the velocities of compensatory eye movements increased considerably. Normally, these movements are responsible for gaze fixation at the target while the head is still turning. The inadequately high velocities of compensatory counterrolling which evidently resulted from excessive vestibular signals (during the first flight day K_{vor} varied from 1.3 to 1.5, reaching 1.4 on the average) were responsible for disorders in gaze stabilization, target loss, and development of a large number of correction saccades: 2 hours preflight they were seen only in 4% and within 22 hours inflight in 30 to 40% GFRs (Fig. 2).

Increase of vestibular excitation and excess of signals from the semicircular canals were also evidenced by changes in other parameters of the GFR and behaviour on the whole, viz. decrease of the velocity of head movements that provided saccade inhibition, and reduction of the maximum amplitude of head movements performed every day during morning two-hour experimental sessions.

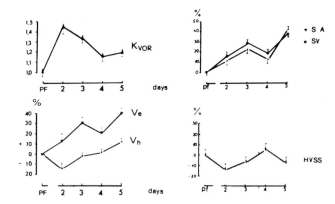

Fig. 1. Changes in the characteristics of the gaze fixation
reaction in the primate during "Cosmos-1514" flight.
On the left-coefficient of gain of the vestibulo-ocular reflex (K_{vor}) and maximum velocity of eye counterrolling (V_e) and head movement (V_n); on the right
- amplitude (SA) and maximum velocity (SV) of the
saccadic movements (above) and head velocity that
supresses saccade (below).

The time-course variations of the above parameters inflight were very similar,
reflecting the processes of adaptation of the control system to the new environment for the vestibular function. As is the case with humans with vestibular les-
sions, these processes included two mechanisms: the behavioural mechanism that
manifested as an increase in the number of GFR complexes with a drastically reduced velocity of head movements, and the neurophysiological mechanism which was
responsible for the inhibition of the transfer function in the vestibulo-oculomotor reflex arc. It should be noted that K_{vor} in the GFR system remained elevated throughout the flight and after its completion.

It is evident that the problem needs further study.

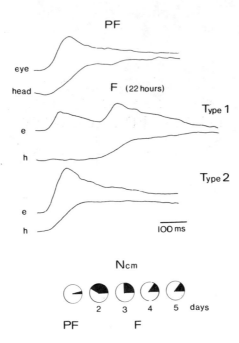

Fig. 2. Fragments of experimental records, obtained preflight (PF) and inflight (F). Type I - fragment gaze
fixation with corrective saccade, Type II - without
it. Below - number of corrected movements in different days of flight.

BIBLIOGRAPHY

Bizzi, E. (1975). Basic Mechanism of Ocular Motility and Their Clin. Implica-
    tions. Proc. Int. Symp. Stockholm, 1974, Oxford e.a., 469-471.
Bizzi, E., Kalil R., Tagliasco V., Morasso P. (1972). Central programming and
    peripheral feedback during eye-head coordination in monkey. Bibl. Ophthal.,
    82, 220-232.
Gualtierotti T., Bracchi F., Rocca E. (1972). Orbiting frog otolith experiment
    (OFO-A). Final report at the data reduction and control experimentation.
    Piccin Medical books, NASA.

OCULAR ALIGNMENT,
RETINAL CORRESPONDENCE,
FUSION, BINOCULARITY

Mutual Interactions between Accommodation and Convergence are Reduced by Tonic Adaptation

C. M. Schor and J. Kotulak

University of California, School of Optometry, Berkeley,
CA 94720, USA

INTRODUCTION

The vergence system has a fast response to disparity stimuli, followed by a slower tonic adaptation, that is illustrated by changes in the phoria (open-loop vergence error) (Schor, 1979; 1983). This phasic-tonic organization results in a stimulus velocity sensitivity for disparity vergence and a stimulus amplitude sensitivity for vergence adaptation. A similar phasic - tonic organization has been suggested for the accommodative system (Schor, Johnson, and Post, 1984), however several controlled studies of tonic adaptation of accommodation have only revealed minor aftereffects in darkness (0.5 diopters) after long and strenuous accommodation (Ebenholtz, 1983; Baker, Brown, and Garner, 1983; Schor, Johnson, and Post, 1984). Darkness is used as a means of observing the open-loop accommodative response or dark focus of accommodation (Leibowitz and Owens, 1978). Other means for opening the accommodative loop such as an empty field (Ganzfeld) and pinhole pupil would be expected to reveal greater aftereffects because the decay time constant for relaxing accommodation to the resting focus is significantly longer under these conditions than in darkness (Phillips, 1974). We have compared the amplitude and duration of accommodative aftereffects under light and dark open-loop conditions. Our results confirm a durable and robust adaptation of tonic accommodation that is temporarily masked in darkness.

The stimulus amplitude sensitivity for tonic elements of accommodation and vergence are believed to result in a stimulus velocity sensitivity of optical reflex accommodation and disparity vergence as a result of the negative feedback loops of these two motor systems (Schor, 1983). The difference in stimulus sensitivity of phasic and tonic mechanisms was used to determine the site of crosslink interactions known as accommodative vergence and vergence accommodation. A frequency response analysis revealed that like the phasic mechanisms of optical reflex accommodation and disparity vergence, both crosslink interactions were stimulus velocity sensitive. This result suggests that the crosslinks originate in the feed-forward paths of accommodation and vergence, after the phasic elements and before the tonic elements of the two motor systems. Accommodative vergence was found to change the phoria (with the vergence loop opened), and vergence accommodation changed the tonic level of accommodation (with the accommodative loop opened). This result indicates that crosslink summing junctions are also located between the phasic and tonic integrators in the feed-forward paths of accommodation and convergence. A step response analysis revealed an amplitude-dependent nonlinearity of the tonic integrators that influenced the stimulus velocity sensitivity of crosslinks. The nonlinearity resulted from a limiting stimulus window or low saturation range for input amplitudes to the tonic integrators. This stimulus window also set the threshold stimulus amplitude for crosslink interaction. Stimuli within the window resulted in tonic adaptation and stimuli greater than the window resulted in accommodative vergence and vergence accommodation.

METHODS

Apparatus. Two serially-arranged, opto-electronic systems, one for stimulus presentation and the other for response measurement, were used. The stimulus-presentation system was capable of independent control of the inputs to accommodation and vergence and of rendering those inputs either statically or dynamically, and under either closed-loop or open-loop conditions. The response-measurement system was capable of continuous and simultaneous monitoring of the outputs of accommodation and vergence and of producing high-resolution recordings using objective infrared recording techniques.

Experimental Procedures. Six different experiments were conducted. In the <u>first study</u>, tonic accommodation was adapted monocularly with a 2-D stimulus, using a short (5 second) and a long (60 second) adaptation period. After the adaptation period, the duration was measured for the decay accommodation to the resting focus, under 3 open loop conditions; (1) a Maxwellian view, which projected a pinhole pupil into the plane of the subject's entrance pupil (2) a bright empth field produced by an opal-glass diffuser in the target plane, and (3) darkness. In the <u>second study</u>, tonic accommodation was adapted monocularly for 2 minutes, using adapting stimuli of 1, 2, 4, and 6 diopters. Immediately following the adaptation period, tha accommodative loop was opened with a Maxwellian view; the magnitude of the tonic aftereffect was measured 45 seconds lator. In the <u>third study</u>, accommodation was adapted monocularly for 1 minute with a 2 diopter stimulus. After the adaptation period, the accommodative loop was opened for 1.5 minutes using a Maxwellian view, interrupted by several short (3-5 second) periods of darkness. In the <u>fourth study</u>, the CA/C frequency response was always measured with the accommodative loop open, so that any change in accommodation could be ascribed to a change in vergence. A binocular Maxwellian view was used to open the accommodative loops of both eyes. The vergence stimulus was a temporally-modualted sine wave. The CA/C frequency response was obtained under two conditions: (1) with the vergence loop closed (referred to as the "closed-loop" condition) and (2) with the vergence loop opened by feedback of the output of the eye-movement monitors (referred to as the "open-loop" condition). The CA/C ratio was defined as the change in accommodation in diopters divided by the change in vergence in meter angles (the response CA/C ratio). The AC/A frequency re sponse was always measured with the vergence loop open, so that any change in vergence could be attributed to a change in accommodation. The vergence loop was opened by extinguishing the light source of the left eye. The accommodative stimulus was a temporally-modulated sine wave. The AC/A frequency response was obtained under two conditions: (1) with the accommodative loop closed (referred to as the "closed-loop" condition) and (2) with the accommodative loop opened by feedback of the output of the dynamic, infrared optometer (referred to as the "open-loop" condition). The AC/A ratio was defined as the change in vergence in prism diopters divided by the change in accommodation in diopters (the response AC/A ratio). In the <u>fifth study</u>, aftereffects of vergence on accommodation, a nd of accommodation on vergence were examined. Subjects binocularly fused a bar pattern through a binocular Maxwellian view (so that the accommodative loops of both eyes were opened). Vergence responses to 10 prism diopters, base out, were stimulated for either 5 seconds or 2 minutes, and then the left eye was occluded by turning off its target. Both accommodation and vergence were monitored objectively during and after the adaptation period. Subjects accommodated to a 2 diopter stimulus presented only to the right eye for either 5 seconds or 2 minutes and then the accommodative loop was opened using a Maxwellian view. Both accommodation and vergence were monitored during and after the adaptation period. In the <u>sixth study</u>, linearity of AC/A and CA/C ratios was tested by comparing their responses to small and large sinusoidal stimuli to accommodation and vergence respectively.

RESULTS

Duration of Aftereffects in Three Open-Loop States. The vertical arrows in Fig.
1 marked A and B beneath the recordings indicate when the adapting period began
and when the accommodative loop was opened respectively. The decay rate of the
accommodative response was faster for all three, open-loop conditions following
short-term adaptation (5 seconds) than it was following long-term adaptation (1
minute). It is also evident that the longest durations of the aftereffect were
found with the Maxwellian view and the shortest durations occurred in darkness.
Durations were similar for Maxwellian view and empty field. The duration of the
dark aftereffect following 1 minute of adaptation (7.3 seconds) was an order of
magnitude less than the duration of the Maxwellian-view aftereffect (69.3
seconds).

Gain of Tonic Adaptation. The amplitude of the tonic aftereffect was measured as
a function of the amplitude of the adapting stimulus. Subjects were adapted for
2 minutes to accommodative stimuli of 1, 2, 4 and 6 D. The accommodative loop
was opened by Maxwellian view and the difference between the baseline resting
focus and the instantaneous accommodative response at 45 seconds (i.e. the tonic
aftereffect) was calculated. The gain of tonic accommodation was defined as the
ratio of the tonic aftereffect at 45 seconds (described above) over the response
amplitude just prior to opening the accommodative loop. The gain was fairly
independent of stimulus amplitude (0.5 and 1.0 for two subjects).

Decay of Tonic Accommodation Interrupted by Darkness. After adapting
accommodation monocularly for 1 minute to a 2D stimulus the decay of tonic
aftereffects was monitored in Maxwellian view that was interrupted by brief
periods of darkness. Figure 2(top) illustrates that during darkness
accommodation decayed rapidly to the resting focus. However, when the Maxwellian
view was reinstated, the accommodative response increased to the level it had
been when there was no previous dark period and it decayed at a much slower rate.
After 70 seconds of opening the accommodative loop, the accommodative response
remained at the same resting focus under both Maxwellian view and dark
conditions. Figure 2 (bottom) illustrates a more sustained aftereffect of tonic
accommodation after 2 minutes of adaptation to a 3 D stimulus. This tonic
aftereffect of accommodation in Maxwellian view continued for several minutes.
During that period accommodation went to the resting focus whenever the target
was interrupted with darkness and the response returned to the adapted state
whenever the target reappeared in Maxwellian view or the eye viewed a lighted
empty field.

Closed loop frequency response. The solid curves in Fig. 3 plot the "closed loop"
gain and phase of accommodative vergence and vergence accommodation responses to
a range of temporal frequencies (0.025-1.25Hz). Stimulus amplitudes for
accommodation and vergence were 2 D (peak to peak) and 10 PD (peak to peak)
respectively. There is a low-frequency rolloff of both the response AC/A and
CA/C ratios.

At high temporal frequencies both accommodation and resulting accommodative
vergence were reduced in amplitude. Accommodative vergence was reduced slightly
more than accommodation such that the ratio of these two responses (AC/A) was
attenuated slightly at high temporal frequencies. In contrast, the closed loop
response CA/C ratio of both subjects continued to increase as temporal frequency
increased because even though the responses of both motor systems was reduced at
high temporal frequencies, disparity vergence was attenuated more than vergence
accommodation.

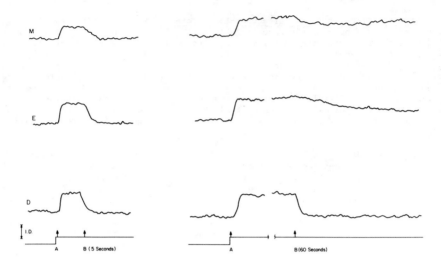

Fig. 1. Different time constants for relaxation of accommodation under 3 different open-loop conditions (Maxwellian view (M), empty field (E), and darkness (D)) after stimulating accommodation monocularly for either 5 or 60 seconds. Arrows marked A and B beneath the recordings indicate when accommodation was stimulated and when the loop was opened respectively. Incomplete relaxation of accommodation after long-term stimulation demonstrates a tonic aftereffect.

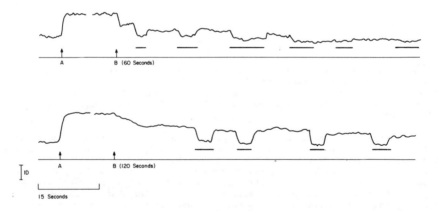

Fig. 2. The decay of a tonic aftereffect of accommodation is shown during open-loop (Maxwellian view) conditions interrupted by brief periods of darkness (underlined segments). Adaptation was for 1 minute to a 2 D stimulus (top) or for 2 minutes to a 3 D stimulus (bottom). During dark periods accommodation went to its resting level but it returned to the adapted state with the Maxwellian view.

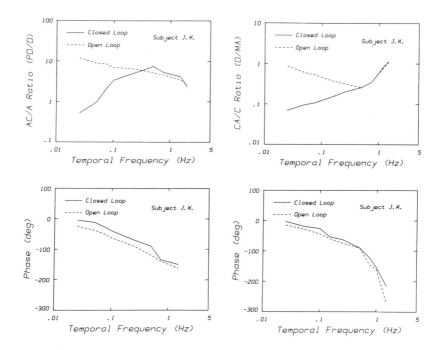

Fig. 3. Gain and phase plots for accommodative vergence and vergence accommodation responses to sinusoidal blur and disparity stimuli presented under open loop (dashed line) and closed loop (solid line) conditions. Gain is the response AC/A and CA/C ratio. Phase lag equals the difference between response and stimulus phase. Stimulus amplitude for open and closed loop conditions were ±0.5 and ±1.0 D respectively for accommodation and ±1 PD and ±10 PD for vergence respectively.

Open loop frequency response. There was no low-frequency rolloff of either accommodative vergence or vergence accommodation under "open-loop" conditions. At high temporal frequencies there was little difference between the open and closed loop responses. The difference between open and closed loop response ratios at low temporal frequencies demonstrated that the derivative or velocity-sensitive element of the closed-loop response is a characteristic of the negative-feedback loop, which was eliminated in the open-loop condition. The derivative element is not shared by the negative-feedback loop for accommodation or for vergence since neither of these systems has a low-frequency rolloff (Rashbass and Westheimer, 1961; Krishnan, Phillips and Stark, 1973).

Aftereffects of vergence on accommodation. During adaptation to the BO prism, there was a convergence increase of 10 PD and an accommodative increase of 0.75 D. As expected, when the left eye was occluded after wearing the prism for a short period (5 seconds), there was a rapid (10 second) decay of both vergence and vergence accommodation. However, when the left eye was occluded after wearing the prism for 2 minutes, there was a residual esophoria (an aftereffect of tonic vergence) and also a prolonged increase in accommodation (an aftereffect of tonic accommodation). Both aftereffects usually decayed slowly over a 1-1.5 minute period; however, occasionally the esophoria decayed rapidly (within 10 seconds) while the accommodative aftereffect persisted for over 1 minute. This dissociation of aftereffects indicates that both accommodation and vergence are adapting separately to the disparity vergence response and that the aftereffect of vergence accommodation is not the result of tonic vergence stimulating accommodation. Vergence effort could stimulate tonic adaptation of accommodation if the CA/C cross link entered the accommodative loop prior to the site of tonic accommodation.

Aftereffects of accommodation on vergence. During monocular adaptation to the 2 D stimulus there was an accommodative response of 1.5 D and an accommodative vergence response of 7.5 PD. When the accommodative loop was opened after 5 seconds of adaptation, there was a rapid (10 second) decay of both accommodation and accommodative vergence. When the accommodative loop was opened after 2 minutes of adaptation, there was a residual increase of accommodation (tonic aftereffect of accommodation) as well as an esophoria (tonic aftereffect of vergence). Both aftereffects usually decayed slowly over a 1-1.5 minute period to their resting levels; however, as in the previous experiment, the two responses occasionally had markedly different time courses, in which accommodation persisted longer than convergence by 40-80 seconds or vice versa. This dissociation in the time courses indicates that vergence and accommodation are adapting separately to reflex accommodation and that the aftereffect of accommodative vergence is not the result of tonic accommodation stimulating vergence. Accommodative effort could stimulate tonic adaptation of vergence if the AC/A crosslink entered the vergence feedforward loop prior to the site of tonic vergence adaptation.

An amplitude dependent non-linearity was revealed by comparing responses to small and large stimuli at low (.06 Hz) and high (0.25 Hz) frequencies. At the low frequencies, the response AC/A ratio incresed from 2 PD/D to 5.6 PD/D when the accommodative response was increased from 0.87 D to 2.25 D. At the higher stimulus frequency, the response AC/A ratio remained the same (5.4 PD/D) when the accommodative response was increased from 0.75 D to 2.00 D. Similarly, at a low temporal frequency (0.06 Hz) the CA/C ratio increased from 0.1D/MA to 0.6D/MA when the amplitude of the disparity vergence response increased from 5 to 10 PD. At higher temporal frequencies the CA/C was independent of the response amplitude of disparity vergence.

DISCUSSION

Model of phasic-tonic accommodation. Figure 4 is a block diagram representing the interaction between tonic and "reflex" accommodation (Heath, 1956), a model that is homeomorphic to the model proposed for vergence adaptation (Schor, 1979). In Fig. 4, tonic accommodation receives input from reflex accommodation as well as from the vergence-accommodation crosslink, as indicated by our results. The tonic element is in parallel with the fast, neural integrator for reflex accommodation. The response of this system to a step input is initially controlled by the fast, neural integrator. This response is gradually taken over by the slower, tonic integrator, which is responsible for the prolonged, tonic aftereffects observed under open-loop conditions.

Model of crosslinks between accommodation and vergence. The model in Fig. 5 describes control of crosslink interactions between accommodation and vergence by subcomponents of these two motor systems. The model illustrates that the crosslink between accommodative and vergence occur between tonic and phasic elements in their feedforward paths. This organization of the take off points for crosslinks, places the tonic integrator for accommodation in the feedback path of accommodative vergence and the tonic integrator for vergence in the feedback path of vergence accommodation which results in the stimulus velocity sensitivity of the phasic elements and their crosslink interactions.

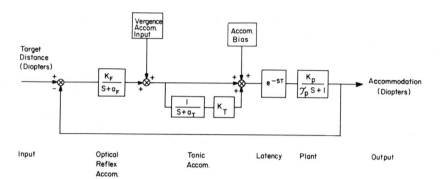

Fig. 4. System model representation of phasic and tonic control elements of the accommodative system. The model illustrates two inputs to tonic accommodation which are reflex accommodation, modeled here as a fast (phasic) neural integrator, and vergence accommodation. Together, the sum of these inputs with tonic accommodation drive the plant or lens-cillary body, modeled here as a first order lag element. The variable gain (Kt) of the tonic integrator is light dependent. Tonic aftereffects of accommodation are masked in darkness when Kt is reduced. A separate bias source is responsible for baseline resting focus in the absence of tonic adaptation.

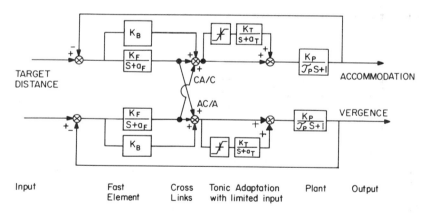

Fig. 5. System model representation of synchenetic interactions between accommodation and vergence. The two motor systems are interconnected at points in their feed-forward paths located between phasic and tonic neural integrators.

Since the frequency response of both accommodative vergence and of vergence accommodation rolls off at the low end under closed-loop conditions, it might be expected that the responses of accommodative vergence and of vergence accommodation to step inputs could not be sustained. However, it has been observed that the response to a step of sufficient amplitude (2 D for accommodative vergence or 5 PD for vergence accommodation) is sustained over an extended time course. This is possible because the tonic integrators of both systems have an amplitude-dependent nonlinearity, in which the effects of large step inputs on tonic adaptation are diminished by a limiting stimulus window or low saturation of input amplitudes. The saturation nonlinearity has the beneficial effect of reducing the low-frequency rolloff that would otherwise be present as a consequence of the differentiator-like behavior of an integrator in a feedback loop. In addition, the residual low-frequency rolloff that is not eliminated by the nonlinearity in the originating loop would be compensated for by adaptation of the tonic element in the destination loop.

The results clearly demonstrate that the AC/A and CA/C ratios are not static values. The amplitude of these ratios increased as dynamic control of accommodation and vergence shifts from an adaptive tonic element to a faster phasic controller that drives crosslink interactions. In this complementary relationship, tonic elements function to sustain motor responses of accommodation and vergence that are initiated by phasic elements and their crosslink interactions.

REFERENCES

Baker, R., B. Brown, and L. Garner (1983). Time course and variability of dark focus. Invest. Ophthalmol. Vis. Sci., 24,1528-1531.
Ebenholtz, S.M. (1983). Accommodative hysteresis: a precursor for induced myopia. Invest. Ophthalmol. Vis. Sci., 24, 513-515.
Krishnan, V.V., S. Phillips, and L. Stark (1973). Frequency analysis of accommodation, accommodative vergence and disparity vergence. Vision Res., 13, 1545-1554.
Leibowitz, H.W. and D.A. Owens (1978). New evidence for the intermediate position of relaxed accommodation. Docum. Ophthal., 46,133-147.
Phillips, S. (1974). Ocular neurological control systems: accommodation and the near response triad. Ph.D. Dissertation, University of California, Berkeley.
Rashbass, C., and G. Westheimer (1961). Disjunctive eye movements. J. Physiol., 159, 339-360.
Schor, C.M. (1979). The relationship between fusional vergence eye movements and fixation disparity. Vision Res., 19, 1359-1367.
Schor, C.M. (1983). Fixation disparity and vergence adaptation. In C.M. Schor and K. Ciuffreda (Ed.), Vergence Eye Movements; Basic and Clinical Aspects. Butterworth, Boston. Chap. 14, pp.465-516.
Schor, C.M., C.A. Johnson, and R.B. Post (1984) Adaptation of tonic accommodation. Ophthal. Physiol. Opt., 4, 133-137.

ACKNOWLEDGMENTS

This project was supported by Grant # R01 EYO3532-04 from the National Eye Institute of the National Institutes of Health.

Neurophysiological Correlates of Convergence and Its Tonic Adjustment

L. E. Mays and C. A. Tello

Departments of Physiological Optics and Psychology, and the
Neurosciences Program, University of Alabama at Birmingham,
Birmingham, AL 35294, USA

INTRODUCTION

Binocular vision requires that the two eyes maintain precise alignment on visual targets at different distances. The vergence eye movement control system accomplishes this by generating horizontal eye movement commands that move the eyes equal magnitudes but in the opposite direction. There is evidence that indicates that this system is relatively independent of the conjugate eye movement systems. Recently, we described cells with a pure vergence signal in the mesencephalic reticular formation near the oculomotor nucleus (Mays, 1984). The activity level of these cells is closely coupled to the vergence angle, and is unrelated to conjugate movements or the absolute position of either eye in the orbit.

Models of the vergence system have postulated the existence of a neuronal integrator which has as its input a signal proportional to binocular disparity (Rashbass and Westheimer, 1961, Zuber and Stark 1966, Krishnan and Stark, 1977). Work by Schor (1979a, 1979b) suggests that there is also a slow time-constant integrator responsible for the level of tonic convergence. Figure 1 is a simplified model showing these two integrators. The input to this system is target vergence, from which vergence is subtracted to yield disparity. The disparity signal must undergo some sensorimotor transformation, since not every occurrence of binocular disparity results in a vergence movement. A relatively fast integrator receives an input signal which is proportional to disparity. The output of this integrator is a vergence position signal. The fast integrator is responsible for generating vergence movements in response to changes in disparity. Schor's experiments indicate that the slow integrator receives its input from this fast fusional integrator. The time constant of the slow integrator is such that it is effectively charged only by prolonged fusional convergence. The result of the increased output of the slow integrator is an increase in the phoria. According to this model, the actual vergence angle is determined by the sum of the outputs of these two integrators.

The purpose of the present experiment was to determine if the activity of mesencephalic convergence cells represent the output of the fast integrator alone (shown as point 1 in Fig. 1), or the summed output of the integrators (shown as point 2 in Fig. 1). According to the model, cells at points 1 and 2 should behave similarly as long as the output of the slow integrator remains constant. If the output of the slow integrator were to increase, the output of the fast integrator (at point 1) must <u>decrease</u> to maintain a given vergence angle. Cells at point 2 should be unaffected by changing the balance between the slow and fast integrators.

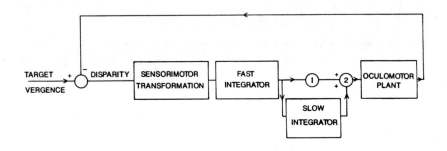

Fig. 1. Model of the vergence system showing fast and slow integrators.

METHODS

Extracellular single unit recordings were made in three rhesus monkeys (<u>Macaca mulatta</u>) trained to look at visual targets for a liquid reward. The animals viewed the targets binocularly through a mirror stereoscope. The targets were small lighted crosses displayed on TV monitors at a distance of 62 cm. Using this display it is possible to manipulate horizontal and vertical target position as well as target vergence. The horizontal and vertical positions of both eyes were measured using the eye coil technique. In this experiment, the monkeys tracked target steps to the left or right with saccades or made symmetrical vergence movements in response to disparity steps. The direction and amplitude of target motion, target duration, and the trial type (saccade or vergence) were randomized. Each trial lasted 3 to 5 s, and was followed by an inter-trial interval of 4 to 7 s during which no visual stimulus was present.

Tungsten microelectrodes were advanced in the midbrain while the animal tracked the targets. When a convergence cell was encountered, the relationship between its firing rate and vergence angle was determined. This was done by computing the firing rate and vergence angle over a number of 100 ms periods of steady fixation following symmetrical convergence movements. The converged position was held no longer than 3 s and convergence trials were intermixed with saccade trials at the normal target vergence (for 62 cm) of 2.2°. The phoria was estimated by having the animal monocularly fixate targets at a distance of 62 cm. The firing rate during the phoria test was also measured.

Convergence adaptation was accomplished by requiring the monkey to view horizontal target steps as target vergence was gradually increased from the normal value of 2.2^O by 6° or 8°. Periodically, the phoria was assessed by measuring eye position during monocular viewing. After 15-30 min of trials at one of the larger target vergence angles, an increased esophoria of from 3° to 7° was evident. Presumably, vergence adaptation would have progressed more rapidly with longer trial durations, but this was not practical with our training and data collection procedures.

Once behavioral evidence of vergence adaptation was seen, the firing rate-vergence angle relationship was reassessed by introducing vergence test trials, interleaved with conjugate (saccadic) step trials. These vergence test trials required the animal to look briefly to targets at lesser vergence demands from the adapted vergence angle. Thus, the monkey was required to diverge from its adapted position. This was necessary to attain vergence angles comparable to those measured prior to adaptation. The duration of the divergence never exceeded 3 s on a trial.

RESULTS

The activity of a convergence cell during a 5° convergence prior to adaptation is shown in Fig. 2. The horizontal positions of the left and right eyes (HR and HL)

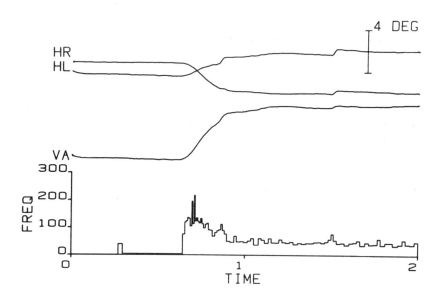

Fig. 2. Activity of a convergence cell during a convergence movement.

are shown, along with the vergence angle (VA). The vertical eye position traces have been omitted for clarity. The instantaneous firing rate of the cell (in spikes per second) is also shown (FREQ). Prior to the movement the vergence angle is about 2.2^O. The firing rate associated with this angle is nearly zero. Some convergence cells, like this one, display a burst of activity during the movement, followed by a relatively steady firing rate after the new vergence angle is attained. Other convergence cells did not exhibit such a burst. The burst was never included in the determination of the rate-position curve.

The behavior of the same cell during a 3° rightward saccade is shown in Fig. 3. As with other convergence cells, there is no change in firing rate unless there is a change in vergence angle. This trial, along with other control trials, demonstrates that convergence cells carry a vergence signal and do not simply encode the position of the eye in the orbit.

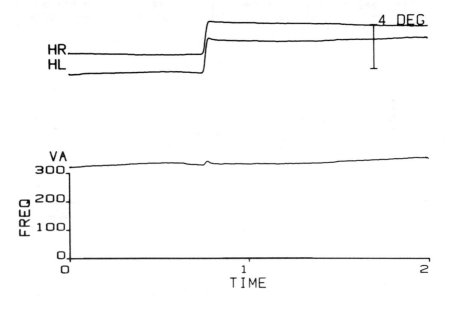

Fig. 3. Activity of the same cell shown in Fig. 2 during a conjugate eye movement.

The relationship between vergence angle and firing rate for this cell is shown in Fig. 4. Each point on the plot is the average firing rate and vergence angle during a 100 msec period of fixation. The points designated by asterisks (*) represent data taken prior to convergence adaptation. A linear regression line indicates that there is a linear relationship between firing rate and vergence angle. The slope of the line is 7.0 spikes/s/deg, the y-intercept is 1.2°, and the correlation coefficient is 0.95. The firing rate during monocular viewing coincided with this regression line.

The open circles (o) in Fig. 4 show the relationship between firing rate and vergence angle for the same cell after adaptation. Convergence adaptation increased the esophoria by approximately 5°. The regression line for the post-adaptation data is nearly parallel to the pre-adaptation data (slope = 6.3 spikes/s/deg) but is offset to the right by about 5° (x-intercept = 6.2°). The correlation coefficient is 0.87. The firing rate associated with the new phoria fell on the this regression line. These results indicate that behavioral adaptation occurs (as evidenced by a change in the phoria) and this adaptation is associated with a similar degree of adaptation in the firing rate of the cell.

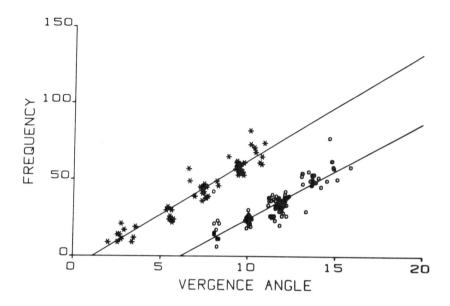

Fig. 4. Firing rate-vergence angle relationship before and after convergence adaptation.

Although these data are for a convergence cell which burst during the movement, similar patterns were seen in convergence cells which carried a pure vergence signal with no burst. Approximately 80% of the convergence cells showed some evidence of adaptation. For some cells, the shift in firing rate was less than that expected based on the change in the phoria. Other cells showed a decrease in the slope of the rate-vergence angle line following adaptation. We do not yet know if this change in slope signifies a change in the gain of the cells, or represents a soft saturation in the firing rate.

Figure 5 shows the rate-position relationships for another convergence cell before (*) and after (o) adaptation. Although the phoria shifted nearly 5°, the rate-position lines are relatively unchanged. The post-adaptation slope is slightly reduced, but this difference is not statistically significant.

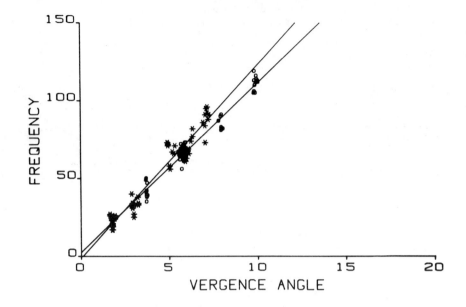

Fig. 5. Firing rate–vergence angle relationship before and after convergence adaptation for a different convergence neuron.

DISCUSSION

The observation that most convergence cells decrease their firing rate for a given vergence angle following adaptation is consistent with the model in Fig. 1. If all convergence cells had showed a shift in their rate–vergence angle curves equal to the change in the phoria, this would suggest that convergence cells receive an input only from the fast vergence integrator and not from the slow, tonic vergence system. This, then, would place them at point 1 in Fig. 1. However, the observations that some cells do not show adaptation, and that others adapt less that the expected amount, suggests that some convergence neurons might receive an additional input from the slow integrator. This would place some cells at or close to point 2.

Mesencephalic convergence cells appear to be near the end stage of processing of vergence movements. The vergence signal they carry is closely coupled to the eye movements and leads them in time (Mays, 1984). Convergence cells are often found within 1 mm of the medial rectus subdivision of the oculomotor nucleus. Although we do not know the pattern of their connections, we note that are well-suited to provide the vergence signal needed by medial rectus motoneurons. The observation that so many of these convergence cells decrease their firing rate during adaptation suggests that the medial rectus motoneurons may receive a tonic signal from a slow integrator directly.

ACKNOWLEDGEMENTS

Supported by NIH grants RO1 EY03463 and P30 EY03039.

REFERENCES

Krishnan, V.V. and L. Stark (1977). A heuristic model for the human vergence eye movement system. IEEE Trans. Biomed. Eng. BME-24, 44-49.

Mays, L.E. (1984). Neural control of vergence eye movements: Convergence and divergence neurons in the midbrain. J. Neurophysiol., 51, 1091-1108.

Rashbass, C. and G. Westheimer (1961). Disjunctive eye movements. J. Physiol. 159, 339-360.

Schor, C. M. (1979a). The influence of rapid prism adaptation upon fixation disparity. Vision Res. 19, 757-765.

Schor, C. M. (1979b). The relationship between fusional vergence eye movements and fixation disparity. Vision Res. 19, 1359-1357.

Zuber, B.L. and L. Stark (1968). Dynamical characteristics of the fusional vergence eye-movement system. IEEE Trans. Sys. Sci. Cyber. SSC-4, 72-79.

Motor and Sensory Compensation for Prisms and Surgical Correction in Convergent Strabismus

B. Bagolini*, M. R. Zanasi** and R. Bolzani**

*Department of Ophthalmology, Catholic University, Rome, Italy
**Department of Ophthalmology, University of Modena, Italy

In comitant strabismus, children do not experience diplopia because in binocular vision they develop sensory adaptations to the ocular deviation known as suppression and anomalous retinal correspondence (a.r.c.).

Rather recently a sensorimotor anomaly present in binocular vision was studied which is also probably an expression of an adaptation to the angle of deviation.

Sensory adaptation. Suppression under the form of more or less large scotomata in the visual field of the deviated eye, present only in binocular vision, is the main reaction of squinting children to the ocular deviation preventing them from seeing double. Anomalous retinal correspondence (a.r.c.) follows the occurrence of suppression. It consists of a variation of the spatial localization of the retinal elements of the deviated eye which is only present in binocular vision. Anomalous retinal correspondence (a.r.c.) has apparently the finality of restoring binocularity in spite of a deviated eye. These two adaptational phenomena are unstable and not always detectable by the various tests. They can be more easily detected in casual seeing with the help of the striated glasses test which leaves normal surroundings almost unchanged. Under casual seeing conditions, it appears that suppression predominates in large angle deviation, while a.r.c. predominates in small angle strabismus with little or no suppression detectable (Bagolini and Capobianco, 1965; Bagolini, 1976). These results are summarized in Fig. 1. When no or little suppression is detectable, anomalous binocular vision may be achieved in spite of a deviated eye through collaboration between anomalous corresponding retinal points. Fusion of the images appears to be possible in spite of the fact that they stimulate retinal points which are not anatomically corresponding but have acquired a functional anomalous correspondence. The intensity of this anomalous collaboration can be measured by suitable techniques.

A high degree of strength can be achieved, particularly in small angle deviation and microstrabismus, mimicking fairly closely normal binocular vision. A simple way to evaluate the intensity of suppression scotomata or the intensity reached by a.r.c. (supporting anomalous binocular vision) is to detect when these two sensory stata are interrupted by a progressively stronger obstacle to the binocular collaboration until diplopia appears. By placing filters of progressive density in front of the deviated eye, the binocular status achieved by the patient is more and more dissociated (Bagolini, 1976) and diplopia will suddenly appear. The predominant binocular sensory status (suppression or a.r.c.) is diagnosed in casual seeing with the striated glasses test while the

151

patient looks at a pen light.   The filters (Fig. 2) of minimal density capable
of eliciting diplopia give us information about the strength of the predominant
adaptational phenomenon.

Sensorimotor adaptation. When a base out prism is placed in front of one eye of
a subject with convergent strabismus in order to optically correct the angle of
strabismus, a slow increase in the convergent deviation frequently occurs
(Bagolini, 1966; Bagolini, 1976).   The prism correction may be partially or
totally compensated.   For example, a strabismic deviation of 10 diopters
corrected with a base out prism of 10 diopters, after a certain period of time,
may increase its angle so that the deviation becomes again of 10 diopters while
wearing the prism. The angle of strabismic deviation is therefore increased
from 10 to 20 prism diopters.

This behavior implies an increase in the tonus of the medial recti determining
an increase in the angle of strabismus.   This increase in the tonus of the
medial recti is solicited by a shift of the retinal image induced by a prism.
It is, therefore, a sensorimotor reaction which occurs only in binocular vision.
It seems that while in a.r.c. it is the spatial localization of the retinal
elements that is changed, in this sensorimotor reaction, it is the motor value
of the retinal elements which changes in binocular vision.   In my experience,
this sensorimotor reaction which I will call anomalous movements (a.m.), is more
deeply rooted in long standing strabismus and when the a.r.c. is present is more
deeply rooted at the filter test previously described.   For this reason and
because of the fact that by appropriate exercises we can weaken or even make
these a.m. disappear (Bagolini, 1966; Adelstein and Cuppers, 1970; Bagolini,
1967), I believe they are an expression of a sensorimotor adaptation to the
angle of deviation rather than the cause of the angle of deviation.   The a.m.
are convergent movements when elicited by base out prisms but, also, though to a
lesser degree, they may become divergent movements or vertical movements when
base in or vertical prisms are placed in front of one eye (Campos and Zanasi,
1978).   This behavior strongly suggests that a.m. are fusional by nature. The
difference between these a.m. and normal fusional movements is related to the
time these a.m. take to show up in comparison to normal fusional movements. The
normal fusional movements are quick enough to be seen with the naked eye. The
a.m. are very slow.   Anomalous movements cannot be seen, but they can be
inferred by the fact that measuring the angle of strabismus using the cover-test
we note a.m. increase in a time that goes from a few minutes to several hours.
We cannot see them just as we cannot see the slow movement of the hands of a
clock.

The aim of a.m. seems to be to restore an anomalous binocular vision interrupted
by prisms, bringing the retinal images again over anomalous corresponding
retinal points.   Incidentally, Ogle and Prangen (1953) have demonstrated a rapid
and a slow component in normal fusional movements, a concept shared by Schor
(1983).   Are a.m. an expression only of the slow component of fusional
movements?

From a practical point of view, it is important to realize how strongly a.m. may
develop in various patients. The measurement of their strength is achieved by
finding the maximum prism the patient is capable of compensating for by
overconverging. By steps of 10 prism diopters, first the angle of deviation is
corrected and then overcorrected if the angle continues to increase. The prism
increment by steps of 10 diopters is continued until it is possible to find a
prism that is so powerful as to not cause compensation. Fresnel prisms are
usually used for this test. For each step a maximum period of observation of 2
hrs. is sufficient for those cases that do not compensate for the prism
correction or overcorrection in less time.   The increase in the angle of
deviation is detected by the cover-test. We found the following possibilities:
1) no prism correction or even undercorrection is compensated for (this means
that no a.m. have developed);

2) the patient is able to compensate only for a prismatic undercorrection of the angle of deviation;

3) the patient is able to compensate for the full prismatic correction of the angle deviation;

4) the patient is able to compensate even for strong prismatic overcorrection of up to 60 diopters and more of overcorrection (it is evident that in this last case a.m. have reached remarkable strength);

5) the prismatic correction in a few cases (usually postoperative) may cause a decrease in the angle of deviation.

This progressive prism compensation test (p.p. test) gives a fairly good idea of the strength these a.m. have reached. Figure 3A exemplifies a case of microstrabismus which could compensate, though partially, for both a 20 and a 40 diopter overcorrection of the angle of esotropia. Figure 3B shows another microstrabismus case which could compensate for 20 diopters of overcorrection but not for 40 diopters of overcorrection. The second case has weaker a.m.

It may be interesting to see how cases with positive results from the p.p. test may react to surgery. The effect of surgery on the position of the retinal images is similar to that obtained using prismatic correction. Jampolsky (1971), using the P.A.T. test, made the important statement that patients with a positive P.A.T. test may react less efficiently to surgery. The P.A.T. test, however, indicates only if a.m. are present but does not attempt to measure this strength.

The p.p. test was performed on 61 esotropic patients wearing the full hypermetropic correction, with angle deviations ranging from 12 to 22 diopters of deviation for distant vision. All patients had good visual acuity and had no impairment of rotation in both eyes. In all patients, a 4 to 5 mm recession of one medial rectus was performed in the non-dominant eye. The cases that post-operatively developed normal binocular vision were not included in this group. In Fig. 4 the surgical results plotted against the degree of positivity of the p.p. test are reported. In the vertical axis the percentage of postoperative angle decrease is reported. The horizontal axis shows the cases having no a.m. on the left side. Moving toward the right, the cases having progressively stronger a.m. are reported through to those cases that compensated for 60 or more prism diopters.

It has been statistically proven (p 0.001) that less satisfactory in the sense of undercorrection, were obtained when a.m. were more strongly developed. In 65 more cases with large angle strabismus a bilateral medial rectus recession was performed and the results were the same. The surgical results were less satisfactory when the p.p. test was highly positive.

In summarizing, there are purely sensory adaptation phenomena to strabismic deviation, such as suppression and a.r.c. There is also a sensorimotor phenomenon believed here to be an adaptational reaction to the angle of deviation. This phenomenon is probably fusional in nature and is called here with the term of anomalous (fusional) movements (a.m.). The aim of a.m. is probably that of bringing retinal images over anomalous corresponding retinal points. Independently from their interpretation, it is possible to state:

1) a.r.c. is an expression of a variation of retinal spatial localization;

2) a.m. is an expression of a variation of retinal motor value;

3) both a.r.c. and a.m. are phenomena present only in binocular vision.

From the practical point of view, it is important to measure the strength acquired by these a.m. This can be done by using progressive prisms (p.p. test) and to see what amount of prism the esotropic patient is able to compensate for. When a.m. are strongly developed, they constitute an important drawback to surgical alignment of the eyes. It is important to realize that when a.m. are present, they are always accompanied by well-rooted sensorial anomalies and normal binocular vision cannot usually be obtained. Surgery is then performed only for esthetic purposes.

CONCLUSION

Sensory motor adaptation has been studied by examining the behavior of patients with convergent strabismus to prismatic correction of their angle deviation. There are cases which compensate, by increasing their angle deviation, for an amount of prisms much greater than their deviation. There are other patients, instead, that do not compensate for prisms and finally a few patients who may even decrease their angle deviation (usually postoperative cases).

Some evidence that these disjunctive compensating movements may be fusional in nature is discussed. They may tend to maintain an anomalous binocularity frequently supported by an anomalous retinal correspondence.

The difference with normal fusional movements lies mainly in their greater slowness. The strength of these sensory motor compensating movements is studied by finding the maximal amount of prisms they are able to compensate for. One hundred twenty-six operated esotropic patients divided into two groups according to their preoperative angle deviation are reported. The postoperative percentage of angle decrease has been plotted against the preoperative strength of these compensating movements. Statistical evidence is given for 61 patients with preoperative small angle deviation showing that these disjunctive compensating movements play an important role in postoperative results. Sixty-four patients unreported here with larger angle deviation behave in the same way.

REFERENCES

Adelstein, F.E. & Cuppers, C. (1970) Le traitment de la correspondence retinienne anormale a l'aide des prismes. Ann. Oculist. (Paris), 203, 445.

Bagolini, B. (1976). Part I: Sensorial anomalies in strabismic patients (suppression, anomalous correspondence, amblyopia). Doc. Ophthal., 41, 1.

Bagolini, B. (1976). Part II: Sensorio-motorial anomalies in strabismus (anomalous movements). Doc. Ophthal., 41, 23.

Bagolini, B. (1967). Discussion of Hugonnier's paper in:Symposium sur l'ambliopie strabique. Liege. Doc. Ophthal., 23, 445.

Bagolini, B. (1966). Postsurgical treatment of convergent strabismus with a critical evaluation of various tests. Int. Ophthal. Clinic, 6, 33.

Bagolini, B. & N.M. Capobianco (1965). Subjective space in comitant squint. Ophthal., 59, 430.

Campos, E. & M.R. Zanasi (1978). Die Anomalen Fusionbewegungen: der Sensomotorische Aspect des Anomalen Binokularsehens. Graefes Arch. Ophthal., 205, 101.

Jampolsky, A. (1971). A simplified approach to strabismus diagnosis. In Symposium on Strabismus. Trans. New Orleans Academy Ophthal., C.V. Mosby, St. Louis, p. 34.

Ogle, K.N. & A. Prangen (1953). Observations of vertical divergences and hyperphorias. Arch. Ophthal., 49, 313.

Schor, C.M. (1983). Fixation disparity and vergence adaptation. In C.M. Schor & K.J. Ciuffreda (Eds.), Vergence Eye Movements, Butterworths, Boston, p. 465.

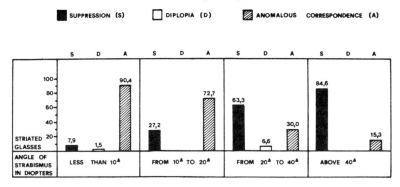

Fig. 1.   Clinical findings obtained in casual seeing with the striated glasses
test in a group of 165 esotropic patients.   The same group was divided
according to the amplitude of the angle of strabismus in prism diopters
into 4 groups.   At the striated glasses test, it is evident that anomalous
binocular vision (harmonious a.r.c.) is frequent in small angle
strabismus, while in large angle strabismus, patients avoid diplopia with
suppression.   More dissociating tests, such as Worth 4-dot and major
amblyoscope, would give different results for reasons explained in the
bibliographical reference 2.

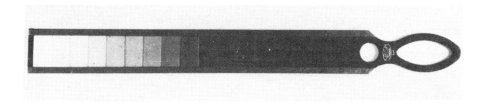

Fig. 2.   A bar of filters useful for measuring the deepness of a.r.c. (when the
patient sees one light crossed by two beams at the striated glasses test)
or the intensity of suppression (when the patient sees the light crossed
only by one beam).   The filters are red because it is sometimes useful to
identify the eye to which the image belongs.

A

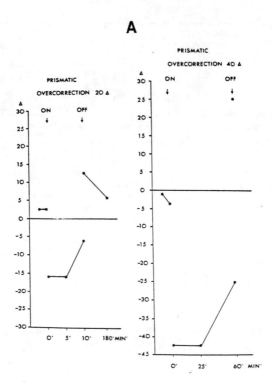

Fig. 3A.   This figure shows a case of microstrabismus.   Dots indicate the angle
of deviation at the cover test read on the vertical axis.   ON indicates
application of base out prisms in front of both eyes.   OFF indicates
removal of prisms.   It is evident that an overcorrection of 20 prism
diopters causes an increase of the angle of strabismus in a few minutes
(read on the horizontal axis).   This increase diminishes slowly in more
than 2 hours.   The same patient compensates well for 40 prism diopters.

B

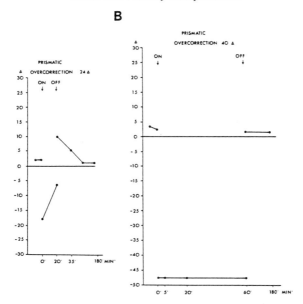

Fig. 3B. This figure shows instead a patient who compensates for 24 diopters of overcorrection but not for 40 diopters of overcorrection.

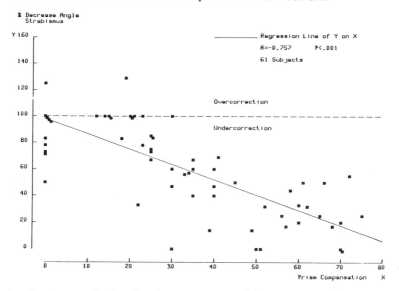

Fig. 4. In the vertical axis the percentage of improvement after surgery is indicated. In the horizontal axis, the preoperative prism compensation from 0 to 80 diopters going from left to right is indicated. The postoperative percentage of improvement, indicated for the various patients by the symbol (■), is plotted against the preoperative amount of prism compensation. Above the line of 100% correction, indicating orthotropia, are located the overcorrected cases.

It is statistically evident (p<0.001) that the greater the prism compensation, the less the surgical correction obtained.

Spatial Localization in Strabismus: a Theoretical Treatment[1]

L. Matin

Department of Psychology, Columbia University, New York,
NY 10027, USA

A. TWO MECHANISMS MEDIATE THE BINOCULAR NONIUS DISCRIMINATION

The presently conventional model for processing of stereodepth information is based on the use of binocular retinal disparity information by binocularly controlled neural units in area 17 of visual cortex. The loss of stereodepth discrimination by the strabismic is reasonably dealt with by this model, although the case is not completely closed. However, processing of the binocular nonius discrimination is not as readily dealt with by the conventional model. The binocular nonius discrimination is a discrimination between the visual directions of two monocular inputs, one to each eye (typically, these are two vertical lines). Since neither of the two items in the binocular nonius stimulus is binocularly viewed, there is no binocularly fused stimulus and so also no binocular retinal disparity information from a binocularly fused target; thus the argument which connects stereodepth and binocular control of cortical units does not apply. Further, there is no other simple reason for assuming that binocular control of cortical units would be central to the nonius discrimination. However, although not enough information is presently available to allow us to state precisely the extent to which losses in stereodepth and in the binocular nonius discrimination parallel each other quantitatively, there is some reason to believe that the relation is a close one. If this is so, it would suggest the presence of a mechanism common to the processing of both.

The extraordinary precision with which stereodepth can be discriminated by the normal individual transforms to about 2 seconds of binocular retinal disparity. The loss of stereodepth in the strabismic can be complete. However, although the strabismic's loss in discrimination of the binocular nonius is severe it is not at all complete, falling only to a level of precision in the range of many minutes or of degrees of arc from the several seconds of arc in the normal individual[2]. Thus, although the tight coupling between the superimposed neural maps of the two retinas at visual cortex area 17 appears to be necessary for stereodepth and for the binocular nonius' normally high precision, the relation between the visual directions of stimuli to the two eyes continues to be perceived when these binocular connections are likely to be sparse or

---

[1] Supported by NEI research grant EY 03198.
[2] Measures of precision of the binocular nonius are sparse in the published literature. For the normal observer the best values reported are 20 seconds of arc of binocular retinal disparity at 1º retinal eccentricity, growing to 2 minutes at 12 degrees eccentricity (Ogle, 1950). Where values are given for (Footnote 2 continued at bottom of next page.)

absent. But if binocular connections are sparse or absent, the mechanism
remaining to mediate the binocular nonius discrimination in the strabismic
does not depend on the integrity of binocular control of units in area 17.

Although the question of how an intact area 17 contributes to the binocular
nonius discrimination (and so how the loss of binocular connections contributes to the deterioration of the binocular nonius discrimination) can be
dealt with by an extension of the conventional model focused on the neuro-
anatomy and neurophysiology of visual cortex, such an extension will not be
developed here. Instead, the present note focuses on delineation of the
second mechanism inferred above. Although the ability of such a second mechanism to guide the binocular nonius discrimination is crude relative to the
precision that has been lost in conjunction with the loss of stereodepth, it
is significant both for the light it can throw on localization in strabismus
and for what it can tell us about spatial localization in the normal observer.

B. ARC AND THE LOSS OF BINOCULAR CONTROL IN STRIATE CORTEX

The functional adaptation to the strabismic's vergence deviation must center
about dealing with two disparate pieces of information regarding the location
of an object arising from a visual projection system whose anatomy and
physiology suggest that it was designed to yield only one perceived location
for each visual object. One form which this could take is anomalous retinal
correspondence (ARC), a condition in which it is said that the directional
values associated with stimulation of the two retinae are transformed so as to
more closely correspond to the pairing of actual locations stimulated by a
single object when the strabismic deviation is in force. ARC has been
considered to be a consequence of a shifting of cortical connections between
the maps of the two retinae so that, for example, in harmonious ARC, if the
vergence deviation is X degrees the resulting shift of connections between the
two monocular cortical maps would be X degrees. But if binocular connections
in striate cortex do not exist in strabismus who manifest loss of
stereodepth, as the conventional model suggests, then ARC cannot be due to a
shifting of the nonexistent connections. It will be more reasonable to search
elsewhere for the basis of ARC; the model below will suggest a basis.

C. OUTLINE OF A MODEL FOR SPATIAL LOCALIZATION IN STRABISMUS

The considerations (above) regarding the binocular nonius discrimination and
----

(Footnote 2 continued from previous page.)
the strabismic in visual angle units they are invariably much larger than
this (at best in the many-minute range; more often in the degree range). Some
workeres have flashed the nonius targets alternately and required the observer
to set the direction of apparent motion to vertical, indicating that this is
desirable (possibly necessary) in order to obtain reliable nonius settings by
the stabismic (Boucher, 1967; Flom, 1980). Precision for some strabismics is
not different than for the normal observers in the same study (Flom, 1980).
But Flom (1980) also notes that some previous workers found the perceptions
of strabismics in the nonius uncertain, and quotes Ogle as saying "...the
subjects are so indefinite as to what or how they see objects where precise
determination is necessary." The detailed empirical picture is in part
complicated by the variations in deficit among strabismics and by the role of
variable vergence movements. In addition, differences in structure and
visibility of the background employed during measurement are also likely to
play a role. Nevertheless, there is no indication that strabismics with
substantial stereoloss will be capable of nonius discriminations with
precisions of 20 seconds under any conditions, even after removing the effect
of variable vergence movements either by image stabilization or by measurement
and calculation, and some reason to believe that they will not.

ARC converge on the support of a model for dealing with some essential aspects of spatial localization by both the strabismic and the normal observer. The essentials of this model will be briefly outlined in terms of three statements. The main reasons for proposing the model are described in the next section: (1) "Visual patterns" are developed and passed on to perception through a "pattern processor" that consists of a series of stages beginning with area 17. (2) Eye position information (EPI) is combined with pattern information (RI =retinal information; indicating derivation of visual patterns from light at the retina) after the neural representation of the visual pattern emerges from the pattern processor; perception of the pattern only occurs in a stage following the point at which output of the pattern processor is combined with EPI. (3) Binocular combination of pattern information occurs in area 17. If binocular control of units in area 17 is lost, binocular formation of visual patterns is not possible. Instead, each monocular RI is passed through a separate monocular pattern processor and separately combined with an EPI signal. EPI signals can be derived from different sources for the two eyes and thus differ in magnitude and consequent influence on localization.

When binocular control of units in area 17 is available as in the normal, nonstrabismic individual, the model indicates that the binocular nonius stimulus will emerge from the pattern processor as a single binocular visual pattern; EPI will be combined with this binocular pattern only after its emergence from the pattern processor. For this case, any variations in EPI will have no influence on the binocular nonius discrimination since such variations will influence localization of both lines in the binocular pattern equally and leave the difference in perceived location between them unchanged.

However, when binocular control of units in area 17 is absent as in (the present extreme version of) the strabismic observer, the model indicates that the output of each of the two monocular processors is separately combined with an EPI signal. The difference in the results of the two combinations yields the material on which the binocular nonius discrimination is based. As noted above, in this case it is possible for a different EPI signal to be combined with each of the two different outputs from the two monocular pattern processors. Any variation between the two EPI signals would yield a corresponding variation in the difference between the two monocular signals that are compared in the binocular nonius discrimination -- a variation that cannot occur for the normal individual for whom there is only a single binocular pattern to be combined with the EPI. This EPI-based variation in the difference between the two monocular signals generates a similar variation in the offset perceived in the binocular nonius discrimination and will be measured experimentally as a decrease in its precision.

The model thus generates a difference in precision of the binocular nonius discrimination between the normal individual and the individual who is deficient in binocularity in area 17. In order for this difference to correspond quantitatively to that observed between normals and strabismics, three things should be true: (1) Discriminations of location within an output of the pattern processor should be at least as precise as the binocular nonius discriminations of normal individuals. (2) There should be an empirical way of deciding whether EPI involved in localization with one eye is the same as EPI involved in localization with the other eye; the evidence should indicate a common EPI for the two eyes in the normal observer and different EPIs for at least some strabismics. (3) The variations between EPI signals to the two monocular systems of strabismics should be quantitatively related to the decreased precision of the binocular nonius discrimination by strabismics in comparison to normal observers. Reasons for believing that the three conditions do hold are described in the next section.

D. BASIS FOR THE MODEL

This section describes the reasons for believing that the characteristics of the model described in the immediately previous paragraph do hold:

1. The pattern processor assumed by the model is sufficiently precise

The monocular discrimination of direction of vernier offset reaches a precision of 2 seconds of arc. Since the stereodepth discrimination also reaches a level of precision that translates into 2 seconds of arc of binocular retinal disparity, it is reasonable to think that stereoscopic acuity is based on the same properties of the matrix of monocular connections that underlies the precision of monocular vernier acuity. But the similarity of the limits of precision for the monocular vernier and the stereodepth discriminations for the normal observer strongly implies that the matrix of binocular connections involved in producing the binocular result perceived in depth for the normal observer is also as fine or finer than that involved in the monocular vernier discrimination; if this were not so stereoscopic acuity would necessarily fall to lower levels of precision than the precision of the monocular vernier discrimination in the normal observer.

The binocular nonius discrimination in normal observers is normally found to reach a precision that is somewhat less than the precision of either the monocular vernier or stereoscopic depth discrimination. Although the conditions under which the best reported values of the binocular nonius (20 sec.) have been obtained were quite good, they were less than optimal and it is likely that smaller values could be reached. However, it is unlikely, even under the best conditions, that precision of the binocular nonius discrimination can reach the same level of precision as either the monocular vernier or as the binocular retinal disparity involved in steroscopic depth. The gap between the precision of the nonius on the one hand and precisions of the vernier and stereo discriminations on the other hand is probably unbridgeable.

Thus, there are excellent reasons for believing that the output of the theoretical pattern processor proposed for normal observers on the binocular nonius discrimination is precise enough to support the level of precision actually obtained on the binocular nonius by normal individuals. We need not at this point deal with other questions that come to mind regarding this pattern processor such as: what are the details of construction of the entire mechanism controlling the binocular nonius discrimination in normal observers, or: why does its precision not reach the level of precision of the monocular vernier or of the stereodepth discriminations.

2. Visual localization by the strabismic with each eye uses
   different EPI

There is good reason to believe that in normal observers the same EPI signal is normally involved in visual localization with each of the two eyes, but that for at least some strabismics the EPI signal involved in visual localization can be different for each of the two eyes. One aspect of this background is the following: If more than a single EPI signal were involved, perceptual adaptation to the presence of a laterally displacing prism should be possible for viewing with one eye alone without adaptation occurring for viewing with the other eye alone. (This unilateral separability of adaptation would be like that which can be obtained for each of an individual's two arms under conditions for which the perceptual adaptation to a laterally displacing prism is due to adaptation of position information regarding the arms.) However, although some attempts to obtain uniocular perceptual adaptation to the wearing of prisms have been made in normal observers, no such adaptation has ever been reported under conditions in which the actual positional relation between the two eyes was not modified. On the other hand uniocular prism adaptation has been obtained in some strabismic observers (Mann, Hein, and Diamond, 1979). Further, rapid perceptual adaptation of EPI does occur for viewing with the operated eye following uniocular strabismic surgery that produces a changed positional relation between the two eyes (Rogan, Eggers, and Matin, 1983). This result could not have been obtained unless the EPI for

viewing with each of the two eyes of strabismic observers was separately
adaptable.

The separation of EPI for the two eyes of strabismic observers is further
shown by the preoperative results in Fig. 1 which displays the difference
between monocular auditory/visual localization matches in the horizontal plane

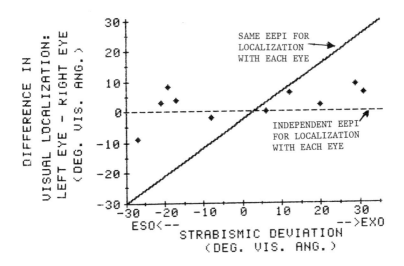

Fig. 1. The left eye-right eye difference in horizontal location of a
         sound chosen by the strabismic observer to match a monocularly-
         fixated target light located at eye level in his median plane is
         shown on the ordinate, and is plotted against the strabismic
         deviation of the observer on the abscissa. Each point is the
         result for one of the 10 comitant observers. When the observer
         changed the fixating eye, both eyes changed horizontal position by
         an angle equal to the strabismic deviation. The horizontal dashed
         line is the locus for which no difference in auditory/visual match
         occurs between the two eyes. The diagonal line is the locus for
         which the difference in match between the two eyes is equal to the
         strabismic deviation (Rogan, Eggers, and Matin, 1983).

made with each eye by 10 comitant strabismics (preoperative measurements;
Rogan, Eggers, and Matin, 1983). During the measurements the observer,
monocularly viewing in complete darkness, fixated the single small target
visible at eye level in his median plane and picked the sound source that
appeared to lie in the same egocentric direction as the visual target from
a horizontal array of loudspeakers (stimulus presented over one loudspeaker
at a time) which gave no visible clue to the observer as to which member
of the array was excited. Since the observer had to turn his eyes by the strabismic deviation in order to change the eye that was fixating (eye patch worn
over nonfixating eye), if a common EPI signal was employed for the auditory/-
visual match with each eye, the localization match with one eye should have
differred from that of the other eye by an amount equal to the strabismic
deviation (diagonal line). If the auditory/visual match was the same with each
of the two eyes, (dashed line), it would imply that the EPI employed for localization with each of the two eyes was different. The results clearly rule out
any possibility that EPI is the same for localization with each of the two eyes.

Thus, the evidence supports the idea that the strabismic is thrown back on a mechanism for comparison of visual locations across the two eyes which is like intersensory discriminations of location (e.g., auditory/visual, limb pointing/auditory, limb pointing/visual). The key point of the comparison is that in an intersensory discrimination of location, local sign information regarding location of each stimulus on the sensing organ is combined with information about the position of the sensing organ relative to its platform on the body, and this combination occurs at a stage prior to the one in which the intersensory comparison of locations is generated. The suggestion implies that the strabismic carries out an "intermodal discrimination" when he performs a binocular nonius discrimination.

3. A quantitative implication of the model

Since precision of a discrimination can be measured by the reciprocal of its variance, for an intersensory discrimination I, the variance S^2_I, should be given by

(1) $$S^2_I = S^2_1 + S^2_2 - 2r_{12} \cdot S_1 \cdot S_2$$

where S^2_1 and S^2_2 are the variances of localization for each of modalities 1 and 2 separately and r_{12} is the correlation between variations in localizations between modalities 1 and 2. Results for intersensory discriminations of location have fitted this formulation sufficiently closely so that, at least to an order of magnitude appropriate to the present theoretical development, we may accept it here. When the correlation between variations in the two modalities is zero, the last term in equation (1) vanishes and the formulation implies that intersensory discriminations of location can be no more precise than the precision of localization with the less precise modality alone. The intersensory case will be dealt with further following a brief consideration of the monocular vernier and binocular nonius discriminations in the context of equation (1).

The variance addition rule given above for intersensory discrimination also applies to deriving the variance of monocular localization from the variances of RI and EPI. For example, for the monocular vernier discrimination: Let variable 1 be the offset of the two lines in the vernier target (difference in RI), and let variable 2 be the difference in eye position information applied to localizing the two lines (difference in EPI), respectively. For this case I becomes the intramodal discrimination of location between the two lines. Since the same value of EPI is involved when viewing two lines with a single eye[3], the variance of the difference between the EPI values applied to the location of each of the lines is zero and the variance of the discrimination equals the variance of RI alone. From this point of view, as proposed by the model above, the high precision of the monocular vernier discrimination is seen to be a consequence of two things: (1) high precision of spatial resolution of the system processing RI, and (2) elimination of the low precision EPI from the equation by virtue of the fact that different parts of the retinal metric of a single eye lie on the same platform in space. That the high precision of the vernier discrimination is limited by the system processing RI and unconcerned with EPI for simultaneously-viewed lines in the vernier target is well-supported by the reduction in vernier acuity with retinal eccentricity.

The analysis of the binocular nonius discrimination in the normal individual

----

[3]Variation in the difference between two values of EPI being equal to zero is indistinguishable from the assertion of the model above that EPI is applied after the difference in RI is taken. Thus, if a single source of EPI is applied after the difference in RI is taken or if two different sources of EPI with identical values are each applied to the separate RI values before the difference is taken, the same result will be obtained.

is identical to the analysis of the monocular vernier case in the immediately
previous paragraph but needs to be concerned with the following additional set
of considerations: Whether the lower precision of the binocular nonius is due
to the influence of uncorrelated eye movements between the two eyes or less
capable projection system processing remains to be determined. [At this
juncture, a strong argument can be made for th influence of uncorrelated eye
movements -- an argument that would need to (and, making use of available
evidence, can be made to) stand up against the fact that the precision of
stereodepth is similar to the precision of the monocular discrimination and
thus better than precision of the binocular nonius discrimination.]

If the system processing EPI is inherently noisy, the use of different EPI in
connection with the RI for localization with each eye would lead to a
nonnegligible value of variance in the binocular nonius discrimination.
Similarly, for the auditory/visual discrimination of location EPI would be
employed for localizing with the viewing eye prior to comparison with the
auditory target. Such a use of EPI would be necessary, of course, since,
although both eye and ears are on a common platform, ocular mobility produces
a change in the portion of the retina stimulated from a given object but no
change in auditory cues to localization. Again, if EPI is inherently noisy, it
would lead to nonnegligible values of variance in the auditory/visual
discrimination of location. (There is ample evidence that proprioception is a
noisy modality and that it is particularly true for EEPI. But space does not
permit the development of this point here.)

E. INFLUENCE OF BACKGROUND IN ARC

The present model, in conjunction with the results of several recent
experiments (Matin, Picoult, Stevens, Edwards, Young, and MacArthur, 1980,
1982; Matin, Stevens, and Picoult, 1983; Matin and Fox, 1986), leads to an
interpretation of ARC. The aspects of those experiments that are central to
the proposed explanation of ARC are:

(1) Experiments with curarized observers

Observers whose extraocular muscles were made paretic by systemically-in-
jected curare exhibited gross errors in perception of egocentric visual
directions that were linearly related to eccentricity of the eye in the orbit
(Matin, et. al., 1980, 1982, 1983). These included errors in the elevation of
visually perceived eye level and of the horizontal direction of the visually
perceived median plane; both kinds of errors reached magnitudes of as much as
30^0. It was shown that these perceptual errors were a consequence of EEPI
taking on values that were appropriate to the normal magnitude of ocular
deviation produced by a command to turn the eyes, but not appropriate to the
reduced ocular deviations that were produced by the extraocular muscles whose
junctional efficiency had been reduced by the curare. The perceptual errors
were measured with the use of several movable target lights in an otherwise
dark visual field.

However, when the experimental room was illuminated normally, the errors of
egocentric visual direction were not manifested by the curarized observers.
Since distances between pairs of visual targets were not misperceived by the
curarized observers in the dark field, for any given eye position the errors
in egocentric visual direction were essentially rigid rotations of visually
perceived space relative to physical space (i.e., a rigid rotation from the
normal relation between visually perceived space and physical space). Thus,
the presence of a normally illuminated and structured visual field
reestablished the normal relations between egocentric visual directions and
physical directions in space for the curarized observer.

(2) Experiments with normal observers

In subsequent experiments (Matin and Fox, 1986) normal observers set a light
to visually perceived eye level in a room whose walls and ceiling were pitched
toward or away from the observer. Errors (as large as 20°) equalled .5 of room
tilt and were directed toward the normal to the tilted wall (away from the
normal to gravity). Thus the influence of a structured visual field on the
"zero point" of egocentric coordinates is not limited to curarized observers,
but is a normally occuring event on normal individuals in normal environments.
Although, for the normal observer in darkness, the elevation of perceived eye
level is solely determined by the output of the mechanism that combines information regarding the direction of gravity with EEPI (extraretinal eye position
information) and with RI, the .5 slope of the results with the tilted room
demonstrates that, when a visual field is present, the field's pitch
contributes equally to the resulting perception.

(3) Visible backgrounds and ARC

Consider a hypothetical case in which vertical EEPI is separable but different
in magnitude for the two eyes of an individual who -- for simplicity -- has no
actual vertical deviation between his two eyes. For a given posture of the two
eyes; this should lead to a difference in monocular settings of a visible target to perceived eye level in darkness that is equal to the difference in EEPI.
But, making use of the result in the previous paragraph, since EPI for each
eye equals the average of the EEPI for that eye with the value based on the
normal to the orientation of a pitched wall in front of the observer, if the
same wall is viewed by both eyes, the final disparity between EPI values for
use in localization between the two eyes will be reduced by 1/2. Thus, viewing
a common visual field with both eyes should reduce the disparity in perceived
eye level between the two eyes by 1/2 relative to the disparity in darkness.

In normal observers a single value of EEPI is sufficient to produce the same
horizontal localization of an object in darkness when viewing with either eye
(within the limits required for matching with audition, for example). But if
horizontal localization in darkness is to be common to each of the two eyes of
the strabismic the values of EEPI must differ by the magnitude of the strabismic deviation; if the same value of EEPI were employed with each of the eyes
of the strabismic, the difference in localization would equal the strabismic
deviation (Fig. 1; main diagonal). As noted above, it appears that the eye position information of some strabismic observers does adapt, bringing visual
localization by one eye closer to that of the other. What has adapted there is
the EEPI component of EPI. But, substantial differences in localization still
are obtained between the two eyes, even for monocular viewing. If a structured
visual field contributes to defining the location in physical space that serves
as the horizontal origin of egocentric coordinates as it does for vertical
location (it does for curarized observers, but the result has not yet been
demonstrated in normal observers: Matin, et. al., 1980, 1982, 1983), a similar
reduction in disparity of localization in horizontal localization should
result between the two eyes of the strabismic when viewing a structured visual
field for whom any disparity exists in darkness. But a reduced disparity of
localization is a measure of ARC. This set of inferences thus also leads to a
prediction of the generally (but not universally) accepted conclusion that ARC
is more frequently obtained the more natural viewing conditions.

F. CONCLUSIONS

The present formulation proposes a model for spatial localization which
suggests that when binocular control of single neural units in visual cortex
is present, as in normal nonstrabismic observers, visually perceived location
of a binocularly presented visual pattern is produced from the combination of
eye position information with the binocularly formed visual pattern. However,
if binocular control of single neural units in visual cortex is lost, as is
likely to be the case for some strabismics, it is suggested that eye position

information is first combined with the monocular visual pattern information
from each eye before any synthesis takes place across the two eyes.

The model thus permits eye position information used by each of eyes to be
different. Two main kinds of predictions are discussed. Both appear to be
confirmed: (1) Comparison of visual directions across the two eyes (nonius
discrimination) by the strabismic who has lost binocular control in striate
cortex should be less precise than in the normal individual because a main
source of variability in the discrimination by the strabismic arises from
variation in the difference in the eye position information used by the two
monocular systems. The model suggests that the high precision of the nonius
discrimination in the normal observer is related to the fact that in the
normal observer the offset in the binocular nonius pattern does not depend on
eye position information. (2) Separate values of extraretinal eye position
information can guide localization in each of the two eyes of strabismics but
not of normal observers. This is in agreement with several findings: the difference in localization between the two eyes of strabismic observers (measured against the same auditory standard) is much smaller than the strabismic
deviation; rapid perceptual adaptation of visual direction occurs to surgical
repositioning of the relation between the two eyes of a strabismic; monocular
wearing of a laterally displacing prism leads to monocular adaptation of
direction by the strabismic but not by the normal observer.

A basis for ARC is developed from the conjunction of the model with findings
showing that eye position information (EPI) used in egocentric visual localization is based on an average from two inputs: (1) visual field structure;
(2) extraretinal eye position information (EEPI). The use of (1) should reduce
the disparity between eye position signals employed by the two monocular
channels of the strabismic by 1/2. The model is thus concordant with the
generalization that ARC is more readily obtained in more natural environments.

REFERENCES

Boucher, J.A. (1967). Common visual direction horopters in exotropes with
anomalous correspondence. Amer. J. of Optom. & Arch. of Am. Acad. of Optom.
44, 547-572.

Flom, M.C. (1980). Corresponding and disparate retinal points in normal and
anomalous correspondence. Amer. J. of Optom. & Physiol. Opt. 57, 656-665.

Mann, V.A., Hein, A., and Diamond, R. (1979). Patterns of interocular transfer
of visuomotor coordination reveal differences in the representation of visual
space. Percept. & Psychophy. 25, 35-41.

Matin, L., Picoult, E., Stevens, J.K., Edwards, M. W. Jr., Young, D., and
MacArthur, R. (1980). Visual-context dependent mislocalizations under curare-
induced partial paralysis of the extraocular muscles. Invest. Ophthalm. & Vis.
Sci., 19, 81.

Matin, L., Picoult, E., Stevens, J.K., Edwards, M. W. Jr., Young, D., and
MacArthur, R. (1982). Oculoparalytic illusion: visual field dependent spatial
mislocalizations by humans with experimentally paralyzed extraocular muscles.
Science, 216, 198-201.

Matin, L., Stevens, J.K., and Picoult, E. (1983). Perceptual consequences of
experimental extraocular muscle paralysis. Ch. 14 in: Spatially Oriented
Behavior. Hein, A. and Jeannerod, J. (Eds) Springer-Verlag, pp. 243-262.

Matin, L. and Fox, C. Elevation of perceived eye level is influenced by
visual field structure.Submitted for presentation at East. Psychol. Assoc.,
April, 1986, New York.

Ogle, K.N. (1950). Researches in Binocular Vision. Hafner, New York.

Picoult, E., MacArthur, R., Young, D., Edwards, M. W. Jr., Stevens, J. K., and
Matin, L. (1980). Relation between visual and auditory maps of space in room
illumination and in darkness. Invest. Ophthalm. & Vis. Sci., 19, 164.

Rogan, M., Eggers, H., and Matin, L. (1983). Pre- and postoperative visual
localization by strabismic observers. Invest. Ophthalm. & Vis. Sci., 24, 83.

Eye Movements and Neural Remapping During Binocular Fusion

M. T. Hyson*, B. Julesz** and D. H. Fender***

*Hy Tech, 1155 N. Verdugo Rd. Glendale, California, USA
**Bell Laboratories, Inc., Murray Hill, New Jersey, USA
***California Institute of Technology, Pasadena, California, USA

INTRODUCTION

How we derive a sense of depth from the separate images of the two eyes is a fundamental problem in vision. While it was once thought that there was a fixed one-to-one relationship between physical points on the retinas and the perceived binocular image, we now know that the correspondence is plastic, subject to dynamic muscular and neural components and altered by the prior stimulation history, eye motions and the state of fusion. This paper explores the eye movements observed during the misalignment of binocular images during normal vision and their relationship to the percepts of depth and fusion. The results show that fusion and depth are maintained in spite of large, constantly changing misalignments of the retinal images caused by eye movements. To explain these observations, we postulate that there is a cortical neural remapping process which, once the retinal images have been fused, rapidly alters the neural correspondence of the images to preserve the percept of depth and fusion despite ever changing physical retinal alignments.

Fender and Julesz (1967) used contact lenses and an optical system to cancel eye motions and present stabilized images that did not move on the retinas. They found that stereopsis of random dot stereograms was possible. Once stereopsis had been achieved with the images in close correspondence on the retinas, the images could be mismatched relative to one another by about 2 degrees while maintaining fusion and the perception of depth. At larger misalignments, fusion was lost. The images had then to be returned to nearly corresponding positions before fusion could be regained. They called this **hysteresis** and speculated that a cooperative process or a neural memory distinct from that needed for fusion was involved. Fender and Julesz moved their images quite slowly but natural eye motions are much faster, moving the images rapidly on the retinas, changing the mapping to the cortex in times as short as 30 ms, the duration of a fixational saccade. Their results suggested that remapping and hysteresis might operate in normal viewing conditions, but such experiments were not done.

Hyson, Julesz and Fender (1983) measured both motor and neural hysteresis during normal binocular vision. This paper summarizes those results. Two vectograph random dot stereograms were placed in registration so an observer saw a fused image and stereoscopic depth. The images were then moved apart in a temporal direction causing an increasing misalignment of the images until fusion was lost. Then the images were moved back together until fusion was regained. The observer saw a percept that was motionless and appeared on the midline despite both target and eye movements so long as fusion was maintained. This implies complex processing of the image by the brain to determine which image changes are movements of the world, the head, or rotations of the eyes. These coarse changes must be distinguished by the visual system if fine differences of depth near threshold are to be seen despite this "noise".

Hyson Julesz and Fender (1983) defined several parameters needed to describe their results. **Image separation** was the angular separation of the two vectographs. It is synonomous with the term "disparity" in Fender and Julesz. In a stabilized image, any image separation on the retinas that allows fusion must be a neural remapping, since images falling on different areas of the retinas and cortex still result in the same percept. Under stabilization, the difference betweeen image position where fusion was lost and where it was regained was then a **neural remapping hysteresis**. In our experiments during normal vision, eye motions often introduced retinal image misalignments. We therefore defined a **vergence error** as a difference between the eyes' vergence and the image separation. This may not be the same as neural remapping because a stereoscopic memory that held depth and fusion information during short duration changes in vergence could make a true remapping unnecessary. Fender and Julesz found evidence of such a memory because they observed that fusion could survive an occlusion of one eye's image for up to 1 second if the retinal image misalignment was small and not near fusional limits. **Neural remapping** was therefore defined to include only those vergence errors that persisted for at least 10 seconds without loss of fusion. This constraint should eliminate the effects of any short term stereoscopic memory by giving it time to fade. **Neural remapping hysteresis** was then defined as the difference between the neural remapping at the time of loss of fusion and at the time of refusion as the images were brought back into closer alignment.

METHODS

The stimulus was a pair of 1000 x 1000 pixel random dot stereogram vectograph transparencies 18 cm square subtending 9.8 degrees with a maximum disparity of 1.2 degrees and eliciting a percept of a spiral in depth seen in front of the background. The vectographs were transilluminated at 315 ± 48 fL by fluorescent lights placed behind a diffusing screen. A lead screw mechanism allowed the vectographs to be aligned and then separated in opposite horizontal directions up to 10 degrees. A linear potentiometer attached to the vectograph frames measured image separation.

Eye movements were recorded to ±2 min arc using scleral contact lenses carrying pinlights on stalks attached to each lens. The pinlights cast shadows on two pair of photomultipliers so that their voltages varied with both vertical and horizontal eye rotations. The observer indicated various perceptual states by pressing three signal buttons grouped near the left hand which produced three voltage levels. A pair of buttons near the right hand activated an ac synchronous motor (forward or reverse) to move the vectographs.

Voltage signals of the four photomultipliers, the potentiometer output and the three buttons were amplified and digitized at 50 samples per second with 8-bit accuracy. The data were processed with a PDP/11 and Tektronics 4001 graphics display. The potentiometer output was scaled to degrees of image separation. The eye rotations were calibrated from data taken while the observer fixated a 5 x 5 array of points which was viewed before and after an experimental session. The centroid of the 25 fixations were selected using the graphics display. Then a second order polynomial of two variables was derived that related the voltages recorded and the known positions of the fixation points. This was applied to the original eye movement data to yield digital data records of the horizontal and vertical rotations of the visual axes of both eyes, in degrees, at each 20 ms interval during the experiment.

An experimental session began with an initial calibration using the 5 x 5 dot array. This was usually followed by three runs where the vectographs were moved slowly apart horizontally from a position of registration until fusion was lost and then slowly returned to their original registered positions. The session ended with a final calibration. While the images moved at a fixed speed of 10 min arc/second, the observer could move the images an arbitrary distance back and forth at will. The maximum image separation was approached carefully in an attempt to find the maximum separation at which fusion could be maintained. At 10 second intervals throughout the experiment, the observer fixated the tip of the stereoscopic spiral image (the point of maximum disparity) or the center of the field and during each fixation, pressed the high, medium or low voltage button to indicate strong fusion and percept of depth, fusion with weak percept of depth or loss of fusion, respectively. Between fixations of the spiral's tip the observer scanned the pattern freely. The data recorded where the eyes were looking at all times ensuring that the observer followed this protocol.

RESULTS

Figure 1 shows a run from observer C for some 300 seconds. The top trace shows the vergence of the visual axes. This was calculated as V = L - R where L and R were the left and right eye rotations, respectively. L and R were measured from the original positions of the visual axes when the vectographs were in register. An observer with a 65 mm interocular distance needed a convergence of 3.6 deg to fuse the background of the registered images. This value should be added to the values in the diagrams if the true vergence of the eyes is desired. The traces contain spikes, some of which are saccades and others blinks. The middle trace, vergence error, E, was calculated as E = V - I where V is the vergence and I is the image separation. The equation defines an overly converged position as positive. The bottom trace shows the image separation between the vectographs during the run.

In the period from 0 - 160 s, vergence error varied about zero with a period of 2.5 seconds and an amplitude of about 1 deg. For the period indicated by the heavy bar, vergence error oscillated about 18 times, often exceeding 2 deg for at least 10 s, showing that neural remapping occured. Vergence

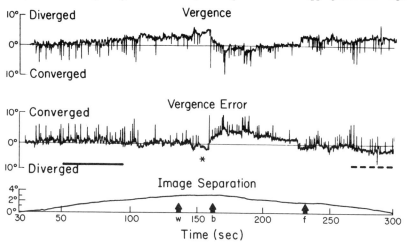

Fig. 1. Vergence and vergence error during the separation of a stereo pair. Top: vergence showing the visual axes diverge to follow the targets. Middle: vergence error, positive values mean the images were separated farther than the visual axes. A heavy bar marks oscillations of vergence error. Long periods of neural remapping are marked * and with a dashed line. Bottom: image separation. Arrows (w, f, b) mark weak depth percept, break of fusion, and refusion respectively.

returned to zero at about 160 s when fusion was lost but took 10 s to do so. Fusion was regained at about 230 s as the images were moved back closer to registration. This is associated with a rapid change of vergence of about 4 degrees. The arrows and letters (w, b and f) in the lower trace indicate when the percept was that of weak depth, loss of fusion and refusion, respectively. Note that the observer's responses occured about 6 seconds after obvious changes of vergence, showing there was a large delay before changes in vergence and fusion were perceived.

Figure 2 shows a vergence error record for observer C on at an expanded scale. The upward pointing spikes are caused by blinks. The record shows several rapid changes of vergence that we call vergence saccades. The vergence changed when the observer voluntarily looked from the spiral's tip to the background, a change of disparity of about 2 deg, roughly the same magnitude as the vergence saccades. These fast changes of vergence are unlikely to be the result of occulomotor errors, which are only a few minutes of arc (St-Cyr and Fender 1969). The vergence saccades deviated from and then returned to a baseline at a vergence error about 2 deg overconverged. Kowler and Steinman (1979) observed that voluntary monocular fixation drifted in the direction of the next position of a predictably jumping target. Our results show that vergence also drifted in a direction that anticipated the next vergence saccade (marked by an arrow) suggesting that the vergence changes were anticipated and might have a similar voluntary component.

Figure 3 shows the data of Fig. 1 plotted as vergence error vs image separation for the entire 300 second run. Time is not represented explicitly. In these diagrams, if the eyes' vergence remained at its original value, the data would lie along the diagonal line in the diagram whereas if the vergence error were always zero, the data would lie on the horizontal axis. Actual trajectories were more complex. The trajectory has several phases, marked by the labeled arrows in Fig. 3 and schematized in Fig. 4.

Phase-a Tracking. Starting with the images overlayed, the observer moved the images apart 2.3 deg. Vergence error varied erratically around zero, with a maximum excursion of about 2 deg.

Phase-b Increasing vergence error. The observer had fusion but a weaker depth percept. In this case the visual axes were overdiverged. Usually the axes ceased to diverge at this phase, leaving them over converged. Since the vergence error was non-zero for more than 10 s while the images were still fused, neural remapping must have occured. Neural remapping regions are marked by asterisks in Fig. 3.

Phase-c Loss of fusion. In this record, a transient divergence of the visual axes, marked †, was followed by loss of fusion. Vergence returned near its original value, as shown by the record returning to the diagonal line.

Phase-d Search. The vergence oscillated and appeared to hunt as the vectographs were brought back together. At about 2 deg image separation, the magnitude of oscillation and and the vergence error decreased.

Phase-e Refusion. A divergent movement, marked ▼, caused the visual axes to pass through zero-vergence-error and fusion was regained.

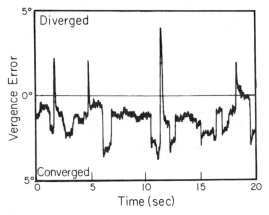

Fig. 2. Expanded vergence error record. Transient movements across zero are blinks, but other rapid changes of vergence error were caused by convergent or divergent saccades. The arrow marks anticipatory vergence drift.

Phase-f Return. Fusion was maintained as the vectographs were returned to their starting points. In this case, the visual axes were overdiverged for the remainder of the run -- another example of neural remapping.

Figure 5 is another vergence error plot for the same observer. Vergence error averaged zero out to an image separation of 6.4 degrees (phase-a). In Phase-b, from 6.4 deg (marked ■), to loss of fusion at 8.4 deg, the average slope of the vergence error increase was parallel to the diagonal (vergence error = image separation) line. This shows that the visual axes had stopped diverging. The images became increasingly misaligned as image separation increased until, at loss of fusion, the images were misaligned 1.9 deg. Hence neural remapping maintained fusion with 1.9 degrees of retinal image misalignment. In Phase-f there was no sustained overdivergence. Rather, phase-f overlayed phase-a. Figure 6 shows a schematic of Fig. 5.

Data measured from time and vergence error plots are summarized in Table 1. The Fusion Lost column is the image separation at which fusion was lost. The next two columns show the maximum neural remappings found in phase-a. The minimum range is 2.5 deg., more than twice the disparity of the target. Therefore, some parts of the images were misaligned by at least 1.3 deg yet fusion and depth were seen. In other runs and observers even larger misalignments were tolerated. Maximum Tracking Angle is where the visual axes ceased to diverge and marked the end of phase-a. Since the eyes were converged 3.6 deg when the images were registered at the beginning of the run, it will be seen that only one observer tracked the vectographs to a point where the visual axes were parallel and only once tracked to 2.8 deg beyond parallel.

The magnitude of neural remapping at loss of fusion differed from the neural remapping at refusion. Since refusion always occured when vergence error (and remapping) were zero, the Neural Hysteresis (last column) is the maximum neural remapping just before loss of fusion and is equivalent to the hysteresis measured by Fender and Julesz under stabilized conditions. Note that both convergent and divergent hysteresis occured.

DISCUSSION

The visual system tolerates binocular misalignments under stabilized conditions while maintaining fusion and extracting depth information. Fender and Julesz (1967) found that for 3.4 deg square random dot targets, 1.9 deg was tolerated. But what of normal vision? Would normal scanning motions improve or detract from this tolerance? Stabilized vision is such a strange condition that any measurements should probably be checked in normal vision as well. Using 9 deg random dot sterograms, we found an extended Panum's area in normal vision.

We found a neural remapping of binocular correspondence that can maintain fusion in the face of large retinal image mismatches. A short term binocular memory could maintain fusion by simply ensuring that briefly the vergence error was reduced to zero every few seconds refreshing the fusion signal. We find this unlikely since alignment occurs only every 12 to 18 seconds in both fused and

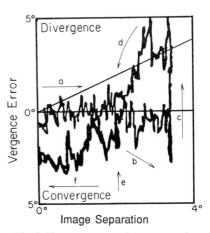

Fig. 3. Vergence error vs image separation trajectory. Arrows mark phases described in the text. Fusion was lost at † and regained at ▼. Some periods of neural remapping are marked by *.

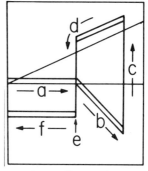

Fig. 4. Schematic of the phases and the vergence error trajectory of Fig. 3.

refused phases. Even so, we accepted only vergence error lasting at least 10 seconds with fusion as evidence of a neural remapping.

Neural remapping occured even with the images overlayed, as the vergence varied ± 3 deg. Even though vergence error often dropped to zero, at times, remappings of 3 deg occured. When the visual axes ceased to diverge as the images were separated, the remapping averaged 2.6 deg, roughly the same as the remapping found in other phases of the run.

After fusion was lost, the visual axes returned to their original positions at the start of the run leaving them overconverged. At about 4 deg of vergence error, the eyes diverged rapidly, reducing vergence error to zero and regaining fusion. A few seconds later the observer reported fusion and strong percept of depth. We conclude that the system knows at 4 degrees of vergence error what magnitude and direction of vergence change is required to regain fusion. In Fig. 5 we see that refusion occured immediately after the vergence error in Phase-d reached the same value as at loss of fusion. Refusion therefore occurs just after previously remapped parts of the retinas correspond. After reactivation of previously remapped areas, a divergent pair of saccades aligns the images. This implies that the vergence system maintains or receives information regarding the positions of the images even while they are unfused.

Vergence is usually acheived by smooth movements alone, but there have been some saccades reported. (Clark and Crane 1978) We found many fast convergent and divergent motions we call vergence saccades. While our data does not have the resolution to show the waveforms in detail, some 2 degree changes of vergence occur in about 20 ms, which is quite fast and in the range of saccadic motions. These fast vergence changes are associated with scanning of a target with multiple depth planes. To our knowledge, no one has recorded binocular eye movements where more than one depth plane was present.

CONCLUSION

The fusional hysteresis described by Fender and Julesz (1967) is of stategic importance to the understanding of binocular vision. Stabilized image experiments have shown a large degree of plasticity in retinal correspondence but few of these results have been corroborated in normal vision. Burt and Julesz (1980) found a hysteresis effect in normal vison but it was only 50% larger than Panum's area. They used dynamically changing random dots which might account for the smaller

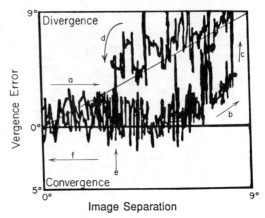

Fig. 5. Vergence error vs image separation for another run of the same observer. Phases marked as before. Fusion was lost after axes overconverged. Loss of tracking marked ●; refusion marked ▼.

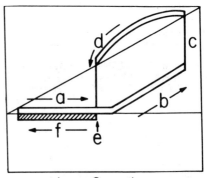

Fig. 6. Schematic of Fig. 5 showing phases of the vergence error trajectory.

hysteresis obtained. Hyson, Julesz and Fender (1983) found large neural remappings in normal vision. Crone and Hardjowijoto (1979) found fixation disparities of 100 min arc with random dot stereograms using nonius lines although these were not bright after-images as suggested by Flom (1985). Schor, Wood and Ogawa (1984) found that fusional limits corresponded a point where the lowest frequency components of the image were 90 deg out of phase.

From this we see that Panum's area changes depending on both the size and complexity of the stimulus. Our limits are similar to those of Crone and Hardjowijoto but smaller than Schor *et al.* This may be explained by the size, complexity and disparity gradients of the stimulus used as suggested by Burt and Julesz (1980). It seems clear that low spatial frequency components are more important to fusion than are high frequencies. Our data show an increased Panum's area consistent with the above studies. We did not explicitly measure a shift of Panum's area although that was possible. Our data also show a fusional hysteresis similar to Fender and Julesz (1967) but larger than that found in other studies. This difference remains unexplained. The small or abscent hysteresis of other studies may be the result of the speed with which retinal misalignments were introduced and the amount of time they were held. Slow movements would allow more adaptation to

TABLE 1. Binocular Eye Movement Parameters

Subject & Run No.	Fusion Lost (deg)	Neural Remapping		Maximum Tracking Angle (deg)	Neural Remapping Hysteresis (deg)
		Convergent (deg)	Divergent (deg)		
A 008	3.4	3.4	4.4	1.7	2.0
015	2.8	5.1	2.3	0.8	1.9
017	3.5	3.2	2.7	1.8	1.7
B 510	0.8	1.3	1.2	0.3	2.2
512	1.4	1.6	2.3	1.0	0.8
532	2.8	2.1	1.2	1.8	2.7
C 542	3.5	2.1	4.6	2.0	3.8*
545	3.8	1.5	3.2	2.3	2.8*
582	5.3	2.0	3.2	3.5	1.4
592	8.6	5.7	5.0	---	3.3*
594	8.3	3.0	1.9	6.4	4.1
D 552	2.6	2.6	3.4	1.4	3.7*
563	7.9	5.7	1.6	0.4	3.0
Mean	4.2	3.1	2.8	2.0	2.6
Standard Deviation	2.6	1.6	1.3	1.6	1.0

* Fusion lost after overdivergent eye motion

changes. Our images were moved slowly and held for minutes at a time in a displaced region.

A change of Panum's area and a changing correspondence of the retinal images that preserves the perception of image relationships like size, depth, and direction a **neural remapping** that compensates for vergence errors, since differing areas of the retina and cortex are processing the images at various times while the percept remains constant. Obviously the correspondence between the retinas, the cortex and the percept are changing. In computer image processing terms, neural location pointers representing where the centers of the images are on the cortex and retinas, at least, must change. For large images and large displacements on the retina, the images will fall on areas with various cortical magnifications. To perceive a constant image size then requires changing the scale of different portions of the image. All these processes make necessary at least a shifting and scaling operation that occurs within a time perhaps as short as the duration of a saccade, but certainly within our criterion of 10 sec. Even a changing Panum's area implies a neural remapping because the region on one retina acceptable as a possible matching region on the other retina is changed.

Why should the visual system need have a neural remapping process? In computing binocular depth, the visual system must first eliminate matching noise which is especially severe in the case of random dot stereograms. Each dot element has a 50% chance of matching any other element in the other eye's image. Before this can be done, the system must eliminate coarse misalignments. As Nelson (1975) has shown "imperfection of the occulomotor system presents an enormous obstacle to successful disparity detection". The constantly changing vergence errors of fixation are about 10 min arc, larger than the tuning of disparity detectors, so a remapping or filtering system is needed. Once these remappings are complete, fine disparity differences can be analyzed. While the results of Schor et al. show the importance of low frequencies in fusion, in our images, many dots at many planes of depth were matched and assigned a location in space. This implies a neural remapping process within the extended Panum's area that simultaneously permitted fine depth detail to be seen once low frequencies were matched.

However, the magnitude of remapping we found is about 3 degrees, surely more than enough for fixation errors. This implies that remapping may have additional functions. Perhaps the remapping allows the exploration of other possible matchings without losing the ones already made, allowing the system to dynamically converge on the best global solution without being trapped by sub-optimal local matches.

Fusion has three basic processes with different time constants. The first is a short term memory that preserves stereopsis in the face of an occlusion of one eye for about one second. The second is the neural remapping which compensates for changes of vergence during intervals of up to 20 seconds between brief retinal alignments. This allows the visual system to extract fine disparity features on the order of seconds of arc in the face of vergence variation of degrees. Third, we find that vergence saccades, initiated with the images some 4 deg misaligned can place the retinal images in correspondence after almost 2 minutes of diplopia. This may imply a longer term memory for at least low spatial frequencies of the last successful correspondence of the retinas.

We must now rework the concept of Panum's area, the horopter, fixation disparity and the like, realizing that many of these appear to have no fixed neural substrate and are plastic, dynamic and probably arise from cooperative effects among whole populations of cells. Any robust model of stereopsis must account for these results.

ACKNOWLEDGEMENTS

My thanks to Cliff Schor, Merton Flom and Leonard Matin for their thoughtful discussions.

REFERENCES

Burt, P. and Julesz, B. (1978). Extended Panum's fusional area for dynamic random dot stereograms. Presentation at ARVO, Sarasota, FL. Apr. 30-May 5.
Burt , P. and Julesz, B. (1980) A disparity gradient limit for binocular fusion. Science, 208, 615-617.
Crone, R. A., Hardjowijoto, S. (1979) What is normal binocular vision? Documenta Ophthalmologica, 47.1, 163-199.
Clark, M. H. and Crane, H. D. (1978). Dynamic interactions in binocular vision. In J. W. Senders, D. F. Fisher and R. A. Montey (Ed's), Eye Movements and the Higher Psychological Functions. Erlbaum, Hillsdale, NJ.
Fender, D. H., and Julesz, B. (1967). Extension of Panum's fusional area in binocularly stabilized vision. J. Opt. Soc. Am., 57, 819-830.
Flom, M. (1985) Personal Communication.
Hyson, M. T., Julesz, B. and Fender, D. H. (1983). Eye movements and neural remapping during fusion of misaligned random-dot stereograms. J. Opt. Soc. Am., 73, 1665-1673.
Kowler, E. and Steinman, R. M. (1979). The effect of expectations on slow occulomotor control -- I. Periodic Target Steps. Vision Res., 19, 619-632.
Nelson, J. I. (1975). Globality and stereoscopic fusion in binocular vision. J. Theor. Biol., 49, 1-88.
Schor, C., Wood, I. and Ogawa, J. (1984) Binocular sensory fusion is limited by spatial resolution. Vision Res., 7, 661-665.
St-Cyr, G. J. and Fender, D. H. (1969). The interplay of flicks and drifts in binocular fixation. Vision Res.,9, 245.

Absolute and Relative Disparity: a Re-evaluation of Their Significance in Perception and Oculomotor Control

H. Collewijn*, C. J. Erkelens* and D. Regan**

*Department of Physiology I, Faculty of Medicine, Erasmus
University Rotterdam, P.O. Box 1738, 3000 DR Rotterdam,
The Netherlands
**Departments of Ophthalmology and Medicine, Dalhousie
University, Gerard Hall, 5303 Morris Street, Halifax, NS,
Canada B3J 1B6

Binocular vision enables us to appreciate the threedimensional structure of the
world, not only under static conditions but also when we or the objects we regard
are in motion. Although it is well known that a reasonably normal binocular
oculomotor control system is a necessary condition for developing and using
binocular vision optimally, there are puzzling discrepancies between the resolution of depth vision and the precision of oculomotor control. Our main purpose
here is to relate oculomotor with visual data, and to dismiss some of the more
obvious notions on binocular depth discrimination as too simplistic. More
detailed accounts of our work are published elsewhere (Erkelens and Collewijn,
1985a,b,c; Regan, Erkelens and Collewijn, 1985a,b; Erkelens and Regan, in press).

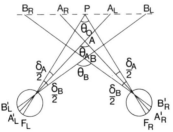

Fig. 1. Definitions of vergence and disparity angles. See text.

A basic concept in binocular vision is disparity as the basis for stereopsis. In
Fig. 1 the lines of sight intersect in P, the fixation point. θ_O is the angle of
convergence. The targets A and B have binocular parallaxes (henceforth called
"target vergences") of θ_A and θ_B. In the experimental situation these targets
were synthesized from dichoptically presented half-images, backprojected on a
translucent screen (A_R, B_R seen by the right eye only; A_L, B_L by the left eye
only; separation by color filters). For the absolute retinal disparities δ_A and
δ_B of the targets A and B with respect to the fixation point we can write:

$$\delta_A = \theta_A - \theta_O \quad \text{and} \quad \delta_B = \theta_B - \theta_O \qquad (1)$$

However, the targets A and B have also a relative disparity δ_{AB} with respect to
each other, which we can write as:

$$\delta_{AB} = \delta_A - \delta_B = \theta_A - \theta_B \qquad (2)$$

In the latter expression neither ocular vergence nor conjugate eye position are involved, and disparity has thus been abstracted from absolute retinal coordinates. What is the role of absolute and relative retinal disparity in perception and oculomotor control?

Experiments on stereopsis usually test relative disparity: subjects discriminate whether one target is closer or farther than a reference target. The reference target often serves also as a fixation point, which is nearly always used in some form to keep the eyes aligned and properly verged. A first question is whether stereopsis requires the presence of a visible target at point P, or whether the absolute retinal coordinates of a single target with respect to the fovea provide depth information. To test this, one has to resort to the sequential presentation of a single target at various disparities and see whether motion in depth is discriminated, in the absence of any visual frame of reference. Westheimer (1979) performed such experiments, using step disparity changes of single small line targets. Compared to the simultaneous viewing of two lines at different disparities, sequential presentation reduced stereoacuity by a factor of about 10 in three highly trained subjects, raising their threshold for depth discrimination to a disparity – absolute in space, although still relative in time – of about 1 min arc.

This figure seems still quite low compared to oculomotor precision. During voluntary head rotation, high quality recordings of compensatory eye movements have revealed disjunctive components on the order of 30 min arc and more (Steinman, Cushman and Martins, 1982). Even if the lower values found by Duwaer (1982) with afterimage techniques would apply, we should expect to see the world moving in depth whenever we rotate our head. However, during head movements normal observers perceive the world as stable and maintain good stereoacuity (Patterson and Fox, 1984; Steinman and colleagues, 1985). Even during overt oscillopsia due to a maladapted vestibulo-ocular reflex the world is perceived to move sideways, but never in depth.

To avoid a number of complications and possible sources of error occurring with head movements, we further explored these problems in subjects with fixed heads, viewing moving stereoscopic stimuli generated as shown in Fig. 1. Movements of both eyes were recorded with scleral coils, with a resolution better than 1 min arc. Stimulus generation, data sampling and analysis were performed digitally by a DEC PDP 11/10 computer.

In the basic experiment we used a random dot stereogram (size 30 x 30 deg, elements 18 x 18 min arc) containing a concealed central figure (a diamond) with a disparity of 36 min arc relative to the background. Visibility of this figure-background was the criterion for binocular, stereoscopic vision. No other visual references were present. The half-images of the stereogram were oscillated in counterphase with triangular or sinusoidal wave forms at frequencies up to 1.5 Hz and amplitudes up to 5 deg; the latter could be equal or unequal for the two half-images.

Perception of movement
Fusion and stereopsis were maintained as long as the various amplitude-frequency combinations did not raise the velocity of target vergence above a maximum, which varied between subjects (range 6–13.5 deg/s). Only observations obtained below these limits will be discussed. Subjects perceived a constant figure-background depth relation. No motion in depth, either of the stereogram as a whole or of the figure relative to the background was ever seen. When the half images were moving with equal amplitudes, the stereogram was seen completely stationary in space. When the amplitudes were dissimilar, a purely sideways motion of the entire configuration was perceived, without any in-depth component. The perceived velocities were psychophysically quantified by asking the subjects to manually track the perceived motion with an unseen joystick. Binocular percepts were compared with the left and right eye monocular percepts for

similar target motions, presented in a randomized sequence. The binocular percepts of sideways motion proved to be statistically equal to the algebraic mean of the two monocularly perceived motions. The relation was linear in all of 6 subjects with a coefficient of correlation r>0.9 (Erkelens and Collewijn, 1985a). For instance, if the image seen by the left eye was stationary and that seen by the right eye was moving, the binocularly perceived motion was half of that seen with the right eye only. This shows that the rule that the oculocentric direction of a fused image is the mean of the oculocentric directions of the two monocular images, previously described for the static case (Ono, Angus and Gregor, 1977; Sheedy and Fry, 1979) is valid in dynamic conditions as well. In the special case of equal and opposite motion of the half-images the mean direction in direction is zero and indeed no motion is perceived. More complex arrangements (such as motions with 90 deg instead of 180 deg phase shift) proved to obey the rule equally well.

Addition of a stationary reference target (seen by both eyes) to the stereogram half-images moving in counterphase immediately induced strong perception of motion in depth. Unless the reference target was also a large, multi-contoured structure (e.g. a grating), the moving stereogram was still perceived as stationary, and the stationary reference appeared to move in depth.

As a further control experiment, a random-dot stereogram was projected of which the central figure (a diamond) and the background could be moved either together or independently. Changes in relative disparity between figure and background induced vivid motion in depth of the figure relative to the background; thresholds for clear motion for 3 subjects were a few min arc (Table 1, column headed Target vergence, Relative motion). When the figure and background of each half-image were moved together as an ensemble, none of our subjects reported any sensation of depth whatsoever (denoted as "none" in Table 1), even when the stimulus oscillation approached and passed the point of fusional breakdown (Table 1, column "Diplopia").

TABLE 1 Thresholds for Motion in Depth of Stereograms (min arc)

Subject	Target vergence			Retinal disparity	
	Relative motion	Absolute motion	Diplopia	Diplopia	Threshold elevation Absolute / Relative
D.R.	2.9	none	85	72	>25
H.C.	3.7	none	211	139	>38
H.S.	8.8	none	151	137	>16

Eye movements
A trivial explanation for these perceptual observations would be the occurrence of perfect vergence tracking, eliminating any changes in absolute disparity. As expected from previous literature on vergence, our eye movement recordings showed that this was by no means the case. Fig. 2 shows a typical example of sinusoidal counterphase motion (target vergence modulated at 0.25 Hz, 6 deg peak-to-peak, maximal velocity 4.7 deg/s), recorded while the subject perceived the stereogram stationary and in two well-defined depth planes. The vergence trace (difference between left and right eye position) shows reasonably good tracking which is fairly smooth, as saccades are largely conjugate. However, gain was considerably below unity and moreover significant phase lags were present. As a result, there was a substantial modulation of absolute retinal disparity (target vergence minus ocular vergence), amounting to about 0.85 deg in both the crossed and uncrossed directions; the peak-to-peak disparity change was 1.7 deg. Such values were typical. Table 1 shows some of the disparity thresholds for diplopia and loss of stereopsis. The threshold varied between about 1 and 2 deg, depending on the subject but not on the stimulus frequency. Within this range of fusion, no subject reported any perception of motion in depth, although this was vividly perceived with relative disparity changes between figure and background of a few min arc (smaller than the fusional range by a factor 16-38; Table 1).

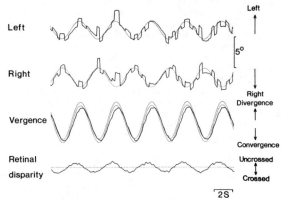

Fig. 2. Relations between eye movements and oscillations of
half-images of random-dot stereogram. Upper two
traces: position of left and right eye (solid lines)
and half-image seen by that eye (dotted lines).
Third trace: Ocular vergence (solid line) and target
vergence (dotted lines) of background (upper curve)
and figure (lower curve). Bottom: absolute retinal
disparity changes caused by vergence tracking error.

At this point the conclusion seems inescapable that for large patterns absolute
disparity changes are not a cue for motion in depth. Only changes in relative
disparity between two visual features or configurations lead to the perception
of relative motion in depth.
A special case seems to be formed by single dot or line targets. We did additional experiments using such targets and confirm Westheimer's (1979) finding that
unreferenced disparity changes of a small, foveal target can be perceived as a
change in distance. However, this perception is degraded compared to the one
based on relative disparity: (1) the threshold is elevated (in our measurements
up to 7x in terms of target vergence; about 3x in terms of retinal disparity
after correction for vergence), (2) thresholds were close to the point of fusional loss for these small targets, (3) even at its strongest, the sensation was
far weaker than when a reference target was present.

We tried to bridge the gap between single and multi-dot targets by using circular multi-dot targets (diameter 28 deg), in which a central dot could be surrounded by a blank annulus of variable width. Two such identical patterns were
shown dichoptically and target vergence was modulated, without any other visual
reference. Without a blank annulus, or when surrounded by a blank annulus of
radius 0.6 deg, a central dot never appeared to move in depth for any stimulus
oscillation amplitude. When the radius of the blank annulus was increased beyond
1-2 deg and oscillation amplitude was raised to just below the point of fusional
breakdown, the central dot appeared to move weakly in depth relative to the surrounding dots. This suggests that the (weak) motion-in-depth sensation elicited
by changes in absolute retinal disparity of a single dot is suppressed by a
lateral interaction of coherently moving neighboring dots, as soon as these are
closer than 1-2 deg.

The control of vergence
Although absolute disparity is not used as a perceptual cue, it does drive
vergence. It is fairly obvious that this must be the case, since proper aligning
of the lines of sight can be achieved only on the basis of retinal coordinates
with the fovea as the origin. It is also clear that absolute disparity must
drive vergence over a reasonably wide disparity range, extending beyond the
perceptual fusional range, in order to be useful.

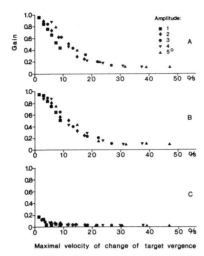

Maximal velocity of change of target vergence

Fig. 3. Mean gain of ocular vergence of 4 subjects as a
function of maximal target velocity, for different
amplitudes. A: stereogram with edges visible; B:
stereogram with edges masked; C: non-fuseable half
images.

Our experiments give some impression of this range for large random-dot stereograms, moving in counterphase. When the half images were moved fast enough to
drive absolute retinal disparities beyond the fusional range, there was no dis-
continuity in the vergence output. As shown in Fig. 3A, vergence gain could be
well described as a uniform function of the maximal velocity of target vergence,
independent of the amplitude. Gain declined progressively with the increase of
velocity, but showed no break in the range around 10 deg/s, above which fusion
was lost. Remarkably, it did not fall to zero even for velocities of almost
50 deg/s. Phase delays were proportional to frequency and well accounted for by
an average delay of 210 ms.

The stereograms offered a unique opportunity to test whether vergence was
driven by features that were easily recognizable monocularly, i.e. the edges
of the pattern, or by the coherent internal structure. Fig. 3B shows similar
data obtained when the vertical, moving edges of both half-images were con-
ceiled by stationary masks. The oculomotor results were exactly as in the
measurements shown in Fig. 3A. This means that vergence was driven by the internal, coherent structure of the stereogram. This was further shown by the
use of non-fuseable half images. One half-image of the stereogram was replaced
by a vertical grating, and the same motion stimuli were applied. Of course,
fusion was absent over the whole velocity range, and not only above 10 deg/s.
However, the difference in oculomotor output with the complete stereogram was
striking (Fig. 3C). Virtually no driving of vergence was obtained, although
edges were visible and both eyes received opposite, large field motion stimuli,
either of which was followed alternatingly by conjugate eye movements, in
parallel with the changes in retinal rivalry. These findings suggest that the
vergence system is driven by corresponding features, even when these have a too
large disparity for perceptual fusion. This implies the existence of a coarse
correlating system with primarily a motor function. Possibly, cortical neuronal
sets such as the "near" and "far" neurons described by Poggio and Fischer (1977)
in the monkey are involved. Although our findings seem to conflict with Westheimer and Mitchell's (1969) finding of vergence responses induced by dissimilar
targets, a real comparison is impossible because they used small, distinct

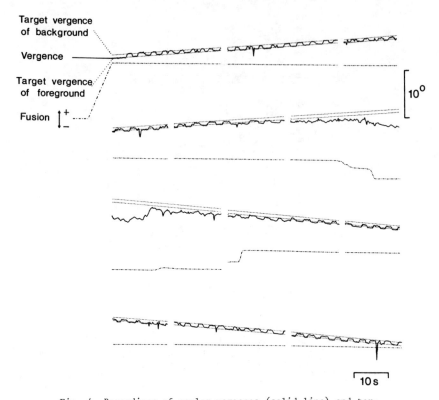

Fig. 4. Recordings of ocular vergence (solid line) and target vergences of figure (lower dotted line) and
background (upper dotted line) of a random dot
stereogram of which the half-images were first
pulled slowly apart beyond the limit of divergence,
and then converged again. Fusion signalled by
stripe-dot line (halfway positions indicate border-
line fusion.

targets whereas we used large, overlapping, multi-contoured patterns. Clearly,
this point deserves a closer investigation.

Another argument for an extended working range for vergence is found from experiments in which half-images of a random-dot stereogram are slowly pulled
apart, beyond the limits of divergence. Fig. 4 shows an example, in which the
subject was instructed to alternate fixation between the figure and the background. Presence or absence of fusion (stereopsis) was signalled by the subject
(lower traces). During target divergence (at 3.7 min arc/s) the subject followed
the figure and background until the limit of divergence was reached. From then
on, the subject first could no longer correctly fixate the background (which had
the larger divergence); subsequently he stopped the alternating fixation movements but continued to see the figure fused, until vergence error (absolute
disparity) exceeded 1-2 deg, when fusion was lost. Disparity continued to increase due to further target separation and divergence relaxed somewhat.
During the return phase, divergence was suddenly restored to its maximum when
the disparity had decreased to about 4 deg. As a result, disparity was quickly
reduced to the limits of the fusional range; complete fusion with recovery of

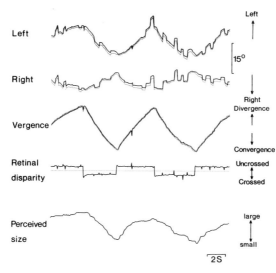

Fig. 5. Perceptual and oculomotor response to open-loop
steps of stabilized half-images of random-dot
stereogram. Upper two traces: position of left and
right eye (solid lines) and (retinally stabilized)
target, seen by that eye. Third trace: ocular vergence (solid line) and target vergence (dotted
line). Fourth trace: imposed steps in absolute disparity; sensitivity 5x higher than in upper traces.
Lower trace: perceived changes in size of stereogram.

the alternating fixation of figure and background was reached only somewhat
later. The return phase showed exactly the same correspondence between eye position and target position as the divergent phase. In our opinion, all deviations
of vergence from correct tracking with maintained fusion are accounted for by
the fusional zone of 1-2 deg; we found no convincing evidence for neural remapping or hysteresis in the vergence system, as proposed by Hyson, Julesz and
Fender (1983); see Erkelens and Collewijn, 1985c.

Perceptual correlates of vergence.
It is an old question whether vergence as such provides an effective cue for
depth. Since in our experiments described above vergence was driven without
vision of motion in depth, the answer seems to be no. However, more stringent
tests were done to test the effects of large vergence movements and exclude some
possible interactions. First, the half-images of the random-dot stereogram were
horizontally stabilized on the retina and vergence was driven open-loop by introducing alternating crossed and uncrossed disparity in steps (Fig. 5). This
elicited triangular vergence motions, so that the shapes of disparity and vergence changes were clearly dissociated. Subjects were asked to signal any motion-
in-depth sensation. None was perceived at any moment, even though vergence exceeded 20 deg. However, perceived size was considerably affected (Fig. 5, lower
trace). During strong convergence, the whole pattern appeared to grow smaller
and dimmer; it expanded and brightened again during divergence. The factor of
shrinkage was informally estimated as about 3 for a convergence of 25°. Such
size changes, reported before by Wheatstone (1852) and Heinemann, Tulving and
Nachmias (1959) were not associated with a sensation of motion in depth.
In a different experiment, the random dot targets were stabilized on the retina
and oscillated at 0.25 Hz through ± 0.5 deg. This induced a large (± 10 deg)

oscillation of ocular vergence. As expected, no motion in depth was seen. Then, the feed-back gain of the stabilization of the surround was either lowered to 0.95 or raised to 1.05 and the same stimulus was applied. This induced similar vergence motions, but in addition a slight modulation of relative disparity of figure vs. background was generated during motion due to the 5% error. All of four subjects reported that the central diamond was now oscillating relative to the background. It was established that the direction of perceived motion was completely determined by the direction of the relative disparity, independently whether it was running in or out of phase with vergence. Also thresholds for the two cases proved to be identical. Thus, we conclude that vergence is not a cue for depth, nor does it interfere with the perception of motion in depth on the basis of relative disparity.

References
Duwaer, A.L. (1982). Assessment of retinal image displacement during head move-
    ment using an afterimage method. Vision Res., 22, 1379-1388.
Erkelens, C.J., and H. Collewijn (1985a). Motion perception during dichoptic
    viewing of moving random-dot stereograms. Vision Res., 25, 583-588.
Erkelens, C.J., and H. Collewijn (1985b). Eye movements and stereopsis during
    dichoptic viewing of moving random-dot stereograms. Vision Res., in press.
Erkelens, C.J., and H. Collewijn (1985c). Eye movements in relation to loss and
    regain of fusion of disjunctively moving random-dot stereograms. Human Neuro-
    biol., in press.
Erkelens, C.J., and D. Regan (1986). Changing target size: its role in the con-
    trol of human ocular vergence. J. Physiol. (London), submitted.
Heinemann, E.G., E. Tulving and J. Nachmias (1959). The effect of oculomotor ad-
    justments on apparent size. Am. J. Psychol., 72, 32-45.
Hyson, M.T., B. Julesz and D.H. Fender (1983). Eye movements and neural remapping
    during fusion of misaligned random-dot stereograms. J. Opt. Soc. Am., 73,
    1665-1673.
Ono, H., R. Angus and P. Gregor (1977). Binocular single vision achieved by
    fusion and suppression. Percept. Psychophys., 21, 513-521.
Patterson, R., and R. Fox (1984). Stereopsis during continuous head motion.
    Vision Res., 24, 2001-2003.
Poggio, G.F., and B. Fischer (1977). Binocular interaction and depth sensitivity
    in striate and prestriate cortex of behaving rhesus monkeys. J. Neuro-
    physiol., 40, 1392-1405.
Regan, D., C.J. Erkelens and H. Collewijn (1985a). Necessary conditions for the
    perception of motion in depth. Invest. Ophthal. Vis. Sci., submitted.
Regan, D., C.J. Erkelens and H. Collewijn (1985b). Visual field defects for ver-
    gence eye movements and for stereomotion perception. Invest. Ophthal. Vis.
    Sci., submitted.
Sheedy, J.E., and G.A. Fry (1979). The perceived direction of the binocular
    image. Vision Res., 19, 201-211.
Steinman, R.M., W.B. Cushman and A.J. Martins (1982). The precision of gaze.
    Human Neurobiol., 1, 97-109.
Steinman, R.M., J.Z. Levinson, H. Collewijn and J. Van der Steen (1985). Vision
    in the presence of known natural retinal image motion. J. Opt. Soc. Am. A,
    2, 226-233.
Westheimer, G. (1979). Cooperative neural processes involved in stereoscopic
    acuity. Exp. Brain Res., 36, 585-597.
Westheimer, G., and D.E. Mitchell (1969). The sensory stimulus for disjunctive
    eye movements. Vision Res., 9, 749-755.
Wheatstone, C. (1852). Physiology of vision. Phil. Trans. R. Soc., 142, 1-17.

Adaptation Processes Resulting from Surgical Correction of Strabismus

G. M. Gauthier*, P. V. Berard**, J. Deransard**,
J. L. Semmlow*** and J-L. Vercher*

*Laboratoire de Psychophysiologie, Université de Provence,
Centre de Saint-Jérome, Rue Henri Poincaré,
13397 Marseille cedex 13, France
**Département d'Ophthalmologie, Hopital Nord,
Marseille, France
***On sabbatical leave from Rutgers University, New Brunswick,
New Jersey, USA

INTRODUCTION

Two main hypotheses exist to explain how we perceive eye-in-orbit position sense. According to the first, proposed by Helmholtz in 1867, the brain receives position information from a signal derived from muscle activation. It is known as the efferent, outflow, or corollary discharge theory. The second theory predicts that the brain receives signals related to the actual length of ocular muscles as detected by tendon organs and spindle-like stretch receptors. Though the specific function of these proprioceptors is unknown, they form the basis of what is known as the inflow or afferent theory.

Both theories predict that, following strabismic surgery, the patient will have problems related to miscalibration of visual orientation and localisation mechanisms. Such problems are seen in patients with ocular paresis (Estanol and Lopez-Rios,1984; Leigh et al., 1982) and in normal subjects wearing magnifying lenses or reversing prisms (Gauthier and Robinson, 1975; Stratton, 1897; Gonshor and Melvill-Jones, 1973). They experience a sensation of instability in the visual world or space inconstancy. After strabismic surgery, space constancy problems might result from the alteration of the normal relationship between retinal image motion, muscle activation and angular deviation. Yet, in the early hours or days following surgery, patients do not report particular discomfort or sensory motor alterations. It is possible that as with the sensorimotor alteration resulting from paretic ocular muscles (Kommerell et al., 1976; Optican and Robinson, 1980; Miles, 1983) these problems recide through activation of appropriate, early-acting adaptive mechanisms.

While sensorimotor recalibration may follow strabismic surgery it is not known if these adaptive processes are based on the same neural mechanisms as those described above. Neurological alteration of these mechanisms, or disruption of necessary proprioceptive signals, may be responsible for the observed failure of the surgical correction in some cases, or the recurrence, after some time, of the abnormal ocular deviation. Hence, surgical alteration of tendon (resection procedure) and muscle receptors (lenghtening loop procedure) may be important considerations in the interpretation and outcome of these cases. To address these questions, we have investigated sensorimotor changes occurring in the visuo-ocular and visuo-manual systems following surgical correction of strabismus. We hope to establish relationships between certain syndromes, surgical procedures, and outcomes. Our approach consists of measuring the subjective appreciation of the straight-ahead direction as indicated by the eyes and/or the hand, before and after surgical intervention.

185

METHODS

The subjective straight-ahead direction for each eye was determined from the angular position of the eye while attempting to fixate an imaginary target located in the saggital plane. The patient was allowed to practice with a real target, a 0.5 deg. spot of light projected on to a translucent screen via a mirror galvanometer. Prior to the test, the patient was requested to make a series of alternate rightward and leftward saccadic movements in order to prevent "anchorage" of the fixating eye on the target after its extinction. The subject was positioned 57 cm. form the screen, the head immobilized by forehead and chin rests. The horizontal movement of both eyes was monitored by DC coupled EOG cupular electrodes. Both eyes were independently calibrated.

The subjective straight-ahead direction as indicated by the hand was determined in a visual pointing task without view of the hand (visually open-loop: Gauthier et al., 1979; Held and Gottlieb, 1958; Prablanc et al., 1975). Three LEDs were presented on a horizontal board at arm's length. One diode was placed in the midline with the others 10 degrees on either side. The targets were randomly illuminated and the patient indicated the perceived position of the target by moving a slide mechanism connected to a potentiometer which in turn fed the computer. Alternatively, "pointing maps" were constructed by asking the patient to point directly at the target, from under the board, with a colored marker. This procedure allowed us to evaluate the dispersion in both anteroposterior and lateral directions. The regular procedure provided only lateral pointing error.

Patients ranging in age from nine to fifty years participated in the eye and hand tests. They were from the Ophthalmology Department of the Hopital Nord in Marseilles. Patients were tested once during the preoperative day, once early in the postoperative day, and once or twice in the following three to four weeks.

RESULTS

Figure 1 illustrates the pre-operative performance of a right-eye esotropic patient in the gaze direction task using the left eye only. Right and left portions of the record correspond to calibration sequences. When the target was extinguished, the patient made large horizontal saccades then directed his gaze toward the position of the previously shown target. The patient fixated the target as soon as it reappeared on the screen and the saccadic amplitude necessary to recapture the target was the measure of error in the appreciation of the straight ahead direction. Ten to twenty similar trials were averaged for each eye sequentially.

Figure 1: Sensing of straight ahead direction as indicated by the eye. From top to bottom: recordings of horizontal target position, target state, left and right eye horizontal position. Left and right portions of records correspond to 10 degree peak-to-peak calibrations. The right eye was patched. During

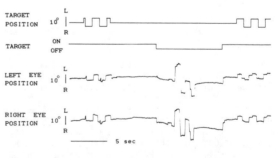

the target extinction period, the patient was told to move his eyes right and left to prevent anchoring of gaze onto the remembered position of the target. When the target was re-illuminated, the Patient recaptured the fixation target with a saccade whose amplitude is a measure of the error of appreciation of straight ahead direction.

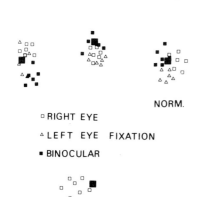

Pointing   maps   (see   methods)
illustrating   the   open-loop
performance of a normal   subject
(upper) and a right-eye eso tropic
patient before surgery are shown in
Fig. 2. Actual target positions are
designated by black squares. The
pointing error for each eye was
taken   as the average over six
pointings for each target.

NORM.

□ RIGHT EYE

△ LEFT EYE FIXATION

■ BINOCULAR

2 C m

STRAB.

2 C m

Figure 2: Sensing of visual target
position as indicated by the hand in
visual open-loop condition. Typical
pointing charts in normal   subject
(top) and in a strabismic Patient
(bottom).

The diversity of the syndromes and the surgical protocols did not permit a
detailed classification of the 24 tested patients. The results were similarly
diversified and not all patients could be definitively classed into a few
categories. However, 16 of the patients could be divided into two groups
defined by the nature of their strabismus, and their pointing errors.

The first class, composed of 11 patients (5 right-eye eso, 3 left-eye eso, 1
right-eye exo, 2 left-eye exo), produced similar errors in gaze and hand
pointing. Before and after surgery, these patients made no errors in either
eye or hand tests when the sound eye was used. When using the strabismic eye
to position gaze before surgery, they made errors of 40% to 70% of strabismic
angle in the direction of the pathological deviation. In the pointing task
these patients demonstrated a systematic error of 25% to 60% of strabismic
error, but in the direction opposite to the pathological deviation. After
surgery, these patients pointed in the vicinity, though with large dispersion,
of the target using either eye. The upper part of Fig. 3 summarizes the average
performance of the patients in this class.

Five patients (3 right-eye eso, 1 left-eye eso, 1 right-eye exo) formed a
second, fairly coherent class. They performed in a similar manner in both eye
and hand tests. Two had alternating strabismus with better than 20/50 visual
acuity. Before surgery, the five patients made no errors, but there was large
inter-trial dispersion in the gaze direction task. After surgery, they made
large errors in the direction of strabismus when using the operated eye. The
lower part of Fig. 3 summarizes the performance of this class in the hand
pointing task showing that preoperative pointing is normal (R1, L1) with both
eyes. After surgery, fixation with the non-operated eye produced no error (L3)
while fixation with the operated eye produced large errors (R3) in the direction
of the previous deviation. The individual error was 20% to 50% of the
strabismic angle.

188   G. M. Gauthier et al.

Patients in these two classes were followed over a one to two month postoperative period. In all but one patient they either refined their performance
(first class) or progressively recovered close to normal visual motor
performance (second class). Adaptation to surgical deviation took place within
a few days, or at most, two to three weeks indicating proper recalibration of
the perceptual and motor mechanisms responsible for sensing eye position and
locating objects in space.

Our data suggest that at least two models apply to the behavior of strabismic
patients in directional tasks such as described above. The patients from the
first group behaved as if the strabismic deviation was caused by an essentially
mechanical factor affecting the resting position of the eye, as represented in
the upper drawing of Fig. 3. When the normal eye looks straight ahead, the
muscles of both eyes are in an equilibrium position and the direction of gaze is
sensed correctly. When the strabismic eye is used to fixate the same target, an
appropriate activation is addressed to the muscles to compensate the
pathological deviation. When this position is attained, the sound eye is
directed to a position equal, but opposite to the strabismic deviation. It is
this compensated position which is sensed as straight ahead. After surgical
rotation of this eye in the orbit, the straight ahead direction is now obtained
in the equilibrium position, and this direction is correctly sensed.

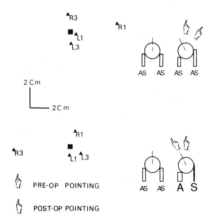

Figure 3: Simple models for
strabismus. Based on our data,
two models may be proposed: a -
pathological deviation appears
to result from mechanical
alteration of the eye resting
position (upper); b - deviation
due to spontaneous hyper-
activation of one (or more)
muscles (lower).

The patients from the second group behaved as if the strabismic deviation was
occasioned by inappropriate nervous activation affecting permanently, and more
or less constantly one muscle, as shown in the lower drawing of the Fig. 3. When
the normal eye looks straight ahead, the other eye is deviated as a result of
the hyperactivation of the affected muscle. (Alternatively, the strabismic
deviation could also result from the hyperactivation of homonymous muscles in
both eyes). When the patient fixates a straight ahead target, a compensatory
activation is addressed to the opposite muscle. The resultant equilibrum
activity is sensed as the correct straight ahead direction. Following surgery,
the actual straight ahead direction is sensed as that corresponding to the
previous resting position of the eye, and the patient tends to make a pointing
error almost equal to the original strabismic deviation. Implicit in this model
is the assumption that position sense is derived either from inflow information
and/or from outflow signals which include the hyperactivity.

CONCLUSION

The analysis of our data is not sufficiently advanced to distinguish between the role of afferent and efferent information in eye position sensing, or to provide details on the adaptive recalibration after surgery. Although it is likely that, as recognized by Steinbach and Smith (1981), tendon organs are necessary for ocular position sensing (as in skeletal muscles: Matthews, 1981), muscle receptors are probably also necessary to provide inflow information matching efferent copy, a key to the maintainance or restoration of appropriate ocular system perception and motor control. We also note that our interpretation of the difference in patient behavior differs from that proposed by Mann et al. (1979) which attributes the difference to the way in which visual space is represented in constant and alternating suppressor patients.

Analysis is still in progress to fit other patients into the two main classes identified thus far, or to develop additional classes based on other criteria. In particular, we are attempting to correlate the effects of surgery as demonstrated by eye and hand pointing tasks with the nature of the strabismus and the surgical correction using criteria such as the action on the sound eye vs. that on the deviated eye, tendon resection and/or recession or muscle lenghtening.

REFERENCES

Estanol B. and Lopez-Rios G. (1984): Looking with a paralysed eye-adaptive plasticity of the VOR. J. Neurol. Neurosurg. Psychiat., 47: 799-

Gauthier G. M., Hofferer J. M., Hoyt W. F. and Stark L. (1979): Visual-motor Adaptation. Quantitative demonstration in patients with posterior fossa involvement. Arch. Neurol., 36: 155-160

Gauthier G. M. and Robinson D. A. (1975): Adaptation of the human vestibulo-ocular reflex to magnifying lenses. Brain Res., 92: 331-335

Gonshor A. and Melvill-Jones G. (1973): Changes of human vestibulo-ocular response induced by vision-reversal during head rotation. J. Physiol. 234: 102-

Held R. and Gottlieb N. (1958): Technique for studying adaptation to disarranged hand-eye coordination. Perceptual & Motor Skills, 8: 83-86

Helmoltz H. Von (1867): Optique physiologique. Masson (Paris)

Kommerell G., Olivier G. and Theopold H. (1976): Adaptative programming of phasic and tonic components in saccadic eye movements. Invest. Ophtalmol. 15: 657-660

Leigh R., Newman S. A., Zee D. S. and Miller N. R. (1982): Visual following during stimulation of an immobile eye (the open-loop condition). Vision Res. 22: 1193-1197

Mann V. A., Hein A. and Diamond R. (1979) Localization of targets by strabismic subjects: contrasting patterns in constant and alternating suppressors. Perception and Psychophysics, 25: 29-34

Matthews P. B. C. (1982): Where does sherrington's muscular sense originate? muscles, joints, corollary discharges? Ann.Rev.Neurosci. 5: 89-218

Miles F. A. (1983): Plasticity in the transfer of gaze. TINS, 6, 2: 57-60

Optican L. M. and Robinson D. A. (1980): Cerebellar-dependent adaptive control of primate saccadic system. J. Neurophysiol., 44: 1058-1076

Prablanc C., Tzavaras A. and Jeannerod M. (1975): Adaptation of the two arms to opposite prism displacements. Quart. J .Exp. Psychol., 27: 667-671

Steinbach M. J. and Smith D. R. (1981): Spatial localization after strabismus surgery: evidence for inflow. Science, 213: 1407-1409

Stratton G. M. (1897): Vision without inversion of the retinal image. Psychol. Rev. 4: 341-360

Effects of Long-term and Short-term Monocular Deprivation Upon Oculomotor Function in the Rhesus Monkey

D. L. Sparks*, M. R. Gurski*, L. E. Mays** and
T. L. Hickey**

*Department of Physiology and Biophysics, Neurosciences
Program, University of Alabama at Birmingham, Birmingham,
AL 35294, USA
**Department of Physiological Optics, Neurosciences Program,
University of Alabama at Birmingham, Birmingham,
AL 35294, USA

INTRODUCTION

This paper presents a brief summary of a series of experiments examining the effects of long-term (LTMD) and short-term (STMD) monocular visual deprivation upon the visual and oculomotor systems of the rhesus monkey. The major goals of the research were: 1) to describe the oculomotor deficits produced by restrictions of sensory-motor linkages during early development; and 2) to examine the electrophysiological and anatomical correlates of observed oculomotor abnormalities. A secondary objective was to compare the sensory and oculomotor deficits to those seen in amblyopic patients. In human amblyopes deficits in the stability of fixation (von Noorden and Burian, 1958; Schor and Hallmark, 1978; Ciuffreda, Kenyon and Stark, 1980; Flom, Kirschen and Bedell, 1980; Schor, 1975), as well as abnormalities in the saccadic (Schor, 1975; Ciuffreda, Kenyon and Stark, 1978), pursuit (Schor, 1875, Ciuffreda, Kenyon and Stark, 1979), vergence (Kenyon, Ciuffreda and Stark, 1981) and optokinetic (Schor and Levi, 1980) oculomotor systems have been observed. The rhesus monkey, with visual and oculomotor systems remarkably similar to those of the human, could serve as an animal model for studying the neural basis of amblyopia if manipulations are found that produce similar sensory and motor abnormalities.

SUBJECTS AND METHODS

This report is based upon findings obtained from 10 monocularly deprived (MD) monkeys (Macaca mulatta). The lids of all MD monkeys were sutured between 8 and 14 days of age and remained closed for either 7 or 14 days for the short-term MD animals (N=5) and for 18-26 months for the long-term MD animals (N=5). Details of the rearing conditions, surgical procedures, behavioral tasks and test conditions are presented elsewhere (Sparks, Mays, Gurski and Hickey, unpublished manuscript).

RESULTS

Informal Testing

Monkeys reared for 18-26 months with one eyelid sutured appeared behaviorally blind when the nondeprived eye was patched. Except for one animal that showed markedly reduced OKN, a pupillary response to light was the only behavior that could be elicited by stimuli presented to the deprived eye. Oculomotor, limb or body movements could not be evoked by moving or stationary visual stimuli (food objects, water bottles, etc) presented in any part of the visual field. The observed behavioral deficits could not be accounted for by optical abnormalities or retinal anomalies.

In contrast to what was observed in the long-term MD animals, oculomotor, limb and body movements could be easily elicited by visual stimuli presented to the deprived eye of short-term MD subjects.

Oculomotor Effects

Optokinetic nystagmus. The effects of monocular deprivation upon optokinetic responses are described in more detail elsewhere (Sparks, Mays, Gurski and Hickey, unpublished manuscript). When visual input was restricted to the deprived eye, 4 of the 5 long-term MD animals failed to produce optokinetic responses (OKN). For these animals, OKN was not present with rotation of the drum in either direction (nasal/temporal or temporal/nasal) at velocities from 10 to 50°/sec, and with stripes up to 15° in width. Normal OKN was observed when the nondeprived eye was viewing the drum. One long-term MD animal displayed slight evidence of OKN when stimuli were presented to the deprived eye. However, even for this monkey, OKN was not seen with nasal/temporal rotation at any drum velocity and eye velocity did not exceed 8°/sec with drum rotations of 30 to 50°/sec in the temporal/nasal direction.

For short-term MD animals with visual input restricted to the deprived eye, drum rotation (in either direction) produced optokinetic nystagmus but the responses were asymmetric. Eye velocity was higher with temporal/nasal rotation.

Fixation. Long-term MD animals did not fixate visual targets when vision was restricted to the deprived eye. When viewing targets with the nondeprived eye, a vertical down-beat nystagmus was observed in both eyes and large drifts in the horizontal position of the deprived eye occurred (see Fig. 1).

Fig. 1.   Instability of the horizontal position of the deprived eye of LTMD animals during attempted
fixation of visual targets. D. Horizontal position
of deprived eye. N. Horizontal position of the
nondeprived eye.

With visual input restricted to the deprived eye, all short-term MD animals exhibited either a vertical (slow phase up) (see Fig, 2A) or oblique (slow phase up and left) nystagmus. Considerable variability in the horizontal and vertical position of the eyes was observed across trials when the animals attempted to fixate the same visual target. Fixation was relatively stable when the non-deprived eye was viewing the target.

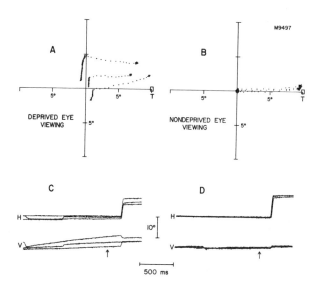

Fig. 2. Typical saccadic movements of STMD animals. The target was presented 10° to the right of the fixation target. Three trials are superimposed in each panel. A and B represent eye movement trajectories when viewing through the deprived eye (A) or nondeprived eye (B). Comparing A and B, note that when the deprived eye was viewing, fixation of the center target (intersection of the axes) was variable, the eyes drifted upward, and saccades were less accurate. C and D represent horizontal (H) and vertical (V) eye position traces for the same trials presented in A and B, respectively. Arrows indicate target onset. Upward deflections of the traces represent rightward (horizontal) and upward (vertical) movements.

Saccades. With vision restricted to the deprived eye, long-term MD monkeys did not make saccades to visual targets presented at any location in the visual field. When the nondeprived eye was uncovered, saccades had normal latencies and normal metrics. Except for the horizontal instability of the deprived eye, saccades appeared to be conjugate.

When viewing targets with the nondeprived eye, short-term MD animals made accurate saccades with normal latencies. When vision was restricted to the deprived eye, latencies were longer, peak saccadic velocity was reduced, and saccades were less accurate. The major deficit was failure of the saccadic system to compensate for upward drifts occurring during the downbeat nystagmus (see Fig. 2).

Pursuit. Under binocular viewing conditions or when vision was restricted to the nondeprived eye, long-term MD animals were capable of performing a smooth pursuit task. Smooth pursuit was not mediated by the deprived eye.

Pursuit responses were mediated by the deprived eye in most short-term MD
animals. However, pursuit gain was lower when the target was traced with the
deprived eye. With target velocities ranging from 5 to 20°/sec, gains ranged
from 0.53 to 0.65 when the deprived eye was viewing the target and from 0.83
0.90 when the nondeprived eye was viewing.

Neurophysiological Findings

Visual stimuli presented to the nondeprived eye appear to generate normal conjugate versional command signals. The burst profile and movement fields of
neurons in the superior colliculus and paramedian pontine reticular formation
are comparable to those seen in normal subjects. Also, stimulation of the
superior colliculus and paramedian pontine reticular formation produced conjugate saccades using normal stimulation parameters.

Surprisingly, during nonconjugate movements (horizontal drift of the deprived
eye), the activity of some cells in the paramedian pontine reticular formation
region was proportional to the position of the deprived eye (Fig. 3). These
cells were not motoneurons innervating the deprived eye since they were

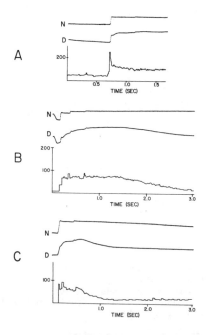

Fig. 3.   Instantaneous spike frequency records of a burst
          tonic neuron isolated in the paramedian pontine
          reticular formation. The activity of the same
          neuron is illustrated for 3 different trials in
          which the time course of the "drift" of the de-
          prived eye differed. It is apparent that the
          activity of this neuron is closely related to the
          horizontal position of the deprived eye.

isolated in the opposite hemisphere. Other cells displayed firing rates proportional to the position of the nondeprived eye (Fig. 4). This implies that there are "left" and "right" eye command signals that are not observed in the normal monkey because versional movements are usually conjugate.

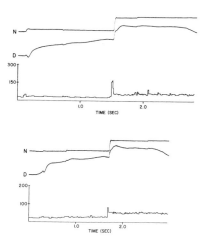

Fig. 4.   Instantaneous spike frequency records of a burst tonic neuron isolated in the paramedian pontine reticular formation. The activity of this neuron is closely related to the horizontal position of the nondeprived eye and is unrelated to the "drift" of the deprived eye.

Recordings from neurons in the intermediate layers of the superior colliculus in short-term MD animals revealed that: 1) the saccade-related burst of activity of some cells was absent when saccades were directed to targets viewed with the deprived eye (Fig. 5); 2) other cells with saccade-related bursts fired less vigorously when targets were presented to the deprived eye; and 3) many collicular neurons increased their firing rate during intersaccadic intervals when fixational "drifts" were present.

DISCUSSION

Unilateral lid closure for 1 or 2 weeks during the first postnatal month produces dramatic visual and oculomotor deficits. The oculomotor deficits are similar to those found in amblyopic patients. With the nondeprived eye patched, short-term MD animals display a marked instability of fixation, an increase in saccadic latency, reduced pursuit gain and asymmetric optokinetic responses - all oculomotor deficits previously observed in amblyopes (Schor, 1983; Flom, Kirschen, and Bedell, 1980). Future papers will explore, in more detail, the adequacy of STMD as a model for studying the neural basis of amblyopia.

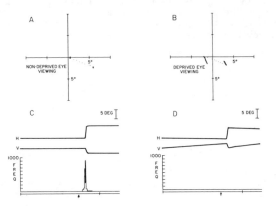

Fig. 5.   The activity of a saccade-related burst neuron recorded in the superior colliculus. A. Saccadic trajectory when viewing through the nondeprived eye. B. Trajectory when viewing with the deprived eye. C. Eye position traces and associated neuronal activity for the trial shown in A. D. Eye position traces and neuronal activity associated with the trial shown in B. Although a saccade to the eccentric target occurred and the trajectory of the movements were well matched, saccade-related activity was not observed when the movement was based upon input to the deprived eye. Arrows indicate target onset. Tic marks represent a time interval of 1 second.

The instability of fixation observed in short-term MD animals with the nondeprived eye patched is associated with an increase in activity of neurons in the intermediate layers of the SC. In normal animals, these cells are quiescent except for a high-frequency burst of activity occurring before saccadic eye movements. This finding, in combination with the recent report of Hikosaka and Wurtz (1985) that lesions of the superior colliculus produce a nystagmus during attempted fixation, suggest that the colliculus plays an important role in the maintenance of stable fixation. Saccadic latencies are longer and the peak velocity of saccades is reduced when visually-triggered saccades are mediated by the deprived eye. These deficits are associated with an alteration in the spatiotemporal pattern of collicular activity: 1) a smaller number of collicular cells discharge before a particular saccade; and 2) the magnitude of the saccade-related bursts observed in those neurons participating in the initiation of the saccade is reduced.

The most surprising result was the finding that in long-term MD animals, in which disjunctive movements frequently occur, some brainstem neurons have firing rates proportional to the position of the deprived eye while other cells discharge at frequencies related to the position of the nondeprived eye. It is usually assumed by oculomotor neurophysiologists that, for versional movements, a single conjugate command is generated for both eyes. However, recent evidence (Snow, Hore and Vilis, 1985; Vilis, Yates and Hore, 1985) suggests that gaze center commands can be adjusted independently for each eye. Also, an unequal dysmetria in the two eyes has been observed following lesions of the medial cerebular nuclei (Vilis and Hore, 1981) and different gain changes in the VOR were measured after unilateral lesions of the flocculus (Ito, Jastreboff and

Miyashita, 1982). Moreover, violations of Hering's law during saccades (Bahill, Ciuffreda, Kenyon and Stark, 1976) have been attributed to independent velocity commands for each eye. Our data add to the accumulating evidence suggesting coordinated, but independent, mechanisms for the control of the orbital position of each eye.

ACKNOWLEDGEMENTS

Supported by NIH Grants EY02293 and EY03039.

REFERENCES

Bahill, A.T., K.J. Ciuffreda, R. Kenyon, and L. Stark (1976). Dynamic and static violations of Hering's law of equal innervation. Am. J. Optom. Physiol. Opt. 53: 786-796.

Ciuffreda, K.J., R.V. Kenyon, and L. Stark (1978). Increased saccadic latencies in amblyopic eyes. Invest. Ophthalmol. Vis. Sci. 17: 697-792.

Ciuffreda, K.J., R.V. Kenyon, and L. Stark (1979). Abnormal saccadic substitution during small-amplitude pursuit tracking in amblyopic eyes. Invest. Ophthalmol. Vis. Sci. 18: 506-515.

Ciuffreda, K.J., R.V. Kenyon, and L. Stark (1980). Increased drift in amblyopic eyes. Brit. J. Ophthal. 64: 7-14.

Flom, M.C., D.G. Kirschen, and H.E. Bedell (1980). Control of unsteady eccentric fixation in amblyopic eyes by auditory feedback of eye position. Invest. Ophthalmol. Vis. Sci. 19: 1371-1381.

Hikosaka, O., and R.H. Wurtz (1985). Modification of saccadic eye movements by GABA-related substances. I. Effect of muscimol and bicuculline in monkey superior colliculus. J. Neurophysiol. 53: 266-291.

Ito, M.P., Jastreboff, and U. Miyashita (1982). Specific effects of unilateral lesions in the flocculus upon eye movements in albino rabbits. Exp. Brain Res. 45: 233-242.

Kenyon, R.V., K.J. Ciuffreda, and L. Stark (1981). Dynamic vergence eye movements in strabismus and amblyopia: asymmetric vergence. Brit. J. Ophthalmol. 65: 167-176.

Schor, C. (1975). A directional impairment of eye movement control in strabismus amblyopia. Invest. Ophthalmol. Vis. Sci. 14: 692-697.

Schor, C. (1983). Subcortical binocular suppression affects the development of latent and optokinetic nystagmus. Am. J. Optom. Physiol. Optics 60: 481-502.

Schor, C., and W. Hallmark (1978). Slow control of eye position in strabismic amblyopia. Invest. Ophthalmol. Vis. Sci. 17: 577-581.

Schor, C.M., and D. Levi (1980b). Disturbances of small-field horizontal and vertical optokinetic nystagmus in amblyopia. Invest. Ophthalmol. Vis. Sci. 19: 668-683.

Snow, R., J. Hore, and T. Vilis (1985). Adaption of saccadic and vestibulo-ocular systems after extraocular muscle tenectomy. Invest. Ophthalmol. Vis. Sci. 26: 924-931.

Sparks, D.L., L.E. Mays, M.R. Gurski, and T.L. Hickey (submitted for publication). Long-term and short-term monocular deprivation in the rhesus monkey: Effects on visual fields and optokinetic nystagmus.

Vilis, T., and J. Hore (1981). Characteristics of saccadic dysmetria in monkeys during reversible lesions of medial cerebellar muclei. J. Neurophysiol. 46: 828-838.

Vilis, T., S. Yates, and J. Hore (1985). Visual patching of one eye produces changes in saccadic properties in the unseeing eye. Dev. Br. Res. 17: 290-292.

von Noorden, G.K., and H. Burian (1958). An electro-ophthalmographic study of the behavior of fixation of amblyopic eyes in light- and dark-adapted state: A preliminary report. Am. J. Ophth. 46: 68-77.

RECOVERY IN VISUO-OCULOMOTOR CONTROL FOLLOWING CORTICAL INJURY

The Effect of Unilateral Ablation of the Frontal Eye Fields on Saccadic Performance in the Monkey

S. -Y. Deng*, M. E. Goldberg*, M. A. Segraves*,
L. G. Ungerleider** and M. Mishkin**

*Laboratory of Sensorimotor Research, National Eye Institute,
Bethesda, Maryland, USA; Department of Neurology, Georgetown
University School of Medicine, Washington, DC, USA
**Laboratory of Neuropsychology, National Institute of Mental
Health, Bethesda, Maryland, USA

INTRODUCTION

The frontal eye fields of the monkey generate neural signals that could provide information for the initiation and guidance of purposive saccades. Three classes of neurons discharge before visually guided saccades: visual cells, which discharge in response to visual stimuli; movement cells, which discharge before purposive saccades but do not require a visual stimulus; and visuomovement cells, which have both movement- and visual-related activity (Bruce and Goldberg, 1985). Electrical stimulation through the recording microelectrode at the site of movement cells yields saccades at thresholds as low as 10uA, and the direction and amplitude of the electrically evoked saccades correlates well with the movement fields of the cells at the stimulation site (Bruce, Goldberg, Bushnell, and Stanton, 1985). Despite this well documented presaccadic activity, frontal eye field lesions have been reported to have little effect on saccadic performance in the monkey. Schiller, True, and Conway (1980) showed that monkeys with bilateral frontal eye field lesions made quite accurate saccades, unless the frontal eye field lesions were combined with a bilateral superior colliculus lesion, in which case the monkeys could not make voluntary saccades beyond a narrow range in the center of the orbit. Schiller and Sandell (1983) subsequently showed that monkeys with frontal eye field lesions could easily make accurate saccades when eye position was perturbed by superior colliculus stimulation in the interval between stimulus presentation and the actual eye movement. The only apparent oculomotor deficit caused by frontal eye field lesions was a mild increase in the latency of saccades.

It would be surprising indeed if the frontal eye fields had no purpose other than to serve as a spare oculomotor command center backing up the superior colliculus, without having some unique function in the control of oculomotor behavior. Since the superior colliculus contains the neural components for the generation of simple, reflexive, visually guided saccades, we postulated that the frontal eye fields would not mediate such simple behavior, but instead were likely to mediate saccades made for reasons more complicated than moving the fovea from one visual target to the next.

METHODS

Two rhesus monkeys (Macaca mulatta) underwent unilateral ablation of the frontal eye fields by subpial aspiration. During the same surgical procedure, they were fitted with a subconjunctival search coil and head-holding apparatus. Surgery

201

was performed aseptically under general anesthesia. They were allowed to
recover for at least one week and were then trained to look at a spot of light
and make saccades from target to target. Eye movements were measured using the
magnetic search coil method. Behavioral control and eye movement sampling at
1Khz were done with a PDP11 computer (Goldberg, 1983).

In the experiments described here three saccade tasks were used. These are
shown schematically in Fig. 1.

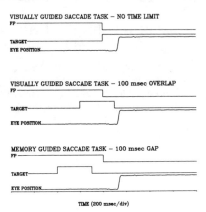

Fig. 1. Behavioral paradigms used in this study. Fixation
point (FP), target, and eye position traces are shown for
each paradigm. Upper position of FP and TARGET traces
signifies light on.

1) Visually guided no-time-limit task: The monkey begins by fixating the central
spot. After 700 to 1400 msec the fixation point disappears and a peripheral
target appears and stays on for the duration of the trial. The monkey must make
a saccade to fixate the new target, and is rewarded either for making a saccade
of the proper amplitude and direction or for fixating the target spot for one
second. 2) Visually guided overlap task: The target light appears 800 msec
after the monkey has achieved fixation and stays on for 300 msec. Two hundred
msec after the target appears, the fixation point disappears; this is the cue
for the monkey to make a saccade to the target. The target disappears 100 msec
later (100 msec overlap), and the monkey therefore makes the saccade in total
darkness. It is rewarded for making a saccade of proper amplitude and
direction. 3) Memory guided gap task: The target light appears 600 msec after
the monkey has achieved fixation, remains on for 300 msec, and then disappears.
One hundred msec later the fixation point disappears (100 msec gap), and the
monkey is rewarded for making a saccade to where the target had been. In both
the gap and overlap tasks the monkey sees the stimulus for the same amount of
time, and the saccade itself is made in total darkness. In all tasks, the cue
to make the saccade is the offset of the fixation point. The trial aborts and
the monkey receives no reward if it breaks fixation before this cue.

Monkeys performed between 2000 and 6000 saccade trials per day. During formal
data collection the monkeys had to make saccades from a standard fixation point
in the center of gaze to a target at one of up to 48 positions. The target was
a spot of light from a LED back projected onto a tangent screen, forming an
image 0.5° of arc in diameter with a luminance of roughly 1.4 cd/m^2. The target
and fixation lights provided the only illumination in the room. Targets were
presented in an unpredictable fashion by the computer. Calibration was
accomplished by having the monkey fixate the various targets. The coil signal
was accurate without cosine correction to 30° on either side of the center of
gaze. Most saccades occurred within limits of 15° on either side of the

fixation point. Eye movement data were digitally filtered and differentiated
off-line. Data analysis was performed on a PDP 11/44 UNIX system.

After the experiments were finished the monkeys were deeply anesthetized and
perfused transcardially with normal saline followed by 10% formol-saline. The
brains were then removed, sectioned on a freezing microtome, stained with cresyl
violet, and the lesions reconstructed.

RESULTS

Histology: Figure 2 shows a reconstruction of one of the lesions. The lesion
was confined to the most posterior part of the anterior bank of the arcuate
sulcus and the operculum of the prearcuate gyrus posterior to the principal
sulcus. All of the data illustrated are from this monkey, although the results
from the second monkey were generally similar.

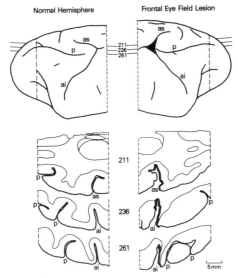

Fig. 2. Reconstruction of representative frontal eye field
lesion. Lesion is indicated by blackened area on lateral
view of the brain and by heavy black lines on individual
sections. Abbreviations: ai, inferior limb of arcuate
sulcus; as, superior limb of arcuate sulcus; p, principal
sulcus.

Immediate postoperative appearance: The day after surgery the animals appeared
normal on gross examination, and had a full range of eye movements. However
they had a mild contralateral neglect as manifested by a tendency to choose
stimuli in the hemifield ipsilateral to the lesion when stimuli were presented
simultaneously in both hemifields, and a tendency to respond less quickly to
stimuli in the contralateral hemifield. Three trained observers who did not
know the side of the lesion correctly identified it after examining the monkeys.
By the time formal training took place, however, the clinical deficit was no
longer apparent.

Visually guided no-time-limit task: After recovery, the monkeys were trained on
the visually guided no-time-limit task. The monkeys learned to perform this
task within a week, without significant difference either in performance or rate
of learning between saccades into the two hemifields. Figure 3 illustrates the

monkey's performance in the no-time-limit task. The grid of final eye positions
reproduces the grid of target positions. Note that no trials ended with the eye
near the origin (0,0), indicating that the monkey made a saccade on every trial.
There was also no difference in the latency of saccades into either hemifield at
the time formal testing began.

VISUALLY GUIDED -- NO TIME LIMIT

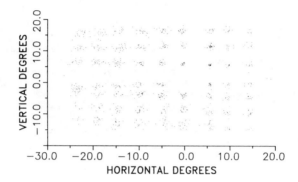

Fig. 3. Visually guided no-time-limit task. Each dot
represents the final eye position of the first saccade made
to the target in each trial, with corrective saccades
ignored. Target positions were spaced 5° apart on a
rectangular grid from -25° to +15° along the horizontal
meridian, and from -15° to +15° along the vertical
meridian. Positions to the left of 0° on the horizontal
meridian are contralateral to the cortical ablation.

Visually guided overlap task: The monkeys were then trained on the visually
guided overlap task. They learned the task with little difficulty when the
stimulus was presented in the hemifield ipsilateral to the lesion, and, having
learned the task, they performed it immediately when the stimulus was in the
hemifield contralateral to the lesion. Saccade amplitudes were somewhat shorter
and their accuracy worse than saccades performed in the no-time-limit task.
However, there were no significant differences in these measures between the two
sides in the overlap task. Figure 4 shows the monkey's performance in the
visually guided overlap task for targets in both hemifields. In this task,
unlike the previous one, the monkey occasionally neglected to make a saccade
during a trial, as can be seen by the collection of final eye positions near the
origin (0,0).

Memory guided gap task: Once the monkeys learned to make saccades in the
visually guided overlap task, they quickly learned within one training session
of several thousand trials to perform saccades to remembered targets presented
in the hemifield ipsilateral to the lesion. Two normal monkeys learned to
perform the memory guided task in one hemifield, and then generalized in one
trial to perform the task for stimuli in the opposite hemifield. The monkeys
with unilateral frontal eye field lesions had severe difficulty learning in the
memory guided task when those targets were in the hemifield contralateral to the
lesion, after they had already easily learned to perform the task for stimuli in
the hemifield ipsilateral to the lesion. When the stimuli appeared in the
hemifield contralateral to the lesion the monkeys would behave as if the target
light had not appeared: they would make random saccades into the ipsilateral
hemifield or make no saccades at all. The monkey whose data are illustrated
required a month of training to learn the task in the hemifield contralateral to
the lesion. Trials requiring memory guided saccades into the contralateral
hemifield had to be intermixed with simpler tasks. Otherwise, the monkey would

stop working entirely in the memory guided gap task. The second monkey took
five training sessions of several thousand trials each to learn the gap task
after it had already learned to perform the task for targets in the hemifield
ipsilateral to the lesion.

VISUALLY GUIDED -- 100 msec OVERLAP

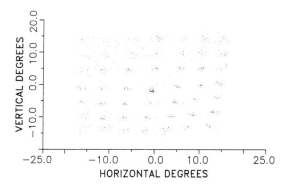

Fig. 4. Visually guided overlap task. Same conventions as
Fig. 3, except that in this case the grid of target
positions extends from -15° to +15° along both the
horizontal and vertical meridians.

MEMORY GUIDED -- 100 msec GAP

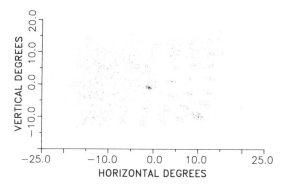

Fig. 5. Memory guided gap task. Spacing of target grid is
identical to that of Fig. 4.

Even when the monkeys began to make memory guided saccades into the hemifield
contralateral to the lesion, the accuracy of those saccades was seriously
impaired. Figure 5 shows memory guided saccades collected seven weeks after the
initial training for this task, and three months after the lesion. The saccades
in Fig. 5 were performed a day before the saccades in Fig. 4. Whereas in Fig. 4
the array of postsaccadic eye positions describes the array of targets, in Fig.
5 the array of targets is only described for the hemifield ipsilateral to the
lesion.

The performance of individual saccades. Not only were memory guided saccades
into the contralateral hemifield inaccurate, they frequently had irregular
velocity profiles and were slower than normal saccades. Figure 6 compares
ipsilaterally and contralaterally directed saccades for the visually guided
overlap and memory guided gap tasks. The morphology of the individual saccades
for both memory guided and visually guided saccades to targets in the hemifield
ipsilateral to the lesion, and the morphology of visually guided saccades to
targets in the hemifield contralateral to the lesion is normal. The memory
guided saccade into the hemifield contralateral to the lesion, however, is
highly irregular. Although many saccades were less irregular than the example
illustrated, the peak velocity–amplitude relationship for memory guided saccades
into the affected hemifield shows both a greater scatter and a lower velocity
than either visually guided saccades into that field or any saccades into the
unaffected field. Figure 7 shows the velocity-amplitude scatter plots for the
visually guided and memory guided saccades illustrated in Figs. 4 and 5.

Saccade latency also is affected by the frontal lesion. The distributions for
memory guided and visually guided saccades to targets in the hemifield
ipsilateral to the lesion are identical. For saccades into the hemifield
contralateral to the lesion, however, the monkey tended to delay visually–guided
saccades and make memory-guided saccades prematurely.

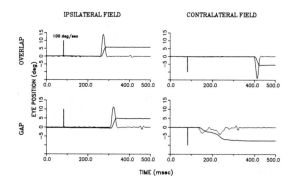

Fig. 6. Saccade morphology for gap and overlap tasks. The
horizontal components of eye position (solid line) and
velocity (dotted line) are shown for single saccades into
each hemisphere for the gap and overlap tasks.

DISCUSSION

These results show that there is a robust and long-lived deficit in some aspects
of saccadic performance after unilateral frontal eye field ablation in the
rhesus monkey. Although the frontal eye fields are not needed for performance
of visually guided saccades, they are clearly important for the learning and
performance of saccades to remembered targets. Initially, the monkeys behaved
as if they did not know what to do in response to the signal to make the
saccade. When they finally learned to move their eyes to where the target had
been, their saccades were relatively inaccurate, slow, and had irregular
velocity profiles.

The frontal eye fields could contribute to this function in either of two ways.
First, the frontal eye fields may be specifically involved in motor memory and
mechanisms necessary for the ordering of behavior in time (Fuster, 1980). The
operated monkey´s inability to suppress an inappropriate saccade to the target
before the fixation light disappears is in keeping with this interpretation.

Neurons have been described in the frontal eye fields that maintain a signal
evoked by a possible saccade target long after the target has disappeared, and
which, in fact discharge through memory intervals longer than those used in this
experiment (Bruce and Goldberg, 1985). Another possibility is that the frontal
eye fields serve as a means of transmitting the results of complicated cortical
processing to the oculomotor system. Guitton, Buchtel and Douglas (1985) have
shown that humans with unilateral frontal eye field lesions from epilepsy
surgery have great difficulty directing their eyes away from a flashed stimulus,
although no trouble directing their eyes toward it. Lesser, Leigh and their
coworkers (1985) found that patients could make contralateral saccades during
unilateral carotid amytal injections, but that saccades to visual stimuli were
much more easily performed than those to verbal command alone. These other
experiments argue that the deficit is a more general one that does not involve
only memory processes. This conclusion is supported by the finding that, unlike
the substantia nigra (Hikosaka and Wurtz, 1983), the frontal eye fields do not
contain any neurons activated exclusively in relation to memory guided saccades
(Bruce and Goldberg, 1985).

VISUALLY GUIDED -- 100 msec OVERLAP

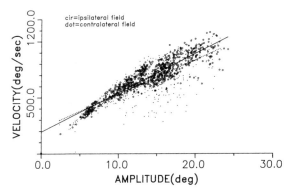

MEMORY GUIDED -- 100 msec GAP

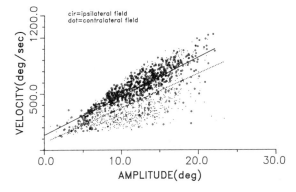

Fig. 7. Scatter plots of amplitude versus velocity for
overlap (top) and gap (bottom) tasks. Each circle
represents a saccade into the hemifield ipsilateral to the
lesion and each dot a saccade into the hemifield
contralateral to the lesion. Least-square regression lines
are shown for contralateral (dotted line) and ipsilateral
(solid line) trials for each task.

The finding that the saccade dynamics were impaired by a cortical lesion was unexpected. Robinson's classic model of the saccadic system (Robinson, 1981) postulates a mechanism that shapes the metrics of the saccade in the brainstem. The higher centers provide targeting and triggering information and leave the saccade motor parameters to the reticular formation. Our results suggest that cortical input is necessary throughout the saccade for those saccades that are generated by the cortex. Carl and Wurtz (1985) showed that patients with hemi-Parkinson's disease have a similar slowing of saccades to remembered targets and they postulated that the deficit could be explained by impaired input to the omnipause neurons (neurons that cease firing before saccades). The frontal eye fields could affect the omnipause neurons either directly by input to the midline pontine region or indirectly by their projection to the caudate which could then affect the substantia nigra (Leichnetz, 1980).

REFERENCES

Bruce, C.J. and M.E. Goldberg (1985). Primate frontal eye fields. I. Single neurons discharging before saccades. J. Neurophysiol., 53, 603-635.
Bruce, C.J., M.E. Goldberg, G.B. Stanton, and M.C. Bushnell (1985). Primate frontal eye fields. II. Physiological and anatomical correlates of electrically evoked eye movements. J. Neurophysiol., 54, 712-732.
Carl, J.R. and R.H. Wurtz (1985). Asymmetry of saccadic control in patients with hemi-Parkinson's disease. Suppl. to Invest. Ophth. and Vis. Sci., 26, ARVO Abst., 258.
Fuster, J.M. (1980). The Prefrontal Cortex : anatomy, physiology, and neuropsychology of the frontal lobe. Raven, New York.
Goldberg, M.E. (1983). Studying the neurophysiology of behavior, Methods for recording single neurons in awake behaving monkeys. In J.L. Barker and J.F. McKelvy (Eds.), Methods in Cellular Neurobiology, Vol. 3, John Wiley, New York. pp. 225-248.
Guitton, D., H.A. Buchtel, and R.M. Douglas (1985). Frontal lobe lesions in man cause difficulties in suppressing reflexive glances and in generating goal-directed saccades. Exp. Brain Res., 58, 455-472
Hikosaka, O.H. and R.H. Wurtz (1983) Visual and oculomotor functions of monkey substantia nigra pars reticulata. III. Memory-contingent visual and saccade responses. J. Neurophysiol., 49, 1268-1284.
Leichnetz, G. (1980). An anterogradely-labeled prefrontal cortico-oculomotor pathway in the monkey demonstrated with HRP gel and TMB neurohistochemistry. Brain. Res., 198, 440-445.
Lesser, R.P., R.J. Leigh, D.S. Dinner, H. Luders, H.H. Morris, R.L. Tomsak, and K.I. Lockwood (1985). Preservation of voluntary saccades after intracarotid injection of barbiturate. Neurology, 35, 1108-1113
Robinson, D.A. (1981). Control of eye movements. In V.B. Brooks (Ed.), Handbook of Physiology, Section 1, The Nervous System, Vol. II, Part 2, Am. Physiological Soc., Bethesda, MD. pp. 1275-1320.
Schiller, P.H. and J.H. Sandell (1983). Interactions between visually and electrically elicited saccades before and after superior colliculus and frontal eye field ablations in the rhesus monkey. Exp. Brain Res., 49, 381-392.
Schiller, P.H., S.D. True, J.L. Conway (1980). Deficits in eye movements following frontal eye field and superior colliculus ablations. J. Neurophysiol., 44, 1175-1189.

Recovery of Oculomotor Function in Monkeys with Large Unilateral Cortical Lesions

R. J. Tusa*, D. S. Zee* and S. J. Herdman**

*Department of Neurology, Johns Hopkins Hospital, Baltimore,
MD 21205, USA
**Department of Physical Therapy, University of Maryland,
Baltimore, MD 21201, USA

INTRODUCTION

An emerging focus of neurophysiological research is on the role of cerebral cortex in the control of eye movements in primates. The results of recordings of activity of cortical neurons during eye movements combined with the effects of focal cortical lesions have suggested that particular cortical structures generate specific types of eye movements. For example, the frontal eye fields (FEF) are thought to be involved in the generation of voluntary saccades (Bruce and Goldberg, 1985). Areas within the parietal-temporal-occipital (PTO) junction are thought to be involved in smooth pursuit eye movements (Newsome and others, this symposium). But the experimental results reported thus far in monkeys would not lead one to predict the types of deficits reported in human patients with large unilateral cerebral lesions: 1) In monkeys, unilateral FEF ablations impair saccades to remembered targets in the contralateral visual hemifield (Goldberg and others, this symposium). In contrast, patients with large unilateral cerebral lesions involving the FEF have a transient paralysis of all saccades contralateral to the lesioned side or at least beyond the midline (Sharpe, 1982). 2) Monkeys with lesions in visual cortex recover the ability to generate accurate saccades to visual targets in their "blind" field (Mohler and Wurtz, 1977). It has been difficult to unequivocally demonstrate such recovery in human patients following visual cortex lesions (Campion and others, 1983). 3) Finally, only small or transient deficits in foveal smooth pursuit, toward the side of the lesion, have been found following PTO lesions in monkeys (Lynch and McLaren, 1982; Newsome and others, this symposium), whereas devastating pursuit deficits toward and mild deficits away from the side of the lesion have been reported in patients following PTO lesions (Troost and Abel, 1982).

It is not clear whether these differences between monkeys and human patients are due to a difference between species, differences in recovery of function, or differences in size and location of lesions. To address these issues we have quantified, using a scleral search coil recording system, both the immediate and long-term effects of large unilateral cortical lesions on the oculomotor performance in 3 adolescent rhesus monkeys trained to fixate and follow a target light.

RESULTS

Extent of Lesions and General Observations

The extent of the lesion in all three animals was similar. All cortical areas known to be involved in visuomotor behavior were aspirated. Cortex at the frontal pole, orbital surface and ventral surface of the temporal lobe was spared. Although the lesion did extend into the underlying white matter the basal ganglia and thalamus were not damaged.

During the initial post-op period, there was a constant, spontaneous eye drift away from the side of the lesion which was independent of orbital position ($\sim2^{\circ}$/s in the light and $\sim10^{\circ}$/s in the dark). In the light, the eyes in the orbit, and the head on the body, were each deviated $\sim20^{\circ}$ toward the side of the lesion. After several weeks, the velocity of the spontaneous eye drift decreased to $\sim1^{\circ}$/s in the light and $\sim5^{\circ}$/s in the dark, and the eye and head deviations each decreased by $\sim10^{\circ}$. No further improvements were observed.

Initation of Saccades and Quick Phases

Initial deficit. Saccades and quick phases of optokinetic (OKN) and vestibular (VOR) nystagmus were recorded as early as 24 hours post-op. No saccades were made to somatic stimuli presented to the side of the face contralateral to the lesion or to auditory stimuli presented in craniotopic space (head coordinate system) contralateral to the lesion. In the light, the animals also did not make saccades into craniotopic space contralateral to the lesion, although they did make spontaneous saccades in all directions within craniotopic space ipsilateral to the lesion. In the dark, however, spontaneous saccades occasionally were made across the midline and back and forth within craniotopic space contralateral to the lesion. In the light, quick phases generated away from the lesioned side began more eccentrically in the orbit than pre-op and did not bring the eyes across the midline. In the dark, however, quick phases generated away from the side of the lesion did bring the eyes across the midline.

These findings suggest that monkeys with large unilateral cortical lesions involving the FEF do not have a paralysis of saccades or quick phases contralateral to the lesioned side. We attribute the paucity of saccades and quick phases generated into craniotopic space contralateral to the lesion to "neglect" of that portion of space and to a deviation of mean eye position toward the lesioned side. It is possible that "saccadic palsies" reported in patients following unilateral cerebral cortical lesions are actually a deviation of mean eye position toward the lesioned side accompanied by a contralateral neglect. DeRenzi (1982) has found a high correlation between ipsilateral eye deviations and contralateral hemispatial neglect in patients with unilateral cerebral cortex lesions.

Recovery. By 4 weeks post-op, the animals spontaneously made saccades beyond 20° into craniotopic space contralateral to the lesion, but only when viewing the tangent screen used for eliciting visually-guided saccades. If the animals were surrounded by a visual environment in which they were not rewarded for looking at a target, such as the inside of an OKN drum, spontaneous saccades were rarely made beyond 10° into craniotopic space contralateral to the lesion, even as long as 1 year post-op. Thus, there appeared to be incomplete recovery of "neglect" of craniotopic visual space contralateral to the lesion.

Visually-Guided Saccades

Visually-guided saccades were examined using a 0.5° target light rear projected onto a tangent screen. Three different saccade paradigms were used. 1) Random target steps in which the target light was unpredictably stepped 5-40° away from fixation. 2) Express saccades in which the fixation light was turned off 200 msec before the onset of the target light 5° away (Boch and others, 1984). 3) Step-ramps in which the target first jumped to a new location up to 20° away, and then moved at a constant velocity (8-60°/s) toward or away from the initial fixation point. In all 3 paradigms, random blank trials were inserted in which the fixation light went out but no new target light came on.

Saccades to targets in the normal visual hemifield. During the acute post-op period, visually-guided saccades made to targets stepped into the normal visual field were hypermetric by 11%-17%. This placed the image of the target in the "blind" visual field. These hypermetric saccades were corrected by the spontaneous 1-2°/s eye drift away from the side of the lesion. The saccadic hypermetria decreased to 5% by 20 weeks post-op and was absent 1 year post-op. The amplitude of visually-guided saccades to targets moving within the normal visual field (step-ramp paradigm) depended upon target velocity, although the saccades were initially hypermetric (Fig. 1).

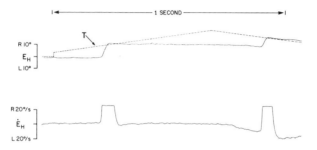

Fig. 1 Saccades made to a target (T) first stepped into the normal visual field and then moved 30°/s toward and then away from the lesioned side in a monkey 1 week post-op. E_H=horizontal eye position; $\dot{E}_H$=horizontal eye velocity (for clarity, the horizontal eye velocity was cut off at 30°/s).

Saccades to targets in the "blind" visual hemifield. Two target light intensities were used including a 3.0 ft L target luminence against a background illumination of 0.1 ft L and a target luminence of 2000 ft L against a background 1 ft L. These target intensities were selected as they are equal to or higher than those that elicit visually-guided saccades in monkeys several months following bilateral occipital lobectomies and in acutely destriated monkeys, respectively (Zee and others, this symposium; Mohler and Wurtz, 1977). In all 3 saccade paradigms, stimuli of either light intensity, stepped into the "blind" visual hemifield elicited a staircase of small saccades. These saccades were searching saccades triggered by the offset of the fixation light and not visually-guided saccades. The saccadic amplitudes did not depend upon target step size and the amplitude and latency of the initial saccades were no different from saccades made when the fixation light was simply turned off (blank trials). This deficit was still present 1 year post-op.

These results suggest that subcortical regions are not sufficient for recovery of visually-guided saccades in monkeys with large unilateral cortical lesions. Recovery of visually-guided saccades in patients with occipital lobe lesions may also depend upon the extent of the lesion, i.e., lesions restricted to striate cortex may result in recovery, whereas more extensive lesions may not. This may explain the discrepancies in the literature on "blindsight".

Saccades to targets stepped vertically. Visually-guided saccades in the pure vertical direction were not made post-op. Instead, oblique saccades were made with a vector directed ~15° off vertical toward the lesioned side, placing the target in the blind visual field. This deficit was still present 1 year post-op.

These results are consistent with the hypothesis that pure vertical saccades are generated by the simultaneous discharge of homotopic loci in both cerebral hemispheres (Robinson and Fuchs, 1969).

Smooth Pursuit

Initial deficit. Smooth pursuit was examined using a 0.5° by 0.5° target light moving in a predictable, triangular waveform ($\pm30^\circ$) rear projected on a screen in front of the animal. A large 20° by 20° target stimulus was also used, to help distinguish pursuit deficits caused by visual inattention or visual field deficits. Target velocities ranged from 2-180°/s. During the first post-op week, pursuit eye velocity to targets moving away from the lesioned side reached a maximum of 30°/s, regardless of target size. Saccadic and not pursuit eye movements were used to track targets moving vertically and toward the lesioned side. By 2 weeks post-op, however, pursuit eye movements began to recover in all directions in all 3 animals. For the large target moving away from the lesioned side, eye velocity saturated between 40-90°/s (160°/s pre-op) and below this level eye velocity was faster than target velocity by ~2°/s. For the large target moving toward the lesioned side, eye velocity saturated between 2-15°/s; below this speed, gain (eye velocity/target velocity) was <0.5. For targets moving vertically, in either direction, eye velocity saturated between 20-30°/s (60°/s up and 90°/s down, pre-op) and below this level the gain was ~0.5. The level of saturation of eye velocity and the gains were ~20% less when small targets were used. During the initial few weeks post-op, smooth pursuit eye movements to both small and large targets moving away from the lesioned side stopped at the midline of the head regardless of head position on the body. We attribute this to "neglect" of craniotopic space contralateral to the lesioned side.

These findings agree with recent clinical studies suggesting a deficit in smooth pursuit in both horizontal directions following an acute unilateral lesion (Troost and Abel, 1982). Based on our findings, it appears that cortical areas in both hemispheres are used to generate horizontal smooth pursuit at high velocities and vertical smooth pursuit at all velocities; whereas cortical areas in only one hemisphere are sufficient to generate smooth pursuit ipsilaterally at low velocities. The deficit in smooth pursuit following a large cortical lesion is much more severe than lesions restricted to area 7a (Lynch and McClaren, 1982) or to area MT (Newsome and others, this symposium). This suggests that either both of these areas must be lesioned to result in a complete pursuit deficit or that other cortical regions are involved in the generation of pursuit.

Sensory versus motor deficits. The pursuit deficits described above were similar to those found when the target was stepped into the normal visual field and moved horizontally. For example, during the first post-op week, the animals did not generate any pursuit eye movements to targets moving toward the lesioned side and did not generate pursuit eye movements above 20°/s to targets moving away from the lesioned side. In spite of this pursuit deficit, the animals were able to accurately detect target velocity and make visually-guided saccades to targets moving 15-60°/s in either direction within the normal visual hemifield. (Note the discrepancy between the animal's ability to use target velocity information to generate saccades but not smooth pursuit eye movements, to targets moving toward the side of the lesion in Fig. 1). It is likely that the saccadic and the pursuit systems share the same sensory afferent pathway for visually-guided eye movements. Thus, the deficit in horizontal smooth pursuit to targets in the normal visual field probably represents a problem in motor control, and not a problem in assessment of target velocity.

Recovery. Although the recovery rates varied among animals, smooth pursuit to both predictable and step-ramp target trajectories improved in all directions, reaching the final level 20-40 weeks post-op. By this time, maximum pursuit eye velocity was normal in all directions in all animals except toward the lesioned side, where pursuit only reached ~100°/s (65% pre-op values). For targets moving

away from the lesioned side, eye velocity was higher than target velocity by
~1°/s, resulting in small back-up saccades. For targets moving toward the lesioned
side, eye velocity was lower than target velocity by ~1°/s, resulting in catch-up
saccades. This pursuit asymmetry probably reflects the addition of a 1°/s
spontaneous eye drift away from the side of the lesion to the pursuit eye velocity
command. For targets moving vertically in either direction, gain returned to
~1.0. The persistent deficit in smooth pursuit toward the lesioned side is similar
to that reported in patients several years following hemidecortication (Troost
and Abel, 1982).

Open loop conditions. Two types of stimuli evoke smooth pursuit; the motion
of images across the retina and the position of images away from the fovea (Pola
and Wyatt, 1980). In order to determine the effectiveness of position information
for generating smooth pursuit in monkeys with large unilateral cortical lesions,
target images were stabilized on the retina. This was done by adding an eye
position signal to the target position. The target was offset from the fovea
at several different eccentricities up to 5.0°. For targets stabilized in the
normal visual hemifield, a series of catch-up saccades and 2-3°/s pursuit movements
were elicited, similar to those generated pre-op. When the target was offset
within 2° from the fovea in the "blind" visual hemifield (the area of foveal
sparing; Bunt and Minckler, 1977), the animals did not make any catch-up saccades,
but did generate pursuit eye movements (Fig 2). (Targets randomly stepped into
the area of foveal sparing also did not generate visually-guided saccades.)
Targets stabilized on the fovea beyond 2° in the blind visual hemifield did not
result in any visual tracking eye movements at all. Thus, following a large
unilateral cortical lesion, target position information in the normal visual
hemifield and up to 2° in the "blind" visual hemifield can mediate smooth pursuit
eye movements. In addition, smooth pursuit, instead of saccades, is used to
correct position error for targets in the area of foveal sparing within the "blind"
visual hemifield.

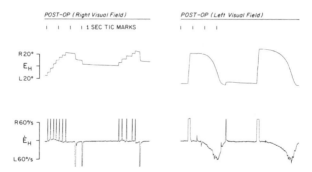

Fig. 2   Visual tracking movements to a stabilized retinal image displaced 1°
from the fovea in a monkey 1 year following a right-sided cortical lesion. E_H=hori-
zontal eye position; $\dot{E}_H$=horizontal eye velocity (cut off at 80°/s for clarity).
Normal catch-up saccades were elicited to targets stabilized in the normal (right)
visual hemifield, but not in the area of foveal sparing within the "blind" (left)
visual hemifield. Instead, pursuit eye movements were elicited in this part
of the visual field reaching velocities up to 60°/s.

DISCUSSION

New Findings

1. In the initial post-op period, spontaneous saccades and quick phases of nystagmus

made in the light, failed to bring the eyes across the midline away from the side of the lesion. In the dark, however, saccades and quick phases did bring the eyes across the midline. We attribute the paucity of saccades and quick phases made into craniotopic space contralateral to the lesion to "neglect" and to a deviation of mean eye position toward the lesioned side.

2. The ability to make visually-guided saccades, including express saccades, to targets stepped into the "blind" hemifield did not recover post-op.

3. Hypermetric saccades were initially made to targets stepped or step-ramped into the normal visual hemifield. This deficit recovered by 1 year post-op.

4. Throughout the post-op period, information about the velocity and direction of target motion within the normal visual hemifield was used to modulate the amplitude of visually-guided saccades.

5. The animals did not make purely vertical visually-guided saccades nor did they recover the ability to do so by 1 year post-op.

6. During the initial post-op period, smooth pursuit could only be initiated away from the lesioned side, did not go above 30°/s, and did not enter craniotopic space contralateral to the side of the lesion. In this direction eye velocity was $1-2^{\circ}$/s higher than target velocity. In time, smooth pursuit eye movements were generated in all directions and were made into craniotopic space contralateral to the lesioned side. By 40 weeks post-op, maximum eye velocity reached pre-op values both vertically and away from the lesioned side, but only reached 65% of pre-op values toward the lesioned side. During horizontal pursuit, eye velocity was $\sim 1^{\circ}$/s higher than target velocity away from the lesioned side and $\sim 1^{\circ}$/s lower toward the lesioned side.

7. Throughout the post-op period, horizontal pursuit but not saccadic eye movements could be generated to targets placed up to 2° into the "blind" visual hemifield (area of foveal sparing).

Many of the oculomotor deficits we have found in monkeys with large unilateral cortical lesions resemble deficits in human patients with cerebral lesions. Thus, we believe the reported differences in oculomotor deficits between small experimental cortical lesions in monkeys and naturally occurring cerebral lesions in human patients are not due to a difference in species, but rather to difference in size and location of lesions.

Summary Diagram

The deficits in **visually-guided eye movements** in monkeys following a large unilateral cortical lesion can be better understood from a very simple diagram, which is tentatively based on data from other chapters in this symposium (Goldberg, Mustari, Newsome, Seagraves, and Zee) (Fig. 3). The intent of this diagram is not to describe all of the potential cortical circuits involved in visually-guided eye movements. Rather, we wish to emphasize the concept that different eye movement abnormalities will occur from defects in either sensory afferent pathways or motor efferent pathways.

Afferent limb. Information about target location within the contralateral visual hemifield and in an area of foveal sparing (FS) in the ipsilateral visual hemifield are probably processed in the geniculostriate system (LGN-17). Information about target velocity for stimuli moving in all directions within the contralateral visual hemifield and in the area of foveal sparing are probably processed by LGN-17 and area MT (Fig. 3).

Efferent limbs. The cortical efferent limb for visually-guided saccades generated in the contralateral direction is not well defined but probably includes cortical area(s) within parietal and occipital cortex (PO) that project to subcortical regions including the deep layers of the superior colliculus (SCdeep). In addition, there is probably a parallel pathway via the frontal eye field to subcortical structures. (Fig. 3; only the PO-SCdeep efferent limb is shown for clarity; double arrows indicate the direction each efferent limb generates eye movements). Cortical areas within one hemisphere also form the efferent limb for smooth pursuit eye movements generated primarily in the ipsilateral direction[*]. The smooth pursuit efferent limb probably includes portions of area MT or adjacent cortical areas such as MST, and its projections to subcortical regions including the dorsolateral pontine nucleus (DLPN) (Fig. 3; for clarity we illustrate a MST-DLPN projection as a possible efferent limb for smooth pursuit).

The efferent limbs are only engaged by one of a potentially large number of stimuli simultaneously being processed in the afferent limb. Therefore, there must be a "target-selection" system interacting with the afferent and efferent limbs. Posterior parietal and frontal cortex are probably important structures in this selection process. Although this system is not shown in Fig. 3, a unilateral lesion involving this system might account for the oculomotor deficits we have attributed to "neglect".

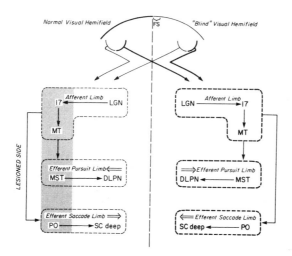

Fig. 3 Simplified diagram illustrating sensory afferent and motor efferent pathways that might be used to generate eye movements in a monkey with a large unilateral cortical lesion. Lesioned side is shaded, see text for details.

Afferent limb defect. No visually-guided eye movements were made to stationary or moving targets located beyond the area of foveal sparing in the "blind" visual hemifield following a large unilateral cortical lesion. We believe this represents an afferent limb defect because it affects both saccadic and pursuit eye movements to targets confined in the visual hemifield contralateral to the lesion.
Plasticity. The animal made searching saccades to stationary and moving targets in the "blind" visual hemifield, although visually-guided eye movements never recovered. Based on these results, it appears that **the afferent limb for visually-guided eye movements cannot be replaced by retinal projections to subcortical efferent structures on the lesioned side** (e.g. retino-SCsup, retino-pregeniculate-SCdeep and retino-pretectal-DLPN projections; Wurtz and Albano, 1980; Weber and Harting, 1980).

Efferent limb defects. During the initial post-op period, smooth pursuit eye movements were not made toward the lesioned side to targets moving in the normal visual hemifield (only saccades were elicited to these targets).

---

[*]Based on our findings, high velocity smooth pursuit eye movements appear to require cortex in both hemispheres. This suggests that the efferent limb has some ability to generate smooth pursuit in the contralateral direction.

216   R. J. Tusa, D. S. Zee and S. J. Herdman

In addition, visually-guided saccades were not made away from the lesioned side to targets in the area of foveal sparing (only pursuit eye movements were generated to these targets). We believe these represent efferent limb defects because the animal apparently "sees" the target, but can only generate pursuit eye movements in one direction and saccades in the other direction. Based on these results, it appears that **information about target position and velocity from the afferent limb in the intact side cannot be relayed to subcortical efferent structures on the lesioned side to generate visually-guided eye movements.**
Plasticity. In time, pursuit eye movements were made to targets moving vertically and to targets moving toward the lesioned side within the normal visual hemifield. In addition, maximum pursuit eye velocity increased to stationary targets in the area of foveal sparing. In contrast, visually-guided saccades in the pure vertical direction or to targets in the area of foveal sparing did not recover. Based on these findings, the smooth pursuit efferent limb on one side appears to have the latent ability to generate eye movements in all directions, whereas the saccadic efferent limb on one side does not appear to have this ability. An alternative explanation would be that information from the afferent limb in the intact side can eventually be relayed to subcortical efferent structures on the lesioned side to generate smooth pursuit eye movements but not visually-guided saccades.

ACKNOWLEDGEMENT

Supported by Teacher-Investigator Award 1K07-NS008004-01 from NINCDS (Dr. Tusa).

REFERENCES

Boch, R., B. Fischer, and E. Ransperger (1984). Express-saccades of the monkey: reaction times versus intensity, size, duration, and eccentricity of their targets. Exp. Brain Res., 55, 223-231.
Bruce, C. J. and Goldberg, M. E. Primate frontal eye fields: (1985) I. Single neurons discharging before saccades. J. Neurophy. 53, 603-635.
Bunt, A. H. and Minckler, D. S. (1977). New anatomical evidence for bilateral representation of the central retina. Arch. Ophthalmol. 95, 1445-1447.
Campion, J., Latto, R. and Smith, Y. M. (1983). Is blindsight an effect of scattered light, spared cortex, and near-threshold vision? Behav. and Brain Sciences, 6, 423-486.
De Renzi, E., Colombo, A., Faglioni, P and Gibertoni, M. (1982). Conjugate gaze paresis in stroke patients with unilateral damage. Arch. Neurol. 39, 482-486.
Lynch, J. C. and McLaren, J. W. (1982). The contribution of parieto-occipital association cortex to the control of slow eye movements. In G. Lennerstrand, D. S. Zee and E. L. Keller (Eds.), Functional Basis of Ocular Motility Disorders, Pergamon Press.
Mohler, C. W. and Wurtz, R. H. (1977). Role of striate cortex and superior colliculus in visual guidance of saccadic eye movements in monkeys. J. Neurophy. 40, 74-94.
Pola, J. and Wyatt, H. J. (1980). Target position and velocity: the stimuli for smooth pursuit eye movements. Vision Res. 20, 523-534.
Robinson, D. A. and Fuchs A. F. (1969). Eye movements evoked by stimulation of frontal eye fields. J. Neurophy. 32, 637-648.
Sharpe, J. A. (1982). Cerebral ocular motor deficits. In G. Lennerstrand, D. S. Zee and E. L. Keller (Eds.), Functional Basis of Ocular Motility Disorders, Pergamon Press.
Troost, B. T. and Abel, L. A. (1982). Pursuit disorders. In G. Lennerstrand, D. S. Zee and E. L. Keller (Eds.), Functional Basis of Ocular Motility Disorders, Pergamon Press.
Weber, J. T. and Harting, J. K. (1980). The efferent projections of the pretectal complex: an autoradiographic and horseradish peroxidase analysis. Brain Res. 194, 1-28.
Wurtz, R. H. and Albano, J. E. (1980). Visual-motor function of the primate superior colliculus. Ann. Rev. Neurosci. 3, 189-226.

No Notion of Motion: Monkeys with Unilateral Striate Lesions Have Long-term Deficits in the Utilization of Stimulus Velocity Information by the Oculomotor System

M. A. Segraves*, M. E. Goldberg*,***, S. -Y.
Deng*, C. J. Bruce*, L. G. Ungerleider**
and M. Mishkin**

*Laboratory of Sensorimotor Research, National Eye Institute,
Bethesda, Maryland, USA
**Laboratory of Neuropsychology, National Institute of Mental
Health, Bethesda, Maryland, USA
***Department of Neurology, Georgetown University School of
Medicine, Washington, DC, USA

INTRODUCTION

Both the saccadic and smooth pursuit systems of the primate require target velocity information to enable the animal to control eye movements appropriately. However, the neural basis for input of velocity information to the oculomotor system is not well understood. Within the macaque's visual pathways, neurons sensitive to target velocity are first found in striate cortex (Hubel and Wiesel, 1968), now considered the origin of a cortical pathway for motion analysis that proceeds from striate cortex to prestriate areas MT and MST (Van Essen and Maunsell, 1983). Thus, lesions of striate cortex should strongly compromise the monkey's ability to use velocity information, and, indeed, in this paper we report that monkeys with unilateral striate ablations have a chronic incapacity for the analysis of velocity information which affects the performance of both the saccadic and smooth pursuit systems.

METHODS

Two adult rhesus monkeys received unilateral striate cortical ablations. Surgery was performed aseptically under general anesthesia. They were allowed to recover for at least three months before beginning behavioral training. One week prior to training, hardware for fixing the head during training was attached to the skull, and a subconjunctival coil was implanted in one eye so that eye position could be monitored with the magnetic search coil technique. The methods of behavioral training and computer control of the experimental paradigm have been described in detail elsewhere (Goldberg, 1983).

RESULTS

Histology. Both brains had complete unilateral removal of striate cortex. A reconstruction of one of the lesions is shown in Fig. 1. There was minimal encroachment into prestriate cortex. Both lesions produced retrograde degeneration throughout the ipsilateral lateral geniculate nucleus.

Eye movements to step-ramp targets. Postoperatively, the monkeys could perform the eye movements involved in smooth pursuit and saccades perfectly well. In particular, they could make accurate saccades to stationary targets in either hemifield, and they could pursue foveal targets moving back and forth with

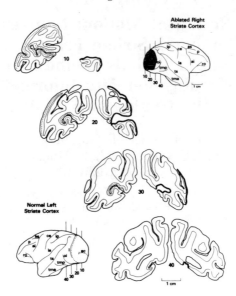

Fig. 1. Reconstruction of representative striate cortical
lesion. The lesion is indicated by blackened area (lateral
view) or heavy black lines (sections). Dashed lines
indicate striate cortical border (lateral view) or extent
(sections).

sinusoidally varying velocities and peak speeds of 125°/sec. However, they were
unable to develop smooth pursuit velocities or to make accurate saccades to
targets moving in the hemifield contralateral to the striate lesion.

Figure 2 illustrates both the saccadic and smooth pursuit deficits during the
monkey's attempt to foveate step-ramp targets. In the step-ramp task (Rashbass,
1961) the visual target is moved instantaneously from the fovea to the retinal
periphery and then begins to move with constant velocity either towards or away
from the fovea. To capture the moving target, the pursuit system must use the
velocity of the peripheral target to generate a pursuit eye movement, and the
saccadic system must adjust the amplitude of the saccade for the ongoing target
velocity. In the unilateral destriate monkey, saccades to both stationary and
step-ramp targets presented in the hemifield ipsilateral to the striate lesion
were accurate (Fig. 2A,B & C), as were saccades to stationary targets presented
in the hemifield contralateral to the lesion (Fig. 2D). However, saccades to
moving targets in the hemifield contralateral to the lesion were inaccurate.
Saccades to targets moving away from the fovea undershot the target (Fig. 2E),
whereas saccades to targets moving towards the fovea overshot the target (Fig.
2F). Saccade error did not correlate with saccade latency, but saccade
amplitude did, suggesting that the monkeys could see the position of the moving
target. However, they acted as if they did not perceive its velocity. The
monkey's smooth pursuit system developed a presaccadic pursuit velocity for
ramps towards and away from the fovea for targets presented in the hemifield
ipsilateral to the lesion (Fig. 2B & C), but not the hemifield contralateral to
the lesion (Fig. 2E & F). Figure 3 shows measurements of pursuit velocity 30
msec after the saccade. For step-ramp targets presented in the hemifield
ipsilateral to the lesion (filled symbols), pursuit velocities 30 msec after the
saccade approached ramp velocity of 30°/sec, whereas velocities for targets

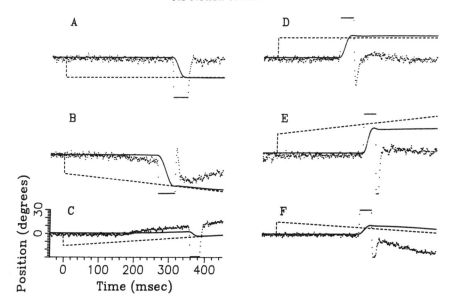

Fig. 2. Saccades to stationary and step-ramp targets. A-C:
Saccades to targets ipsilateral to striate ablation. D-F:
Saccades to targets contralateral to striate ablation. Eye
position, solid line; Target position, dashed line; Eye
velocity, noisy dotted line. Velocity calibration is equal
to position calibration in deg/sec.

moving in the hemifield contralateral to the lesion (open symbols) were similar
to those obtained in the step only condition (crosses & pluses). For the ramp-
away condition in the hemifield contralateral to the lesion, pursuit velocity
was not significantly different from that obtained in the step-only condition
(p=.11770). There was a significant difference between the step-only and ramp-
back conditions in the hemifield contralateral to the lesion (p<.0001); however
the velocity was much less than that obtained for the hemifield ipsilateral to
the lesion. This response may in part be explained by the fact that the target
moves to the hemifield ipsilateral to the lesion after saccades in ramp-back
trials due to overshoot.

Pursuit of stabilized images. To see whether the deficit was limited to the
processing of retinal stimulus velocity or whether it was a more comprehensive
deficit in the analysis of stimulus velocity, we studied the monkeys' generation
of smooth pursuit while they attempted to fixate parafoveally stabilized images.
(Fig. 4). In Fig. 4A, the monkey tracked a target moving to the left at
20°/sec. At time zero, the target was stepped 2° further to the left and eye
position was then continually added to target position, stabilizing the target
image upon the retina 2° to the left of center. In this example, the monkey
continued to pursue the target (response to position error), and pursuit
velocity did not drop to zero until about 1200 msec after the image was
stabilized. When the image was stabilized in the hemifield contralateral to the
lesion (Fig. 4B) the monkey was not able to maintain pursuit, and velocity
dropped to zero in about 250 msec. The time course of this rapid drop in
velocity was very similar to that obtained when the light was simply turned off
(Fig. 4C.). However, the monkey was able to make an accurate saccade to a
stationary target stepped 2° into the hemifield contralateral to the lesion
(Fig. 4D), indicating that he could see the stabilized target.

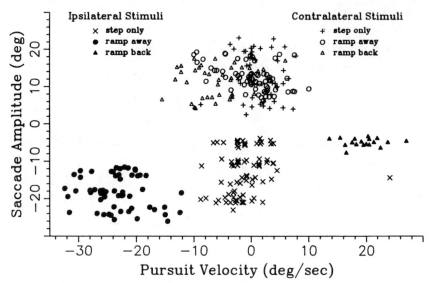

Fig. 3. Pursuit velocity measured 30 msec after saccades to
step-ramp targets presented in both hemifields.

Residual capacity. The observed deficits were present for as long as the
monkeys were studied, six and eighteen months postoperatively. Despite this
apparent global deficit in velocity analysis, there were several indications of
a residual capacity for velocity processing. Although smooth pursuit velocity
following an initial saccade to a step-ramp target was near zero, when the
monkey made multiple saccades to capture a moving target corrective saccades
were frequently followed by a greater pursuit velocity than after the first
saccade, even though the target remained in the hemifield contralateral to the
lesion because of the undershoot of the first saccade. For example, in a
sampling of 31 trials in which a monkey made two horizontal saccades to capture
a target in the hemifield contralateral to the lesion, the mean velocity after
the first saccade was 1.1°/sec, but increased to 4.9°/sec after the second
saccade (means significantly different, p<.0005). Finally, although pursuit
maintenance induced by an image stabilized in the hemifield contralateral to the
lesion was not efficient, the drop in velocity did not occur as rapidly as when
the target light was simply turned off. In a sampling of 150 trials, the mean
time for pursuit velocity to drop to zero with the image stabilized 3° into the
hemifield ipsilateral to the lesion was 995 msec. The mean time to zero
velocity with the image stabilized in the hemifield contralateral to the lesion
was 400 msec. The mean time to zero velocity for trials in which the light went
out during pursuit was 290 msec. All of these means were significantly
different at the p<.00005 level.

DISCUSSION AND CONCLUSIONS

These results demonstrate the crucial importance of the macaque's striate cortex
for the transfer of velocity information to the oculomotor system. The residual
velocity processing after unilateral striate lesions suggests that subcortical
structures or extrastriate cortex may play a role. In the monkey with a
unilateral striate lesion, this extrastriate system seems to operate with low
gain and long latency. However, monkeys with bilateral occipital lesions do not
show as severe a deficit as that demonstrated in these experiments (Zee and
colleagues, this symposium), suggesting that in the absence of a cortical

imbalance, these extrastriate mechanisms are used more effectively.

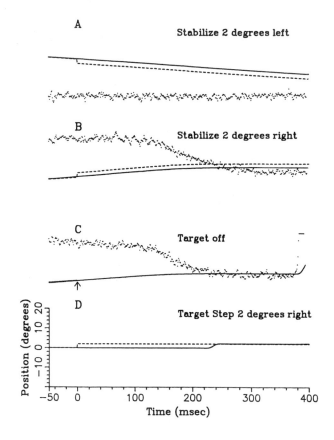

Fig. 4. Tracking stabilized targets. Eye position, solid
line; Target position, dashed line; Eye velocity, noisy
dotted line. Velocity calibration is equal to position
calibration in deg/sec. Initial ramp velocity in A, B and C
was 20°/sec. Arrow in C marks target light off.

REFERENCES

Goldberg, M. E. (1983). Studying the neurophysiology of behavior, Methods for
    recording single neurons in awake behaving monkeys. In J. L. Barker and J.
    F. McKelvy (Eds.), Methods in Cellular Neurobiology, Vol. 3, John Wiley, New
    York. pp. 225-248.
Hubel, D. H. and T. N. Wiesel (1968). Receptive fields and functional
    architecture of monkey striate cortex. J. Physiol., 195, 215-243.
Rashbass, C. (1961). The relationship between saccadic and smooth tracking eye
    movements. J. Physiol., 159, 326-338.
Van Essen, D. C. and J. H. R. Maunsell (1983). Hierarchical organization and
    functional streams in the visual cortex. Trends. Neurosci., 6, 370-375.

The Middle Temporal Visual Area and the Control of Smooth Pursuit Eye Movements

W. T. Newsome*, M. R. Dursteler** and
R. H. Wurtz**

*Department of Neurobiology and Behavior, State University of
New York, Stony Brook, NY 11794, USA
**Laboratory for Sensorimotor Research, National Eye Institute,
National Institutes of Health, Bethesda, MD 20205, USA

INTRODUCTION

Clinical studies of human patients and experimental ablations in monkeys indicate
that the control of smooth pursuit eye movements is, in part, a cortical phenomenon. The pursuit deficits that follow cortical lesions appear to have both
sensory and motor components. Ablations of striate visual cortex result in pronounced pursuit deficits when the pursuit target appears in the damaged portion
of the visual field (Goldberg and colleagues, 1982; Zee and colleagues, 1982;
Segraves and colleages, this volume). This deficit is patently sensory since monkeys perform pursuit in a normal fashion when the target appears in an intact region of the visual field. On the other hand, unilateral lesions of the parieto-
occipital region in humans (see Troost and Abel, 1982) and hemidecortication in
monkeys (Tusa and colleagues, this volume) result in deficits for pursuit of all
visual targets that move toward the side of the lesion regardless of their initial location in the visual field. Such deficits appear to be related to a specific motor aspect of the task rather than to some sensory property of the stimulus. Pursuit deficits following bilateral lesions of the parieto-occipital region of cortex in monkeys have also been documented by Lynch and McLaren (1982).

We have recently produced both the sensory and motor type deficits with small
(<10 mm^2) lesions in the region of the middle temporal visual area (MT), an extrastriate area that lies near the juncture of the parietal and occipital lobes
in monkey cortex. MT is a natural candidate for supplying visual information to
the pursuit system since most MT neurons are selective for the direction and
speed of moving visual targets (e.g. Maunsell and Van Essen, 1983a). Information
about the motion of the target is essential for the guidance of pursuit eye movements. In addition, MT has a robust projection to the dorsolateral pontine nuclei (Maunsell and Van Essen, 1983b) which have been implicated in the control
of smooth pursuit eye movements (Suzuki and Keller, 1984). In our experiments,
we have made small, selective lesions of MT with the neurotoxin, ibotenic acid,
which kills cell bodies without affecting fibers of passage (Olney, 1983).
Lesions placed in the representation of the peripheral visual field in MT result
in a retinotopic deficit for visual motion which is manifested as a reduction in
the speed of the initial phase of pursuit eye movements when the visual target
appears in the damaged portion of the visual field. Lesions of the center of
gaze representation in MT also produce the retinotopic deficit, but in addition,
cause reduced gain for all pursuit movements toward the side of the lesion. Both

of these deficits are transient, and this paradigm should prove useful for studying mechanisms of recovery from cortical damage.

METHODS

Monkeys were initially trained on a visual fixation task (Wurtz, 1969) and then
underwent surgery in which an eye coil, head holder, and recording cylinder were
implanted. Monkeys were then trained on a step-ramp pursuit task (Rashbass, 1961)
in which they were presented with a stationary fixation target followed by a pursuit target whose motion was restricted to the horizontal meridian and whose speed
was 16 deg/sec. When the fixation target was extinguished, the pursuit target
appeared with one of several possible step displacements and moved either toward
or away from the fixation point. The monkey's task was to fixate the first target and then to follow the second target with smooth pursuit eye movements until
the end of the trial. In addition, a second set of trials was randomly interleaved with the first in which the second target remained stationary after its
appearance. In these trials, the monkey simply made a saccade to the stationary
target in order to obtain the reward. All trials were presented in random order
until the monkey completed 10 successful trials for each stimulus condition. The
monkey obtained a liquid reward for each trial in which he maintained his eye position within a small electronic window around the fixation and pursuit targets.
Eye movements were measured by the magnetic search coil technique.

After several training sessions, electrophysiological recording sessions were
conducted and MT was identified by the characteristic direction selectivity of
its neurons and by its characteristic visual topography (e.g. Van Essen, Maunsell
and Bixby, 1981). We made our MT lesions by injecting the neurotoxin, ibotenic
acid, directly into MT. One microliter of ibotenic acid (15 ugm/ul) was injected
through a Hamilton syringe whose needle had been insulated so that physiological
recordings could be obtained at the injection site. Lesions made in this manner
were small (2-12 mm^2) and were generally restricted to MT. We employed the chemical lesion technique because we found in preliminary experiments that surgical
ablation of MT consistently resulted in vascular infarcts into the optic radiation.

Since we could map the visual receptive field at each injection site, we were able
to place each injection on the representation of the horizontal meridian in MT at
a known eccentricity. We therefore knew which portions of the visual field were
likely to be affected by a deficit, and other portions of the visual field served
as within-animal controls. We have presented these methods in greater detail in
previous publications (Newsome and colleagues, 1985a,b).

RESULTS

The Retinotopic Deficit

The top set of traces in Fig. 1A shows ten superimposed responses of a normal
monkey to one step-ramp stimulus. Horizontal eye position is plotted on the
vertical axis, and time is plotted on the horizontal axis. Position of the
visual target is indicated by the broken line, and the monkey's eye position is
shown by the solid traces. The monkey fixated the stationary target for the
first 200 msec of the period illustrated. At time 0, the target stepped 5° to
the monkey's right and moved away at 16 deg/sec. With a latency of around 150
msec, the monkey made a saccadic eye movement to place his eyes near the moving
target and then tracked the target with smooth eye movements until the end of the
trial. It is important to note that the monkey began to track the target with
eye movements of appropriate direction and speed within a few tens of milli-
seconds of the end of the saccade. Since pursuit eye movements are generally
initiated with a latency of 80-100 msec (Lanman, Bizzi and Allum, 1978; Lisberger and Westbrook, 1985), the initial 80 msec of pursuit in the traces of Fig.
1A must be in response to stimulus motion that occurred <u>before</u> the monkey made

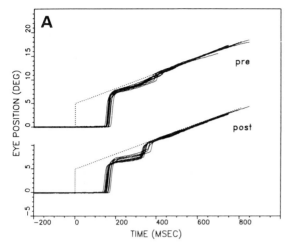

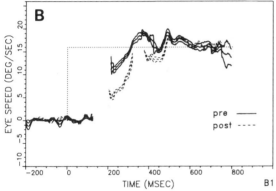

Fig. 1. Effect of an ibo-
tenic acid lesion in peripheral MT on the initiation
of smooth pursuit eye movements. A. Eye movement responses to step-ramp tracking target before (top) and
after (bottom) a lesion.
Horizontal eye position is
plotted on the ordinate and
time on the abscissa. The
dashed lines indicate the
sudden target displacement
(5° to the right) and subsequent motion. The solid
traces are 10 superimposed
eye movement responses to
the tracking target. B.
Averaged eye speed records
for the prelesion (solid)
and postlesion (dashed)
data illustrated in A. Mean
eye speed and the standard
error of the mean are shown
as a function of time. Reprinted from the *Journal of
Neuroscience.*

the saccade. In this particular case, the initial interval of pursuit was made
in response to motion which occurred 5-7 degrees to the right of the fovea.
Clearly, then, one can assay the efficacy of motion at several locations in the
visual field simply by varying the size and direction of the initial target displacement and by measuring the pursuit response within 70 msec of the end of the
initial saccade.

The lower set of traces in Fig. 1A shows the responses of the same monkey 24
hours after an injection of ibotenic acid into MT at the representation of the
horizontal meridian, 6° to the monkey's right. The most striking change in the
response was a reduction in pursuit eye speed during the initial 100 msec following the saccade. This effect is most clearly seen in the eye speed records in
Fig. 1B. The mean eye speed (with the standard error) is plotted against time
for the prelesion (solid) and postlesion (dashed) data shown in Fig. 1A. Following the lesion, the mean eye speed was reduced to about half its normal value
during the initial 100 msec of pursuit. After a corrective saccade, however, the
monkey tracked the target for the duration of the trial with normal pursuit movements. This is presumably because the initial saccade brought the visual target
into an undamaged portion of the visual field. It seems, therefore, that this
deficit did not result from a motor inability to perform pursuit eye movements.

Rather, the deficit appeared to be visual because it only occurred for targets which moved within a restricted area of visual space.

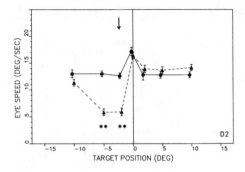

Fig. 2. Mean smooth eye speed measured 70 msec after the end of the initial saccade (ordinate) for target motion at 7 different locations in the visual field (abscissa). Circles connected by a solid line indicate the mean prelesion performance and standard error for 10 trials at each eccentricity. The dashed line shows postlesion performance. Asterisks indicate significant differences in pre- and postlesion performance (p<.001). The vertical arrow indicates the retinotopic location of the lesion in MT. The lesion was made in the right hemisphere. Reprinted from the Journal of Neuroscience.

The retinotopic nature of this deficit is illustrated in Fig. 2. In this experiment an injection of ibotenic acid was made on the horizontal meridian representation in MT, 2.5° to the monkey's left as indicated by the vertical arrow in Fig. 2. The tracking target was stepped to several locations on the horizontal meridian as indicated on the horizontal axis. The mean pursuit speed was measured 70 msec after the end of the initial saccade and is plotted on the vertical axis. Postlesion performance matched prelesion performance at all locations in the visual field except 2° and 5° to the monkey's left. The points for which the monkey's performance was impaired corresponded well to the location of the ibotenic acid injection in MT. Monkeys with such lesions were impaired when initiating pursuit for either leftward or rightward motion as long as the retinal motion occurred within the damaged portion of the visual field. This deficit, which we refer to as the retinotopic deficit, was observed for all MT lesions which did not include the center of gaze representation.

Monkeys with the retinotopic deficit were also impaired in their ability to make saccadic eye movements to moving targets. One can see that the amplitude of the initial saccade in the postlesion traces of Fig. 1A is smaller than the corresponding saccades in the prelesion traces. We measured this effect by defining a quantity called "saccadic error" to be the difference between target position and eye position at the end of the initial saccade. This quantity is plotted against the visual field location of the moving stimulus in Fig. 3A. Postlesion performance closely matched prelesion performance at all positions in the visual field except 5° to the monkey's right, a location which corresponded to the point of the ibotenic acid injection into MT in this experiment (vertical arrow).

These visuomotor deficits that followed MT lesions were selective in that they were only observed for responses to moving visual targets. In Fig. 3B, saccadic error is shown for the control trials in which the monkey made saccades to stationary targets. The monkey's performance was normal at all locations in the visual field, even for the location where saccades to moving visual targets were impaired (Fig. 3A). The deficit thus appears to selectively affect the monkey's use of motion information (retinal slip), leaving oculomotor responses to position information unaffected. This finding is indicative of the selective role played by MT in the cortical processing of visual motion.

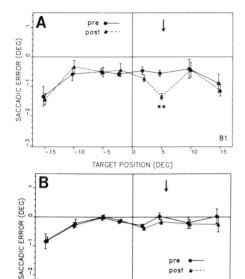

Fig. 3.   Effect of an MT lesion on
the accuracy of saccades to moving
and stationary targets. A. Saccadic
error (ordinate) for saccades to
moving targets at 9 different locations in the visual field (abscissa)
before and after an MT lesion. B.
Saccadic error for saccades to stationary targets at 9 different locations in the visual field. Data were
from the same experiment as those in
A. Double asterisks and the vertical
arrow have the same significance as
in Fig. 2. Reprinted from the
Journal of Neuroscience.

The Directional Deficit

We observed a different pattern of deficits when the MT lesion included the representation of the center of gaze in MT. For such lesions, the retinotopic
deficit was present for central eccentricities in the contralateral hemifield,
but an additional deficit was superimposed upon the retinotopic effect. This
deficit, which we call the "directional deficit", is illustrated in Figure 4.
This animal sustained an MT lesion in the right hemisphere, and had a corresponding retinotopic deficit for central eccentricities in the left hemifield. In
addition, however, the monkey's pursuit gain was reduced for all rightward tracking regardless of the point of initiation.

For example, the eye movement traces in Fig. 4A show prelesion and postlesion
responses to a target that was stepped 5° to the monkey's right with subsequent
motion away from the center of gaze. Following the lesion, the speed of the pursuit movements was reduced and frequent catch-up saccades were necessary to keep
the eyes near the moving target. This effect is clearly seen in the mean eye
speed traces in Fig. 4B. Eye speed was, on the average, 40-50% below normal
throughout the trials. In contrast, leftward pursuit was always normal after the
monkey succeeded in placing his eyes near the moving target (Dursteler and
colleagues, 1984).

This directional tracking deficit is very similar to human deficits reported in
the clinical literature (e.g. Troost and Abel, 1982) as it appears to be related
to a particular aspect of motor behavior (undirectional tracking) rather than to
the visual properties of the stimulus. The directional deficit is not, however,
intuitively explicable by any known property of MT neurons. If anything, one
might have expected pursuit deficits for tracking in the opposite direction, with
a reduced pursuit gain for target motion toward the damaged contralateral hemifield, that is, for leftward motion in the case of Fig. 4.

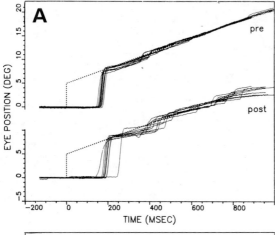

Fig. 4. Effect of a foveal MT lesion on smooth pursuit eye movements. A. Ten superimposed eye movements (solid traces) made in response to a step-ramp tracking target (dashed line) before (top) and after (bottom) an MT lesion. B. Mean and standard error of smooth eye speed (ordinate) as a function of time (abscissa) for the pre- (solid) and postlesion (dashed) responses shown in A. The lesion was made in the right hemisphere.

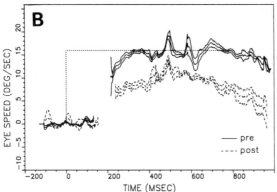

The interpretation of the directional deficit is somewhat complicated by the proximity of the center of gaze representation in MT to an adjacent extrastriate area, MST. MST contains neurons which encode certain aspects of pursuit eye movements (Wurtz and Newsome, 1985), and it is conceivable that the directional deficit results from reversible damage to this area that was not visible in histological sections. Regardless of the precise location of the lesion, our results clearly show that both the sensory and motor pursuit deficits that have been reported following large cortical lesions can be produced by exceedingly small lesions of extrastriate visual areas in the superior temporal sulcus.

Recovery

The monkeys were, in general, fully recovered from both the retinotopic and directional tracking deficits within one week following the lesion. The lone exception to this was for one hemisphere in which we made several injections at the same point in MT over a three week period. This animal failed to recover fully: pursuit initiation was impaired through the final testing session, 3 weeks after the final injection. Histological reconstruction revealed that the lesion created

by the serial injections involved much of MT and a substantial portion of MST on
the anterior bank of the STS as well.

DISCUSSION

We have documented two pursuit deficits which follow small lesions of visual
area MT. The retinotopic deficit is characterized by an impaired ability to
initiate pursuit to, or make saccades to moving visual targets when the motion
occurs in a particular portion of the visual field. The monkey appears to under-
estimate the speed of the moving visual stimulus. The initiation phase of pursuit is reduced in speed, and saccades consistently undershoot the target if motion is away from the fixation position, or overshoot the target if motion is
toward the fixation position. These effects are similar to those which follow
striate lesions (Goldberg and colleagues, 1982; Zee and colleagues, 1982;
Segraves and colleagues, this volume), but unlike striate lesions, the MT lesions
cause no deficits in saccades to stationary targets. The directional deficit,
on the other hand, is characterized by a reduced gain for all smooth pursuit
movements in a particular direction (toward the side of the lesion). This deficit is remarkably similar to the pursuit deficits in humans and monkeys which
follow extensive damage to the parieto-occipital region (Troost and Abel, 1982;
Tusa and colleagues, this volume).

The recovery of normal performance that follows the MT lesions is interesting in
its own right as a model system for studying the mechanisms that mediate behavioral adaptation to cortical damage. For example, it may be that several visual
areas contribute to the control of smooth pursuit eye movements so that damage
to one can be compensated relatively quickly by the others. If so, lesions
placed simultaneously in a small number of visual areas may result in permanent
pursuit deficits, thus identifying the multiple pathways which mediate the cortical control of pursuit.

Alternatively, recovery may be largely mediated by the substantial amount of
neural tissue within MT that survives our small lesions. Larger lesions of MT
should provide a critical test of this possibility. If recovery is indeed shown
to be dependent upon mechanisms within MT, electrophysiological mapping experiments can test for changes in the map of visual space in MT that may underlie
such behavioral adaptation. It will also be interesting to determine whether
sensory feedback is necessary to initiate the process of recovery. What, in
other words, are the effects of visual deprivation during the period between the
lesion and the initial postlesion behavioral testing? Future experiments along
these lines should provide a greater understanding of the cortical pathways that
control pursuit eye movements and of the adaptive changes that permit recovery
from damage to a portion of those pathways.

BIBLIOGRAPHY

Dursteler, M.R., R.H. Wurtz, W.T. Newsome, and A. Mikami (1984). Deficits in
    pursuit eye movements following ibotenic acid lesions of the foveal repre-
    sentation of area MT of macaque monkey. Soc. Neurosci. Abstr., 10, 475.
Goldberg, M.E., C.J. Bruce, L. Ungerleider, and M. Mishkin (1982). Role of the
    striate cortex in generation of smooth pursuit eye movements. Ann. Neurol.,
    12, 113.
Lanman, J., E. Bizzi, and J. Allum (1978). The coordination of eye and head
    movement during smooth pursuit. Brain Res., 153, 39-53.
Lisberger, S.G., and L.E. Westbrook (1985). Properties of visual inputs that
    initiate horizontal pursuit eye movements in monkeys. J. Neurosci., 5,
    1662-1673.
Lynch, J.C. and J.W. McLaren (1982). The contribution of parieto-occipital
    association cortex to the control of slow eye movements. In G. Lennerstrand,
    D.S. Zee, and E.L. Keller, (Eds.), Functional Basis of Ocular Motility

Disorders. Pergamon Press, Oxford. pp. 501-510.

Maunsell, J.H.R., and D.C. Van Essen (1983a). Functional properties of neurons in the middle temporal visual area of the macaque monkey. I. Selectivity for stimulus direction, speed, and orientation. J. Neurophysiol., 49, 1127-1147.

Maunsell, J.H.R., and D.C. Van Essen (1983b). The connections of the middle temporal visual area (MT) and their relationship to a cortical hierarchy in the macaque monkey. J. Neurosci., 3, 2563-2586.

Newsome, W.T., R.H. Wurtz, M.R. Dursteler and A. Mikami (1985a). Deficits in visual motion processing following ibotenic acid lesions of the middle temporal visual area of the macaque monkey. J. Neurosci., 5, 825-840.

Newsome, W.T., R.H. Wurtz, M.R. Dursteler and A. Mikami (1985b). Punctate chemical lesions of striate cortex in the macaque monkey: effect on visually guided saccades. Exp. Brain Res., 58, 392-399.

Olney, J.W. (1983). Excitotoxins: an overview. In K. Fuxe, P. Roberts, and R. Schwarcz (Eds.), Excitotoxins. Macmillan Press, London, pp. 82-95.

Rashbass, C. (1961). The relationship between saccadic and smooth tracking eye movements. J. Physiol. (Lond)., 159, 326-338.

Suzuki, D.A., and E.L. Keller (1984). Visual signals in the dorsolateral pontine nucleus of the alert monkey: Their relationship to smooth-pursuit eye movements. Exp. Brain Res., 53, 473-478.

Troost, B.T., and L.A. Abel (1982). Pursuit Disorders. In G. Lennstrand, D.S. Zee, and E.L. Keller (Eds.), Functional Basis of Ocular Motility Disorders. Pergamon Press, Oxford. pp. 511-515.

Recovery of Ocular Motor Function in Humans with Cerebral Lesions

R. J. Leigh and S. E. Thurston

Cleveland Veterans Administration Medical Center, and
University Hospitals of Cleveland, Case Western Reserve
University School of Medicine, Cleveland, OH 44106, USA

INTRODUCTION

A wide range of repair mechanisms have been demonstrated in ocular motor systems. These mechanisms enable recovery from disorders affecting vestibular, saccadic and vergence eye movements. Even smooth pursuit -- which might be regarded as a "closed-loop" system not requiring any corrective mechanism -- has been shown to be capable of adaptive changes (Optican, Zee and Chu 1985). Limitations to the extent of repair that is possible by such adaptive mechanisms exist. Some are due to fixed patterns of innervation such as that described by Hering's law. Other constraints on repair may be imposed by the ability of the brain to detect its own errors. For example, visual inputs are known to be vital for the adaptive mechanisms that effect repair and recovery in ocular motor systems. Thus, recovery from the effects of cerebral lesions may depend upon the extent of damage to the visual pathways including visual cortex. The demonstration in monkeys of multiple, extrastriate visual areas -- each containing a topological representation of the contralateral visual field and each specialized for analysis of some basic property of the visual stimulus -- suggests that some such areas may have specific influences on adaptation and recovery. It would seem that those visual areas that encode the direction and speed of visual stimuli are particularly important for the adaptive control of eye movements. In the macaque monkey, these visual areas are middle temporal (MT), medial superior temporal (MST) and area 7a of the parietal lobe (Van Essen and Maunsell, 1983).

Certain unilateral cerebral lesions in man cause a characteristic, asymmetric deficit in horizontal smooth pursuit (Figure 1). We have chosen to study this smooth pursuit asymmetry because it persists and seems immune to adaptive mechanisms. We wondered whether the persistence of this disorder was due to deprivation of the visual inputs required for repair or whether it was due to some fixed pattern of innervation within the pursuit system.

Clinicians first recognized tracking asymmetry with unilateral hemispheric lesions when they tested "optokinetic" nystagmus at the bedside using striped tapes or drums. It was noted that less nystagmus was induced when the striped stimulus was moved horizontally towards the side of the lesion. The location of the lesion producing this tracking asymmetry has been specified as "in the

posterior or middle portion of the cerebrum" (Cogan and Loeb, 1949), deep
parietal lobe (Baloh, Yee and Honrubia, 1980; Smith, 1963) and the
supramarginal or angular gyri (Fox and Holmes, 1926).

Quantitative measurements of horizontal smooth pursuit of a small visual
stimulus in patients with unilateral hemispheric disease have demonstrated
that pursuit gain (eye velocity/target velocity) is reduced when the target
moves towards the side of the lesion (Baloh, Yee and Honrubia, 1980; Troost
and colleagues 1972). Pursuit of targets moving away from the side of the
lesion is intact and, for lower target velocities, eye movements may be too
fast, i.e., gain greater than 1 (Sharpe, Lo and Rabinovitch, 1979). Studies
of smooth pursuit asymmetry which involve tracking of targets that move
periodically do not control the location of the visual stimulus on the
retina. This seems an important variable to control since visual information
presented to one hemisphere (the damaged one) may be impaired. Moreover,
studies to date have either employed targets moving at constant velocities or
sinusoidally at a restricted number of frequencies. With such approaches it
is not possible to detect any limitation of smooth pursuit related to target
acceleration (Lisberger and colleagues, 1981). We have set out to study
smooth pursuit asymmetry (SPA) due to cerebral lesions, examining what visual
deficit, if any, it might reflect.

SUBJECTS AND METHODS

We studied 15 patients with unilateral cerebral lesions (age range 35-59
years). Of these, 7 patients had suffered cerebral infarction, 6 patients had
undergone partial temporal lobectomy for intractable seizures, 1 patient had
suffered a penetrating head injury and 1 patient had a solitary metastasis.
All patients had their visual fields mapped on a perimeter or tangent screen
and their visual acuities measured. The interval between the cerebral lesion
and our measurements ranged from one month to 34 years. In addition, we
studied 5 healthy control subjects (age range 27-40 years). Horizontal eye
movements were recorded monocularly using the magnetic search coil method or
binocularly using infrared oculography. The patient's head was held still
during smooth pursuit testing. The stimulus for predictable smooth pursuit
tracking was a laser spot subtending 9 minutes of arc that was rear-projected
onto a semitranslucent tangent screen located 1.5 meters in front of the
subject. During most testing, subjects and patients viewed this stimulus
binocularly. Smooth pursuit was tested using predictable and non-predictable
target motion. The predictable target motion consisted of 1)
constant-velocity, triangular waveforms with velocities of up to 60
degrees/second and amplitudes of $\pm$ 15 degrees. 2) Sine waves with frequencies
of 0.1 to 1.0 Hz and amplitudes of $\pm$ 7.5 or $\pm$ 15 degrees. Non-predictable
target motion consisted of step-ramp stimuli that were presented in a
pseudo-random sequence. Because we were particularly interested in measuring
pursuit of a target moving in the left or right hemifield of vision we
selected stimuli that would avoid the area of central retina where there is
bilateral cortical representation (Bunt and Minkler, 1977) and also stayed out
of the blindspot of either eye. The stimuli consisted of (1) a step of three
degrees followed by a ramp of either 15 or 30 degrees/second away from the
fovea, (2) a step of 9 degrees followed by a ramp of 15 or 30 degrees/second
towards the fovea, or (3) a step of 6 degrees followed by a zero
degrees/second ramp. In practice the step-ramp was achieved as the subject
viewed a central, red light-emitting diode subtending 10 minutes of arc. Each
trial began as the diode went out and a moving target (a slit of light 2.4
degrees high and 4.6 minutes of arc wide) appeared simultaneously in one or
the other peripheral visual field. We chose this method of presenting
step-ramp stimuli since Lisberger and Westbrook (1985) found it to be optimal
for inducing a measurable pursuit response before the subject made a saccade.
For each patient, we checked that the luminence of the slit of light was above
the threshold for detection of similarly located static stimuli during visual

field testing. In normal subjects it was possible to measure pre-saccadic pursuit responses. This response, the first 60-100 msec of smooth pursuit, occurs before there has been time for visual feedback and can be related to stimulation of a specific part of the peripheral retina. The magnitude of this pre-saccadic response depends upon the location of the target on the retina and also may be influenced by whether the target moves toward or away from the fovea (Lisberger and Westbrook, 1985). Thus, in both subjects and patients we compared (1) foveafugal responses from the right and left hemifields, (2) foveapetal responses from the right and left hemifields. During all testing, subjects and patients were encouraged to track targets as best as they could.

RESULTS AND DISCUSSION

The Occurrence of Smooth Pursuit Asymmetry and its Relationship to Visual Field Defects

Of the 15 patients studied, 5 showed a definite asymmetry of horizontal smooth pursuit. The reduction in pursuit gain in these patients always corresponded with target motion towards the side of the hemispheric lesion. Four patients had suffered cerebral infarction and 1 had sustained a penetrating head injury. Four of our patients had right hemisphere lesions, and one had a left hemisphere lesion. In 4 patients, the lesion was localized, using computed tomography, to parieto-temporal cortex. This distribution is similar to that described by Fox and Holmes (1926) in patients showing "optokinetic" asymmetry, but more cases are required to determine a consistent pattern of localization.

The presence or absence of a homonymous visual field deficit per se bore no relation to the finding of SPA; some of our patients showing SPA had homonymous hemianopsia and some did not. Moreover, some patients with homonymous hemianopsia did not have SPA. Similarly, the presence or absence of hemi-visual neglect or inattention was not related to the presence of SPA. Fox and Holmes (1926) also reported a lack of correlation between "optokinetic" asymmetry and homonymous hemianopsia or visual inattention. The finding that SPA is unassociated with visual field deficit or visual inattention does not, however, exclude the possibility of a selective tracking deficit when moving targets are presented into one or other visual hemifield.

Smooth Pursuit Asymmetry is Independent of the Visual Hemifield into which the Visual Stimulus is Presented

We were able to study SPA in 3 patients using step-ramp stimuli. One patient had homonymous hemianopsia and this confounded our attempts to study the initial pursuit response to a visual stimulus presented into one hemifield of vision. The other two patients showed consistent results indicating that their SPA was independent of the visual field into which the stimulus was projected.

Figure 3 shows data from a 35-year-old man (LL) with a right parieto-temporal infarction (same patient as shown in Figure 1). At the time of testing, he was easily able to see the pursuit target in both peripheral fields. When the moving target was presented in one or the other visual hemifield (step-ramp stimuli) a similar asymmetry was evident to that present during tracking of predictable target motion. Because of the different responses in normal subjects to stimuli presented at different retinal locations, it is necessary to compare panels A with B, and C with D. In A and B a pre-saccadic pursuit response is evident (see velocity record) and is greater for leftward target motion. The average acceleration, over the first 100 msec. of the responses is 45 degrees/second^2 to the right (A) and 90 degrees/second^2 to the left (B). Such differences were apparent in every trial of type A and B conducted

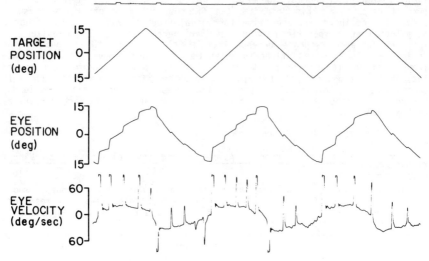

Fig. 1.   Smooth pursuit asymmetry (patient LL). Time marks
at top are in seconds. Rightward movements are
indicated by upward pen deflection.

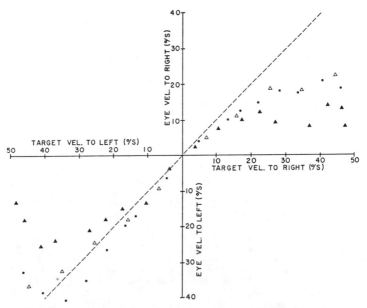

Fig. 2. Smooth pursuit of targets with predictable movement
by patient LL. ± 15° triangular, ●; ± 15° sines,
△; ± 7.5° sines,▲.

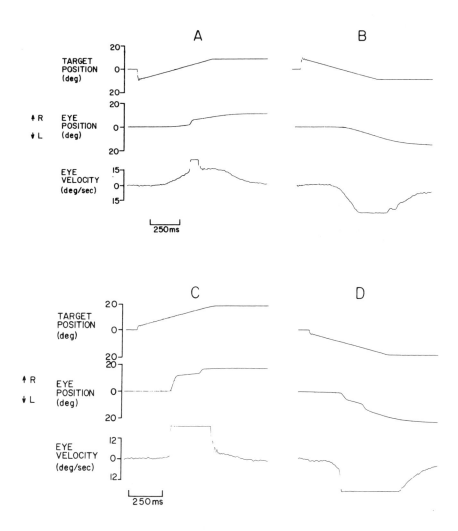

Fig. 3.   Pursuit responses to step-ramp stimuli in patient
LL.   Note that the target (slit of light) only
became visible after the step had occurred (see
"Methods").

in this patient. In C, the pre-saccadic response is too small to be reliably measured but for leftward target movement (D) a pre-saccadic acceleration of 75 degrees/second^2 is evident. In this patient, pre-saccadic acceleration of the eye was evident in 75% of trials such as D but in less than 15 percent of trials such as C. In a second patient (LB), a 59-year-old man with a right parietal lobe infarction, pre-saccadic responses were abolished for all trials with target movement to the right. For leftward target movement (trials type B and D), a pre-saccadic response was always present. Thus, in these two patients, the pursuit asymmetry was present in response to stimuli presented in either visual hemifield. This deficit is different from that produced by discrete lesions of MT (Newsome and colleagues, 1985) or lesions of striate cortex (Goldberg and colleagues, 1982).

Smooth Pursuit Asymmetry and the Brain's Estimate of Target Velocity

Is SPA due to a general deficiency in motion detection -- an impairment of the brain's ability to estimate target velocity? If this is the case, then one would expect ocular motor tasks, in addition to smooth pursuit, that require an estimate of target velocity to be impaired. Such a deficit might constrain the capabilities of adaptive mechanisms. On the otherhand, SPA might be a disorder of a specific ocular motor system.

To try and make this distinction, we measured the accuracy of saccades made to moving targets during step-ramps in two patients showing SPA but no visual field defect. In this situation, the brain must utilize information on target position and speed in planning saccades (Newsome and colleagues, 1985). For trials in which the target ramped towards the fovea, saccadic latencies were variably prolonged so that the target had passed over the fovea before a saccade occurred (Figure 3A) or else no saccade occurred (Figure 3B). However, for trials with target ramps away from the fovea, saccadic latencies were fairly constant and a comparison could be made of responses for rightward and leftward target motion (Figure 3C and D). We compared saccadic error (target position - eye position) at the end of the first saccade of each trial. In both patients saccadic error was significantly greater for step-ramps directed away from the side of the lesion (P < 0.05). This is apparent in the two trials shown in Figures 3C and 3D. On the other hand, saccades to step displacements of the target (without a subsequent ramp) did not show an asymmetry.

This preliminary data suggests, therefore, that SPA is independent of any general impairment of the ability to estimate target velocity. Both patients showed deficient smooth pursuit when tracking targets moving to the right in either hemifield of vision. On the otherhand, saccades were significantly more hypometric when target motion was to the left in the left visual hemifield than with target motion to the right in the right visual hemifield. Saccades to stationary targets presented in the right or left visual hemifields were made with equal accuracy.

Dynamic Properties of Smooth Pursuit Asymmetry

To investigate the dynamic properties of SPA we studied the relationship between eye velocity and target velocity with the three types of predictable stimulus motion in two patients. Representative data from one patient (LL) is shown in Figure 2. (1) Both patients had a left-right asymmetry of pursuit gain that was consistent for triangular-stimulus target velocities of up to 30 degrees/second for patient LL and 20 degrees/second for patient LB. In patient LL, pursuit to the left had a gain greater than 1 for targets of up to about 30 degrees/second (see Figure 2). To the right, pursuit gain was approximately 0.7 within this same range. For patient LB, pursuit gain to the left was approximately 0.9 and to the right was 0.4. (2) Above 30 degrees/second for LL and 20 degrees/second for LB, pursuit gain for tracking of triangular-waveform targets declined. This might represent either the transient acceleration of the turn-around points of the triangular wave or a true velocity saturation (Meyer, Lasker and Robinson, 1985). (3) When targets with variable accelerations (sine waves) were used, it was found that both patients showed lower and more variable gain with higher target acceleration and that this "acceleration-saturation" deficit was greater for pursuit of targets moving towards the side of the lesion. Thus SPA could be mainly attributed to a change in "steady-state" gain rather than a change in "acceleration saturation". Troost and colleagues (1972) and Sharpe, Lo and Rabinovitch (1979) reported similar findings when they studied SPA following hemidecortication. Pursuit deficits due to "acceleration saturation" have been reported with more posterior cerebral lesions (Leigh and Tusa, 1985).

A striking feature in patient LL was that he tracked targets to the left with a gain of greater than 1, even at target velocities of over 30 degrees/second. This was evidenced by the presence of "back-up" saccades (see Figure 1). Patient LB showed the same phenomenon, but only at lower target velocities. The patients described by Sharpe and colleagues (1979) also tracked targets moving away from the side of their hemidecortication with gain values of greater than 1. Their findings could probably be explained on the basis of a static bias (manifest as nystagmus during attempted fixation of a stationary target) superimposed upon a normal contralateral pursuit gain. In our patient LL, intermittent right-beating nystagmus was present, during attempted fixation of a stationary target, with slow phase velocity of 1 degree/second or less. During pursuit to the left, however, eye velocity exceeded target velocity by as much as 6 degrees/second. Thus, in this patient, the enhanced contralateral pursuit could not be explained simply on the basis of a "static bias"; further studies seem appropriate to settle this point.

Why Does Smooth Pursuit Asymmetry Persist?

SPA may be observed immediately following a cerebral injury. In some patients (for example the case reported by Leigh and Tusa, 1985) SPA partially or completely resolves following resolution of cerebral edema. It may, however, persist and we have recorded it in one patient 34 years after injury of the right temporal-parietal cortex. In addition to the SPA, the accompanying nystagmus, with slow phases directed away from the side of the lesioned hemisphere, may also persist. The persistence of SPA seems to imply some limitation of adaptive mechanisms. The preliminary evidence presented here suggests that SPA is independent of any general deficit of the brain to use information on retinal image motion. Moreover, the finding of increased pursuit gain when tracking targets moving away from the side of the lesion might represent an attempt to put things right.

Optican, Zee and Chu (1985) have recently demonstrated that although smooth pursuit is a closed-loop system, it does show an ability to perform plastic-adaptive changes in response, for example, to the visual consequences imposed by extraocular muscle paresis. One finding of this study was that the increase in pursuit gain applied to tracking in both directions; this bidirectional change may have been adaptive in their patients. Asymmetrical changes in pursuit can be induced in normal subjects (Carl and colleagues - this symposium) but our patients with SPA seemed to have lost this ability.

SUMMARY

We have studied the asymmetry of horizontal smooth pursuit that persists after unilateral, cerebral lesions to determine how it is related to disturbance of visual inputs. Our preliminary findings suggest that this type of smooth pursuit asymmetry (1) is independent of homonymous hemianopsia or hemi-visual neglect, (2) occurs in response to stimuli presented in either visual hemifield, (3) is independent of any general deficiency of the brain to estimate the speed of moving targets, (4) principally reflects an asymmetry of the internal (open loop) gain of the pursuit system, (5) may point to a limited ability of these patients to make asymmetric changes in pursuit gain in response to visual requirements.

ACKNOWLEDGEMENTS

We are grateful to S.G. Lisberger, J.R. Carl, C. Kennard, L.A. Abel, L.F. Dell'Osso, R.B. Daroff, R. Lesser, S. Landgraf and A. Ziegler for advice and technical help. Supported by the Veterans Administration and Evenor Armington Fund.

REFERENCES

Baloh, R. W., R. D. Yee and V. Honrubia (1980). Optokinetic nystagmus and parietal lobe lesions. Ann. Neurol., 7, 269-276.
Bunt, A.H. and D. S. Minckler (1977). Foveal sparing. New anatomical evidence for bilateral representation of the central retina. Arch. Ophthalmol., 95, 1445-1447.
Cogan, D. G. and D. R. Loeb (1949). Optokinetic response and intracranial lesions. Arch. Neurol. Psychiat., 61, 183-187.
Fox, J. C. and G. Holmes (1926) Optic nystagmus and its value in the localization of cerebral lesions. Brain, 49, 333-371.
Glickstein, M., J. L. Cohen, B. Dixon, A. Gibson, M. Hollins, E. Labossiere and F. Robinson (1980). Corticopontine visual projections in macaque monkeys. J. Comp. Neurol., 190, 209-229.
Goldberg, M. E., C. J. Bruce, L. Ungerleider and M. Mishkin (1982). Role of the striate cortex in generation of smooth pursuit eye movements. Ann. Neurol., 12, 113.
Leigh, R. J. and R. J. Tusa (1985). Disturbance of smooth pursuit caused by infarction of occipitoparietal cortex. Ann. Neurol., 17, 185-187.
Lisberger, S. G., C. Evinger, G. W. Johanson and A. F. Fuchs (1981). Relationship between eye acceleration and retinal image velocity during foveal smooth pursuit in man and monkey. J. Neurophysiol., 46, 229-249.
Lisberger, S. G. and L. E. Westbrook (1985). Properties of visual inputs that initiate horizontal smooth pursuit eye movements in monkeys. J. Neuroscience, 5, 1662-1673.
Meyer, C. H., A. G. Lasker, and D. A. Robinson (1985). The upper limit of human smooth pursuit velocity. Vision Res., 25, 561-563.
Newsome, W. T., R. H. Wurtz, M. R. Dürsteler, and A. Mikami (1985). Deficits in visual motion processing following ibotenic acid lesions of the middle temporal visual area of the macaque monkey. J. Neuroscience, 5, 825-840.
Optican, L. M., D. S. Zee and F. C. Chu (1985). Adaptive responses to ocular muscle weakness in human pursuit and saccadic eye movements. J. Neurophysiol., 54, 110-122.
Sharpe, J. A., A. W. Lo and H. E. Rabinovitch (1979). Control of the saccadic and smooth pursuit systems after cerebral hemidecortication. Brain, 102, 387-403.
Smith, J. L. (1963). Optokinetic nystagmus. Thomas, Springfield, IL.
Troost, B. T., R. B. Daroff, R. B. Weber and L. F. Dell'Osso (1972). Hemispheric control of eye movements. II. Quantitative analysis of smooth pursuit in a hemispherectomy patient. Arch. Neurol., 27, 449-452.
Van Essen, D. C. and J. H. R. Maunsell (1983). Hierarchical organization and functional streams in the visual cortex. Trends in Neurosciences, 6, 370-375.

Adaptation to Frontal Lobe Lesions

J. A. Sharpe

Division of Neurology, Playfair Neuroscience Unit, and the
Neuro-ophthalmology Unit, Toronto Western Hospital,
Departments of Medicine and Ophthalmology, University of
Toronto, Toronto, Canada

INTRODUCTION

The frontal eye field (FEF) of subhuman primates contains neurons that discharge before saccades: movement cells, visuomotor cells, and visual cells (Bruce and Goldberg, 1985). These three cell types have little or no discharge before spontaneous saccades. Some cells show slowly building anticipatory discharge before saccades to predictable stimuli. Ablation of one FEF causes only transient ipsilateral deviation of the eyes and contralateral neglect (Latto and Cowey, 1971). Stimulation of the supplementary motor area (SMA) of the dorsomedial frontal cortex elicits contralateral saccades and SMA units discharge before both visually triggered and spontaneous saccades (Schlag and Schlag-Rey, 1985).

Homologues of the simian FEF and SMA are demonstrated by cerebral blood flow studies in man. Blood flow in lateral frontal cortex and a zone presumed to be the SMA increases during repeated saccades (Burde, Fox and Raichle, 1983). Paresis of voluntary saccades is attributed to frontal lobe damage (cf. Sharpe, 1982) but confirmation by modern radiologic and quantitative oculographic study is scanty. Patients with chronic cerebral hemidecortication have mild slowing and prolonged latencies of saccades in both horizontal directions (Sharpe, Lo and Rabinovitch, 1979) and inaccuracy of contralateral saccades (Troost, Weber and Daroff, 1972). Patients with frontal lobectomy for epilepsy (Guitton, Buchtel and Douglas, 1985) and Alzheimer's disease (Fletcher and Sharpe, 1985) exhibit a visual grasp reflex consisting of difficulty suppressing saccades toward novel stimuli and making voluntary saccades away from them. Oculographic investigation can quantify behavioural deficits caused by cerebral hemispheric disease (Sharpe, 1982). This chapter reviews effects of unilateral frontal lobe lesions on the latency, accuracy, and speed of saccades and considers their adaptation.

FRONTAL LOBE LESIONS: PATIENTS AND METHODS

Horizontal saccades were measured in 8 patients, aged 32 to 69 (mean 45, SD 11) with unilateral frontal lobe lesions. Five were right sided and three left sided. Six patients with infarcts or hematomas, either hypertensive or spontaneous, were studied two weeks to six months after onset of symptoms. Two patients with tumors, one metastatic and one a low grade glioma, were studied two weeks and 16 years, respectively, after symptom onset. Study was deferred for at least two weeks, after any ipsilateral deviation of the eyes had recovered. Patients were selected from a larger group with frontal lobe damage because: 1) they were receiving no anticonvulsant or other neuroactive drugs; 2) they were alert and cooperative; 3) they were free of other neurologic disease; and 4) lesions were identified by CT scan to be confined to one frontal lobe, without shift of midline structures or other mass effects. The lesions involved frontal cortex and white matter, not necessarily the prefontal cortex or supplementary motor area, but they were positioned to involve projections from these areas. Eleven age-matched volunteers (mean age 50, SD 9) served as control subjects.

Eye position was recorded by infrared limbus reflection technique with the head immobilized. Analogue signals of eye and target position were digitized at 200 hertz for analysis by a PDP 11/73 computer in five patients and in all control subjects, or from recordings on an inkjet rectilinear polygraph in three patients. Light emitting diode targets on a stimulus arc were stepped at regular or pseudorandom intervals, amplitudes and directions. Saccadic peak velocities, durations, latencies and accuracies were determined as previously described (Sharpe, Lo, and Rabinovitch, 1979; Zackon and Sharpe, 1984). Statistical analyses of group data were performed by Mann Whitney U tests and comparison of contralateral and ipsilateral values for individual subjects by two-tailed t tests.

PEAK VELOCITIES

Scatter plots of peak velocities (PV) of saccades of various amplitudes were fitted to a best fit exponential curve: PV = $V(1-\exp[-A/C])$ where A is amplitude at any corresponding PV, V is the asymptotic peak velocity and C is a constant defining the curve. V values of contralateral and ipsilateral saccades were not significantly different for the patient group (Fig. 1). Two patients had subnormal peak velocities in both directions (below 355 deg/sec; normal V -2 SD). Contralateral saccades were significantly slower than ipsilateral saccades in two patients. The side or duration of lesions did not affect the slowing. A patient with a left frontal glioma for 16 years and a patient with a right infarct for two weeks had slowed contralateral saccades. When compared with peak velocities of patients studied 8 to 12 years after cerebral hemidecortication, slowing of contralateral saccades was more marked after decortication than after frontal lobe lesions (Fig. 1). This suggests that non-frontal areas of the cerebrum also modulate the speed of saccades.

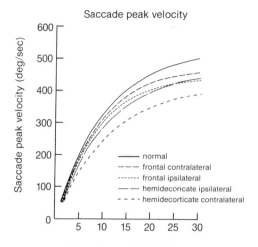

Fig. 1.   Peak . velocities   of both   contralateral
           and   ipsilateral   saccades   were
           significantly   slowed   in   group   of   5
           hemidecorticate   patients   but   not   in
           group of 7 frontal lobe patients.

Deng and associates (1984) found slow saccades to remembered
positions of targets flashed into the field contralateral to FEF
lesions in monkeys; slowing lasted over 10 months. Visually guided
saccades were normal. The FEF contributes to the dynamic features
of saccades toward remembered targets, as well as to triggering and
targetting. Visually guided saccades were slow in four of these
patients, suggesting that other frontal lobe areas, perhaps the
SMA, modulate the activity of brainstem medium lead burst units.
Slowing after recent (two weeks) or longstanding (16 years) lesions
illustrates limited adaptation to frontal lobe lesions.

SACCADE DURATIONS

When compared to those of normal subjects, durations of saccades in
the patient group were significantly prolonged (p < 0.05)
contralateral to frontal lobe lesions. Three patients had
abnormally long duration saccades in both directions (> normal mean
+2 SD). Contralateral saccadic durations were significantly longer
in four individual patients (p < 0.02 to < 0.001).

The durations of saccades are dictated by the firing duration of
medium lead burst units in the pons. Saccade durations were
prolonged in patients studied two weeks, four weeks, six months,
and 16 years after diagnosis. Although normal saccade durations in
three patients may exemplify adaptation to unilateral frontal lobe
damage, prolonged durations in five patients demonstrated
incomplete adaptation.

SACCADE LATENCIES

1. Predictable Targets

Saccades to 20 degree targets at regular intervals were delayed
contralateral to frontal lobe lesions (Fig. 2). Contralateral
mean latency was 342 msec, SD 89 and ipsilateral mean latency was
245 msec, SD 47 (normal mean latency 220 msec, SD 32).

2. Unpredictable Amplitude and Direction Targets

When targets stepped in unpredictable directions and amplitudes of
5, 10 or 20 degrees at 3 second intervals, normal subjects had
longer latencies than when timing was unpredictable. Although the
patient group had greater saccadic delay than the normal mean,
the delay was not significant. Contralateral and ipsilateral
delay did not differ for the group (Fig. 2).

3. Unpredictable Amplitude, Direction and Timing

Saccades to targets moving unpredictably were delayed in both
directions (p < 0.02; Fig. 2) without significant group difference
between contralateral and ipsilateral delay. Two patients had
significantly longer latencies to contralateral targets.

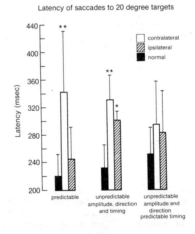

Fig. 2.   Graphs of mean saccade latencies to
          target steps of predictable and
          unpredictable amplitude, direction and
          timing. Target steps of 20 degrees are
          selected from variable amplitude
          paradigms. *p < 0.02, **p < 0.01
          compared with normal latencies.

Saccadic Delay

Overall, four patients had significantly greater delay in dispatching saccades to targets in the field of gaze contralateral to frontal lobe lesions. Three patients had abnormal delay in both directions. Although four patients had latencies within the normal range, in two of them contralateral delay was significantly greater. Only two had normal symmetrical latencies. Considered under each condition of target predictability, contralateral delay was significantly greater than ipsilateral delay when target motion was predictable (Fig. 2).

Inability to direct and sustain activity toward future goals is a feature of bilateral frontal lobe disease (Luria, 1969). In a patient with a right frontal lobe tumor, Luria, Karpov and Yarbuss (1966) reported a paucity of saccades during picture scanning. In the present study, unilateral frontal lobe damage impaired the ability to dispatch contralateral saccades when the time and location of target appearance could be anticipated. Under this condition, ipsilateral saccades, presumably dispatched with the participation of the opposite intact frontal lobe, had normal latencies. All patients with prolonged latencies to predictable targets had right sided lesions, consistent with a major role of the nondominant hemisphere in vigilance (Heilman and Valenstein, 1972). Loss of neurons that develop anticipatory increase in their discharge before saccades (Bruce and Goldberg, 1985) may be a pathologic correlate of delayed contralateral saccades to predictable targets.

In addition, saccades were delayed in both directions when target amplitude, direction and timing were unpredictable (Fig. 2). Although the group differences between contralateral and ipsilateral delay were not significant, four individual patients had significantly longer delay to contralateral targets under those unpredictable conditions. Bilateral delay also occurs after complete cerebral hemidecortication (Sharpe, Lo and Rabinovitch, 1979). The delay of ipsilateral saccades is not readily explained by transcallosal influences on the intact frontal lobe since, at least in the FEF, sites where microstimulation elicit contralateral horizontal saccades are not connected to the opposite FEF via the corpus callosum (Bruce and Goldman-Rakic, 1984).

Normal subjects can make express saccades at latencies of about 100 msec if a target is extinguished well before a new target appears (Fischer and Ramsperger, 1984). FEF lesions in the monkey do not impair the ability to make express saccades but superior colliculus ablation abolishes them (Schiller, Sandell and Maunsell, 1984), suggesting that express saccades are processed by direct retinocollicular projections, without cerebral hemispheric participation.

Ipsilateral deviation of the eyes occurred acutely in 3 patients but recovered rapidly, within 3 days. Subsequently, delay of contralateral saccades was evident in patients who had transient ipsilateral deviation. Neither ipsilateral deviation nor delay of contralateral saccades occurred in patients with frontal lobe

neoplasms. In such patients, adaptation to the insidious
pathologic process could occur, but adaptation was incomplete:
bidirectional delay occurred 6 months to 16 years after onset of
symptoms from infarction or neoplasm.

Rehabilitation of saccades appeared complete to clinical
examination. This adaptation may be mediated by intact areas of
the damaged hemisphere or by the opposite hemisphere.
Bidirectional saccades are within the repertoire of one hemisphere,
as evidenced by saccadic function after hemidecortication (Sharpe,
Lo and Rabinovitch, 1979). When ipsilateral gaze deviation
persists for many days, previous damage to the opposite frontal
lobe may be responsible(Latto and Cowey, 1971; Steiner and Melamed,
1984). Persisting delay of contralateral saccades, or of
bidirectional saccades, after unilateral frontal lobe damage
exemplifies limited adaptation by spared cortical projections from
the damaged hemisphere and from the opposite hemisphere.

                        ACCURACY OF SACCADES

Saccades to 20 degree predictable targets were inaccurate in both
directions. Amplitudes of initial saccades to targets in the
contralateral field were subnormal (mean 16.9 deg., SD 2.1) but did
not differ from those to ipsilateral targets (mean 16.0 deg., SD
2.8; normal 19.0 deg., SD 1.0) in agreement with the findings of
Pykko and associates (1984). Inaccuracy was recorded up to five
months after a frontal hematoma. Refixations consisted of a series
of hypometric steps. When timing and amplitudes of target motion
were unpredictable, the accuracy of saccades was within the normal
range in both directions.

Unilateral FEF ablation in monkeys causes inaccuracy of
contralateral saccades, not ipsilateral saccades, to remembered
target positions; however, contralateral saccades to visual targets
are accurate (Deng and others, 1984). More extensive frontal lobe
damage in humans impairs the precision of saccades to predictable
targets in both directions.

Since saccades to unpredictably moving targets were accurate after
unilateral frontal lobe damage, target error signals must also be
delivered to the brainstem from intact cerebral areas, such as
prestriate and inferior parietal cortex. In contrast, hypometria
of saccades to predictable targets exemplifies defective execution
of motor programs that involve anticipation. Hypometric saccades
to predictable targets might be the behavioural correlate of
damage to frontal lobe neurons that display anticipatory build up
of their discharge before saccades.

                        CONCLUSIONS

Unilateral frontal lobe lesions cause defects in programming
saccades. Although the frontal lobe is not essential for
generating voluntary or optically evoked saccades, mild slowing of

saccades attests to frontal lobe influences on brainstem generation of fast eye movements. Delay of contralateral saccades to predictable targets and bidirectional delay of saccades to unpredictable targets are manifestations of unilateral frontal lobe involvement. Bidirectional inaccuracy of saccades to predictable targets can persist for months after frontal lobe damage.

When contrasted with transient ipsilateral deviation of the eyes and neglect of the opposite hemifield of movement after acute lesions, saccadic function undergoes remarkably rapid rehabilitation. Manifestations of destruction of parts of the nervous system are threefold: they reflect functions of the damaged area, functions of the rest of the brain, and adaptive capacities of the rest of the brain. These saccadic changes illustrate visual and ocular motor adaptation and some of its limits.

ACKNOWLEDGEMENTS

Supported by Medical Research Council of Canada Grants ME5509 and MT5404. The author is grateful to P. Nguyen and A. W. Lo for technical assistance and to R. Armstrong for manuscript preparation.

REFERENCES

Bruce, C. J. and P. S. Goldman-Rakic (1984). Columnar organization of callosal connectivity in the Macaque frontal eye fields and its relation to elicited eye movements. Soc. Neuroscience Abstr., 10, 59.
Bruce, C. J. and M. E. Goldberg (1985). Primate frontal eye fields. I. Single neurons discharging before saccades. J. Neurophysiol., 53, 603-635.
Burde, R. M., P. T. Fox, and M. E. Raichle (1983). Cortical regulation of saccadic eye movements in man demonstrated by positron emission tomography. Soc Neuroscience Abstr., 9, 751.
Deng, S.-Y., M. A. Segraves, L. G. Ungerleider, M. Mishkin, and M. E. Goldberg (1984). Unilateral frontal eye field lesions degrade saccadic performance in the rhesus monkey. Soc. Neuroscience Abstr., 10, 59.
Fischer, B. and E. Ramsperger (1984). Human express saccades: extremely short reaction times of goal directed eye movement. Exp. Brain Res., 57, 191-195.
Fletcher, W. A. and J. A. Sharpe (1985). Alzheimer's disease: saccadic eye movement dysfunction., Ann. Neurol. 18, 142.
Guitton, D., H. A.Buchtel, and R. M. Douglas (1985). Frontal lobe lesions in man cause difficulties in suppressing reflexive glances and in generating goal-directed saccades. Exp. Brain Res. 58, 455-472.
Heilman, K. M. and E. Valenstein (1972). Frontal lobe neglect in man. Neurology, 22, 660-664.
Latto, R. and A. Cowey (1971). Fixation changes after frontal eye field lesions in monkeys. Brain Res., 30, 25-36.

Luria, A. R., B. A. Karpov, and A. L. Yarbuss (1966). Disturbances
    of active visual perception with lesions of the frontal lobes.
    Cortex 2, 202-212.
Luria, A. R. (1969). Frontal lobe syndromes. In P. J. Vinken and
    G. W. Bruyn (Eds.). Handbook of Clinical Neurology, Vol. 2,
    North-Holland, Amsterdam. pp. 725-757.
Pykko, I., A.-I. Dahlen, L. Schalen, and B. Hindfelt (1984).
    Eye movements in patients with speech dyspraxia. Acta
    Otolaryngol., 98, 481-489.
Schiller, P.H., J.H. Sandell, and J.H.R. Maunsell (1984). Effect
    of superior colliculus and frontal eye field lesions on
    saccadic latency in the monkey. Soc. Neuroscience Abstr., 10,
    60.
Schlag, J., and M. Schlag-Rey (1985). Unit activity related to
    spontaneous saccades in frontal dorsomedial cortex of monkey.
    Exp Brain Res., 58, 208-211.
Sharpe, J. A., A. W. Lo, and H. E. Rabinovitch (1979).
    Control of the saccadic and smooth pursuit systems after
    cerebral hemidecortication. Brain, 102, 387-403.
Sharpe, J. A. (1982). Cerebral ocular motor deficits. In G.
    Lennerstrand, D. S. Zee, and E. L. Keller (Eds.),
    Functional basis of ocular motility disorders. Pergamon Press,
    Oxford. pp. 479-488.
Steiner, I., and E. Melamed (1984). Conjugate eye deviation
    after acute hemispheric stroke: delayed recovery after previous
    contralateral frontal lobe damage. Ann. Neurol., 16, 509-511.
Troost, B. T., R. B. Weber, and R. B. Daroff (1972). Hemispheric
    control of eye movements. Quantitative analysis of refixation
    saccades in a hemispherectomy patient. Arch. Neurol., 27,
    441-448.
Zackon, D. H., and J. A. Sharpe (1984). Midbrain paresis of
    horizontal gaze. Ann. Neurol., 16, 495-504.

Adaptation of Gaze to Eccentric Fixation in Homonymous Hemianopia

W. H. Zangemeister, F. Dannheim and K. Kunze

University Clinic Hamburg, Eppendorf, Department of Neurology,
D2 Hamburg 20, Martinistr. 52, FRG

INTRODUCTION.
Patients with homonymous hemianopia (HH) display typical
disabilities to acquire visual targets in their blind hemifield. In
a HEAD FIXED situation they develop characteristic strategies of
ocular motor control to overcome the HH defect (3). In a more
natural HEAD FREE situation they show additional difficulties to
cope with their HH defect (9). These include stair-step and one-step
overshoot/backdrift saccadic strategies for target
acquisition in the blind hemifield (BHF), which is also used in a
head fixed condition, these patients demonstrate a significant side
asymmetry of compensatory eye movements (CEM); CEM gain i.e.ratio of
eye to head velocity is increased for gaze shifts to BHF and
decreased for gaze shifts to SHF (seeing hemifield). Often this may
cause large 'maladaptive' gaze errors. HH patients therefore tend to
minimize or avoid head movements.
Experimentally normal subjects can be forced to use a similarly
deranged behavior of ocular motor control. When normal subjects (Ss)
learn to achieve eccentric gaze fixation using secondary visual
feedback (2VFB), i.e. gaze position is displayed simultaneously with
the target, they demonstrate similar strategies to superpose target
and 2VFB-target (11). Initially they use stairstep saccades and
macrosaccadic square wave oscillations that were earlier described
(5,7) as transient responses to achieve and maintain eccentric
fixation. After some training they become adapted to the task and
now use slow and fast drifts to achieve eccentric fixation; they use
microsaccadic square wave jerks or a nystagmus like pattern of small
eccentric saccades with following backdrifts to maintain eccentric
fixation.
We reasoned that early adaptation to and use of eccentric fixation
could help hemianopic patients to cope better with their disability.
Also they might be able to make better use of their head movements,
which they otherwise avoid (9). To test this hypothesis we compared
gaze responses of three normal subjects and three patients with full
dense homonymous hemianopia. We compared first their initial
transient responses to the task of eccentric fixation using 2VFB.
Then, after some training in head fixed and head free situations, we
looked for their adaptive responses. The results were compared with
earlier findings (3,9,10,11).

METHODS.
Normal subjects and patients. Three normal subjects (age 25,29,40
all male) served as comparision. They all had full uncorrected visual
acuity (20/20) and no history of earlier neurological or eye diseases.
The three patients (age: 40 female,51 male,46 male) were all admitted
because of occlusion of right posterior cerebral artery; this was con=
firmed by CT-scans and angiography. They all showed a complete dense
left homonymous hemianopia, that was quantified by Octopus perimetry
during their stay in our clinic;it was rechecked before checking their
eye movements for this study. Neurological examination did not reveal
additional disturbances except for discrete reflex asymmetries in two
cases. All patients showed 20/20 visual acuity with correction.

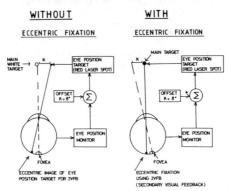

Fig.1: Setup for achieving eccentric fixation using 2VFB

Setup and recording equipment (cf.Fig1). Ss set in a comfortable
chair with their head either fixed by a head rest and four head
constraints (H.FIXED condition), or with head free to move (H.FREE
condition) in a dimly lit room in a viewing distance of 100cm to a se=
micircular white screen.One eye was patched, in patients this was the
eye contralateral to the HH (right eye). Horizontal eye movements were
recorded by monocular DC electrooculography (EOG) with a resolution of
one degree.Head movements were recorded using a tight head band linked
through two universal joints to a low torque ceramic potentiometer of
infinite resolution. A white light spot of 1 deg visual angle served as
the primary target; it was controlled by a mirror galvanometer linked
to a signal generator that would generate horizontal steps of various
amplitudes (+-5 to 30deg) and frequencies (0.01 - 1.5Hz). After cali=
bration of eye and head movements including electronic summation to
obtain gaze position a second -red laser- target of 0.3deg vis. angle
was displayed. It was controlled by another mirror galvanometer that
was linked to gaze position output through a low pass filter. After
calibration Ss were asked to fixate the white center target and then to
fixate the red laser spot as soon as it would appear. At first the laser
spot had the same position as the white target when the eye fixated the
target (feedback gain of 1,no offset). After 30 sec of practising Ss had
to close their eyes. The position of the laser spot was now changed by
an offset of about 8 deg off the center to the right i.e. towards the
SHF in case of HH patients (Fig.1,left). The Ss was then required to
accurately fixate the target, so that the laser spot was superimposed
upon it (Fig.1,right). The same procedure was repeated several times
with predictable and nonpredictable positions of the main white target
and different offsets (4 deg,12 deg) of the red laser spot for eccentric
2VFB to right to obtain transient responses. Eccentric offset of 2VFB
was then fixed. In this way adaptive responses to continuously applied
eccentric fixation to different targets using 2VFB were tested.

öAfter a pause the head free condition began,with essentially the
same procedure as with head fixed.Each set of trials lasted about 10
minutes.

RESULTS and DISCUSSION.

HEAD FIXED (Fig.2).
Transient responses. Normal Ss demonstrated transient
stairstep patterns of normal latency and 3 to 4 steps when they were
firstly exposed to eccentric fixation using 2VFB (upper left). To
maintain this, they used saccadic square wave oscillations (upper
right) of decreasing amplitude.
With non eccentric fixation HH patients demonstrated the earlier
described (3) typical responses (Fig.2,lower left). Non predicted
targets were fixated by multiple stairsteps of variable initial
delay (0.3-0.5sec), and of variable total duration (up to 1.9sec).
In case the target was lost, typically the target recovery strategy
(3) was used (lower right), consisting of irregular macrosaccadic
'oscillations'.

HEAD FIXED CONDITION: GAZE POSITION = EYE POSITION

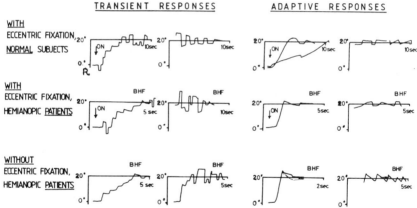

Fig.2: Gaze responses in head fixed condition.
        R.=right,ordinates=gaze position,abszissae=time.On=2VFB on

A similar strategy of mostly irregular square wave oscillations
occurred when HH patients tried to achieve and maintain
eccentric fixation without training (transient;middle left). Initial
capture of target using 2VFB for eccentric fixation was sometimes
achieved by very time consuming multiple stairsteps.
Adaptive responses. After some training using always the same
offset of 8 deg to the right, normal Ss tended to use slow or
fast drifts instead of stairsteps to achieve eccentric fixation more
rapidly (upper left). To maintain eccentric fixation, very small
saccadic oscillations or slow drifts together with small oppositely
directed saccades - a nystagmus like pattern - were used (upper
right). In contrast, HH patients used large overshooting
saccades followed by some slow backwards drift and small corrective
saccades, when position of the eccentric 2VFB target was predictable

öand the task had been trained. Maintenance of eccentric fixation was done by more irregular behavior of varying slow and fast drifts intercepted by small saccades. The former strategy resembled the strategy that was used by patients when predictable targets in the BHF were captured with foveal fixation (right, middle and lower). Of special interest was, that one patient with a longstanding acquired HH had developed a nystagmus like pattern to 'lock' on targets on the side of the BHF. A similar behavior has been described before (9,10).
HEAD FREE (Fig.3).
Transient responses. With head free to move (2nd set of experiment) Ss had of course undergone some training of the basic task. Also, the accuracy of the offset of the eccentric target was not as good as with head fixed due to limitations of the experimental setup. *Normal* Ss generally used a stairstep of only two saccades as transient responses, and then tried to match gaze position and target position using small irregular head oscillations rather than saccades to lock on target. In this way they made use of their compensatory eye movements (CEM, pursuit eye movements plus vestibular ocular reflex (VOR)) to keep on target. This included some degree of erratic, sometimes greatly off target leading gaze movements (upper left).

HEAD FREE CONDITION: GAZE POSITION = HEAD+EYE POSITION

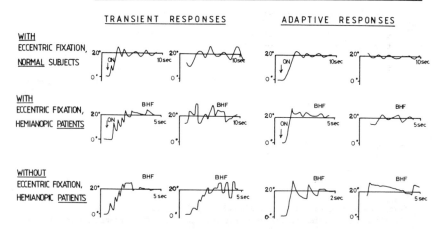

Fig.3: Gaze responses in head free condition.

With and without eccentric fixation HH *patients* used the same strategy of multiple stairsteps with fast CEMs during the head movement. CEM gain (ratio of eye to head velocity) was high for gaze shifts to the BHF, low for shifts to the SHF. They initially tried to maintain eccentric fixation in this transient state by avoiding head movements partly(left,lower),other when center fixation was permitted. Here,they completely avoided head movements.
Adaptive responses. *Normal* Ss soon learned to suppress larger saccades and to use small head movements to achieve and maintain eccentric fixation on the target (upper right). After some training they showed a gaze type III (8) like pattern when capturing a predictable target.

HH *patients* preferred to use gaze type I with eccentric
fixation. With training they were able to suppress the
asymmetrically high CEM gain that occured with gaze shifts to the
BHF (middle right). `Locking on` the target,however, was done using
a non regular combination of small head movements and some small
saccades on top of CEMs. When non eccentric fixation was used,
capturing the target was done through a large saccade with fast CEMs
driving the target off the fovea even in this adapted state after
some training. For maintaining the target in view head movements
were avoided and a strategy of saccades with slow backdrift was
used. This appeared to be more efficient than coping with
asymmetrically CEMs of asymmetrical gain generated by head
movements.
LATENCIES.
Latencies to achieve eccentric fixation ranged in *normal* Ss
around 30 to 40 sec without training, around 5 to 10 sec after
training. HH *patients* needed considerably longer (up to 80 sec)
to achieve eccentric fixation, especially in the head free
condition. After some training, however,they had almost similar
latencies as *normal* Ss.
In *patients* acquisition of the primary target (predicted *and*
non predicted) improved considerably after training (down to
0.25sec). This included a change of strategies from multiple
stair-step to one-step gaze shifts. Subjectively they felt easier
with head free to move and made therefore more often use of head
movements than was expected from earlier studies.

We conclude that *short term* adaptation to eccentric 2VFB could
optimize hemianopic patients' *long term* adaptation to the visual
field defect. Eccentric 2VFB is a useful experimental task and it
may help patients with acquired hemianopia to cope better, and
perhaps faster, with their difficulties to acquire targets in their
blind hemifield.

REFERENCES.
1. Kirschen,DG,Flom,MC (1978). Visual acuity at different retinal
loci of eccentrically fixating functional
amblyopes.Am.J.Optom.55:144-150
2. Mandelbaum,JL,Sloan,LL (1947).Peripheral visual
acuity.Am.J.Ophthalmol.30:581
3. Meienberg,O,Zangemeister,WH,Rosenberg,M,Hoyt,WF,Stark,L
(1981).Saccadic eye movement strategies in patients with homonymous
hemianopia.Ann.Neurol.9:537-544
4. Sansbury,RV,Skavenski,AA,Haddad,GM,Steinman,RM (1973).Normal
fixation of eccentric targets.J.Opt.Soc.Am.63:612-614
5. Stark,L.,Vossius,G.,Young,LR (1962).Predictive control of eye
tracking movements.IRE Trans.HFE 3:52-57
6. Steinbach,MJ (1969).Eye tracking of self-moved targets:The role
of efference.Exp.Psychol.82:366-376
7. Young,LR,Stark,L (1963).Variable feedback experiments testing a
sampled data model for eye tracking movement.IEEE Trans.HFE-4:38-51
8. Zangemeister,WH,Stark,L (1982).Gaze types: Interaction of eye and
head movements in gaze.Exp.Neurol.77:563-577
9. Zangemeister,WH,Meienberg,O,Stark,L.,Hoyt,WF (1982).Eye - head
coordination in homonymous hemianopia.J.Neurol.225:243-254
10.Zangemeister,WH,Stark,L (1983).Pathological types of eye - head
coordination in neurological disorders.Neuro-ophthalmology 3:259-276
11.Zeevi,YY,Peli,E,Stark,L (1979).Study of eccentric fixation with
secondary visual feedback.J.Opt.Soc.Am.69:669-675

The Physiological Response Properties of Single Pontine Units Related to Smooth Pursuit in the Trained Monkey

M. J. Mustari*, A. F. Fuchs* and J. Wallman**

*Regional Primate Research Center, University of Washington,
Seattle, WA 98195, USA
**Department of Biology, City University of New York,
New York, NY 10031, USA

INTRODUCTION

It is well established that the cerebellar flocculus is required by the oculomotor system for normal smooth pursuit eye movements. This important floccular role has been demonstrated in lesion studies where either large cerebellar lesions including the flocculus (Westheimer and Blair, 1974) or small lesions restricted mainly to the flocculus (Zee and co-workers, 1981) have produced long-lasting deficits in smooth pursuit. In accord with these lesion effects, single unit recording studies (Miles and Fuller, 1975; Lisberger and Fuchs, 1978) have demonstrated that floccular Purkinje cells discharge during smooth pursuit eye movements with their firing rate proportional to eye velocity. visual signals are required to generate these smooth pursuit eye movements and the flocculus of the monkey has been shown to receive a visual mossy fiber input (Noda, 1981) with activity proportional to visual stimulus velocity.

Anatomical tracer studies have revealed that the primate flocculus receives a major projection from the basilar pons (Brodal, 1978; Langer and co-workers, 1985) including the dorsolateral pontine nucleus (DLPN) which is the subject of this report. The dorsolateral pontine nuclei receive visual input from both primary and visual association areas (Brodal, 1978; Fries, 1981; Glickstein and co-workers, 1980). Thus the dorsolateral pontine nucleus has the appropriate afferent and efferent connections to provide the flocculus with signals that could be involved in smooth pursuit and other types of eye movement.

METHODS

Briefly, a scleral search coil for measuring eye movements (Fuchs and Robinson, 1966) and a recording chamber permitting access to the dorsolateral pontine nucleus, were surgically implanted in four monkeys (Macaca nemestrina) under asceptic conditions. The monkeys were trained to either fixate a stationary target spot or track a moving target spot, rear projected onto a tangent screen (70x50 deg) for an applesauce reward. During fixation of the stationary target spot, a second visual stimulus could be presented for receptive field testing.

Single units were recorded with tungsten microelectrodes using conventional methods. Target and eye position signals, unit discharge and other relevant signals were saved on analog tape for subsequent off-line data analysis. All units encountered in the vicinity of the DLPN were subjected to a variety of tests which included: 1) movement of a full field (70x50 deg) visual background during fixation, 2) turning a stationary visual sitmulus on and off during fixation, 3) smooth pursuit of a small target spot against a dark background, and 4) smooth pursuit of a small target which was turned off briefly (200-500 msec) against a dark background. The velocity and direction of both the visual stimuli and/or the eye movement were varied to find the optimal conditions for each unit. Units activated with our testing regime were often found in clusters surrounded by units whose discharge we could not effect.

Lesions were placed on representative electrode tracks where units which discharged during smooth pursuit eye movements were encountered. At the conclusion of the experimental series each animal was deeply anaesthetized and perfused with saline followed by 10% formalin. Frozen sections were cut at 50 um and every section mounted on microscope slides and stained for histological study.

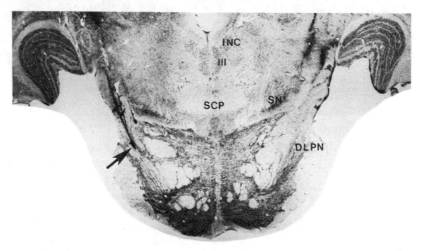

Fig. 1.   Histological section cut in the stereotaxic plane.
DLPN dorsolateral pontine nucleus, SCP superior
cerebellar peduncle, III oculomotor nucleus. Electrode Track (arrow).

All of the units (N=125) described in this study were histologically confirmed to be within the confines of the dorsolateral pontine nucleus (Nyby and Jansen, 1951). Figure 1 shows an example of one of our electrode tracks, with a marking lesion at a location where units that discharged during smooth pursuit eye movement were recorded (arrow).

RESULTS

For those DLPN units which discharged with either eye movement or visual stimulation, 90% (N=112) discharged during smooth pursuit of a small target spot against a dark background (smooth pursuit in the dark). Three unit response types have been encountered: 1) units that respond to visual stimulation only, 2) units that respond to eye movement only and 3) units which respond to both eye movement and visual stimulation.

The response of a DLPN unit with mixed visual and eye movement responses is shown in Fig. 2. During vertical smooth pursuit in the dark (Fig. 2a), the discharge pattern (typical for most DLPN units) is characterized by a direction-specific response. The response shows irregular bursts and pauses (Figs. 2, 3), neither of which could be attributed to either saccades or retinal slip. Note that the bursting in Fig. 2c is still apparent during the second cycle where the target was turned off briefly (target blank) and therefore no visual stimulus was present and no saccades occur (last half of the first off pulse).

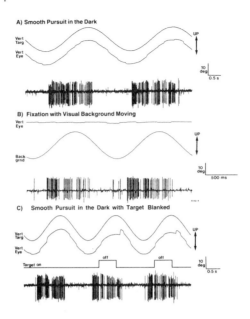

Fig. 2. Response of a DLPN unit during smooth pursuit
in the dark A, full field background movement B,
and during smooth pursuit in the dark with
the target turned off as indicated.

The visual response of the same unit is shown in Fig. 2b. The animal fixated a stationary target spot while a full field visual background was moved vertically, over the same amplitude (+/- 10 degs) and at a similar velocity as that of the target in Fig. 2a, revealing a direction-selective response. The same direction-selective discharge could be revealed with a small (2 deg diameter) test spot in this and most other DLPN units. Some units demonstrated spatial summation within their receptive fields and large visual stimuli were most effective for plotting their receptive fields.

The response during smooth pursuit of a target spot in the dark could be related to the eye movement itself or could be the result of visual activation by movement of the target's image across the retina (retinal image slip) during pursuit. In an effort to dissociate these effects the target was turned off (blanked) on some cycles during smooth pursuit for such brief periods (200-500 msec) that smooth tracking was maintained without a target. Figure 2c compares the response of the unit during smooth pursuit in the dark when the target spot is blanked briefly (400 ms) during part of the cycle (last two cycles) with the response during normal tracking (first cycle). Although the eye velocity drops during the target blank, the monkey maintains his tracking relatively well and the unit continues to discharge throughout the target blank. This result demonstrates that there is a motor component to this unit's discharge, since any visual input during the target blank has been completely eliminated. This result, along with the unit's response to full field visual stimulation and the fact that it also had a large (entire tangent screen) visual receptive field indicates that this unit has mixed visual and movement components to its discharge. In 14 units tested with target blanking, 6 showed no drop in discharge during the blank. Thus units in the DLPN with eye movement related activity seem rather common.

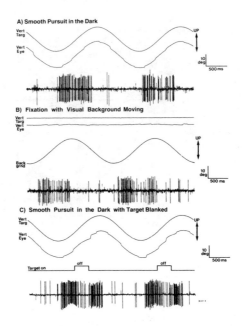

Fig. 3. Response of a DLPN unit during smooth pursuit
in the dark A, full field background movement B,
and smooth pursuit in the dark with the target blanked.

Figure 3 illustrates a DLPN unit dominated by visual inputs. During smooth pursuit in the dark, this unit, like the one of Fig. 2, demonstrates direction selectivity and bursty firing that occurs throughout the preferred half cycle (up). Also, like the unit in Fig. 2, this unit is direction selective and responds to upward movement of a full field visual background during fixation. However, unlike the unit of Fig. 2, during a target blank, the response of this unit falls nearly to the resting rate (Fig. 3c) although the tracking remains quite reasonable. When the target is turned back on, the unit demonstrates an on response. These results suggest that the response of this unit has little, if any, eye movement component. When this unit was tested with a small spot during fixation, a large receptive field covering the entire tangent screen was revealed.

The preferred eye movement direction of units was tested by having the animal track horizontal, vertical and oblique target movements (+/- 45 degs from horizontal). The preferred visual direction was tested similarly during fixation with full field background movement. Figure 4 shows three representative eye movement directional tuning curves taken from three different DLPN units. Units A and B are directionally selective with mostly up and down selectivities respectively. Unit C has an elevated response with respect to its resting rate for all directions tested and is considered directionally nonselective. Most of the units that discharged during smooth pursuit in the dark were direction selective, with considerable variability in the sharpness of their directional tuning. The preferred direction (arrows 4) for each unit was defined by the angle at which the fitted directional tuning curve reached its maximum and often was intermediate to one of the actual directions tested. Directional tuning was assessed quantitatively in 22 units and qualitatively in 80 others revealing that all directions of eye movement were represented.

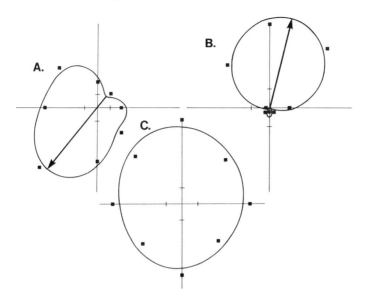

Fig. 4. Eye movement directional tuning curves for
three DLPN units. Tic=10 spikes/sec.
Arrows indicate best direction.

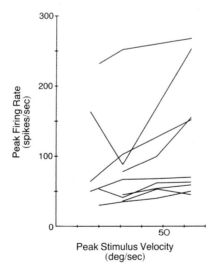

Fig. 5. Visual velocity sensitivity of DLPN units.
Abscisa, peak eye velocity (degs/sec),
ordinate, peak firing rate (spikes/sec).

The visual velocity sensitivity of units was tested by moving a full field background at different frequencies (0.25-1.0 Hz) over a constant amplitude (+/- 10 degs) while the monkey fixated the stationary target spot. Figure 5 shows the velocity tuning curves produced by plotting the peak firing rate against peak stimulus velocity. There was no consistent relationship between firing rate and stimulus velocity across units. Seven of nine units showed little if any consistent change of firing rate over the range of velocities tested. Therefore the discharge of the large majority of DLPN units does not seem dependent on retinal slip velocity. This suggestion was tested directly by measuring the retinal slip velocity (target velocity minus eye velocity) that was associated with smooth pursuit of the target spot and looking for a relation between retinal slip velocity and unit discharge. For 10 units with an identified visual sensitivity we found that there was no consistent relation between unit discharge and regions of high retinal slip velocity.

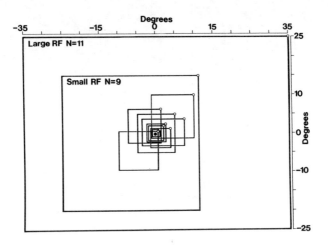

Fig. 6. Visual receptive fields of 20 DLPN units.
Large receptive fields cover entire tangent screen.
All receptive fields include the fixation point (center dot).

Figure 6 shows the visual receptive fields of 20 DLPN units that were plotted with a small test spot while the animal fixated the target spot. The receptive fields were either very large, covering the entire tangent screen, or relatively small. All the visual receptive fields we have encountered included the fixation point and most were direction selective. For seven units where binocularity was tested, all were binocular. Although not studied in detail, some of the very large visual receptive fields had local regions in which a particularly intense response was elicited. The size of the receptive field was not related to whether the unit also had eye movement sensitivity.

DISCUSSION

The results obtained in this study demonstrate that the dorsolateral pontine nucleus has a population of units that discharge during smooth pursuit eye movements. Some of the units encountered there are visually dominated and such units have been reported in earlier work (Mustari and co-workers, 1984; Suzuki and Keller, 1984). This is the first report of units in the dorsolateral pons that have a response related to eye movement in the absence of a visual stimulus, as demonstrated during smooth pursuit with the target blanked. Although we have used the target blanking test on relatively few units (n=14) almost half of them displayed a discharge that continued throughout the target blank and must therefore be related to eye movement per se.

The neural activity we have recorded in the DLPN could have many sources. The DLPN of the monkey has been shown in anatomical studies to receive inputs from the visual association cortex, posterior parietal cortex (Nyby and Jansen, 1951; Brodal, 1978; Glickstein and co-workers, 1980; Weber and Yin, 1984) and the middle temporal visual area (Fries, 1981; Maunsell and Van Essen, 1983). Thus DLPN units with small visual receptive fields could receive their input from area 17 or 18. Units with large visual receptive fields could receive convergent input from primary visual cortex and/or from other areas such as the middle temporal visual area, where units with such fields and a preference for moving stimuli of a particular velocity and direction have been reported (Maunsell and Van Essen, 1983; Zeki, 1974). Although no reports of the response properties of units in the middle temporal visual area of the behaving primate exist, recent chemical lesion studies (Newsome and co-workers, 1985) support a role for this area in smooth pursuit. There have been several reports on the posterior parietal cortex of the behaving monkey showing unit activity reminiscent of the activity reported here. These studies have reported units that discharge during smooth pursuit eye movements (Sakata and co-workers, 1983) as well as units that continue to discharge through a target blank during smooth pursuit eye movements (Kawano and co-workers, 1984).

This study supports the suggestion that the dorsolateral pontine nucleus may act as a staging area for both visual and eye movement related activity to be sent to the flocculus for use in the generation of smooth pursuit eye movements.

REFERENCES

Brodal, P. (1978). The corticopontine projection in the rhesus monkey: Origin and principles of organization. Brain 101, 251-283.

Brodal, P. (1982). Further observations on the cerebellar projections from the pontine nuclei and the nucleus reticularis tegmenti pontis in the rhesus monkey. J. Comp. Neurol. 204, 44-55.

Fries, W. (1981). the projection from striate and prestriate visual cortex onto the pontine nuclei in the macaque monkey. Soc. Neurosci. Abs. 7, 762.

Fuchs, A. F., and D. A. Robinson. (1966). A method for measuring horizontal and vertical eye movement chronically in the monkey. J. Appl. Physiol. 21, 1068-1070.

Glickstein, M., J. L. Cohen, B. Dixon, A. Gibson, M. Hollins, E. Labossiere, and F. Robinson. (1980). Corticopontine visual projections in macaque monkeys. J. Comp. Neurol. 190, 209-229.

Kawano, K., M. Sasaki, and M. Yamashita. (1984). Response properties of neurons in the posterior parietal cortex of monkey during visual-vestibular stimulation. I. Visual tracking neurons. J. Neurophysiol. 51. 340-351.

Langer, T. P., A. F. Fuchs, C. Scudder, and M. C. Chubb. (1985). Afferents to the flocculus of the cerebellum in the Rhesus Macaque as revealed by retrograde transport of horseradish peroxidase. J. Comp. Neurol. 235, 1-25.

Lisberger, S. G., and A. F. Fuchs. (1978). Role of the primate flocculus during rapid behavioral modification of the vestibuloocular reflex. I. Purkinje cell activity during visually guided horizontal smooth-pursuit eye movements and passive head rotation. J. Neurophysiol. 41, 733-763.

Maunsell, J. H. R., and D. C. Van Essen. (1983). Functional properties of neurons in middle temporal visual area of the macaque monkey. I. Selectivity for stimulus direction, speed, and orientation. J. Neurophysiol. 49, 1127-1147.

Miles, F. A., and J. H. Fuller. (1975). Visual tracking and the primate flocculus. Science 189, 1000-1002.

Mustari, M. J., A. F. Fuchs, and J. Wallman. (1984). Smooth pursuit related units in the dorsolateral pons of the rhesus macaque. Soc. Neurosci. Abs. 10, 987.

Newsome, W. T., R. H. Wurtz, M. R. Dursteler, and A. Mikami. (1985). Deficits in visual motion processing following ibotenic acid lesions of the middle temporal visual area of the macaque monkey. J. Neurosci. 5, 825-840.

Noda, H. (1981). Visual mossy fiber inputs to the flocculus of the monkey. Ann. N. Y. Acad. Sci. 374, 465-475.
Nyby, O., and J. Jansen. (1951). An experimental investigation of the corticopontine projection in Macaca mulatta. Skrifter utgitt av det Norske videnskaps. Akademi: Osla J'mat-Natury. Klasse H. 3, 1-47.
Sakata, H., H. Shibutani, and K. Kawano. (1983). Functional properties of visual tracking neurons in posterior parietal association cortex of the monkey. J. Neurophysiol. 49, 1364-1380.
Suzuki, D. A., and E. L. Keller. (1984). Visual signals in the dorsolateral pontine nucleus of the alert monkey: Their relationship to smooth-pursuit eye movements. Exp. Brain Res. 47, 145-147.
Van Essen, D. C., J. H. R. Maunsell, and J. L. Bixby. (1981). The middle temporal visual area in the macaque: myeloarchitecture, connections, functional properties and topographic representation. J. Comp. Neurol. 199, 293-326.
Weber, J. T., and T. C. T. Yin. (1984). Subcortical projections of the inferior parietal cortex (Area 7) in the stump-tailed monkey. J. Comp. Neurol. 224, 206-284.
Westheimer, G., and S. M. Blair. (1974). Functional organization of primate oculomotor system revealed by cerebellectomy. Exp. Brain Res. 21, 283-284.
Zee, D. S., A Yamazaki, P. H. Butler, and G. Gucer. (1981). Effects of ablation of flocculus and paraflocculus on eye movements in primate. J. Neurophysiol. 46, 878-899.
Zeki, S. M. (1974). Functional organization of a visual area in prestriate cortex of monkey. Brain Res. 14, 271-291.

The Role of Direction Selective Cells in the Nucleus of the Optic Tract of Cat and Monkey During Optokinetic Nystagmus

K.-P. Hoffmann and C. Distler

Abt. f. Vergleichende Neurobiologie, Universitaet Ulm, Oberer
Eselsberg, D-7900 Ulm, FRG

Considerable evidence has accumulated suggesting that in mammals such as rats, rabbits and cats, direction selective cells in the nucleus of the optic tract (NOT) and in the dorsal terminal nucleus of the accessory optic tract (DTN), signal retinal slip during horizontal optokinetic nystagmus (OKN) (Collewijn, 1975; Hoffmann, 1982; Precht, 1982). These neurons can easily and unequivocally be identified by antidromic activation from the inferior olive and monosynaptic orthodromic activation via slowly conducting retinal axons. The unique feature of this subcortical pathway is the complete bias of neurons on one side of the brain to respond only to one direction of stimulus movement in the visual world. Neurons on the right side prefer rightward, and those on the left leftward, movement. The receptive fields of these neurons are very large and in the cat always include the area centralis, i.e. they extend into both nasal and temporal retina. The velocity range over which these neurons respond differs depending on the species investigated. Very low stimulus velocities (less than 0.1°/s) can always activate the neurons, but the upper cut-off velocities increase from 10-50°/s in rat and rabbit, to about 100°/s in the cat. In the mammalian species investigated so far, large area random dot patterns or gratings have proved to be optimal stimuli. Small spots or single lines induce little or no response (rat: Cazin et al., 1980; rabbit: Collewijn, 1975; cat: Hoffmann and Schoppmann, 1981).

A model has been put forward which attributes the differing properties of NOT neurons in the cat versus the rat or rabbit, to the development of a strong cortical input to the midbrain in the cat (Hoffmann, 1980). This is of course a trend which is probably continued in the evolution of primates.

As a result of cortical input to NOT and DTN cells in the cat the following three new properties arise:

1. Most of these cells become binocular, i.e. they can be activated by either eye.

2. The cells respond vigorously to stimulus velocities above 10°/s.

3. Relatively small optokinetic stimuli (less than 10 x 10°) are effective when centered on the area centralis.

That these properties depend on the cortical input was demonstrated by their absence after decortication (Hoffmann, 1982; Grasse et al., 1984).

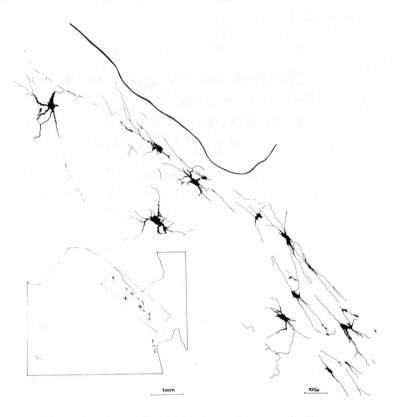

Fig. 1. Camera lucida drawings of neurons in the nucleus of the optic tract of the squirrel monkey. These neurons were labelled by injecting horseradish peroxidase into the ipsilateral inferior olive and reacting the midbrain sections with tetramethylbenzidine. The cells are found lateral to the representation of the fovea in the superior colliculus and medial or ventral to the pulvinar (see inset).

A direct proof for the involvement of these NOT and DTN neurons in the optokinetic nystagmus was achieved by neurophysiological recordings in the fully awake cat (Hoffmann and Huber, 1983). For this investigation a search coil was implanted around the eye to record eye movements in a magnetic field. In addition, head restraining bolts and a recording chamber were attached to the skull to be able to lower a recording electrode into the midbrain. Optokinetic nystagmus was elicited by a large area random dot pattern. The onset of strong direction selective responses in NOT and DTN neurons during optokinetic nystagmus began within less than 100 ms after the onset of stimulus movement. Neurons on the left side of the brain increased their firing rate during slow phases of OKN directed to the left, and neurons on the right side during slow phases to the right. The activity of the neurons dropped to spontaneous rates within 100 ms when the stimulus was switched off even though a clear after nystagmus (OKAN) could be observed. In addition, slow eye movements evoked by the vestibulo-ocular reflex in the dark did not influence

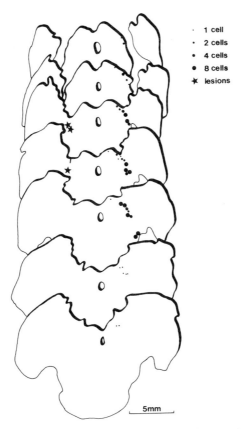

· 1 cell
· 2 cells
• 4 cells
● 8 cells
✷ lesions

5mm

Fig. 2. Serial reconstruction of the region of
the nucleus of the optic tract in the pretectum and the
dorsal terminal nucleus of the accessory optic tract.
Drawings of 0.1 mm thick frontal sections are arranged
from posterior (top) to anterior (bottom). Dots on the
right correspond to the frequency of retrogradely
labelled cells in the section whereas the asterisks on
the left mark the recording sites of direction selective
cells which could be antidromically activated from the
inferior olive.

the discharge rate of these neurons. NOT and DTN cells therefore seem to be
exclusively visually sensitive, and only to a particular direction of retinal
slip. Electrical stimulation through the recording electrode led to clear OKN
with slow phases in the same direction as during visual optokinetic stimulation
in the preferred direction of the neurons at the stimulation site, i.e. if the
electrode had recorded from the right NOT-DTN region, electrical stimulation
elicited OKN with rightward directed slow phases. Stimulation on the left side
elicited slow phases to the left. If, however, an electrolytic lesion was
placed at the recording site of direction selective cells in the NOT-DTN
region, a clear deficit was found in response to sinusoidal horizontal movement
of the optokinetic stimulus. Stimulus movement towards the side of the lesion
was less effective in eliciting OKN than movement away from the side of the

lesion. When the optokinetic stimulus moved in the same direction for a long time these deficits were difficult to detect.

All the features described above clearly indicate a major role for these neurons during OKN in cat, and there are now a number of findings suggesting that such a pathway might be present in primates as well (Zee, in this volume). Our next step was the anatomical identification and physiological characterisation of NOT-DTN neurons in monkeys. Anticipating a projection from such neurons to the dorsal cap of the inferior olive, we injected horseradish peroxidase into the inferior olive of 3 squirrel monkeys and 3 macaque monkeys. The results of such injections are shown in Figs. 1 and 2. Clearly there are neurons in the NOT-DTN region of the monkey midbrain which project to the inferior olive. The location of these cells within the brachium of the superior colliculus allows them to sample visual information from a large number of retinal and/or cortical fibers. In physiological experiments, these neurons were identified by their axonal projection. Stimulating electrodes were inserted into the inferior olive in 2 squirrel monkeys and one macaque monkey. A second pair of stimulating electrodes was placed in the optic chiasm. Only these neurons which could be activated both antidromically from the inferior olive and orthodromically from the optic chiasm were studied. These recording sites are marked by asterisks in Fig. 2.

The antidromic latencies of these monkey NOT-DTN neurons ranged from 1 to 5 ms and the orthodromic latencies from 6 to 10 ms. Whereas the antidromic spikes could be elicited reliably with very low currents it was difficult to activate the cells satisfactorily from the optic chiasm. Especially when compared to results in the cat (Hoffmann and Schoppmann, 1981), the direct retinal input to NOT-DTN cells in the monkey seems rather weak. On the other hand, the visually elicited responses were very strong and brisk. We suggest that these cells in the monkey receive their major input from the cortex. Further support for this suggestion will come from the description of the receptive field properties. As found in the cat, the neurons in the NOT-DTN region of the monkey also responded strongly to horizontal movements of large area random dot patterns. To our great surprise, in the monkey these neurons were equally sensitive to a small spot moving through their receptive field. The smallest spot tested was less than $0.1°$ in diameter and elicited a clear response when it moved across the central retina. The response was strongest when the spot moved across the fovea (Fig. 3). The receptive fields sometimes subtended more than $40°$ and always included the fovea. Therefore they extended far into both nasal and temporal hemifields. All receptive fields were binocular and stimulation of either eye alone was sufficient to drive the cells. As was the case in the cat, all cells antidromically activated from the inferior olive had the same (ipsilateral) preferred direction. The responses to directions other than horizontal could vary. Some neurons preferred upwards movements and other downward movements. As a population these neurons gave a very strong direction specific response to horizontal stimulus movement which declined equally with deviation in either direction from horizontal. In addition, we found no clear difference between the velocity tuning measured with random dot patterns or single spots. Both types of stimuli elicited strong direction specific responses at velocities between 0.1 and several hundred deg/s. With most velocities tested we also observed a suppression of the spontaneous activity for the (null)direction opposite to the preferred direction. The modulation of cell discharge rates (difference between activity in the preferred and in the null direction) was strongest for stimulus speeds between 10 and $80°/s$. The modulation depth increased by about 5-10 spikes/s with each doubling of stimulus velocity in this range.

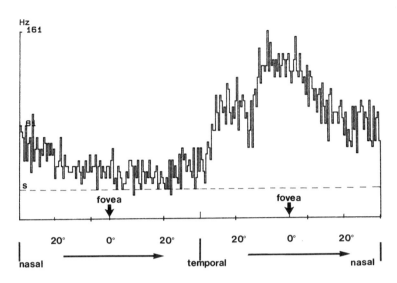

Fig. 3. Direction selective response of a monkey
NOT neuron to movement of small spot of light. The
animal was anesthetized and paralyzed, and the stimulus
was presented monocularly. Discharge rate is plotted on
the Y-axis and stimulus position in the visual field is
plotted along the X-axis. The horizontal broken line
marks the spontaneous activity in the dark. Spontaneous
activity in the light corresponds to the values at the
beginning and end of the histogram. As the spot moves
from nasal in the visual field towards the fovea the
discharge rate declines, but increases again as the
stimulus moves away from the fovea. The discharge rate
is clearly increased above the spontaneous level only
with movements from temporal to nasal. The peak rate
occurs when the stimulus moves across the fovea.

DISCUSSION AND CONCLUSIONS:

The neurons described above in the anesthetized monkey have enough properties
in common with neurons in the awake cat's NOT-DTN region to suggest that they
relay a signal encoding retinal slip in the monkey's optokinetic pathway. By
their projection to the inferior olive these cells also provide visual climbing
fiber input to the flocculus of the monkey's cerebellum. We have argued that
cells in the NOT-DTN region must receive a strong cortical input because they
are all binocular and respond to very high stimulus velocities, despite a weak
retinal input. Which cortical areas project to these cells as well as the
properties of NOT-DTN cells after decortication await further investigation.
David Zee reported at this meeting that the OKN of rhesus monkeys shows
substantial modifications after decortication. Tested monocularly, only slow
movements from temporal to nasal in the visual field elicited OKN. This
result, taken together with our knowledge about the correlated changes in OKN
and receptive field properties in NOT-DTN in the cat after decortication, would
suggest that the cortex also contributes binocularity and responses to high
stimulus velocities to NOT-DTN cells in the monkey. The asymmetry in monocular
OKN (slow phases only to the right when the left eye is tested and only to the
left when the right eye is tested) after decortication in the monkey would

suggest that each eye is connected by direct retinofugal fibers primarily to the contralateral NOT-DTN. These results strongly support previous claims of separable cortical and subcortical optokinetic pathways in primates as well as lower mammals (Ter Braak and Van Vliet, 1963).

REFERENCES

Cazin, L., W. Precht, and J. Lannou (1980). Firing characteristics of neurons mediating optokinetic responses to rat's vestibular neurons. Pflug. Arch., 386, 221-230.
Collewijn, H. (1975). Direction selective units in the rabbit's nucleus of the optic tract. Brain Res., 100, 489-508.
Grasse, K., M. Cynader, and R. M. Douglas (1984). Alterations in response properties in the lateral and dorsal terminal nuclei of the cat accessory optic system following visual cortex lesions. Exp. Brain Res., 55, 69-80.
Hoffmann, K.-P. (1982). Cortical versus subcortical contributions to the optokinetic reflex in the cat. In Functional basis of ocular motility disorders, ed. G. Lennerstrand et al., pp. 303-310, Oxford/New York: Pergamon.
Hoffmann, K.-P., K. Behrend, and A. Schoppmann (1976). A direct afferent visual pathway from the nucleus of the optic tract to the inferior olive in the cat. Brain Res., 115, 150-153.
Hoffmann, K.-P., and H. P. Huber (1983). Responses to visual stimulation in single cells in the nucleus of the optic tract (NOT) during optokinetic nystagmus (OKN) in the awake cat. Neurosci. Abstr., 9, 1048.
Hoffmann, K.-P., and A. Schoppmann (1981). A quantitative analysis of the direction-specific response of neurons in the cat's nucleus of the optic tract. Exp. Brain Res., 42, 146-157.
Precht, W. (1982). Anatomical and functional organisation of optokinetic pathways. In Functional basis of ocular motility disorders, ed. G. Lennerstrand et al., pp. 291-302, Oxford/New York: Pergamon.
Ter Braak, J. W. G., and A. G. M. Van Vliet (1963). Subcortical optokinetic nystagmus in the monkey. Psychatr. Neurol. Neurochir., 66, 277-283.

Acknowledgements:
This work was supported by DFG grant Ho 450/17.

The Acute and Chronic Effects of Bilateral Occipital Lobectomy Upon Eye Movements in Monkey

D. S. Zee, R. J. Tusa, S. J. Herdman, P. H. Butler
and G. Gücer

School of Medicine, Johns Hopkins University, Baltimore,
MD 21205, and School of Medicine, University of Maryland,
Baltimore, MD 21201, USA

There is considerable controversy about the amount of preservation and the degree of restoration of visual function in human beings with cerebral lesions that include visual cortex (Campion, Latto and Smith, 1983). In monkeys, however, the evidence is compelling that a number of visual functions can be performed in the absence of striate cortex (Keating, 1980; Pasik and Pasik, 1982). Little is known, though, of the ocular motor performance of such animals. For these reasons we examined ocular motor behavior in four monkeys before and after bilateral occipital lobectomy to determine both the acute deficits as well as the capabilities for recovery.

Summary of Major Findings

The immediate effects of removal of the occipital lobes were not unexpected. The animals appeared blind and were unable to fixate upon or track targets of interest. The monkeys did show, however, residual optokinetic responses with characteristics similar to those of afoveate, phylogenetically-older animals such as the rabbit (Collewijn, 1981).

The long-term effects of occipital lobectomy were somewhat surprising and paradoxical. On the one hand, three of four monkeys recovered the ability to produce smooth pursuit and all four recovered the ability to make saccades to small targets. This occured in the absence of any sign of recovery of an ability to recognize objects of interest. On the other hand, three monkeys gradually lost ability to hold their eyes still. They developed spontaneous and gaze-evoked nystagmus and wandering drifts and oscillations of the eyes. Two animals also gradually lost some ability to generate optokinetic responses.

Methods and Extent of Lesions

Eye movements were recorded using the search coil technique. Four rhesus monkeys, ages 2 1/4 - 3 1/2 years, were trained to fixate and follow targets and then, in a one-stage procedure, both occipital lobes were removed at the level of the prelunate gyrus and the remaining calcarine cortex aspirated. Subsequent histological examination showed that in two animals (1 and 2) striate cortex had been totally removed and retrograde degeneration in the lateral geniculate body was complete. In the other two animals (3 and 4) there were small remnants of striate cortex. In all animals much of prestriate cortex had been removed but portions of area 'MT' were spared.

Optokinetic Responses

All animals demonstrated residual optokinetic responses when first tested
in the postoperative period. In one animal (no. 2) only a bare remnant
of optokinetic nystagmus (OKN) could be elicited; the maximum slow-phase
velocity was 4 deg/sec. In the other three animals OKN was much better
preserved. Its characteristics (in the first few postoperative weeks) were
as follows:

1) In response to a constant-velocity drum rotation the initial jump in
slow-phase velocity (usually attributed to the pursuit system) was absent.
Instead, there was a prolonged rise to the steady-state value and as slow-phase
velocity approached drum velocity, i.e. as retinal slip velocity diminished, the rate of change of slow-phase velocity increased. In monkey 1,
for example, with a 30 deg/sec drum rotation it took as long as 120 seconds
for slow-phase velocity to reach the steady-state value of 28 deg/sec,
an average acceleration of less than 0.25 deg/sec/sec.. In contrast, preoperatively, in response to a drum velocity of 120 deg/sec (which, because
of the initial 'pursuit' component produced retinal slip velocities of
about 40 deg/sec) it took less than 45 seconds to rise to the steady-state. The
maximum slow-phase velocity of optokinetic afternystagmus (OKAN) was greater
preoperatively than could ever be reached postoperatively (in monkey 1,
84 deg/sec versus 58 deg/sec). The time constant of OKAN, however, appeared
unaffected by surgery.

2) Higher slow-phase velocities could often be reached with a slowly accelerating stimulus (to keep retinal slip velocities low) than with a large-
amplitude, constant-velocity stimulus. In monkey 1, slow-phase velocity
reached 58 deg/sec if the drum was slowly accelerated (0.25 deg/sec/sec)
to 60 deg/sec but only 3 deg/sec if the drum velocity was immediately stepped
to 60 deg/sec and kept there.

3) During sinusoidal drum rotation no appreciable response was elicited
at a stimulus frequency of 0.22 hz. As stimulus frequency was progressively lowered the slow-phase velocity of OKN increased and the phase lag
decreased. In monkey 4, for a 10 deg/sec amplitude stimulus, at 0.04 hz
the gain (eye vel/drum vel) and phase lag were 0.4 and 60 deg, respectively;
at 0.015 hz they were 0.95 and 12 deg, respectively. At a given frequency
the gain decreased as the amplitude of the stimulus increased. In monkey
4, at a stimulus frequency of 0.015 hz, the gain was 0.75 for a 20 deg/sec
amplitude stimulus and 0.25 for a 40 deg/sec amplitude stimulus.

4) During monocular viewing, optokinetic stimuli moving temporo-nasally
elicited better OKN than those moving naso-temporally (in monkey 1, a maximum
slow-phase velocity of 30 deg/sec versus 8 deg/sec). During monocular viewing
of the stationary drum there appeared "latent nystagmus"; a conjugate drift
of 2-4 deg/sec such that the slow phase of the viewing eye was directed
nasally.

These results are compatable with the idea that primates have an underlying
optokinetic system organized like that of afoveate animals (Zee and colleagues,
1982; Waespe, Cohen and Raphan, 1983). Occipital lobectomy, by abolishing
the initial, "pursuit" component of OKN, revealed the afoveate optokinetic
response. Many of the optokinetic responses of our lesioned monkeys can
be explained by assuming that extrastriate visual information is transmitted
to the accessory optic nuclei (AON) and nucleus of the optic tract (NOT). In
these structures neural activity related to retinal slip is transformed
in a nonlinear way (Hoffmann, this symposium) so that lower retinal-slip
velocities lead to relatively higher rates of neural discharge. The output

of the retinal-slip nonlinearity is then filtered by an intact velocity storage mechanism in the vestibular nuclei. In fact, the gain and phase measurements of our lesioned monkeys during sinusoidal OKN were close to those reported for many of the neurons in the vestibular nuclei during sinusoidal optokinetic stimulation in intact monkeys (Boyle, Büttner and Markert, 1985). Our findings also suggest that cortical inputs supply the immediate, "pursuit" component of OKN, as well as balance out inherent directional asymmetries and increase the speed and range of the afoveate optokinetic response.

Within several months the initial component of OKN (maximum slow-phase velocity in the first second of the response to a constant-velocity stimulus) began to recover. In two monkeys, the rate of recovery roughly paralleled that of smooth pursuit of small moving targets. In the other two monkeys, though, the rates of recovery of smooth pursuit and the initial component of OKN were disparate. For example, monkey 2 recovered accurate smooth pursuit (smooth eye velocities up to at least 80 deg/sec) but virtually no initial component of OKN. Monkey 3, in contrast, recovered much of the initial component of OKN, up to 38 deg/sec, but only a rudimentary pursuit capability, to about 10 deg/sec. These findings suggest caution when equating the mechanisms that generate the initial rise in slow-phase velocity in response to a full-field OKN stimulus to those that generate smooth pursuit of small moving targets. The sensory and motor pathways may be the same but factors such as attention and size and location (on the retina) of the stimulus may influence the degree to which the pursuit system is engaged during OKN.

Recovery of Smooth Pursuit

After 3-6 months smooth pursuit recovered to a remarkable degree in three of four animals. During attempted tracking of a small target square (1.0 deg × 1.0 deg), moving in a sinusoidal fashion, all three monkeys showed periods during which peak eye velocity reached peak target velocity (Fig. 1). In fact, the average gains (peak eye vel/peak target vel) were close to those before surgery (Table). Monkey 3, though, who even had some preservation of striate cortex, recovered only a rudimentary pursuit response with gains less than 0.20.

In all animals pursuit performance was more variable and erratic than preoperatively. The eyes often moved much faster or slower than the target imparting a wavering appearance to the eye velocity trace. These fluctuations in eye velocity could reflect some loss in the fidelity and precision with which motion of images upon the retina was being transduced into an internal representation of the movement of the target. Alternatively, the oscillations in eye velocity could emanate from an instability in the pursuit system, perhaps because of an increase in time delays.

To further explore smooth tracking capabilities we recorded the initiation of pursuit in response to step-ramp (Rashbass) stimuli. Postoperatively, monkeys 1, 2, and 4 could generate pursuit responses in either direction using information about target speed from image motion on either hemiretina (Fig. 2). The latency to the onset of pursuit, however, was approximately double the preoperative value (Table). We used the average acceleration of the eye during the first 120 msec of smooth tracking as a measure of "open-loop" performance. We found a striking recovery of the ability of the animals to rapidly bring the speed of the eye up toward that of the target. On individual trials the eye could reach accelerations in excess of 400 deg/sec/sec. Postoperatively, the values for monkeys 1 and 2 fell within the normal range (preoperative responses were not available) and

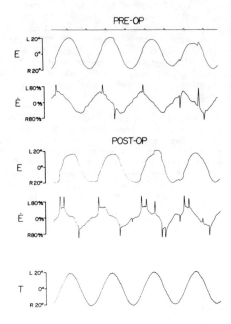

Fig. 1. Smooth pursuit of monkey 1; peak target velocity
= 58.5 deg/sec, time marks at one second intervals.
E = eye position, Ė = eye velocity, T = target position.

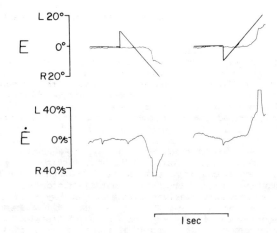

Fig. 2. Postoperative responses of monkey 1 to step-ramp stimuli
(ramp velocity, 60 deg/sec). Target position is superimposed
on the eye position (E) trace. Ė = eye velocity.

TABLE   Postoperative Smooth Pursuit Responses

		Step-Ramp (60 deg/sec)		Sine-wave (60 deg/sec)
		Latency	Initial Acceleration	Gain
Normal range *		115-128ms	154-418 deg/sec/sec	0.88-1.00
Monkey **				
1	R	262	204	0.88
	L	310	191	0.93
2	R	232	278	0.96
	L	236	190	0.95
3	R	--- ***	---	0.16
	L	---	---	0.19
4	R	237	296	0.84
	L	194	280	0.80

* Range of means for three normal animals
** All values are means with n > 8 trials
*** Too few responses to measure

in monkey 4 the postoperative responses were only slightly decreased compared with preoperative values. Thus, while our monkeys did not recover absolutely normal pursuit function, they displayed a remarkable restoration of both the initial and sustained components of the smooth pursuit response.

How does the "cortically blind" monkey see and follow a small moving target in the absence of a geniculostriate pathway? Unfortunately, even in normal monkeys, the anatomical substrate for pursuit is not fully understood. Most evidence points to the superior temporal sulcus with area 'MT' and its environs including area 'MST' as the crucial link between the visual information processed in striate cortex and the pursuit motor commands relayed to the brainstem and cerebellum (Newsome, this symposium).   Other areas, though, both cortical (eg., frontal eye fields and posterior parietal cortex) and subcortical (eg., the pretectal nuclei and superior colliculi) may also participate in the generation of pursuit eye movements.

Perhaps the best explanation for our animals' recovery is that their pursuit was being generated by the spared cortex in the superior temporal sulcus using extrastriate visual information, probably relayed via the pulvinar. The pulvinar receives direct and indirect (via the superior colliculus and pretectal nuclei) retinal projections and itself projects to area 'MT'. The pulvinar, however, also receives direct projections from striate cortex and portions of the pulvinar itself are reported to undergo retrograde degenerative changes after occipital lobe ablations.   Another possible source of visual information to spared cortex is via direct projections to extrastriate cortex from the lateral geniculate nucleus.   We cannot, however, rule out an exclusively subcortical origin for the restored pursuit in our animals although the extremely poor recovery in monkey 3 makes this possibility less likely.

Our completely destriated monkeys recovered much more pursuit function
than do animals with a unilateral striate removal (Segraves, this symposium).
This difference suggests that only a severe loss of striate cortex in both
hemispheres causes enough of a deficit to stimulate alternative mechanisms
to generate pursuit eye movements.

Recovery of Saccades

Within a few months after surgery all animals recovered some ability to
generate visually-guided saccades. The consistency of performance, though,
varied from animal to animal. Nevertheless, when each of the monkeys did
make saccades in response to target jumps, their refixations were nearly
as accurate and as fast as preoperatively, although latencies were moderately
increased. For example, in monkey 2, the mean saccade amplitude for 20
degree target displacements were similar pre- and postoperatively, 18.9
deg and 18.7 deg, respectively, but the standard deviations increased from
0.57 deg to 3.25 deg. Peak velocities for 20 degree saccades did not change,
about 650 deg/sec pre- and postoperatively. Latencies increased from 148
msec preoperatively to 206 msec postoperatively. Standard deviations were
45 msec in both cases.

Vestibular Adaptation

We assessed the ability of our cortically-lesioned monkeys to adaptively
change the gain of their vestibulo-ocular reflex (VOR). We measured VOR
adaptation by recording the VOR gain (peak eye vel/peak head vel) in darkness
before and after four hours of passive, combined, vestibular and optokinetic
stimulation. The chair and drum were both oscillated at 0.25 Hz, 30 deg/sec
amplitude, with the drum and chair either in phase (X0 viewing) to elicit
a decrease in VOR gain, or 180 deg out of phase (X2 viewing) to elicit
an increase in VOR gain. In the first month after surgery three animals
(1,3,and 4) were able to adaptively modulate their VOR gain both up and
down although the degree of change, especially when an increase in gain
was called for, was usually less than that before surgery. For example,
monkey 1 raised and lowered its gain 18% and 47%, respectively, of the
amount it did preoperatively. Two of the monkeys (1 and 3) could adaptively
increase or decrease their gain in spite of no ability to use vision to
make any immediate adjustments in VOR gain during the adaptation period.
In other words, at any particular time, the value of the VOR gain was the
same in the dark, and the light no matter what the particular viewing conditions. Monkey 2 had the least recovery of its adaptive capability in spite
of a remarkable recovery of smooth pursuit. When tested six months postoperatively, during prolonged X2 viewing, the animal could not raise its VOR
gain at all and during prolonged X0 viewing it could decrease its gain
by only 50% as much as preoperatively. In contrast, by six months postoperatively, the other three monkeys could adaptively lower their VOR gain by
the same amount as preoperatively.

Taken together these results support the following conclusions. First,
the ability to adaptively modulate the VOR gain is affected by occipital
lobectomy. There is, however, considerable residual capability, especially
for adjusting the gain downwards, even in monkeys with complete removal
of striate cortex. Secondly, VOR gain adaptation can occur in the absence
of an ability to use visual information to make any immediate adjustments
in slow-phase velocity when visual and vestibular inputs are incongruent.
During prolonged visual-vestibular conflict, the presence of retinal slip
alone suffices to induce some adaptive change in VOR gain.

Loss of Gaze Stability and of Optokinetic Responses

Several months after surgery three of the animals (1-3) began to show disturbances of fixation. Each showed undulating slow drifts of the eyes with
occasional high-velocity drifts up to 30 deg/sec. Monkeys 1 and 2 developed
brief postsaccadic drift as well as gaze-evoked nystagmus. Monkey 2 also
developed a horizontal spontaneous nystagmus with slow-phase velocities
up to 20 deg/sec, even in the light. In addition, in monkeys 1 and 3 the
upper limit of OKAN began to diminish. For example, in monkey 1 the maximum
slow-phase velocity of OKAN declined from 58 deg/sec immediately postoperatively
to 20 deg/sec six months after surgery.

Mechanisms for the Long-Term Changes after Occipital Lobectomy

Why did some functions slowly deteriorate while others slowly improved
after occipital lobectomy? The explanation may be, in part, related to
the effects in remote anatomical structures that occur after lesions of
visual cortex in young monkeys. Dineen, Hendrickson and Keating (1982) found
that removal of occipital cortex leads not only to retrograde degeneration
in the lateral geniculate body and pulvinar but also transynaptic degeneration
of a proportion of retinal ganglion cells. It may be that chronic "visual
deprivation", either from removal of visual cortex itself or from secondary
degenerative effects on retinal ganglion cells, degrades the ability of
the central nervous system to ensure ocular motor accuracy. Cerebellar
circuits, for example, if deprived of visual sensory feedback may no longer
be able to maintain the long-term stability and reliability of the brainstem
networks that hold the eyes still and ensure appropriate levels and balance of tonic activity in, for example, the brainstem structures in which
OKN is generated.

Dineen, Hendrickson and Keating (1982) also found anatomical reorganization
of the central projections from surviving retinal ganglion cells after
occipital lobectomy. Therefore, recovery of function may be, in part, secondary
to changes in the retinal inputs into the structures that mediate extrastriate visual processing.

Conclusions

1) An optokinetic system organized like that of afoveate animals was found
in monkeys after bilateral occipital lobectomy. There was a poor response
to stimuli that produced high velocities of retinal slip or were comprised
of high-frequency components. These limitations probably reflect the combination
of a nonlinear transformation of information about retinal slip velocity
(which likely occurs in AON and NOT) and subsequent filtering of that information by an intact velocity storage mechanism in the vestibular nuclei. In
intact monkeys, cortical inputs provide the immediate, "pursuit" component
of OKN which overcomes the limited ability of the afoveate optokinetic
system to respond to high-velocity, high-frequency stimuli. Cortical inputs
also directly affect the afoveate optokinetic system: they balance out
inherent temporal-nasal asymmetries and improve dynamic performance and
extend the range of response.

2) The ability to pursue and saccade to small moving or stationary targets
recovered to a remarkable degree in animals without striate cortex. The
mechanism of pursuit recovery is likely via extrastriate visual projections
to areas 'MT' and 'MST' at the parietal-temporal-occipital junction. The
recovery of visually-guided saccades also probably depends on extrastriate
(likely cortical) visual inputs to the superior colliculus or to the frontal
eye fields.

3) Some ability to adaptively modify the gain of the VOR survived removal of striate cortex. This capability appeared to be independent of the ability to make immediate adjustments of slow-phase velocity during conditions of visual-vestibular conflict.

4) Some deterioration of ocular motor performance, especially for holding the eyes still, developed several months after surgery. This loss of function as well as some aspects of recovery of function may be due to remote anatomical effects of removal of occipital cortex such as transynaptic loss of some retinal ganglion cells as well as rerouting of information through spared retinal inputs to extrastriate structures.

References

Boyle, R., U. Büttner, and G. Markert (1985). Vestibular nuclei activity and eye movements in the alert monkey during sinusoidal optokinetic stimulation. Exp. Brain Research, 57, 362-369.

Campion, J., R. Latto, and Y. M. Smith (1983). Is blindsight an effect of scattered light, spared cortex, and near-threshold vision? Behavior Brain Sci., 6, 423-486.

Collewijn, H. (1981). The Oculomotor System of the Rabbit and Its Plasticity. Springer-Verlag, Berlin.

Dineen, J., A. Hendrickson, and E. G. Keating (1982). Alterations of retinal inputs following striate cortex removal in adult monkey. Exp. Brain Res., 47, 446-456.

Keating, E. G. (1980). Residual spatial vision in the monkey after removal of striate and preoccipital cortex. Brain Research, 187, 271-290.

Pasik, P., and T. Pasik (1982). Visual functions in monkeys after total removal of visual cerebral cortex. Contributions to Sensory Physiology, 7, 147-200.

Waespe, W., B. Cohen, and T. Raphan (1983). Role of the flocculus and paraflocculus in optokinetic nystagmus and visual-vestibular interactions: effect of lesions. Exp. Brain Research, 50, 9-33.

Zee, D. S., P. H. Butler, L. M. Optican, R. J. Tusa, and G. Gücer (1982). in A. Roucoux and M. Crommelinck (Eds.) Physiological and Pathological Aspects of Eye Movements. Dr. W. Junk Publishers, The Hague. Effects of bilateral occipital lobectomies on eye movements in monkeys: preliminary observations, 225-232.

BRAINSTEM AND CEREBELLAR
MECHANISMS IN
OCULOMOTOR CONTROL

Vestibulo-cerebellar Control of the Vestibulo-ocular Reflex (VOR)

B. Cohen, T. Raphan and W. Waespe

Departments of Neurology, Mount Sinai School of Medicine (BC),
and University of Zurich (WW) and Computer and Information
Science, Brooklyn College, City University of New York (TR)

INTRODUCTION:

Each part of the vestibulo-cerebellum is closely related to the labyrinths and vestibular nuclei. Although anatomical and physiological differences have been noted between them, it has not been clear how they are functionally related to the VOR. Models of the VOR have resulted in identification of discrete functional components which explain the VOR dynamics. Surprisingly, these components can be related to specific areas of the brainstem and cerebellum. In this paper we relate the function of the two major regions of the vestibulo-cerebellum to a model of the VOR and of visual-vestibular interaction. The model is shown in Fig. 1. It is composed of three main components, a direct vestibular pathway, a direct visual or optokinetic pathway and a velocity storage integrator that is shared in common by both the visual and vestibular systems. The direct pathways are responsible for rapid changes in eye velocity from the visual and vestibular systems, while the velocity storage integrator subserves slow changes and is responsible for the dominant time constant and low frequency characteristics of the VOR (Cohen et al. 1977; Raphan et al. 1979; Waespe et al. 1983; see Raphan and Cohen, 1985 for review).

Fig.1

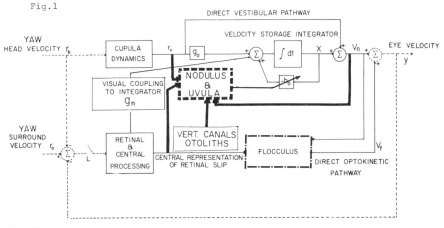

Fig. 1: Model of the VOR and of visual-vestibular interactions.

FLOCCULUS

Knowledge about floccular function has come from studies that show that firing
frequencies of floccular Purkinje cells are related to retinal slip (Noda 1981),
to eye velocity during ocular pursuit (Miles and Fuller 1975; Lisberger and
Fuchs 1978), and to the rapid rise in optokinetic nystagmus (OKN) (Waespe et al.
1981). These studies suggest that the flocculus mediates activity that produces
rapid changes in eye velocity from the visual system during both ocular pursuit
and OKN. Lesion studies strongly support this idea. After flocculus and
paraflocculus lesions there are marked deficits in ocular pursuit (Dichgans et
al. 1978; Zee et al. 1981), and OKN (Zee et al. 1981; Waespe et al. 1983).
Changes in OKN after bilateral flocculus and paraflocculus lesions are shown in
Fig. 2B, D, F. Before lesion the response to a step of surround velocity had a
characteristic initial rapid rise in slow phase eye velocity followed by a slow
rise to a steady state level (Fig. 2A, C, E). After stimulation there was a
rapid fall in slow phase velocity followed by a slow decline during optokinetic
after-nystagmus (OKAN). The rapid rise and fall in velocity are attributable to
activation of the direct visual pathway, and the slow rise and fall to the
velocity storage integrator (Cohen et al. 1977). After flocculectomy and
parafloyculectomy only activity attributable to the indirect visual pathways
remains, and the response after lesion is simulated by the model of Fig. 1 if
the direct visual pathway that includes the flocculus is removed or its gain is
reduced (Waespe et al. 1983).

VISUAL SUPPRESSION

The flocculus and paraflocculus are not only responsible for producing ocular
pursuit, but they also participate in suppressing the VOR when viewing targets
that move and are stabilized with regard to the head. An example of such
suppression is shown in Fig. 3C. Post-rotatory nystagmus was induced by a step
of angular velocity in darkness. When the lights were turned on at t_o, the
stationary visual surround was illuminated, producing visual-vestibular
conflict. The animal's semicircular canals and the vestibular system signalled
that it was moving, but the visual system indicated that it was stationary. In
response to this the animal responded to the visual information, suppressing its
nystagmus. Slow phase velocity dropped suddenly, then more slowly to zero.
Activity related to ocular pursuit that is mediated by the flocculus produces
the initial rapid component of visual suppression (Lisberger and Fuchs 1978).
It is this component of suppression that was lost or severely compromised after
floccular and parafloccular lesions (Waespe et al. 1983).

Concurrently, during visual suppression activity in the velocity storage
mechanism in the vestibular system is rapidly discharged. This produces the
decline in slow phase velocity that follows the initial drop. The loss of
stored activity during visual suppression is demonstrated in Fig. 3C by the
continuous decline in eye velocity when the animal was in light, and by the
failure of eye velocity to recover when the lights were out after the period of
visual suppression at t_1 (Raphan et al. 1979).

The rapid discharge of slow phase velocity in the presence of visual-vestibular
conflict implies that there is a process in the VOR that can rapidly shorten the
time constant of the velocity storage mechanism, causing stored activity to be
discharged or "dumped". We have called this process a "dump" mechanism (Cohen
et al. 1977). It is initiated by retinal slip during visual-vestibular
conflict and has been modeled by closing a switch that shortens the time
constant of the feedback loop that includes element h_o during for the period
of exposure to the stationary surround. The model is capable of simulating
effects of visual suppression of both OKAN and post-rotatory nystagmus (Cohen et
al. 1977; Raphan et al. 1979). The ability to alter the time constant of the
velocity storage integrator during visual suppression and cause a discharge of
stored activity is not lost after flocculectomy (Waespe et al. 1983; Waespe and

Fig.2

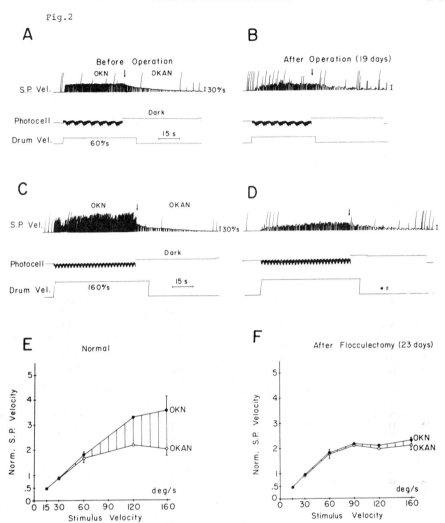

Fig. 2: OKN and OKAN induced by stimulus velocities of 60 and 160 deg/sec before (A,C) and after (B, D) bilateral flocculectomy. Downward arrows and photocell indicate lights out. The initial rapid rise in slow phase velocity at the onset of OKN in the normal animal (A, C) was reduced after flocculectomy (B, D), and the maximum velocity of OKN was the saturation velocity of OKAN. Note that OKN rose more slowly to a steady state level after than before operation, and that OKAN was unaffected by flocculectomy. E, F, Graphs showing OKN (closed circles) and OKAN (open circles) before (E) and after (F) flocculectomy. Stimulus velocity is on the abscissa and slow phase velocity, normalized with regard to a stimulus velocity of 30 deg/sec, is shown on the ordinate. Note that OKN steady state velocities fell after flocculectomy (F) to approximately the value of OKAN. OKAN was unaffected by the lesions. The vertical bars indicate the rapid drop in eye velocity at the end of OKN and the onset of OKAN. This is a measure of activity in the direct optokinetic pathway. (From Waespe et al. 1983).

280   B. Cohen, T. Raphan and W. Waespe

Cohen 1983). This suggests that this function must be performed in the VOR itself or elsewhere in the vestibulo-cerebellum.

TILT SUPPRESSION

There is another way to discharge activity from the velocity storage mechanism. If the position of the head is changed or tilted during post-rotatory nystagmus or OKAN, there is a rapid loss of nystagmus (Raphan et al. 1981). In the example shown in Fig. 3B, the animal was rotated about a vertical axis in darkness and stopped. During the post-rotatory nystagmus it was suddenly tilted at t_o. In response the time constant of the decline in slow phase velocity became shorter and stored activity was lost. The loss of stored activity is demonstrated by the failure of slow phase velocity to recover when the animal was brought back to the upright position at t_1. We have postulated that visual suppression and tilt suppression utilize the same mechanism in dumping activity from the storage integrator (Raphan et al. 1981). The ability to dump activity during head tilt is preserved after flocculectomy (Waespe et al. 1983). This indicates that the flocculus is not part of the mechanism that discharges or adapts the velocity storage mechanism. This is also shown by the essentially normal response of vestibular nuclei neurons to conflict stimulation after flocculectomy (Waespe and Cohen 1983). That is, activity of vestibular nuclei neurons induced by a step of angular velocity declined more rapidly in a conflict situation than in darkness.

The nature of the mechanisms utilized during tilt dumps is currently under investigation. Initial studies indicate that duration and angle of tilt are both important factors in determining the duration and extent of the dump of stored activity. This would not be produced simply by introducing a single short time constant for the period of the tilt. Rather a graded mechanism is implied. This has been represented in the model shown in Fig. 1 by a controller which modifies the parameter h_o.

NODULUS AND UVULA

The failure of the flocculus to affect velocity storage suggested to us that other regions of the vestibulo-cerebellum might subserve the dumping function, and experiments were undertaken to explore this possibility. Four monkeys were studied after bilateral removal of the nodulus and ventral uvula (Waespe et al. 1985). Eye movements were recorded with electrooculography, and the eye position signal was electronically differentiated and rectified to obtain a signal proportional to eye velocity. In this paper we consider only horizontal eye movements. Stimuli were given in the three-axis vestibular and optokinetic stimulator that has been described previously (Raphan et al. 1981).

There were no effects of the lesions on the step gain of the VOR (Compare Fig. 3A & D, for example), and the initial rapid rise in OKN was of normal configuration and gain. The steady state gain of OKN was also essentially unaffected. Effects on the VOR time constant, however, were dramatic. After nodular and ventral uvular ablation all previous habituation of the VOR was lost, and its time constant became as long as in naive animals. This is shown in Fig. 3D by the prolongation of the response to a step of angular velocity in darkness. (Note the difference in time base of Fig. 3A and 3D). OKAN was similarly prolonged. In addition, the dominant time constant of the VOR or of OKAN could no longer be habituated, regardless of how often or how long the animal was tested. This suggests that the nodulus and uvula contain neural mechanisms that control and adapt the dominant time constant of the VOR.

Nodulo-uvulectomy also had a striking effect on visual and tilt suppression. Although animals retained the rapid drop in eye velocity during visual suppression presumably mediated by the flocculus, they could no longer discharge stored eye velocity rapidly (Fig. 3F). Animals also completely lost the

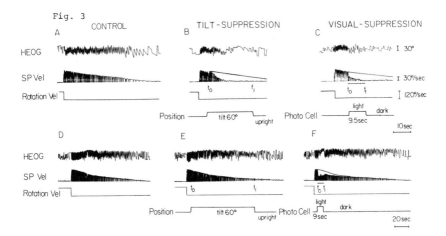

Fig. 3

Fig. 3. Visual suppression (C, F) and tilt suppression (B, E) of post-rotatory
nystagmus (A, D), before (A-D) and after (D-F) surgical ablation of the nodulus
and ventral uvula. The top trace is the horizontal EOG and the second trace is
rectified slow phase velocity of nystagmus. The dotted line in each panel shows
the velocity that would have occurred had the animal not had exposure to the
stationary visual surround (C, F) or been tilted (B, E) as shown in A & D. The
third trace in each panel is rotational velocity. The fourth trace in C, F is
the photocell, recording darkness and light. At t_o the lights were on,
exposing the stationary surround. At t_1 the animal was back in darkness.
A, B and D, E were recorded entirely in darkness. In B and E the fourth trace
is chair position. At t_o the animal was moved into the right side down
position, and at t_1 it was moved back to the upright position. Note that
after nodulectomy (D-E) the time course of decline of slow phase velocity was
not substantially altered by visual or tilt suppression. (From Waespe et al.
1985).

ability to alter the time constant of nystagmus when tilted during post-rotatory
nystagmus (Fig. 3E). Each of the effects, shown in Fig. 3E and F for
post-rotatory nystagmus, were also present during OKAN. That is, after
nodulo-uvulectomy animals lost the ability to rapidly alter OKAN slow phase
velocity during exposure to a stationary visual surround, and tilting the head
had no effect on the decline in slow phase velocity during OKAN. Thus, the dump
mechanism in the model of Fig. 1 was inactivated or lost by removal of this
region of the vestibulocerebellum.

An interesting finding in three of the four animals after lesion was the
presence of periodic alternating nystagmus in darkness (Waespe et al. 1985).
Such nystagmus is found in humans after posterior fossa lesions and has been
postulated to be due to an instability of the integrators in the vestibular
nuclei on the two sides (Leigh et al. 1981). This implies that the nodulus and
uvula also stabilize the velocity storage integrators in the VOR, presumably by
suppressing commissural pathways that appear to play an important role in
producing velocity storage (deJong et al. 1982; Galiana et al. 1984).
Periodic alternating nystagmus in humans has been treated successfully in some
cases with baclofen (Halmagyi et al. 1980). In the monkey baclofen also
abolished the periodic alternating nystagmus (Waespe et al. 1985). This
occurred in conjuction with a reduction in the dominant time constant of the
VOR. We have subsequently found that baclofen also has a dose-specific effect

of the VOR in the normal animal (Helwig et al. 1985). Baclofen is a GABA agonist, acting on GABAb synapses. It seems likely that the output of the Purkinje cells of the nodulus and uvula utilize GABAb receptors in stabilizing or "dumping" the velocity storage mechanism. We have also found that stimulation in the region of the nodulus and uvula causes a reduction in the time constant of the VOR and of OKAN on one side, in much the same way as during tilt or visual suppression (Solomon et al. 1985). This is further evidence that mechanisms to control or adapt velocity storage originate in the nodulus and uvula.

These concepts have been incorporated in the model of Fig. 1. The nodulus and uvula, shown in the box enclosed by the heavy dashed lines, receive direct input from the labyrinths (Brodal and Hoivik 1964; Carleton and Carpenter 1982). Both otolithic as well as semicircular canal activity has been recorded in the nodulus (Precht et al. 1976a, b; Marini et al. 1979), but it is not known whether this input is from the labyrinth or from the vestibular nuclei, which also project heavily to this region (Brodal and Torvik 1957). Presumably, the input from the vertical canals and otolith organs are used to estimate the onset, duration and extent of the changes in head position with regard to gravity. There is also visual input to the nodulus and uvula (Maekawa and Simpson 1973). Takeda and Maekawa (1985) have shown that the input related to retinal slip that reaches the flocculus from the inferior olive, also reaches the nodulus and uvula. This visual input could be compared to the vestibular input to determine if conflict was present to initiate dumping of velocity storage during visual-vestibular conflict. If this occurred, it could provide a neural basis for conflicts that might lead to motion sickness. This would be of interest since it is known that motion sickness suceptibility is reduced after nodulectomy (Bard et al. 1947). The output of the nodulus and uvula project to caudal portions of the vestibular nuclei and to the prepositus nucleus (Angaut and Brodal 1967; Brodal and Brodal 1985), and are largely separate from the projections from the flocculus (Precht et al. 1977; Langer et al. 1985) Presumably, the nodular and uvular Purkinje cell axons contact cells in the vestibular nuclei that are responsible for velocity storage. If correct, then these neurons may lie in the caudal portions of the vestibular nuclei.

In summary a theoretical scheme for understanding the VOR is presented. In this scheme the VOR is controlled by the vestibulo-cerebellum in two ways:

1. The flocculus and probably the paraflocculus produce rapid changes in eye velocity from the visual system, and are responsible for ocular pursuit, the rapid rise in OKN and for rapid components of visual suppression of the VOR. In addition, the flocculus may also raise or lower the VOR gain to maintain or suppress ocular compensation for head movement (See Miles and Lisberger 1981, and Ito 1984, for review). Although not considered here, the flocculus may be important for parametric control of saccadic eye movements, for helping maintain positions of fixation and for providing adaptive control of saccades and post-saccadic drifts.

2. The nodulus and uvula, on the other hand, appear to have little role in mediating rapid changes in eye velocity, whether induced by the visual or vestibular system. Rather they appear to be primarily involved in controlling velocity storage, habituating its dominant time constant, discharging stored activity rapidly when it is inappropriate, and stabilizing the storage mechanism so that the feedback processes that are involved in integration between the two sides do not go into oscillation. They also appear to play an important role in producing long term adaptation of the VOR, since plastic changes in the VOR time constant are lost after these parts of the vestibulo-cerebellum are destroyed. It is now of interest to determine how head position is sensed by the nodulus and uvula, how the mechanism of dumping is initiated and realized, and how the dominant time constant of the VOR is adapted as a result of visual-vestibular conflict.

REFERENCES

Angaut, P. and Brodal, A. (1967) Arch. Ital. Biol. 105, 441-479.
Bard, P., Woolsey, C.N., Snider, R.S., Moutcastle, V.B. and Bromiley, R.B.
    (1947) Fed. Proc. 6, 72.
Brodal, A. and Hoivik, B. (1964) Arch. Ital. Biol., 102, 1-21.
Brodal, A. and Torvik, A. (1957) Arch. Psychiatr. Nervenkr. 195, 550-567.
Carleton, S.C. and Carpenter, M.B. (1984) Brain Res. 294, 281-298.
Cohen, B., Matsuo, V., and Raphan, T. (1977) J. Physiol. (Lond.), 270, 321-344.
deJong, J.M.B.V., Cohen, B., Matsuo, V., and Uemura, T. (1980) Exp. Neurol. 68,
    420-442.
Dichgans, J., Von Reutern, G.M., and Rommelt, U. (1978) Arch. Psychiat. Nervenkr.
    226, 183-199.
Galiana, H.L., Flohr, H. and Melvill Jones, G. (1984) J. Neurophysiol. 51, 242-259.
Halmagyi, G.M., Rudge, P., Gresty, M.A., Leigh, R.J. and Zee, D.S. (1980)
    Ann. Neurol. 81, 609-611.
Helwig, D., Cohen, B. and Raphan, T. (1985) Soc. Neurosci. Abstr, 11, 694
Ito, M. (1984) The Cerebellum and Neural Control, Raven Press, New York.
Langer, T., Fuchs, A.F., Chubb, M.C., Scudder, C.A. and Lisberger, S.G. (1985)
    J. Comp. Neurol. 235, 26-37.
Leigh, J., Robinson, D.A., and Zee, D.S. (1981) Ann. N.Y. Acad. Sci. 374, 619-635.
Lisberger, S.G. and Fuchs, A.F. (1978) J. Neurophysiol., 41, 733-763.
Marini, G., Provini, L. and Rosina, A. (1975) Brain Res. 99, 367-371.
Miles, F.A. and Lisberger, S.G. (1981) Ann. N.Y. Acad. Sci. 374, 465-475.
Miles, F.A. and Fuller, J.H. (1975) Science, 189, 1000-1002.
Noda, H. (1981) Ann. N.Y. Acad. Sci. 374, 465-475.
Precht, W., Volkind, R., Maeda, M., and Giretti, M.L. (1976a) Neuroscience, 1,
    301-312.
Precht, W., Simpson, J.I. and Llinas, R. (1976b) Pluegers Arch. 367, 1-6.
Precht, W., Volkind, R. and Blanks, R.H.I. (1977) Exp. Brain Res. 27, 143-160.
Raphan, T., Matsuo, V., and Cohen, B: (1979) Exp. Brain Res., 35, 229-248.
Raphan, T., Cohen, B., and Henn, V. (1981) Ann. N.Y. Acad. Sci., 374, 44-55.
Raphan, T. and Cohen, B. (1985) In: Adaptive Mechanisms in Gaze Control, Facts
    Theories, edited by A. Berthoz and G. Melvill Jones, Elsevier, Amsterdam
Solomon, D., Raphan, T. and Cohen, B. (1985) Soc. Neurosci. Abstr. 11, 693.
Waespe, W., Buettner, U., and Henn, V. (1981) Exp. Brain Res. 43, 337-348.
Waespe, W., Cohen, B., and Raphan, T. (1983) Exp. Brain Res. 50, 9-33.
Waespe, W. and Cohen, B. (1983) Exp. Brain Res., 51, 23-35.
Waespe, W., Cohen, B., and Raphan, T. (1985) Science, 228, 199-202.
Zee, D.S., Yamazaki, A., Butler, P.H., and Gucer, G. (1981) J. Neurophysiol.,
    46, 878-87.

Supported by NS 00294 and EY 04148

Multidimensional Organization of the Vestibulo-ocular Reflex (VOR)

T. Raphan and B. Cohen

Department of Computer and Information Science, Brooklyn
College of CUNY, Brooklyn, New York and Department of
Neurology, Mount Sinai School of Medicine of CUNY, New
York, USA

Introduction:

The vestibular system generates compensatory eye movements for movements of the
head and environment in a head based coordinate frame. However, the central
nervous system probably encodes motion of the head and environment in coordinate
bases related to semicircular canal orientation (Simpson & Graf, 1981). The
information is then transformed to the extra-ocular muscle coordinates to
generate compensatory eye movements (Pellionisz, 1985;Robinson, 1983). Recent
attempts at modelling the three dimensional behavior of the VOR have been
restricted to describing the static transformations that map the head velocity
vector into canal based coordinates and finally into an eye movement motor
command (Robinson, 1983;Pellionisz, 1985), and the dynamics of the visual and
vestibular systems and the effects of gravity on the system via the otolith
organs have not been considered in a three dimensional scheme. The purpose of
this paper is to show how multidimensional system theory can be utilized to
formulate a model of the three dimensional dynamical transformations during
visual-vestibular interaction and how gravity effects these transformations.

Experimental basis of the generalized model:

Initial studies of the dynamics of the VOR were done for rotations about a
vertical axis in the upright position and gravity was not a factor. Under these
circumstances vestibular and visual systems complement each other to maintain
stable retinal images (See Wilson & Melvill-Jones, 1979; Henn et al, 1980 for
review). The complementary function is shown in Fig. 1A, B. For steps of
rotation about a vertical axis in darkness slow phase eye velocity decays to
zero with a time constant of 10-15 sec (Fig. 1A). This is followed by a post
rotatory nystagmus with identical characteristics when the rotation stops.
For a step in surround velocity there is a quick rise in slow phase eye velocity
followed by a slow rise to a steady state level (Fig. 1B)(Cohen et al, 1977).
The slow rise in velocity during OKN complements the decline in slow phase
velocity during per rotatory nystagmus in darkness. When the lights are turned
off, at the end of OKN there is after-nystagmus whose time course is similar to
that of post rotatory nystagmus in darkness but is in the opposite direction.
The two summate and cancel after rotation in light. A detailed mathematical
analysis of these responses has shown that a common velocity storage integrator
is utilized in these responses and in the visual-vestibular interactions (Raphan

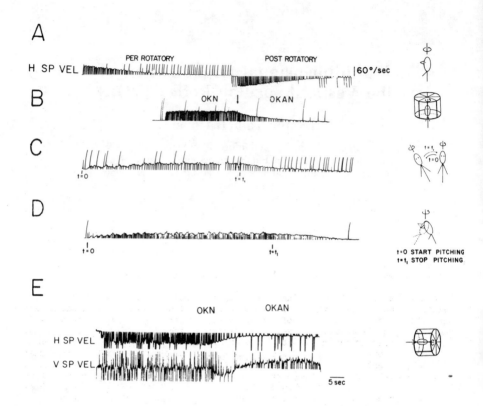

Fig. 1. A. Horizontal slow phase eye velocity response to a step in yaw head velocity in darkness. During rotation eye velocity jumps rapidly and then decays to zero. When the rotation stops, there is a post-rotatory response with characteristics similar to that of the per-rotatory nystagmus. B. Slow phase eye velocity in response to a step in surround velocity. There is a quick rise in slow phase velocity during optokinetic nystagmus (OKN) followed by a slow rise to a steady state value. When the lights are shut off, optokinetic after-nystagmus (OKAN) continues in darkness. C. Response to off-vertical axis rotation. The animal was rotating in darkness and slow phase velocity had declined to zero. When the animal is tilted at t_o, slow phase velocity increases to a steady state level. When the animal is tilted back to the vertical at t_1 slow phase velocity declines to zero. D. Response to pitch while rotating. Again the animal was rotating in darkness and slow phase velocity had declined to zero. At t_o pitching is introduced and slow phase velocity increases to a steady state level. When pitching stops at t_1, slow phase velocity decreases to zero. The responses in A-D are mediated by horizontal velocity storage. E. OKN and OKAN with the subject left side down. During stimulation in light only horizontal OKN is induced with slow phase phases away from gravity and there is no vertical component. During OKAN in this position, however, a vertical component develops with prominent downward slow phases. This is followed by a strong secondary upward OKAN.

et al, 1977;Robinson, 1977; Raphan et al, 1979;Waespe et al, 1983). Recent evidence indicates that velocity storage can be activated by many types of stimuli, and that it has a three dimensional gravity-dependent structure that is capable of storing information to produce eye movements in a wide range of planes (Raphan and Cohen 1985).

One type of gravity related response which has been linked to otolith function is the response to off-vertical axis rotation (OVAR). After an animal has been rotated about a vertical axis until per-rotatory nystagmus decays to zero, if the axis of rotation is tilted the nystagmus returns to a steady state level over a time course similar to that of OKAN (Fig. 1C). During the period of OVAR there is a sustained horizontal nystagmus for as long as rotation persists. When the animal is returned to the upright position, the nystagmus decays to zero velocity with a time constant approximately equal to that of OKAN and per and post rotatory nystagmus (Fig. 1C)(Benson and Bodin, 1966; Guedry, 1965; Raphan et al., 1981; Young and Henn, 1975). This suggests that velocity storage is utilized during OVAR to generate the continuous horizontal nystagmus. Labyrinthine lesions as well as unit recordings from semicircular canal afferents support the contention that the otoliths generate the signals necessary for the continuous nystagmus during OVAR (Money and Scott, 1962; Correia and Money, 1970; Cohen et al., 1983;Goldberg and Fernandez, 1981; Raphan et al., 1981). It has been postulated that sequential excitation and inhibition of otolith hair cells by the rotating gravity vector generates a travelling wave whose velocity is estimated centrally. This input reaches the velocity storage integrator which generates the continuous horizontal nystagmus.

Pitching the head while rotating about a space vertical axis is another gravity related response that induces continuous horizontal nystagmus. The dynamics and the steady state velocity of this nystagmus are similar to those of OVAR, suggesting involvement of the velocity storage mechanism (Fig. 1D). Canal plugging experiments and unit activity recorded in the eighth nerve provide decisive support for this idea and demonstrate that the vertical semicircular canals are primary effectors in producing this response (Raphan et al., 1983;Raphan et al, 1985). However, as the input to the vertical canals during pitch while rotating is sinusoidal, it must be rectified to produce a steady state eye velocity. It has thus been postulated that the otoliths contribute to the rectification, by conveying information about the attitude of the head with regard to gravity to central structures.

Gravity also effects the dynamics of of the VOR by modifying the vertical and horizontal modes of the velocity storage integrator. During optokinetic nystagmus, velocity storage is present for vertical nystagmus when animals are on their sides, but disappears when animals are upright (Matsuo et al., 1981; Matsuo and Cohen, 1984). Moreover, a vertical component of velocity storage can be activated by a pure horizontal optokinetic stimulus resulting in oblique OKAN when animals are on their sides (Fig. 1E) (Raphan & Cohen, 1983).

In summary, the data suggest that velocity storage is a three dimensional dynamic system which processes semicircular canal, otolith and visual inputs to produce compensatory eye movements in all planes. The model will consider the dynamic transformations of head and surround velocity signals to an eye velocity command and the effects of gravity on the processing. The metric transformation to eye muscle coordinates can then be considered as a separate problem (Pellionisz & Llinas, 1980; Robinson, 1983;Pellionisz, 1985).

Three Dimensional Model of the Visual-Vestibular Interaction:

The generalized model of the VOR that we will consider is shown in Fig. 2A. The inputs $\underline{r}_v$ and $\underline{r}_o$ are 3 dimensional head velocity and optokinetic velocity vectors in a head based coordinate system. $\underline{r}_1$ is a linear

acceleration vector also referenced to a head based coordinate system. The
model parameters have been generalized to matrix and system operators. The
manner in which this generalization can be effected is considered next as we
discuss each part of the model.

Semicircular Canal Kinematics: Head to Canal Coordinate Transformations
(T_{can}):

Each semicircular canal is an inertial mechanism that responds to angular motion
with a component along the normal to the canal plane. Thus, the central nervous
system receives information about angular head movement relative to a coordinate
system whose axes are defined by the normals to the canal planes. In order to
achieve good ocular compensation, the eyes must rotate so as to oppose head
movements. Therefore, compensatory eye movements must be made in planes of head
rotation. These can be conveniently expressed as horizontal, vertical, and
torsional rotations relative to a head coordinate system defined by the normals
to the horizontal stereotaxic, sagittal and coronal planes. The central nervous
system receives information from the semicircular canal in canal coordinates.
Therefore, the first transformation that will be considered is the one from head
coordinates to canal coordinates. Fig. 2B shows the geometrical relationship
between the head coordinate and canal coordinate bases. The components of a
vector in the canal coordinate basis is a measure of the excitation of each
semicircular canal. Therefore, when the head is rotated, a transformation must
take place centrally from canal coordinates to which head movements are
referenced, to head coordinates which serve as a reference for eye movements.
In the monkey the lateral canals are tipped up approximately 15-25° above the
horizontal steriotaxic plane (Reisine et al, 1985;Blanks et al, 1985;Bohmer et
al, 1982). The anterior and posterior canal planes are approximately orthogonal
to the horizontal canal plane and are rotated 45°. If the 15° value is
utilized (Reisine et al, 1985), the coordinate transformation from head
coordinates to canal coordinates can be approximately described by the following
transformation:

$$
\begin{bmatrix} x_c \\ y_c \\ z_c \end{bmatrix} = \begin{bmatrix} .707 & .683 & -.183 \\ -.707 & .683 & -.183 \\ 0 & .259 & .966 \end{bmatrix} \begin{bmatrix} x \\ y \\ z \end{bmatrix} \qquad (1)
$$

or in vector notation

$$
\underline{r}_v = T_{can}\ \underline{r}_h \qquad (2)
$$

where $\underline{r}_v$ is the canal excitation vector and $\underline{r}_h$ is the head velocity
vector. It should be noted that angular velocity components along the x y z
axes corresponds to pitch, roll and yaw, respectively. Positive directions for
angular velocities along these axes correspond to pitch forward, clockwise roll
(to the left side), and rotation to the left respectively. The positive
direction for the canal axes excitations x_c, y_c, z_c, correspond to the
excitatory direction for the left labyrinth. This convention establishes a
right handed coordinate system. Although this development assumes an orthogonal
coordinate basis for the canals, there is evidence that there is some degree of
nonorthogonality albeit small. This may have an effect on the way central
vestibular neurons are excited. A nonorthogonal basis can be handled by
assuming a more general transformation T_{can} with different elements in the
matrix representing the transformation.

Optokinetic Input $(T_{can}, \mathbf{\Upsilon}(\underline{e}))$:

When full-field visual stimuli are presented, the stimulus vector can be defined as the corresponding head movement which would give compensatory eye movements. Thus, pure upward visual excitation corresponds to a downward head movement and would be represented as a vector along the positive x axis. Visual motion to the right would be a vector along the z axis. Visual rotation corresponding to roll would be along the y axis. The vector associated with the stimulus in canal coordinates (x_c, y_c, z_c) can be obtained by substituting (x, y, z) into Eq. (1) and solving for x_c, y_c and z_c. This could be translated into canal coordinates by central processing (Simpson et al, 1981). In this way signals from both the visual and peripheral vestibular system could be combined centrally under a common basis. The nonlinear matrix operator $\mathbf{\Upsilon}(\underline{e})$ that operates on the central representation of slip will be assumed to be a diagonal matrix whose elements are the same type of nonlinear functions found for horizontal OKN (Waespe et al, 1983). Once the vestibular and optokinetic signals are transformed to a common co-ordinate basis, the dynamical aspects of the peripheral and central processing can be considered.

Dynamic Aspects of Semicircular Canal Kinematics (D_{can}):

Each semicircular can be described approximately by a first order linear differential equation (Raphan and Cohen, 1981).

$$\frac{d}{dt} r_v + \frac{1}{t_c} r_v = - \frac{d}{dt} u \qquad (3)$$

where r_v is the eighth nerve output and u is the input angular head velocity along the normal to the canal plane. Eq 3 can be put into state form

$$\frac{d}{dt} x_{cup} = -\frac{1}{t_c} x + \frac{1}{t_c} u$$

$$r_v = x_{cup} - u \qquad (4)$$

where x_{cup} is the state of the cupula (the sum of the eighth nerve output and the component of angular velocity along the normal to its plane). If Eq 4 is applied to each canal then the state equations are given by:

$$\begin{bmatrix} \dot{x}_{ant} \\ \dot{x}_{pos} \\ \dot{x}_{lat} \end{bmatrix} = \begin{bmatrix} -1/t_c & 0 & 0 \\ 0 & -1/t_c & 0 \\ 0 & 0 & -1/t_c \end{bmatrix} \begin{bmatrix} x_{ant} \\ x_{pos} \\ x_{lat} \end{bmatrix} -1/t_c \begin{bmatrix} u_{ant} \\ u_{pos} \\ u_{lat} \end{bmatrix} \qquad (5)$$

$$\begin{bmatrix} r_{v\ ant} \\ r_{v\ pos} \\ r_{v\ lat} \end{bmatrix} = \begin{bmatrix} x_{ant} \\ x_{pos} \\ x_{lat} \end{bmatrix} + \begin{bmatrix} u_{ant} \\ u_{pos} \\ u_{lat} \end{bmatrix} \qquad (6)$$

where it is assumed that the cupula time constant of all the canals are identical and that there is no cross coupling between canal afferents at this level. This can conveniently be represented in vector form as

$$\dot{\underline{x}}_{cup} = -\frac{1}{t_c} \underline{x}_{cup} + \frac{1}{t_c} \underline{r}_c \qquad (7)$$

$$\underline{r}_v = \underline{x}_{cup} + \underline{r}_c$$

In addition since

$$\underline{r}_c = T_{can} \underline{r}_h \qquad (8)$$

A

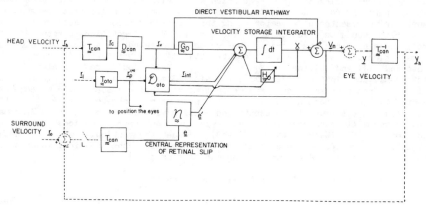

B

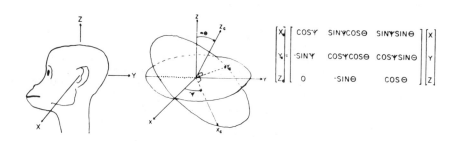

XYZ - HEAD BASED CO-ORDINATES
$X_c Y_c Z_c$- CANAL BASED CO-ORDINATES

X_c- NORMAL TO ANTERIOR CANAL PLANE
Y_c- NORMAL TO POSTERIOR CANAL PLANE
Z_c- NORMAL TO HORIZONTAL CANAL PLANE

Fig. 2. A. Three dimensional dynamical model of visual-vestibular interaction. Head and surround velocity are transformed into canal based coordinates (T_{can}). The canal excitation vector $\underline{r}_c$, is then dynamically transformed into a signal $\underline{r}_v$ representing the eighth nerve canal excitation vector. The visual slip signal is also converted into canal coordinates by T_{can} to generate a central representation of retinal slip, $\underline{e}$. Both $\underline{r}_v$ and $\underline{e}$ activate a multidimensional representation of velocity storage which combines with the direct vestibular pathway to generate eye velocity in canal coordinates. This representation of eye velocity is transformed back into head coordinates by the transformation T_{can}^{-1} to generate eye velocity in head coordinates which can combine with head and surround velocity. The three dimensional structure of the direct optokinetic pathway has been left out for simplicity. B. Transformation equations that relate head coordinates to canal coordinates, T_{can}.

Then Equation 7 can be represented as

$$\dot{x}_{cup} = -\frac{1}{t_c} x_{cup} + T_{can} \underline{r}_h$$

$$\underline{r}_v = x_{cup} + T_{can} \underline{r}_h \qquad (9)$$

This is a standard linear system and given any angular head velocity vector $\underline{r}_h$ in head coordinates and any starting state the eighth nerve excitation vector from the canals $\underline{r}_v$ can be obtained (Zadeh & Desoer, 1964). This equation not only describes the coordinate basis transformation from head to canal coordinates but also defines the dynamic transformations as well. We will next consider the generalized velocity storage integrator and how it is coupled to by the multidimensional vestibular and visual excitations.

The Integrator (H_o) and Its Coupling:

The internal dynamics of the velocity storage integrator can be represented by the matrix differential system:

$$\dot{x} = H_o \underline{x} + G_o \underline{r}_v + \eta (T_c \underline{e}) + \underline{r}_{int} \qquad (10)$$

The direct pathway through the flocculus (Zee et al., 1980; Waespe et al., 1983) has been left out so as to concentrate on those signals which are known to converge onto the integrator. The vector $\underline{e}$ is the retinal slip, $\eta(\underline{e})$ is a nonlinear matrix operator, G_o is the coupling matrix from the eighth nerve to the integrator and H_o is the matrix representing the dynamics associated with the integrator. It will be assumed that G_o and $\eta(\underline{e})$ are diagonal matrices. This is reasonable first approximation since there is no reason to believe that the coupling to the integrator from the semicircular canals or visual system is anything but in canal coordinates. If it is assumed that there are gravity dependent off-diagonal terms in H_o it would explain the cross coupling efects of gravity during optokinetic excitation. It should be noted that $\underline{y}$ is the vector velocity command in a canal based coordinate frame presumably coded in the firing frequencies of vertical and horizontal second order vestibular nuclei neurons. This signal must be converted to an eye muscle excitation command to rotate the eyes (Pellionisz , 1980; Robinson, 1983). In order to obtain the appropriate compensation this must closely approximate the inverse coordinate transformation that exists from head to canal coordinates.

Otolith Kinematics (Static and Dynamic Responses, D_{oto}):

The otolith organs, utricle and saccule, respond to a linear force vector, $\underline{r}_l$ which is produced by linear acceleration or gravity. Each cell of the utricular macula responds to a linear force vector and is maximally excited by force along its polarization vector (Fernandez and Goldberg, 1975). Thus when the head is tilted, the gravitational force field excites those cells which have polarizations along the gravitation field. Those which have polarizations othogonal to the gravitational field will not be excited (Shotwell et al 1981). The polarization vectors are distributed over all angles but about 70 percent of the cells have polarizations for ipsilateral side down (Fernandez and Goldberg, 1975). The dynamics of the utricular afferents are very rapid, responding to a sudden head tilt in 15 msec. Regularly firing afferents maintain a level of firing proportional to the force while irregularly firing cell adapt back to their spontaneous level. Thus the vector that inputs to the central nervous system from $\underline{r}_{(n)}$ the transduction by the otolith organs is a spatially distributed n-vector, $\underline{r}_{(n)}^p$, which under normal circumstances approximately describes the head position with regard to gravity. This vector can generate direct compensatory eye position changes as the head moves with regard to gravity. In addition, it must be combined with information from the semicircular canals and possibly from 2nd order vestibular nuclei neurons by the system operator

D$_{oto}$. The output of the system operator is the signal vector which charges the integrator, r_{-int}.

In summary, a model has been presented that is a natural extension of the model of visual-vestibular interaction for rotations about a vertical axis. It is an experimentally testable mathematical structure which should help elucidate the functional dynamics of the VOR.

References:

Benson, A.J., Bodin, M.A., (1966) Aerospace Medicine, pp. 144-154.
Blanks, R.H.I., Curthoys, I.S., Bennett, M.L., Markham, C.H., (1985) Brain Res., 300:315-324.
Bohmer, A., Henn, V., Suzuki, J. I., (1982) In Physiological and Pathological aspects of eye movements. A. Roucoux and M. Crommelinck, eds., Dr. W. Junk Publishers, The Hague, Boston, London, 127-130.
Cohen, B., Matsuo, V., Raphan, T., (1977) J. Physiol. 270: 321-344.
Cohen, B., Suzuki, J.I., Raphan, T., (1983) Brain Res. 276: 159-1164.
Collewijn, H., (1975) Brain Res. 100:489-508.
Correia, M.J., Money, K.E., (1970) Acta-oto-laryngolica. 69: 7-16.
Fernandez, C., Goldberg, J.M., (1975a) J. Neurophysiol. 39: 970-984.
Goldberg, J.M., Fernandez, C., (1981) Ann. N.Y. Acad. Sci. 374: 40-43.
Guedry, F.E., (1965) Acta-otolaryngol. 60:30-48, 1965.
Henn, V., Cohen, B., Young, L.R., (1980) Neurosciences Research Program Bull., M.I.T. Press, Cambridge, Mass.
Matsuo, V., Cohen, B., Raphan, T., deJong, V., Henn, V., (1979) Brain Res. 176: 159-164.
Matsuo, V., Cohen B., (1983) Exp. Brain Res. 53:197-216.
Money, K.E., Scott, J.W., (1962) Amer. J. Physiol. 202: 1211-1220.
Pellionisz, A., Llinas, R., (1980) Neuroscience, 5:1125-1136.
Pellionisz, A., (1985) In: Berthoz, A. and Melvill-Jones, G. (Eds.), Reviews in Oculomotor Research, Elsevier/North Holland.
Raphan, T., Matsuo, V., Cohen, B., (1979) Exp. Brain Res. 35: 229-248.
Raphan, T., Cohen, B., (1981) In Models of Oculomotor Behavior and Control. B. Zuber (ed), CRC Press, Inc., West Palm Beach, Fla., pp. 91-109.
Raphan, T., Cohen, B., Henn, V., (1981) Ann. N.Y. Academy of Sci., 374: 44-55.
Raphan, T., Cohen, B., Suzuki, J.I., Henn, V., (1983) Brain Res. 276: 165-172.
Raphan, T., Cohen, B., (1983) Neuroscience Abstract 95: 10, 1983.
Raphan, T., Cohen, B., (1985) In: Berthoz, A. and Melvill-Jones, G. (Eds.), Reviews in Oculomotor Research, Elsevier/North Holland.
Raphan, T. Waespe, W. and Cohen, B. (1985) Neuroscience Abstr.
Reisine, H., Simpson, J.I., Rudinger, D., Henn, V., (1985) Neurosc. Abstr.
Robinson, D., (1977) In: Baker, R., Berthoz, A. (eds), Control of Gaze by Brain Stem Neurons. Elsevier/North Holland, Amsterdam, pp. 49-58.
Robinson, D.A., (1983) Biol. Cybern.
Shotwell, S.L., Jacobs, R., Hudspeth, A.J., (1981) Ann. N.Y. Acad. Sci. 374:1-10.
Simpson, J.I., Graf, W., (1981) Ann. N. Y. Academy of Sci., 374:
Simpson, J.I., Graf, W., Leanard, C., (1981) In: Progress in Oculomotor research, pp. 475-484, Fuchs, A.F., Becker, W. (eds.) New York, Elsevier.
Waespe, W., Cohen, B., Raphan, T., (1983) Exp. Brain Res. 50: 9-33.
Wilson, V., Melvill Jones, G., (1979) Plenum Press, New York.
Young, L.R., Henn, V., (1975) Fortchr. Zool., 23: 235-246.
Zadeh, L., Desoer, C.A., (1963) Mcgraw Hill.
Zee, D.S., Yamazaki, A., Eutler, P.H., Gucer, G., (1980) J. Neurophysiol. 46: 878-899.

Supported by NEI Award EYO4148, FRAP Award 6-652237 and NINCDS 00294

The Eye Velocity Signal of Floccular Purkinje Cells During Optokinetic Nystagmus and Smooth Pursuit

W. Waespe and V. Henn

Department of Neurology, University of Zürich,
8091 Zürich, Switzerland

INTRODUCTION

Movement of an entire visual surround elicits optokinetic nystagmus (OKN) and foveation of a small moving target induces smooth pursuit eye movements (SP). In primates, OKN is followed by a strong after-nystagmus (OKAN) in darkness, whereas after-effects of SP are minimal (Lisberger and co-workers, 1981). The hypothesis has been put forward that during OKN the primate visual system couples to the oculomotor system via "direct" and "indirect" pathways (Cohen and co-workers, 1977). The terms "direct" and "indirect" were chosen to describe the dynamics of the OKN slow phase velocity response. Single cell recordings and lesion studies will be reported in support of the hypothesis that floccular Purkinje cells (P-cells) are part of the "direct" visual-oculomotor pathways. Slow phase velocity of OKN in response to a step in stimulus velocity has two dynamically different components (Fig. 1A): A rapid initial change in velocity (a) is followed by a slower rise (b) to a steady state level (Cohen and co-workers, 1977; Lisberger and co-workers, 1981). When the light is turned out, eye velocity rapidly drops (c) to a value (d) from which it slowly decays in darkness as OKAN. Fast changes in slow phase velocities (a,c) and upper ranges of constant velocities are attributed to activation of "direct" pathways (Cohen and co-workers, 1977). Activity within the "indirect" visual-oculomotor pathways is thought to induce slow changes in eye velocity (b) and low steady state velocities of OKN (d). A key element is a "velocity storage" mechanism by which activity related to slow phase velocity is stored during OKN and which is responsible for the occurrence of OKAN. The maximal initial velocity of OKAN is called its saturation velocity (Cohen and co-workers, 1977). In monkey it is usually between 50 and 70 deg/s (Waespe and co-workers, 1983; Lisberger and co-workers, 1981). The contribution of "direct" pathways to steady state OKN velocities is judged from the fast drop after lights out (c) and the contribution of "indirect" pathways from the initial velocity of OKAN (d). Up to a stimulus velocity of about 60 deg/s the "direct" pathways contribute little to steady state OKN velocities. In an intact animal, there are neurons in the vestibular nuclei (i.e. "central neurons") which are not only modulated during vestibular stimulation, but also during optokinetic stimulation up to 60 deg/s and during OKAN (Waespe and Henn, 1977a, 1977b).

Bilateral labyrinthectomy or cutting of the vestibular nerve (vestibular neurectomy) abolishes completely and permanently OKAN and changes the dynamics of OKN (Fig. 1B; Cohen and co-workers, 1982; Waespe and Wolfensberger, 1985). This is

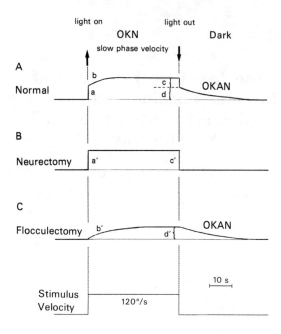

Fig. 1. Scheme of time course of slow phase velocity of
optokinetic nystagmus (OKN) and after-nystagmus
(OKAN) in response to a step in stimulus velocity.
Upward and downward arrow lights on or out.

probably effected by the functional inactivation of central vestibular neurons
due to loss of the resting discharge input from the vestibular nerve (Collewijn,
1976; Robinson, 1981). It is assumed that vestibular neurectomy disrupts activity in the "indirect" pathways which transmit the slow changes in OKN velocity
including OKAN. Flocculectomy on the other hand reduces significantly all fast
changes in slow phase eye velocity during OKN (Fig. 1C). It also reduces peak
steady state eye velocities of OKN to values which correspond to the OKAN saturation velocity (d' in Fig. 1C; Waespe and co-workers, 1983). Flocculectomy
severely disrupts activity within the "direct" pathways of OKN.

        RESULTS

For experimental set-up, identification of neuronal activity, analysis and anatomy we refer to the original publications (Waespe and co-workers, 1981, 1985;
Waespe and Henn, 1981; Büttner and Waespe, 1984).

Normal Monkey

114 P-cells were recorded in 9 flocculi of 6 monkeys. Resting discharge averaged
79 imp/s (range 23-142). The simple spike (SS) activity of about 90% of the P-
cells was modulated with fast eye movements. Units were selected by their response to visual suppression of vestibular nystagmus. All these neurons were also
tested for their responses to constant optokinetic stimulation at 120 deg/s. Only

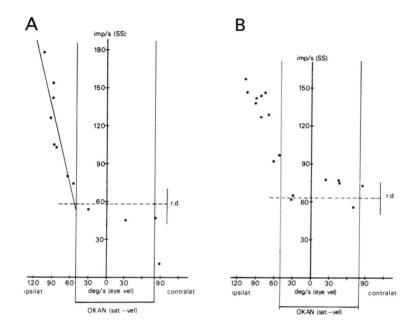

Fig. 2. Firing rate (ordinate) as a function of slow phase
velocity (abscissa) during constant velocity OKN.
r.d. = resting discharge (average: dashed line,
range: vertical line). The regression line in A
crosses the average r.d. at a threshold velocity
of 52 deg/s .

35 P-cells (31%) were found to be tonically modulated during steady state OKN and
only for eye velocities above the OKAN saturation velocity. Average firing rate
(SS activity) as a function of slow phase velocity during constant velocity OKN
is shown in Fig. 2 for two P-cells in one monkey. The saturation velocity of OKAN
(vertical lines in Fig. 2) in this particular monkey was approximately 50 deg/s
for slow phases of OKN to the ipsilateral side (on-direction) and approximately
80 deg/s to the contralateral side (off-direction). Each point represents the
average activity of at least 10 slow phases. As long as eye velocity does not
exceed the OKAN saturation velocity, P-cell activity remains within the range
of the resting discharge. For eye velocities above the OKAN saturation velocity the firing rate changes monotonically with increasing eye velocities. The
firing rate-eye velocity relationship is characterized by the parameters threshold and sensitivity. Regression lines were fitted as shown in Fig. 2A. In the
on-direction the slopes of the regression lines for 8 P-cells recorded in the
same monkey are shown in Fig. 3A (thin lines). The range of eye velocity sensitivity, given by the slope of the regression line, ranged between 0.54 and 2.95
imp·sec^{-1}/deg·s^{-1} with an average of 1.43 (thick line). The extrapolated regression lines intercepted levels of average resting discharges (abscissa) at velocities between 17 and 52 deg/s (all values in the on-direction) with an average
threshold velocity of 33 deg/s (Fig. 3A). The P-cells in Fig. 2 were, except one
point in A, not inhibited with slow phase velocities in the off-direction. This
is due to the failure of the monkey to produce OKN velocities in the off-direction substantially above the OKAN saturation velocity of 80 deg/s (even at 160
deg/s stimulus velocity).

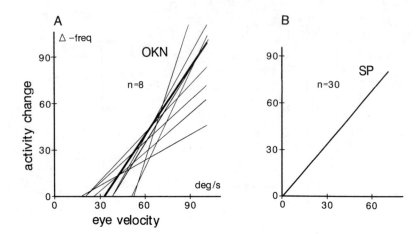

Fig. 3. A: Frequency changes (regression lines fitted
to firing rate-eye velocity curves as shown in
Fig. 2A) as a function of eye velocity in the
on-direction (for single P-cells: thin lines,
average: thick line) during steady state OKN.
The OKAN saturation velocity was 50 deg/s.
B: Averaged frequency changes (regression line)
as a function of eye velocity during SP.

During SP P-cells are modulated already at an eye velocity of 8 deg/s (Miles
and co-workers, 1980) and the threshold velocity is near zero. The eye velocity
sensitivity of P-cells during SP was 1.14 imp·s^{-1}/deg·s^{-1} (n=30, Fig. 3B). All
these 30 P-cells were not modulated during OKN velocities below the OKAN saturation velocity. P-cells were also not modulated in relation to image slip velocity
during OKN-suppression when the monkey prevents the occurrence of OKN by fixating
a single stationary target. The P-cells analysed in Fig. 3 during OKN and SP were
recorded in different monkeys.

The results suggest that in normal monkey
1. P-cells code eye velocity during constant velocity OKN only for eye velocities
   above the OKAN saturation velocity.
2. P-cells code eye velocity during SP over the whole range of eye velocities.
3. P-cells modulated during SP and OKN belong to the same group.
4. P-cells are not modulated in relation to the velocity of whole-field image
   slip during OKN-suppression.
5. P-cells are not modulated during OKAN in relation to slow phase eye velocity.

Neurectomized Monkeys

84 P-cells were recorded in 3 flocculi of 2 monkeys. Resting discharge averaged
72 imp/s (range 25-145). As in normal monkey, about 90% of P-cells were also
modulated with fast eye movements. Each P-cell was responsive to optokinetic
stimulation. 33 of the 84 P-cells were in addition also tested for their responses during SP. Over 90% of the P- cells increased firing rates with eye
velocity during SP as well as with slow phase eye velocity during OKN to the
ipsilateral side, in a way similar to that of the normal monkey. In all except

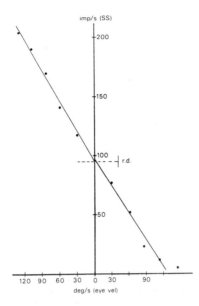

imp/s (SS)

Fig. 4. Firing rate (ordinate) as a function of slow phase
velocity during steady state OKN (abscissa). Firing
rate increased with eye velocity to the ipsilateral
side (on-direction) and decrease with eye velocity
to the contralateral side. Continuous lines are
least-squares regression lines fitted separately
to values in the on- and off-direction.

3 P-cells modulation during OKN was bidirectional with a decrease in firing rate
for slow phases to the contralateral side. This behavior is quite different than
that of the normal monkey. With a few exceptions P-cells were not modulated in
relation to whole-field image slip during OKN-suppression. Figure 4 displays
average firing rates of a typical P-cell as a function of eye velocity during
constant velocity OKN. The crossing point of the extrapolated regression line
with the average resting discharge (horizontal dashed line) is again referred to
as threshold velocity. The regression lines for 10 P-cells for eye velocities in
the on-direction are shown in Fig. 5A (thin lines). The slopes and sensitivities
averaged 1.37 imp·s^{-1}/deg·s^{-1} (thick line) with a range between 0.87 and 2.23.
The average threshold velocity was 3.9 deg/s (range 11 deg in the off-direction
to 14 deg in the on-direction, Fig. 5A). The depth of modulation of P-cells during steady state and sinusoidal OKN and during sinusoidal SP as well were comparable. The eye velocity sensitivity averaged 1.23 imp·s^{-1}/deg·s^{-1} (thick line,
range 0.38-2.8) during SP and 1.11 imp·s^{-1}/deg·s^{-1} during sinusoidal OKN (thin
line, range 0.4 to 3.10) for the same P-cells (Fig. 5B, n=16). During smooth
pursuit at 0.25 and 0.33 Hz peak firing rate was approximately in phase with eye
velocity with an average phase lag of 1.5 deg (range 31 deg phase lead to 18 deg
phase lag). During OKN at 0.1 and 0.2 Hz peak firing rate led peak eye velocity
by 10.5 deg (range 23 deg phase lead to 7 deg phase lag).

The results suggest that in vestibular neurectomized monkey
1. P-cells code eye velocity during constant velocity OKN for any eye velocity
   as threshold velocity and OKAN saturation velocity are zero.

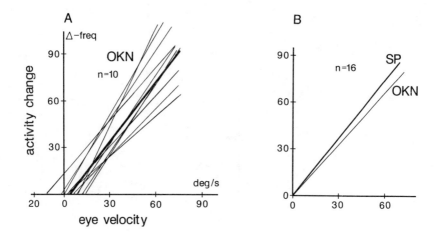

Fig. 5.   A: Frequency changes (regression lines fitted
          Fig. 4) as a function of eye velocity. Same dis-
          play as in Fig. 3A. B: Average frequency changes
          (regression line) as a function of eye velocity
          during SP (thick line) and during sinusoidal OKN
          (thin line) for the same 16 P-cells.

2. P-cells code eye velocity during SP over the whole range of velocities with
   a sensitivity comparable to that in normal monkey.
3. P-cells modulated during SP are always also modulated during OKN and vice-
   versa; they code eye velocity during SP and OKN at any eye velocity with
   comparable strength.
4. P-cells encoding eye velocity during SP and OKN belong to the same group.
   There are no further subgroups which encode eye velocity during SP and OKN
   separately.

        DISCUSSION

In normal and vestibular neurectomized monkeys the dominant parameter which can
be related to SS activity of a group of floccular P-cells is velocity of visually
induced slow eye movements. These eye movements may be induced either by movement
of a small target light (SP) or by movement of the entire visual surround (OKN).
However, in normal monkey P-cells are modulated during steady state OKN only for
eye velocities above a threshold velocity of 40-60 deg/s which approximately
corresponds to the OKAN saturation velocity. P-cells are not modulated during
OKAN in relation to eye velocity (Waespe and Henn, 1981). After neurectomy OKAN
is absent and the average threshold velocity is zero. P-cells are modulated during steady state OKN already for a range of eye velocities which does not cause
a modulation in normal monkey. Sensitivity of SS activity to eye velocity during
steady state OKN is comparable for eye velocities above the threshold velocity
which is between 50 and 70 deg/s in normal monkey and zero in vestibular neurectomized monkey. During SP eye velocity sensitivities are comparable in normal and
neurectomized monkeys with values between 0.8 and 1.28 imp·s^{-1}/deg·s^{-1} (Lisberger
and Fuchs, 1978; Büttner and Waespe, 1984). Thus, neurectomy has apparently no
effect on the behavior of P-cells during SP eye movements but it dramatically

affects the modulation of the same P-cells during steady state OKN. Furthermore, activity of floccular P-cells reflects rather oculomotor parameters and not sensory input parameters.

The hypothesis has been put forward that OKN slow phase velocity in normal monkey has two dynamically different components, a fast and a slow one. The results strongly suggest that the two components depend on different neuronal populations. Firing rate of floccular P-cells is modulated in relation to the fast component only. The results furthermore support the idea that it is the smooth pursuit system which may generate the fast component in the OKN slow phase velocity response.

Lisberger and Fuchs (1978) and Miles and co-workers (1980) assumed that the signal of P-cells during SP, VOR and VOR-suppression is produced by the summation of a "head velocity" and an "eye velocity" signal. The two signals are carried by two separate mossy fiber channels. The signals in the two channels are opposite in sign, and may cancel each other. This is the case during VOR as the gain of the VOR is almost unity. The eye velocity signal is assumed to originate in burst-tonic and tonic neurons in the brainstem, and it is therefore combined with an eye position signal. The authors further assumed that the "head velocity" signal originates in primary vestibular neurons. We have suggested that the main vestibular MF input to the flocculus originates not from primary vestibular neurons but from a subgroup of neurons (central vestibular neurons) in the vestibular nuclei (Waespe and co-workers, 1981). Firing rate of these neurons changes during OKN monotonically up to stimulus velocities of about 60 deg/s when saturation occurs. During OKAN, firing rate of these neurons is related to eye velocity (Waespe and Henn, 1977a, 1977b). It is assumed that activity changes of central vestibular neurons reflect activity within the "indirect" visual-oculomotor pathways (for review: Raphan and Cohen, 1985). The apparent difficulty in explaining the behavior of P-cells during OKN and OKAN is resolved if the "head velocity" signal originates not from primary but from central vestibular neurons. The flocculus is then continuously informed to the extent that central vestibular neurons or the "indirect" visual-oculomotor pathways contribute to eye velocity during OKN and OKAN (for details: Waespe and co-workers, 1985).

CONCLUSIONS

Evidence has been presented to support the hypothesis that the two dynamically different components, the slow and fast component, in the OKN slow phase velocity response depend on different neural populations. The time course of changes of firing rate of floccular P-cells in normal and neurectomized monkeys closely follows the time course of the fast component. Consequently, flocculectomy severely reduces the fast component, whereas the slow component is preserved (Waespe and co-workers, 1983).

There is strong evidence that one of the main functions of the flocculus in primates may be the computation of a signal to induce or suppress following eye movements during visual-vestibular interaction. To be able to do the necessary computation, the minimal requirements are two different MF channels, one which carries an "eye velocity" signal and another which carries a "vestibular" signal. However, the "vestibular" signal is complex and reflects the amount to which a subgroup of neurons in the vestibular nuclei, which we had called central vestibular neurons contribute to eye velocity during head movements, suppression of VOR, OKN, and OKAN. The modulation of flocculuar P-cells can be interpreted only together with the modulation of central vestibular neurons. Whenever the signal carried by these neurons is inappropriate to induce or suppress eye movements for stable vision, floccular P-cells are activated. In this sense, floccular P-cells and central vestibular neurons behave complementary to each other during visual-vestibular interaction.

APVOS-K

REFERENCES

Büttner, U. and W. Waespe (1984). Purkinje cell activity in the primate
    flocculus during optokinetic stimulation, smooth pursuit eye movements and
    VOR-suppression. Exp. Brain Res., 55, 97-104.
Cohen, B., V. Matsuo, and T. Raphan (1977). Quantitative analysis of the veloc-
    ity characteristics of optokinetic nystagmus and optokinetic after-nystagmus.
    J. Physiol. (Lond.), 270, 321-344.
Cohen, B., J. Suzuki, T. Raphan, V. Matsuo, and V. DeJong (1982). Selective
    labyrinthine lesion and nystagmus induced by rotation about off-vertical
    axis. In G. Lennerstrand and E. L. Keller (Eds.), Functional Basis of
    Cellular Disorders, Pergamon Press, New York. pp. 337-346.
Collewijn, H. (1976). Impairment of optokinetic (after-)nystagmus by labyrinth-
    ectomy in the rabbit. Exp. Neurol., 52, 146-156.
Lisberger, S. G. and A. F. Fuchs (1978). Role of primate flocculus during rapid
    bevavioral modification of vestibulo-ocular reflex. I. Purkinje cell activity
    during visually guided horizontal smooth-pursuit eye movements and passive
    head rotation. J. Neurophysiol., 41, 733-763.
Lisberger, S. G, F. A. Miles, L. M. Optican, and B. Eighmy (1981). Optokinetic
    response in monkey: Underlying mechanisms and their sensitivity to long-term
    adaptive changes in vestibuloocular reflex. J. Neurophysiol., 45, 869-890.
Miles, F.A., J. H. Fuller, D. J. Braitman, and B. M. Dow (1980). Long term
    adaptive changes in primate vestibulo-ocular reflexes. III. Electrophysio-
    logical observations in flocculus of adapted monkeys. J. Neurophysiol.,
    43, 1437-1476.
Raphan, T. and B. Cohen (1985). Velocity storage and the ocular response to
    multidimensional vestibular stimuli. In A. Berthoz and G. Melvill Jones
    (Eds.), Adaptive Mechanisms in Gaze Control: Facts and Theories, Chap. 8.
    Elsevier, North-Holland, Amsterdam. pp. 123-143.
Robinson, D. A. (1981) Control of eye movements. In Handbbok of Physiology, the
    Nervous System II/2. Am. Physiol. Soc., Bethesda, Md. pp. 1275-1320.
Waespe, W. and V. Henn (1977a). Neuronal activity in the vestibular nuclei of
    the alert monkey during vestibular and optokinetic stimulation. Exp. Brain
    Res., 27, 523-538.
Waespe, W. and V. Henn (1977b). Vestibular nuclei activity during optokinetic
    after-nystagmus (OKAN) in the alert monkey. Exp. Brain Res., 30, 323-330.
Waespe, W. and V. Henn (1981). Visual-vestibular interaction in the flocculus
    of the alert monkey. II. Purkinje cell activity. Exp. Brain Res., 43, 349-
    360.
Waespe, W., U. Büttner, and V. Henn (1981). Visual-vestibular interaction in
    the flocculus of the alert monkey. I. Input activity. Exp. Brain Res., 43,
    337-348.
Waespe, W., B. Cohen, and T. Raphan (1983). Role of the flocculus and para-
    flocculus in optokinetic nystagmus and visual-vestibular interactions:
    Effects of lesions. Exp. Brain Res., 50, 9-33.
Waespe, W., D. Rudinger, and W. Wolfensberger (1985). Purkinje cell activity
    in the flocculus of vestibular neurectomized and normal monkeys during opto-
    kinetic nystagmus (OKN) and smooth pursuit eye movements. Exp. Brain Res.,
    60, (in press).
Waespe, W. and W. Wolfensberger (1985). Optokinetic nystagmus (OKN) and opto-
    kinetic after-responses after bilateral vestibular neurectomy in the monkey.
    Exp. Brain Res., 60 (in press).

The Transition Between Pre-motor Eye Velocity Signals and Oculomotor Eye Position Signals in Primate Brain Stem Neurons During Pursuit

R. Eckmiller

Department of Biophysics, Division of Biocybernetics,
University of Düsseldorf, FRG

INTRODUCTION

Saccadic and smooth pursuit eye movements are controlled by separate classes of pre-motor neurons. The most likely candidates for these different tasks are burst neurons for saccades (for references,see: Robinson,1981) and eye velocity neurons for pursuit (Eckmiller and Bauswein,1985). Burst neurons and eye velocity neurons have two main features in common: a)they are located in the vicinity of the oculomotor nuclei and b)they carry eye velocity signals without an eye position component. Since oculomotor motoneurons encode absolute eye position (in addition to eye velocity), it is generally assumed that a process of 'neural integration'(conversion of eye velocity into eye position signals) occurs.

This paper presents single unit data from a new class of pre-motor neurons, the Intermediate Phase neurons, having several characteristic functional properties that suggest they are involved in the process of neural integration during both saccadic and smooth pursuit eye movements. A new model of the neural integrator is proposed which closely matches the dynamic properties of these neurons as well as those of motoneurons.

METHODS AND RESULTS

The experimental data are based on the analysis of single unit recordings from 35 intermediate phase neurons in four monkeys (Macaca fascicularis) while sitting with their heads fixed in a rotatable primate chair. Animals had been trained to keep a small visual target on the fovea under three conditions: a)Smooth Pursuit: foveal pursuit eye movements during sinusoidal target movement (10 deg amplitude at frequencies between 0.2 and 1.4 Hz), b)VOR(Light): pursuit of a stationary target during head rotation (chair rotation about the vertical axis) with the same amplitude and frequency range as in a), and c)VOR-Suppression: fixation of the target which moved with the sinusoidally rotating chair. Monocular eye movements were recorded with an infrared oculometer (Bouis,Karlsruhe) or with implanted Ag/AgCl electrodes.

Recording Sites

Electrode tracks were stereotaxically positioned perpendicular to the horizontal plane. In many cases single unit recordings from intermediate phase neurons appeared to be from cells (rather than fibers) as judged by the spike polarity and duration. Several small electrolytic lesions (20μA, 20sec) were generated

at different recording sites in each animal. Histology was performed on serial
sections (25μm thick, alternating cell and fiber stains) of Celloidin embedded
brain tissue following perfusion under deep barbiturate anesthesia.

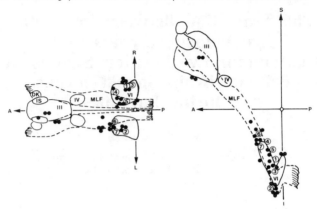

Fig. 1   Horizontal and sagittal plane of the brain stem with
         recording sites of 35 intermediate phase neurons,seven
         of which are numbered for later reference in the text.

Fig.1 indicates the 35 recording sites schematically in the horizontal and
sagittal planes. The neural structures of the oculomotor nuclei (III.,IV.,VI.)
and the medial longitudinal fasciculus (MLF) are indicated for orientation.
The main group of recording sites was close to, but not in, the VI.nucleus. These
recording sites are located within various neural structures (Langer et al.,1985;
McCrea et al.,1979) such as the supragenu nucleus (suprageniculate nucleus or
supragenu of the prepositus nucleus), the prepositus hypoglossi nucleus (see also:
Cannon and Robinson, this volume), the raphe nucleus, as well as a region rostro-
dorsal to the VI.nucleus within the MLF. The recording sites at the ventral
border of the VI.nucleus coincide with those of pursuit neurons (Eckmiller and
Mackeben,1980), which (together with eye velocity neurons) have also been described
more recently at locations along the dorsal border of the VI.nucleus (Eckmiller
and Bauswein,1985).

Functional Properties of Intermediate Phase ('Integrator') Neurons

The range of dynamic properties of individual intermediate phase neurons forms a
continuum between those of eye velocity neurons with no eye position component
(Eckmiller and Bauswein,1985) and those of oculomotor motoneurons. In other words,
eye position sensitivity during fixation is small for neurons with phase lead
values close to 90 deg during Smooth Pursuit or VOR, but considerably larger for
neurons with smaller phase values (close to 30 deg). Neurons were classified as
intermediate phase neurons if eye position sensitivity had values larger than
0.5 Imp per sec/deg at phase values close to 90 deg (distinction from eye velocity
neurons) or if they exhibited signs of a leaky integrator behavior in the impulse
rate following saccades and had phase values above 30 deg at 0.8 Hz (distinction
from motoneurons). Fig.2 illustrates three recording episodes from each of two
intermediate phase neurons during Smooth Pursuit (top traces: target movement,
horizontal eye movement, and instantaneous impulse rate IR in Imp per sec),
VOR(Light), and spontaneous horizontal eye movements (bottom traces). Recordings
on the left are from neuron no.5 with an eye position sensitivity of only 1.5
Imp per sec/deg at a presumed recording site in the right supragenu nucleus (see
Fig.1). In contrast, neuron D50-1312, which was recorded at the left ventro-medial
border of the III.nucleus, exhibited an eye position sensitivity of 3.8
Imp per sec/deg and an intermediate phase lead of 53 deg at 0.8 Hz.

During spontaneous eye movements the impulse rate of this neuron showed rather slow upward or downward drifts following each saccade (bottom right of Fig.2), reminiscent of a leaky integrator and quite distinct from the impulse rate of a motoneuron.

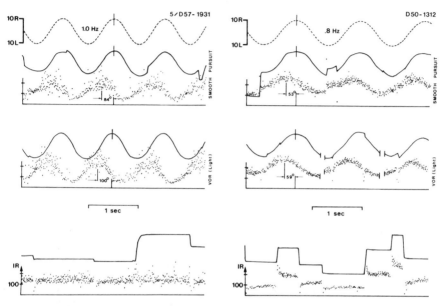

Fig. 2   Recordings from two intermediate phase neurons
(left and right) during Smooth Pursuit, VOR(Light),
and spontaneous eye movements.

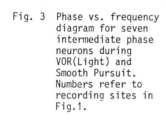

Fig. 3   Phase vs. frequency
diagram for seven
intermediate phase
neurons during
VOR(Light) and
Smooth Pursuit.
Numbers refer to
recording sites in
Fig.1.

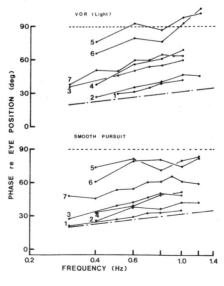

Phase lead values of seven intermediate phase neurons with numbered recording
sites (see: 1-7 in Fig.1) are plotted as a function of frequency in Fig.3. Average
phase vs. frequency characteristics for eye velocity neurons (Eckmiller and
Bauswein,1985) shown as dotted lines at 90 deg lead, as well as motoneurons
(Eckmiller and Mackeben,1978) shown as interrupted lines below 30 deg, were added
for comparison. Note the phase increase with increasing frequency. During VOR-
Suppression, the impulse rate of intermediate phase neurons like that of
motoneurons was not modulated.

Implications for the Neural Integrator

Most existing models of a neural integrator in the oculomotor system (Cannon and
Robinson,1983; Kamath and Keller,1976; Zee et al.,1981) share the concept of a
low pass filter ($F(s) = G / (1 + s T)$) in order to explain various lesion-
induced failures to hold eccentric gaze positions. However, the presented
neurophysiological data, concerned with the neural control of Pursuit and VOR
(Light) as a function of frequency, call for an expansion of the low pass concept.

The phase vs. frequency diagrams in Fig.3 show a clear increase of phase lead
with increasing frequency for all intermediate phase neurons (as well as
motoneurons). Assuming that eye velocity neurons with an impulse rate $IR_{EV}= c \cdot \dot{\theta}$
proportional to pursuit velocity (Eckmiller and Bauswein,1985) provide
the input for intermediate phase neurons (with IR_{IN}), these phase plots can be
approximated (disregarding additional pure time delay) by the following
transfer function:

$$\frac{IR_{IN}(s)}{IR_{EV}(s)} = G_1 \frac{1 + s T_1}{s} . \tag{1}$$

On the other hand, the generally accepted equation describing the dynamic
properties of an oculomotor motoneuron (see: Robinson,1981):
$IR_{MO}= k \cdot \theta + r \cdot \dot{\theta}$ yields the transfer function:

$$\frac{IR_{MO}(s)}{IR_{EV}(s)} = \frac{k}{c} \frac{1 + s \frac{r}{k}}{s} . \tag{2}$$

In this case, eye velocity was replaced by IR_{EV} of an eye velocity neuron as
input signal. It is evident that equations   (1) and (2) are formally identical,
which supports the hypothesis that intermediate phase neurons represent the
missing link between eye velocity and motoneurons. According to this hypothesis,
the neural integrator can be approximately described by the following features:
1)The integrator network consists of a cascade of intermediate phase neurons
('Integrator'neurons).
2)Along this cascade the time constant T_1 (which corresponds to the ratio r/k)
becomes gradually reduced. This means a ' gradual increase of the eye position
component k at the expense of the eye velocity component r from one intermediate
phase neuron to the next.
3)The transfer function of a neural integrator element can be described by the
equation: $F(s) = G_1(1 + s T_1)/s$.
4)In agreement with a previous study (Zee et al.,1981) it is assumed that the
neural integrator network consists of two halves that interact in a push-pull
fashion.

The neural integration process for saccadic eye movements seemingly requires an
additional, parallel path, with the transfer function of a low pass ($G_2/(1 + s T_2)$)
as suggested by several authors (see above). However, this additional path is
assumed here to perform only a leaky integration and to function only for the
generation of saccades. The proposed scheme for a half-element of the neural
integrator is illustrated in Fig.4. Further connections from the output of the
low pass to individual intermediate phase neurons within the cascade (not shown
here) are likely. With regard to a realization of the proposed cascade integrator
model (in contrast to one-step integrator models), several quite simple alternative
neural networks are available.

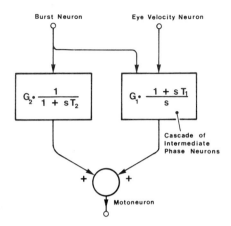

Fig. 4 Model of Neural Integrator in the oculomotor system.
Main path with cascade on the right for all types of
eye movements. Along the cascade, the time constant T_1
becomes gradually reduced.
Addional path on the left for saccadic eye movements.

ACKNOWLEDGEMENTS

Dr. E.Bauswein's contribution to the experiments and data analysis is gratefully
acknowledged, as are Mrs. E.Jaworski's assistance with the histology and
Mrs. A.Thelen's assistance with the animal training.
Supported by the Deutsche Forschungsgemeinschaft, SFB 200/A1.

REFERENCES

Cannon,S., D.A.Robinson, and S.Shamma(1983). A proposed neural network for the
    integrator of the oculomotor system. Biol.Cybern.,49,127-136.
Eckmiller,R., and M.Mackeben(1978). Pursuit eye movements and their neural control
    in the monkey. Pflügers Arch.,377,15-23.
Eckmiller,R., and M.Mackeben(1980). Pre-motor single unit activity in the monkey
    brain stem correlated with eye velocity during pursuit. Brain Res.,184,210-214.
Eckmiller,R., and E.Bauswein(1985). Smooth pursuit eye movements. In H.J.Freund
    et al.(Eds.),Oculomotor and Skeletomotor System,Prog.in Brain Res.,64,in press.
Kamath,B.Y., and E.L.Keller(1976). A neurological integrator for the
    oculomotor control system. Math.Biosci.,30,341-352.
McCrea,R.A., R.Baker, and J.Delgado-Garcia(1979). Afferent and efferent
    organization of the prepositus hypoglossi nucleus. In R.Granit and O.Pompeiano
    (Eds.), Reflex Control of Posture and Movement, Prog.in Brain Res.,50,
    Elsevier,Amsterdam,653-665.
Robinson,D.A.(1981). Control of eye movements. In: Hdb.of Physiology, The Nervous
    System,vol.II,Motor Control, Part 1,Williams § Wilkins,Baltimore,1275-1320.
Zee,D.S., A.Yamazaki, P.H.Butler, and G.Gücer(1981). Effects of ablation of
    flocculus and paraflocculus on eye movements in primate.
    J.Neurophysiol.,46,878-899.

The Final Common Integrator is in the Prepositus and Vestibular Nuclei

S. C. Cannon and D. A. Robinson

Departments of Biomedical Engineering and Ophthalmology, The
Johns Hopkins University, Baltimore, MD 21205, USA

THE FINAL COMMON INTEGRATOR HYPOTHESIS

Early analyses of the vestibuloocular reflex (VOR) proposed that there was a neural circuit to convert the head-velocity information from the semicircular canals into an eye-position signal (Robinson, 1968, 1971). Later single-unit recordings demonstrated that a motoneuron's firing rate modulates according to eye-position with the same gain regardless of whether the eye movement was of vestibular, pursuit or saccadic origin (for review, see Robinson 1981). All of these eye movements are initiated as eye-velocity commands on primary vestibular afferents, pursuit velocity cells, or pontine burst neurons, respectively. The conversion of velocity to position information is performed mathematically by the process of integration. Consequently the generation of the eye-position signal is performed by a population of neurons, named the neural integrator, that must lie somewhere in the pathway from these premotor cells to motoneurons. Robinson (1975) reviewed experimental evidence and theoretical arguments that favored the hypothesis of a single, common, final integrator that is shared by all the conjugate eye-movement systems (see Fig. 1). However conclusive experimental data that demonstrate a single integrator have been lacking because, despite a nearly twenty-year appreciation for the

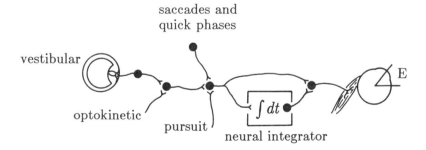

Fig. 1. The final common integrator hypothesis (adapted from Robinson, 1975). All conjugate eye movements (E) are initiated as eye-velocity commands that are converted to eye-position signals by the neural integrator. Both eye-velocity and eye-position commands are relayed to the motoneurons.

S. C. Cannon and D. A. Robinson

necessity of the neural integrator, its anatomical location has been elusive. There has also been one report (Godaux and Laune, 1983) of a neuroleptic agent that, when administered to cats, disabled the integrator for the VOR but did not induce gaze-evoked nystagmus which these authors interpreted as evidence that the integrator for the saccadic system was intact and distinct. Subsequently, independent investigations on monkey (Cannon and Robinson, 1985) and cat (Cheron and colleagues, in press) have simultaneously shown that lesions in the region of the prepositus and vestibular nuclei cause aberrant vestibular, optokinetic, saccadic, and pursuit eye movements, all apparently generated as if there were no neural integrator. These findings support the idea that a single integrator is used by all conjugate eye-movement systems.

METHODS

Eye movements were recorded by the search-coil technique (Robinson 1963) from 4 rhesus monkeys who were trained to fixate or pursue targets for water reinforcement. After brain-stem landmarks were electrophysiologically mapped out through a chronically-implanted recording chamber, 1 - 3 µl injections of neurotoxins were made bilaterally, 0.5 to 2.5mm off the midline, and at levels from 0.5 to 2.5mm caudal to the abducens nucleus. Either ibotenate (10µg/µl) or kainate (1-4 µg/µl) were injected via a 29 gauge cannula. Two to 4 weeks after the last injection, the animals were sacrificed, their brains were fixed in 10% neutral formalin, and alternate 40 µm sections were stained for nissl substance or myelin. The cannula tracks ended in a region extending caudally from the caudal tip of the abducens nuclei through the rostral poles of the medial vestibular nuclei, and medially to the junction between the medial vestibular and prepositus nuclei.

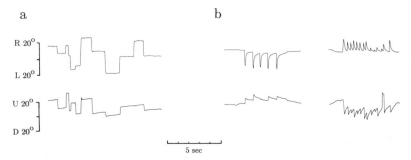

a   b

5 sec

Fig. 2. Spontaneous horizontal and vertical saccades in darkness before (a) and after (b) bilateral injections of ibotenate. In (b) two excerpts from a continuous record are shown to demonstrate that eye position drifts centripetally after both leftward and rightward saccades. R, L, U, D are right, left, up, and down.

RESULTS

1. Saccades

Spontaneous saccades in darkness, recorded just prior to injection, are shown in Fig. 2a. Even in the absence of visual feedback the post-saccadic drift in the horizontal direction was negligible. Since it is the eye-position component of a motoneuron's firing rate that enables the eye to be held eccentrically against elastic restoring forces, the neural integrator was intact. Vertically, the eyes drifted upward with a constant velocity between saccades. This was a pattern of mild downbeat nystagmus found in many normal rhesus monkeys. The record in Fig. 2b is from the same animal approximately 1 hr. after a bilateral injection of 30 µg of ibotenate. Every time the monkey attempted to make a spontaneous horizontal saccade in complete darkness, the eye rapidly drifted centripetally with a time constant of 200 msec. This was simply the response of the extra-ocular muscle plant alone to a burst (the eye-velocity input) with no corresponding step change of innervation (the eye-position command for a saccade, generated by the neural integrator). The integrator for vertical eye movements was deteriorated to a lesser extent, the time constant for these drifts was about 750 msec.

2. Vestibuloocular Reflex

At 24 hrs after bilateral injections of 4 μg of kainate, the VOR in the horizontal plane was measured by rotating the monkey in complete darkness. Figure 3 shows the eye *position* as a function of time during a constant-velocity step of head rotation. The change in eye position had the shape that the slow-phase eye-velocity record would normally have. This occurred because the head-velocity signal sensed by the canals was relayed to the motoneurons without any eye-position component. There was no integrator to convert the initial step increase in the head-velocity signal into a ramp change in eye position (normal slow phases). The brief dips in eye position were resetting saccades. In the absence of an integrator, each saccade was followed by a rapid drift to the offset determined by the canal signal as illustrated in the lower trace. The velocity-storage element of the central vestibular apparatus was also impaired. The cupula time constant seen by the motoneurons was no longer increased centrally to its normal value of 16 to 20 sec; instead the head-velocity signal decayed with a time constant of 6.8 sec which is comparable to the value reported for the cupula alone.

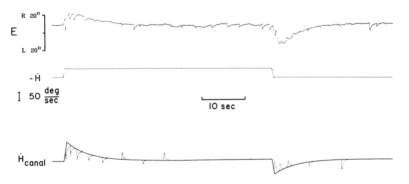

Fig. 3. Eye position, E, recorded during *en bloc* rotation 1 day after bilateral injections of kainate. Middle trace is head velocity, $\dot{H}$. A hypothetical canal signal is shown at the bottom with superimposed saccades as they would appear in the absence of a neural integrator (dashed lines).

3. Pursuit Movements

Figure 4 shows the first few seconds of the eye-position response during constant-velocity, full-field optokinetic stimulation at various times after the injection of kainate. The initial component of the optokinetic response in foveate animals is thought by many to be generated by the pursuit system. In all three cases the initial response was a step change in eye position; that is, the change in eye position again reflected the eye-velocity signal. There was no integrator to convert the velocity-step command into a ramp position signal. In the two records at 22 hr the animal had recovered the ability to generate resetting quick phases, but the saccades still drifted rapidly back (with a velocity that was independent of drum speed) to a step change in null position that was determined by the eye-velocity signal sent to the motoneurons with no accompanying eye-position signal. This drift towards the null point is particularly evident in the middle record. When the light came on, the monkey just happened to generate a saccade that was larger than the offset in null point, determined by the pursuit-velocity signal, so that the eye actually drifted back towards the null point or in the direction *opposite* to that of the opto-kinetic drum.

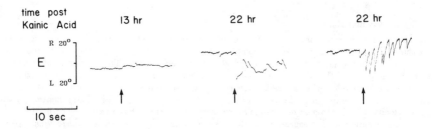

Fig. 4. Pursuit eye movements elicited during the initial response to full-field opto-kinetic stimulation at 13 and 22 hrs after a kainate injection. Arrows indicate the on-set of light; see text for details. Drum velocity in the three records was 40 deg/sec to the right, left, and then right.

4. Optokinetic Response

A longer eye-movement tracing recorded during optokinetic stimulation is shown in Fig. 5. After several seconds the slower-responding, optokinetic system should be operative, but again the eye movements reflect a step input command with superimposed quick phases. The step eye-velocity command was not converted by the neural integrator to a ramp change in eye posi-tion (slow phases). The plateau in eye position to the right was not a saturation artifact nor a limitation of lateral gaze since spontaneous eye movements (not shown) exceeded this limit. The "slow-phase" velocity was independent of the drum speed; it was determined by the leaki-ness of the neural integrator (or the time constant of the muscle plant alone if the neural integrator time constant is less than 200 msec). When the light was extinguished the eye did not immediately return to its baseline null point which implies that the optokinetic system must have been charged since there was some storage. The velocity storage, however, had an abnor-mally small time constant of only 3.5 sec.

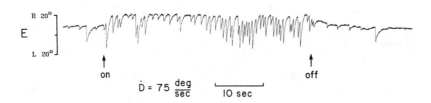

Fig. 5. Eye position recorded during full-field optokinetic stimulation 1 day after a kainate injection; see text for details. $\dot{D}$ is drum velocity.

DISCUSSION

Injections of excitatory neurotoxins caused pronounced abnormalities in eye movements and postural control. The effects, however, were partially reversible over a time course of 72 hrs, and the neural integrator recovered to the extent that the time constant for post-saccadic drift in darkness was 2 to 3 sec which is still an order of magnitude too short. Although dense gliosis was present along the cannula tracks, small spherical regions of cell loss (600 μm dia.) were found at the tip of only a few tracks. Thus apparently these excitotoxins transiently impaired cells in the immediate vicinity, but they were not lethal. Unfortunately this means that we cannot accurately determine the exact anatomical extent of the toxin's influence. Nevertheless, because none of the monkeys developed gaze palsies attributable to damage of the adjacent abducens nucleus, the effects of the injections must have been highly localized. Furthermore, the profound effects of these injections are an important finding even if all we can be certain about is the location of the cannula tip.

CONCLUSIONS

From these data, we conclude that the neural integrator is located in the region of the medial vestibular and prepositus hypoglossal nuclei. Cheron and colleagues (in press) have found similar results from electrolytic lesions of the rostral pole of the prepositus and vestibular nuclei in the cat. Previous lesions of the cerebellum in cat (Robinson, 1974) and of the flocculus in monkey (Zee and colleagues, 1981) also impaired the neural integrator, but these cerebellar lesions never completely eliminated the integrator because the time constant for post-saccadic drift was approximately 1.5 sec which is 7 times longer than the time constant of the muscle plant alone. Our results also confirm the idea that a single, common, final integrator is used by all conjugate eye-movement systems. A more extensive, permanent, histologically-evident lesion must be made with excitotoxins before the question of partial recovery of the neural integrator can be addressed.

ACKNOWLEDGEMENTS

S. Cannon was supported by grants GM 07309 from the General Medical Institute and EY 07047 from the National Eye Institute of the NIH. D. Robinson received support from grant EY 00598 from the National Eye Institute, NIH.

REFERENCES

Cannon, S. C., D. A. Robinson (1985). Neural integrator failure from brain-stem lesions in monkey. *Suppl. to Invest. Ophthalmol. & Vis. Sci., 25*, 181.
Cheron, G., E. Godaux, J. M. Laune, B. vanDerkelen (1985). Disabling of the oculomotor neural integrator by lesions in the region of the prepositus and vestibular nuclear complex. *J. Physiol (Lond.)*, in press.
Godaux, E., J. M. Laune (1983). The saccadic and the vestibulo-ocular reflex in the cat do not share the same integrator. *Neurosci. Lett., 38*, 263-268.
Robinson, D. A. (1963). A method of measuring eye movement using a scleral search coil in a magnetic field. *IEEE Trans. Bio-Med. Electron.* BME-10, 137-135.
Robinson, D. A. (1968). Eye movement control in primates. *Science, 161*, 1219-1224.
Robinson, D. A. (1971). Models of oculomotor neural organization. In P. Bach-y-Rita, C. C. Collins, J. E. Hyde (Eds.) *The control of eye movements.* Academic Press, New York, pp. 519-538.
Robinson, D. A. (1974). The effect of cerebellectomy on the cat's vestibulo-ocular integrator. *Brain Res.* 71, 195-207.
Robinson, D. A. (1975). Oculomotor control signals. In G. Lennerstrand and P. Bach-Y-Rita (Eds.), *Basic Mechanisms of Ocular Motility and Their Clinical Implications.* Pergamon Press, Oxford and New York. pp. 337-374.
Robinson, D. A. (1981). Control of eye movements. In V. B. Brooks (Ed.) *Handbook of Physiology, Vol II, Part 2, The Nervous System*, Williams and Wilkins, Baltimore, pp. 1275-1320.
Zee, D. S., A. Yamazaki, P. H. Butler, G. Gücer (1981). Effects of ablation of flocculus and paraflocculus on eye movements in primate. *J. Neurophysiol.* 46, 878-899.

Adaptive Control of Saccadic and Smooth Pursuit Eye Movements

L. M. Optican

Laboratory of Sensorimotor Research, National Eye Institute,
Bethesda, Maryland, USA

Visual acuity is degraded when images slip on the retina at more than a few degrees per second (Westheimer and McKee, 1975). The vestibuloocular reflex (VOR) operates to stabilize images during head turns. The development of the fovea improved the ability of higher animals to perceive their environment. However, this improved acuity required higher animals to bring the image of an object of interest onto the fovea to see it clearly. Two additional neural systems allow the fovea to be directed at objects of interest: the saccadic system generates rapid eye movements (up to 900°/s) that redirect the gaze toward the object; the pursuit system generates slow eye movements (less than 200°/s) that track smoothly moving objects.

In general, a tracking response requires the synergistic action of all three of these subsystems (VOR, saccades and pursuit). If any one of them fails to function properly, visual acuity will deteriorate. This is because the domains of ocular motor performance (delays, time constants, speeds and accelerations) of these subsystems do not overlap. So, if an ocular motor deficit develops (due to aging, injury or disease), adaptive mechanisms attempt to recalibrate these subsystems to compensate for the deficit.

The study of these adaptive mechanisms has progressed quite far in the study of the VOR, but less is known about the long-term adaptive control of saccadic and pursuit eye movements. Since the input to the VOR is head rotation and its output is eye rotation, the system operates open-loop: i.e., the output does not affect the input. It is intuitively obvious why such a system should be under adaptive control, since any errors that the system makes do not influence the input and hence can not be further reduced by subsequent action of the system. Other ocular motor systems, such as the saccadic and pursuit subsystems, operate closed-loop: i.e. their output (eye movement) affects their input (retinal error). In such systems any errors in performance are reduced by subsequent actions of the system, so it is not immediately obvious why closed-loop systems need to adapt. One disadvantage of allowing the system to reduce errors by subsequent action is that it takes longer to acquire a target. Because of the intrinsic delays in the saccadic and pursuit subsystems (about 250 and 130 ms, respectively), closed loop operation can lead to oscillations of the eyes. By supposing that the goal of the brain is not merely to reduce errors, but also to acquire the target as quickly as possible while avoiding oscillations, we can generalize the need for adaptive mechanisms from open-loop to closed-loop control systems.

Inferring innervation from eye movements. One common method for studying
adaptive changes in innervation is based on the assumption that the two eyes are
yoked during conjugate movements (e.g., saccades and pursuit); this is known as
Hering's law. If one eye is weakened, viewing with that eye will induce changes
in innervation to achieve acceptable ocular motor performance. In the adaptation
studies it is assumed that any changes in innervation will be the same for both
eyes. Thus one can monitor the changes in innervation induced by viewing
monocularly with a weakened eye from the changes in the movements made by the
good eye (when it views) before and after adaptation. Several studies have shown
that monocular patching does cause small changes in the degree of yoking between
the two eyes, which has led to the suggestion that Hering's law may itself be the
consequence of an adaptive mechanism (Snow and others, 1985; Vilis and others,
1985; Zee and colleagues, 1984). The magnitude of the changes in the good eye
after adaptation to viewing with a weak eye can be larger than the changes due to
patching alone. Also, the results from monocular and binocular studies of
adaptation are similar. So, for this discussion, Hering's law will assume to
hold during adaptation.

ADAPTIVE CONTROL OF THE SACCADIC SYSTEM

Early studies of long-term adaptive properties established that the goal of the
saccadic system was to make saccades of the appropriate size with no post-
saccadic drift (Abel and others, 1978; Kommerell and colleagues, 1976; Optican
and Robinson, 1980). The control of saccade amplitude seems to be dependent upon
midline cerebellar structures (vermis and fastigial nucleus), while the
suppression of post-saccadic drift seems to depend upon the cerebellar flocculus
and paraflocculus (Optican and colleagues, 1980; Optican and Robinson, 1980).
The ability to adjust saccade amplitude requires a fairly sophisticated control
system, since there is no simple per- or post-saccadic signal that relates to
saccade error. Instead, some part of the visual system must determine where the
object of interest is on the retina before and after the saccade. This visual
process must then communicate with the saccadic control system and invoke
appropriate adaptive adjustments. One possible scheme for doing this, based on a
corrective saccadic system, has been proposed (Optican, 1982). In this scheme
large saccades were made to fall short intentionally, and the resulting retinal
error was compared with the expected error by a "correction system" that issued a
subsequent corrective saccade. More research must be done to determine what
parameters of the visual scene, and what aspects of the movement errors, are
necessary to elicit action from the adaptive mechanism for saccadic amplitude.

The adaptive mechanism for suppression of post-saccadic drift has been studied in
some detail in our laboratory. Original studies of saccadic plasticity showed
that post-saccadic ocular drift was always suppressed, even when saccade
amplitude was not corrected (Optican and Robinson, 1980). This implied that a
simple measure of post-saccadic ocular drift, such as retinal slip, might be
sufficient to drive the adaptive mechanism. Subsequent studies showed that
optically-induced retinal slip, even in the presence of normal extraocular muscle
proprioception, elicited an adaptive response (Optican and Miles, 1985).

Figure 1 shows an example of spontaneous saccades made in the dark by a monkey
under normal conditions (Fig. 1A), and after it had been exposed to several days
of optically-induced post-saccadic retinal slip (slip onward, Fig. 1B, and
backward, Fig. 1C). Note that the post-saccadic drift occurs with essentially
zero-latency, and has an exponential time course. These characteristics led
Kommerell and colleagues (1976) to propose that the post-saccadic ocular drift
seen in the good eye after compensation for peripheral weakness in a diseased eye
reflected a change in the pulse-step ratio of saccadic innervation. This idea is
based on the fact that the innervation needed to make a saccade consists of two
main components: a pulse of high frequency but brief duration that drives the
eye against the viscous drag of the orbital tissues, and a step of lower
frequency but sustained duration that develops enough muscle force to balance the

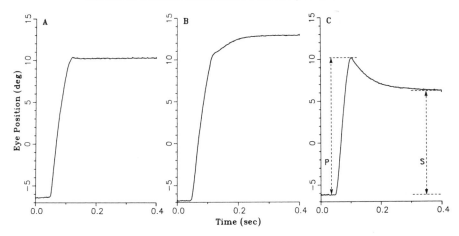

Fig. 1. Optically induced post-saccadic ocular drift. Normal, spontaneous saccade in the dark (A). Spontaneous saccades in the dark after
several days of exposure to an onward (B) or backward (C) exponential
drift that followed every saccade. The amplitude of the rapid part of
the saccade (P) and the final position of the movement (S) are measured
from the saccade's starting point. The portion P is called the saccade,
and the portion (S-P) is called the post-saccadic ocular drift. [From
Optican and Miles, 1985.]

restoring forces in the orbit (Robinson, 1964). Because the step portion of the
innervation determines the final eye position, if the pulse and step are not
matched, the eye will drift after the end of the saccade. If the step is too
small for the pulse, the eye will drift backward, and if the step is too large,
the eye will drift onward.

The idea that controlling the gain of the step of saccadic innervation could
suppress post-saccadic ocular drift was exploited in a simple model of drift-
suppression proposed earlier (Optican, 1985). The basic mechanism was to
integrate any post-saccadic retinal slip, correlated with the direction of the
antecedent saccade, to determine rightward and leftward step gains. After the
step gains were adjusted to suppress post-saccadic retinal slip, one would expect
to see an ocular drift with a time constant determined by the dynamics of the
ocular plant. This time constant is quite long (about 200 ms), and is much
longer than the ocular drift time constants typically observed (40 - 80 ms). One
possibility is that the ocular drift time constant is not determined by the
passive properties of the ocular plant, but depends instead upon the details of
the transition between the pulse and step of innervation. In his original work
on the ocular plant, Robinson (1964) pointed out that this transition should be
an exponential decay. Goldstein (1983) recorded from abducens neurons in awake
monkeys and found that the short time constant of pulse decay was 70 - 90 ms.

To see whether the time constant of the ocular drift was a consequence solely of
the ocular plant dynamics, we tried adapting monkeys to optically induced post-
saccadic retinal slip with different exponential time constants. Our results
showed that, after several days of adaptation, the time constant of the post-
saccadic ocular drift associated with spontaneous saccades made in the dark was
linearly related to the time constant of the adapting stimulus. This implied
that some component of the neural innervation was actively determining the time
constant of the ocular drift. The next question was how to fit this into the
scheme of drift suppression through adaptive control of the step gain.

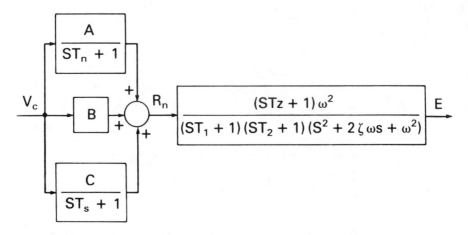

Fig. 2. New model of the final common path. V_c is the velocity command, and E is the eye movement. The blocks on the left represent (from top to bottom) the step, pulse and slide components of the saccadic innervation, R_n. The block on the right is the transfer function of the ocular motor plant. S is the Laplace transform variable.

A new model for the brain stem part of the final common path, through which all eye velocity commands produce eye movements, was proposed (Optican and Miles, 1985). Figure 2 shows a block diagram of this new final common path. The block on the right is the fourth-order, lumped, linear model of the ocular plant dynamics of Robinson (1964). The upper and middle blocks on the left are the neural integrator and feedforward path originally proposed by Skavenski and Robinson (1973). With the earlier final common path, the velocity command was fed to the extraocular muscles directly to form the pulse (with weight B), and it was also integrated to produce a step (with weight A). In the new model, these brain stem paths are augmented by another branch that gives an exponential decay to the transition from the pulse to the step, called the slide (with weight C), Hence saccadic innervation is now approximated by a pulse—slide—step combination. This final common path was combined with a saccadic pulse generator based on previous work (Zee and colleagues, 1976; van Gisbergen and others, 1981) to produce a complete model of the saccadic system.

Figure 3A shows a family of spontaneous saccades made in the dark when a monkey was in its normal state. Most of the model's parameters (i.e., gains and time constants) were taken from the values in Zee and colleagues (1976), and some were adjusted manually to achieve a good fit to the family of normal saccades. Two examples of saccades made after adaptation to optically—induced post—saccadic retinal slip are shown in Fig. 3, B and C. The model could accurately simulate the eye movement when the ocular drift had a long time constant (Fig. 3B) by adjusting only the gains of the step and slide components (gains A and C in Fig. 2). When the ocular drift had a short time constant, however, increasing the gains of the step and slide could not produce a short enough time constant (Fig. 3C, dashed line). A good simulation could only be achieved by changing the gain of the step and both the gain and the time constant of the slide (A, C and T_s in Fig. 2).

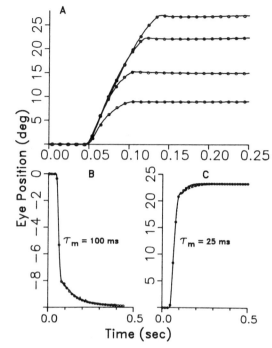

Fig. 3. Simulations of normal and adapted eye movements. Solid lines are spontaneous saccades of a monkey in darkness. The circles are the results of simulating a model with the final common path of Fig. 2. A. A family of normal saccades. B. A saccade made after adaptation to an image motion with a time constant of 100 ms. Eye movement time constant is about 80 ms. C. A saccade made after adaptation to an image motion with a time constant of 25 ms. Eye movement time constant is about 34 ms. The dashed line is the best fit the model can achieve by changing the gain of the step and slide components. The circles are the best fit that can be obtained by changing the gain of the step and both the gain and the time constant of the slide. [Modified from Optican and Miles, 1985.]

ADAPTIVE CONTROL OF THE PURSUIT SYSTEM

The ocular motor response to moving objects depends on how much of the visual field those objects fill. Full-field images are first tracked by a short-latency (about 50 ms) ocular following response, which has been shown to be under adaptive control (Kawano and Miles, 1983). This short-latency system appears to be involved in improving image stabilization (cf. Kawano and Miles, this volume). Our discussion will be concerned with the response to small, smoothly moving objects.

The smooth pursuit response has a latency of about 130 ms and attempts to match eye velocity to target velocity. Weakness of extraocular muscles, caused by injury or disease, reduces the gain of the ocular motor plant so that the tracking response has a lower acceleration than normal. Optican and colleagues (1985) studied patients with unilateral muscle palsies and showed that the initial acceleration (first 130 ms) of the tracking response was under adaptive control. In this study the patient's good eye was used as a control to infer

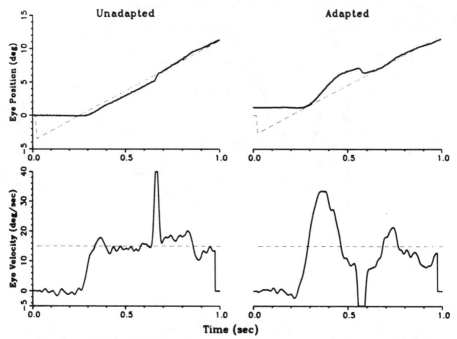

Fig. 4. Effects of adaptation on pursuit movements in central field.
Patient had a unilateral, right abducens nerve palsy. Recordings are
from good eye. Eye velocity obtained by digitally differentiating eye
position record. Target motion was a 15°/s step-ramp (dashed lines). In
unadapted state, weak eye has been patched for 9 days. In adapted state,
weak eye has been viewing for 9 days.

changes in innervation.

After the weak eye had been patched for nine days, pursuit movements of the good
eye in the central field appeared normal (Fig. 4, Unadapted). The eye
accelerated smoothly to the target velocity, and a catch-up saccade was used to
get on target. After 9 days of viewing with the weak eye, the patient´s good eye
showed signs of adaptation (Fig. 4, Unadapted). When the good eye was viewing it
responded to a target ramp with too high an acceleration, resulting in an eye
velocity that overshot the target velocity. The eye went beyond the target,
requiring a back-up saccade.

In normal eye movements in the horizontal plane, the medial and lateral recti
muscles act as pull-relax (or agonist-antagonist) pairs. Since most orbital
deficits do not affect all muscles equally, the weakness will vary according to
the position of the eye in the orbit, and the direction of the eye movement. One
example of such a deficit arises in patients with a unilateral abducens nerve
palsy (that reduces innervation to the lateral rectus muscle). The patient will
then have a reduced muscle gain for abducting movements of the affected eye.
Since most of the action of the lateral rectus muscle is from straight ahead to
temporal, the deficit will be greater for movements starting in the middle and
going temporally. Movements that start nasally and move to the middle are more
dependent on relaxation of the medial rectus muscle (the antagonist) and so are
less affected by the defective VI-th nerve. Thus we see that the abducens palsy

creates an orbital position dependent deficit. For nasally directed movements starting from straight ahead, most of the force comes from the medial rectus (agonist) and the deficit in the VI-th nerve has little effect. For movements starting from an abducted position and moving toward the midline, however, much of the change in force comes from the relaxation of the lateral rectus (agonist). Because of the reduced effectiveness of the VI-th nerve, the reduction in force of the lateral rectus will be less than normal, resulting in an orbital position dependent reduction in acceleration even in the direction away from the palsied muscle.

Optican and colleagues (1985) showed that the pursuit system acceleration was adjusted in a direction and orbital-position dependent way. Hence it appears as if the pursuit system is under adaptive control with the goal of acquiring the target as rapidly as possible, without inducing oscillations. This adaptation may require several days to develop. In response to short periods of adaptation (20 min) Gellman and Carl (1985) showed little change in the early period of pursuit acceleration, although eye velocities during the steady-state period of tracking were changed over this short period (cf. Carl and Gellman, this volume).

PRINCIPLES OF ADAPTIVE OCULAR MOTOR CONTROL

The results of the simulation shown in Fig. 3 demonstrate that a complete understanding of the adaptive control of eye movements must include mechanisms for changing neural dynamics (i.e., time constants) as well as gains. As shown by the direction and orbital position dependence of pursuit adaptation, adaptive mechanisms must also be sensitive to the conditions prevailing when a movement is initiated, and must be able to induce changes in control parameters as a function of such conditions. We can already infer that adaptation occurs to achieve several different goals, such as shortening the time to acquire a target and avoiding oscillations. Perhaps other control strategies remain to be discovered. The future study of adaptive control will reveal more details of the nature of the controlled parameters, and hopefully provide some insight into the underlying adaptive mechanisms.

REFERENCES

Abel, L.A., Schmidt, D., Dell'Osso, L.F., and Daroff, R.B. (1978). Saccadic system plasticity in humans. Ann. Neurol., 4: 313-318.
Gellman, R.S. and Carl, J.R. (1985). Human smooth pursuit: Early responses to sudden changes in target velocity. Soc. Neurosci. Abstr., 11: 79.
Gisbergen, J.A.M. van, Robinson, D.A., and Gielen, S. (1981). A quantitative analysis of generation of saccadic eye movements by burst neurons. J. Neurophysiol., 45: 407-432.
Goldstein, H.P. (1983). The Neural Encoding of Saccades in the Rhesus Monkey. Doctoral dissertation, Johns Hopkins University.
Kawano, K., and Miles, F.A. (1983). Adaptive plasticity in short-latency ocular following responses of monkey. Soc. Neurosci. Abs., 9: 868.
Kommerell, G., Olivier, D., and Theopold, H. (1976). Adaptive programming of phasic and tonic components in saccadic eye movements. Investigations in patients with abducens palsy. Invest. Ophthalmol., 15: 657-660.
Optican, L.M. (1980). Saccadic dysmetria. In Functional Basis of Ocular Motility Disorders, G. Lennerstrand, D.S. Zee, and E.L. Keller, eds. Pergamon, Oxford. Pgs. 441-451.
Optican, L.M. (1985). Adaptive properties of the saccadic system. In Adaptive Mechanisms in Gaze Control: Facts and Theories. A. Berthoz and G. Melvill Jones, eds. Elsevier, Amsterdam. Pgs. 71-79.

Optican, L.M., and Miles, F.A. (1985). Visually induced adaptive changes in primate saccadic oculomotor control signals. J. Neurophysiol., 54: 280-298.

Optican, L.M., and Robinson, D.A. (1980). Cerebellar-dependent adaptive control of primate saccadic system. J. Neurophysiol., 44: 1058-1075.

Optican, L.M., Zee, D.S., and Chu, F.C. (1985). Adaptive response to ocular muscle weakness in human pursuit and saccadic eye movements. J. Neurophysiol., 54: 110-122.

Optican, L.M., Zee, D.S., Miles, F.A., and Lisberger, S.G. (1980). Oculomotor deficits in monkeys with floccular lesions. Neurosci. Abstr., 6: 474.

Robinson, D.A. (1964). The mechanics of human saccadic eye movement. J. Physiol. (London), 174: 245-264.

Skavenski, A.A., and Robinson, D.A. (1973). Role of Abducens neurons in vestibuloocular reflex. J. Neurophysiol., 36: 724-738.

Snow, R., Hore, J., and Vilis, T. (1985). Adaptation of saccadic and vestibulo-ocular systems after extraocular muscle tenectomy. Invest. Ophthalmol. & Vis. Sci., 26: 924-931.

Vilis, T., Yates, S., and Hore, J. (1985). Visual patching of one eye produces changes in saccadic properties in the unseeing eye. Devel. Brain Res., 17: 290-292.

Westheimer, G. and McKee, S.P. (1975). Visual acuity in the presence of retinal-image motion. J. Opt. Soc. Am., 65: 847-850.

Zee, D.S., Chu, F.C., Optican, L.M., Carl, J.R., and Reingold, D.B. (1984). Graphic analysis of paralytic strabismus with the Lancaster red-green test. Am. J. Ophthalmol., 97: 587-592.

Zee, D.S., Optican, L.M., Cook, J.D., Robinson, D.A., and Engel, W.K. (1976). Slow saccades in spinocerebellar degeneration. Arch. Neurol., 33: 243-251.

Ocular Following in the Monkey: Significance of Some Visual Factors, and Plasticity

K. Kawano and F. A. Miles

Laboratory of Sensorimotor Research, National Eye Institute,
Bethesda, Maryland, USA

The ocular following responses elicited by brief, unexpected movements of the visual scene were studied in 10 rhesus monkeys. Test patterns were either random dots or sinewave gratings with the stripes oriented vertically (spatial frequency, F_s, 0.046–1.06cycles/^{o}) back-projected onto a translucent screen, $85^o \times 85^o$. Test stimuli were velocity steps (speed, V, 5–400°/s) of 100 ms duration, applied shortly after spontaneous saccades to avoid saccadic intrusions. It should be noted that animals were never trained to track these movements nor reinforced for doing so. Eye movements were recorded using the electromagnetic search coil technique (Robinson, 1963). To keep them alert, animals were reinforced with fluids for making fast saccades.

Triggered by local luminance changes. Sample response profiles elicited by ramps of various speeds are shown in Fig. 1. Such profiles were irregular and idiosyncratic, but consistent and closely time-locked to stimulus onset. Using random dot patterns, response latencies were short, e.g., when the criterion for onset was an eye acceleration of 100°/s^2, mean latency for 8 monkeys with a 40°/s test ramp was 51.5 ms (± 0.6, SE). Using gratings for which $F_s < 0.5$cycles/^{o}, latency was inversely related to—and solely a function of—contrast and temporal frequency, F_t (where $F_t = F_s * V$): Fig. 2. We conclude from the latter that ocular following is triggered by local changes in luminance.

A gated response? When a sheet of ground glass was interposed between the animal and the screen to blur the random dot pattern, response latency increased progressively—as might be expected—but the amplitude of the initial wave of eye acceleration was either little affected or increased. When used with the sinewave gratings, the ground glass screen simply reduced the contrast of the patterns (range: 0.5–0.003), with very similar consequences for ocular following: Fig. 3. We suggest that these anomalous increases in amplitude with reductions in contrast might be explained if the motion detectors responsible for triggering an ocular following response act as a gate for the tracking system proper. Not until the detectors confirm the existence of motion is the tracking system allowed to go in pursuit. If the detectors take a long time to operate the gate (because of low contrast, for example), and if during this time the tracking system continues to integrate the input errors (presumably retinal image slip) then, when the gate is eventually operated, the accumulated drive signal will result in a brisk onset to tracking. Thus, although there is a delay in the onset of tracking, little is lost. We suggest that such a gating arrangement could endow the system with greater noise immunity, preventing the tracking of spurious signals and thereby improving fixational stability.

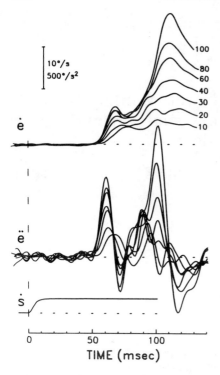

TIME (msec)

TEMPORAL FREQ., F_t (Hz)

Fig. 1. Sample ocular following responses recorded from a monkey using a random dot pattern with velocity steps ranging from 10-100°/s (see numbers by traces). Each trace is an average of 100+ sweeps of the stimulus. $\dot{e}$, eye velocity; $\ddot{e}$, eye acceleration; $\dot{s}$, stimulus velocity. Calibration bar applies to $\dot{e}$ and $\ddot{e}$ traces only.

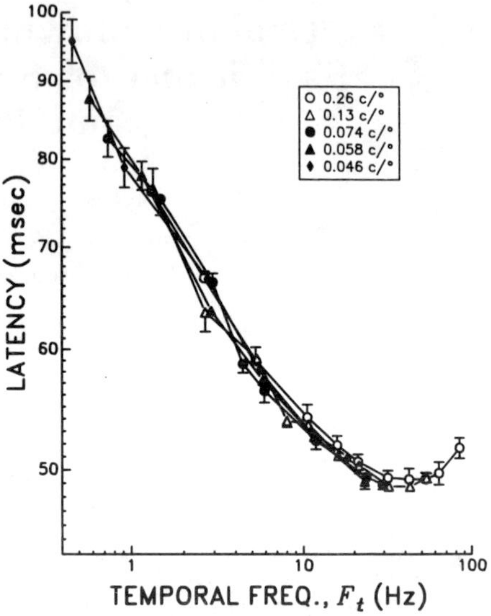

Fig. 2. Ocular following using sinewave grating patterns: Dependence of latency on temporal frequency (F_t), regardless of spatial frequency (F_s: see key) and drift velocity (V). Average data from 3 animals. Lines link points sharing the same F_s. Error bars, $\pm$SE.

Positive reafferent modulation. Contrary to expectation, en masse movement of the visual field was not the optimal stimulus for ocular following (left half of Fig. 4: dashed line). Responses could be improved (by up to 75%) by partitioning the field into central and peripheral regions (center, 20-60° diameter) and, with gaze centered, reversing the image motion in the periphery so that center and surround now saw contrary movement (dotted line). Responses were intermediate if the images in the surround remained stationary (continuous line). Ter Braak (1957), Hood (1975) and Guedry & coworkers (1981) have reported similar effects on human optokinetic responses, though using somewhat different stimuli from those employed here. In the present study, it was also found that any tracking produced by motion in the periphery alone (not shown) was always in the same direction as the stimulus, albeit weak, and we conclude that these anomalous effects of motion in the periphery result from direction selective modulation of the system's sensitivity to motion at the center: in-phase suppression and antiphase enhancement. Direction selective visually driven neurons with a similar center-surround organization have been described in the MT region of cortex in owl monkey (Allman, Miezin & McGuinness, 1985).

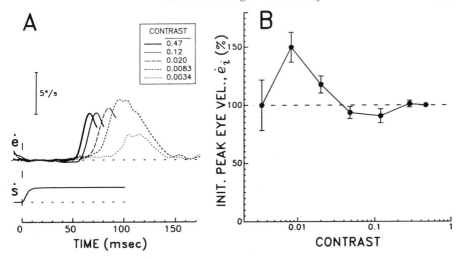

Fig. 3. Ocular following using sinewave grating patterns: Effect of reducing contrast. $F_s=0.264$cycles/^{o}; $V=60^o$/s. A: Sample response profiles from one animal (curtailed to avoid confusing overlaps). Labels and other conventions as in Fig. 1. B: Amplitude data based on measures of $\dot{e}_i$ in 3 animals. Each data set from each animal was first normalized with respect to the response obtained with the highest contrast stimulus (0.47) before averaging. Error bars, $\pm$SE.

We suggest that this peripheral modulation of ocular following assists in the tracking of 'objects'. Further, because this mechanism was only apparent when the central region was large—40° diameter was best—we suggest that, under normal conditions, the objects in question are generally nearby and stationary, their retinal images moving only because the observer moves (reafference); the contrary motion in the surround would then result from parallax due to the background objects being more distant. Thus, we envision a negative feedback tracking system driven by inputs from the central retina and modulated by inputs from the peripheral retina. The latter operates such that motion in the surround that is contrary to that in the center results in an increase in gain: Positive Reafferent Modulation. A block diagram of this scheme is shown in the right half of Fig. 4. Collett (1971, 1972) and Collett & King (1974) have invoked a similar mechanism in the optic lobe of the privet hawk moth to aid the tracking of small moving objects.

Using dichoptic presentation to allow each eye to be stimulated independently revealed that motion in the peripheral field of one eye could modulate the tracking induced by motion in the central field of the other eye (although limited to in-phase suppression): interocular transfer. This provides evidence that some part of the suppressive effect must occur at or beyond a site that receives inputs from both eyes and hence must be mediated by the CNS. In contrast, the antiphase enhancement would seem to occur earlier in the visual pathway, though other factors might account for its lack of transfer.

Post-saccadic enhancement of ocular following. Tracking responses were subject to transient enhancement after saccadic eye movements. Responses were best when the test ramps began 20–30 ms after saccades, and attenuated progressively as the post-saccadic delay interval was increased. Sample response profiles elicited by test ramps initiated at various times after saccades are seen in

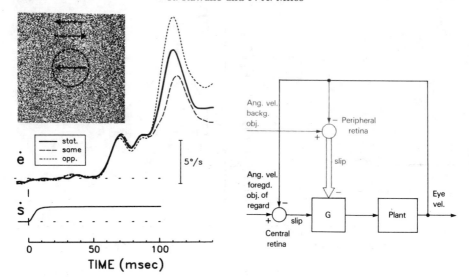

Fig. 4. Positive reafferent modulation. Left: sample response profiles from one monkey. The random dot pattern was partitioned into separate central and peripheral regions such that the dots in each region could be moved independently (boundary stationary). The diameter of the central region was 60°. In all cases, images at the center moved leftwards at 60°/s. Images in the periphery were either stationary (continuous line, ´stat´), or moved in exactly the same way as those at the center (dashed line, ´same´), or moved at the same speed but in the opposite direction (dotted line, ´opp´). Upward deflections represent leftward motion, i.e., the direction of stimulus motion at the center. Labels and other conventions as in Fig. 1. Right: Block diagram of the proposed scheme. Foreground images moving in the central retina are tracked by a negative feedback system whose gain is modulated by the background images moving in the peripheral retina (broken lines).

Fig. 5A; post-saccadic delay intervals (in ms) are indicated by the numbers at the side of each trace. The effect of the antecedent saccade was quantified by measuring the amplitude of the initial peak in the eye velocity profile ($\dot{e}_i$), and averaged data from two animals are plotted in Fig. 5B (open symbols). The decline in responsiveness was roughly exponential: average time constant, 60 ms; average asymptote, 22%. We suggest that this transient enhancement aids the visual suppression of post-saccadic ocular drifts (glissades).

The magnitude of the post-saccadic enhancement was dependent on the amount of retinal stimulation during the antecedent saccade. When this stimulation was compromised—as when a vertical saccade was made on a grating pattern with vertically oriented stripes—subsequent enhancement of ocular following was much reduced. Further, saccade-like conditioning movements of the visual scene (480°/s for 20 ms)—initiated 250 ms after saccades to allow post-saccadic enhancement to subside—improved the ocular following responses to subsequent test ramps: visual enhancement of ocular following. The enhancement here was similar in magnitude and time course to that in the wake of real saccades (closed symbols in Fig. 5B). We conclude that the post-saccadic enhancement of ocular following is largely due to the visual stimulation produced by the saccade sweeping the scene across the retina.

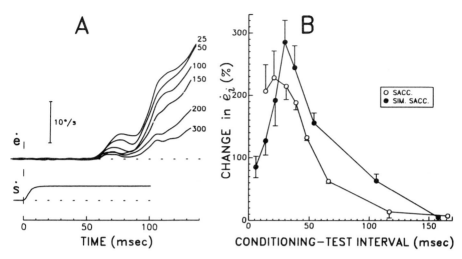

TIME (msec)   CONDITIONING-TEST INTERVAL (msec)

Fig. 5. Post-saccadic enhancement of ocular following. A: Sample
response profiles resulting from 40°/s test ramps applied at various
times after saccadic eye movements. Delay intervals (in ms) indicated
by numbers at side of traces. Labels and other conventions as in
Fig.1. B: Quantitative comparison of the magnitude and time course of
the enhancement in the wake of saccades (open symbols) and saccade-
like movements of the visual scene (closed symbols). Average data
from 2 monkeys. Time on abscissa measured from end of saccades (real
or simulated) to onset of test ramps (60°/s). Amplitude measures
normalized with respect to the unenhanced control (response when test
ramps delivered 250 ms after saccades without prior conditioning)
before averaging. Error bars, ±SE.

Using dichoptic presentation to allow each eye to be stimulated separately
revealed that visual enhancement showed poor interocular transfer: the saccade-
like conditioning movements had to be seen by the same eye that saw the test
stimuli in order to produce appreciable enhancement. This suggests that most of
the enhancement occurs at a point in the visual pathway before the inputs from
the 2 eyes have converged.

Peripheral suppression. Data obtained with the visual field partitioned into
central and peripheral regions (center, 20-60° diameter) and with gaze centered
suggested that the ocular following system and the enhancement mechanism that
modulates it both receive their major inputs from the central 40° of the retina.
Other experiments with the field partitioned (center, 20° diameter) showed that
the conditioning and test stimuli had to be seen by the same region of retina in
order to demonstrate enhancement. Indeed, when the two stimuli impinged on
different regions, suppression was seen. The latter was particularly potent
when the conditioning stimulus was seen by the peripheral retina and the test
stimulus by the central retina: peripheral suppression (Fig. 6). This
suppression was brief, only affecting responses to test ramps initiated during-
-and up to 30 ms after--the conditioning stimulus, and reduced responsiveness on
average by up to 79%. We suggest that peripheral suppression functions to
prevent the ocular following system from tracking the visual disturbances caused
by saccades: saccade-like movements of the central images alone produced small
transient ocular following responses whereas such movements of the peripheral
images or of the whole field did not.

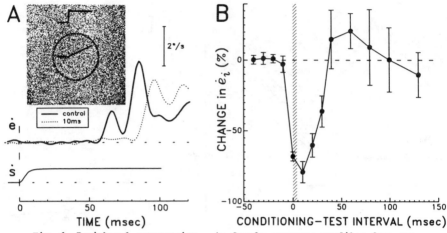

TIME (msec)   CONDITIONING–TEST INTERVAL (msec)

Fig. 6. Peripheral suppression. A: Sample response profiles from one
monkey. The random dot pattern was partitioned into separate central
and peripheral regions such that the dots in each region could be
moved independently (boundary stationary). The diameter of the
central region was 20°. 60°/s test ramps were applied at the center
250 ms after saccades. In half of the cases, an 11° displacement of
the dots in the periphery preceded the test ramp at the center by 10
ms (dotted line), resulting in the suppression of the first wave of
the tracking response, and the delay of subsequent waves. Labels and
other conventions as in Fig. 1. B: Magnitude and time course of
peripheral suppression based on measures of $\dot{e}_i$ (averages for 3
animals). The displacements in the periphery lasted 4 ms and their
occurrence is indicated by shading. Data were normalized with respect
to controls (responses to test ramps applied 250 ms after saccades
without prior conditioning) before averaging. Error bars, ±SE.

Dichoptic presentation was used to permit separate partitioning of the visual
fields for each eye. Saccade–like movements applied to the peripheral field of
one eye suppressed the responses elicited by test ramps applied at the center of
the other eye: interocular transfer of peripheral suppression. The suppression
here was as vigorous as that in the normal binocular situation, indicating that
it must involve interactions at or beyond a site that receives inputs from the 2
eyes and hence must be mediated by the CNS. The peripheral suppression
described here bears a striking resemblance to the suppressive effect of sudden
displacements of the field on visual detection described by MacKay (1970a,
1970b).

Adaptive plasticity. The adaptability of the ocular following responses
elicited by brief movements of the visual scene was studied in 5 rhesus monkeys.
Adapting stimuli were double ramps, each lasting 150 ms: the first ramp was
designed to initiate ocular following and the second to induce consistent visual
errors that would challenge any adaptive mechanism regulating the performance of
such tracking. The second ramp could differ from the first in either speed
(speed steps) or direction (direction steps) depending on the experiment: Fig.
7. Monkeys were repeatedly exposed to these adapting stimuli over a period of 3
days.

Exposure to speed steps involving increases or decreases in speed resulted in
clear increases or decreases, respectively, in the ocular following responses
elicited by the standard 100 ms test ramps: Fig. 8. These changes were specific

A. SPEED STEPS   B. DIRECTION STEPS

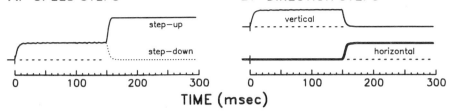

TIME (msec)

Fig. 7. Velocity-step adaptation paradigms (sample stimulus velocity profiles). A: Speed steps. B: Direction steps.

to the direction and, to a lesser extent, the speed of the adapting stimuli. The rate of adaptation was most rapid during the first part of each day, with partial recovery during overnight rest periods. Optican, Zee & Chu (1985) have recently made related observations on human patients with ocular muscle weakness of one eye. These workers found that patients improved the tracking performance of their weak eye when their normal eye was patched for a few days. That this improvement was due to central adaptive mechanisms rather then peripheral recovery was evident when the patch was switched: When obliged to use the normal eye the patient now showed overshooting and oscillation, indicating that the system mediating tracking through that (inexperienced) eye had acquired an abnormally high gain.

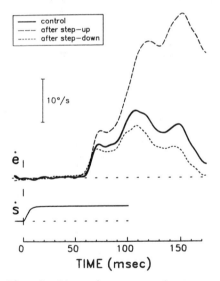

Fig. 8. Adaptation to speed steps. Effect of 3 days of exposure to step-up (dashed line) and step-down (dotted line) speed steps on the response profiles evoked by 40°/s test ramps. Profiles obtained prior to adaptation are shown in continuous line. Labels and other conventions as in Fig. 1.

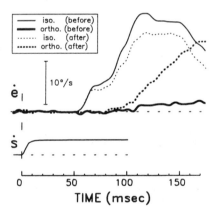

Fig. 9. Adaptation to direction steps. Sample response profiles evoked by 40°/s upward test ramps before (continuous line) and after (dotted line) 3 days of exposure to anticlockwise direction steps. The isogonal component is shown in thin lines/dots (upward deflections representing upward movements), and the orthogonal component in thick lines/dots (upward deflections representing leftward movements). Labels and other conventions as in Fig. 1.

Direction steps consisting of 90° anticlockwise changes in the direction of movement resulted in the emergence of orthogonal components of ocular following (anticlockwise) and the attenuation of the isogonal components: Fig. 9. These changes are reminiscent of those seen in the vestibulo-ocular reflex following cross-axis stimulation (Schultheis & Robinson, 1981; Callan & Ebenholtz, 1982). In the present experiments, the orthogonal responses differed from the isogonal ones in having longer latencies (mean±SD: 71.1 ± 14.8 ms) and smoother response profiles, and in showing no overnight recovery. It is concluded that the ocular following responses of the monkey are subject to extensive visually mediated adaptive regulation.

REFERENCES

Allman, J., F. Miezin, and McGuinness (1985). Stimulus specific responses from beyond the classical receptive field: Neurophysiological mechanisms for local-global comparisons in visual neurons. Ann. Rev. Neurosci., 8, 407–430.

Callan, J. W., and S. M. Ebenholtz (1982). Directional changes in the vestibular ocular response as a result of adaptation to optical tilt. Vision Res., 22, 37–42.

Collett, T. (1971). Visual neurones for tracking moving targets. Nature, 232, 127–130.

Collett, T. (1972). Visual neurones in the anterior optic tract of the privet hawk moth. J. comp. Physiol., 78, 396–433.

Collett, T., and A. J. King (1974). Vision during flight. In G. A. Horridge (Ed.), The Compound Eye and Vision of Insects. Clarendon, Oxford. pp. 437–466.

Guedry, F. E., J. M. Lentz, R. M. Jell and, J. W. Norman (1981). Visual-vestibular interactions: The directional component of visual background movement. Aviat. Space Environ. Med., 52, 304–309.

Hood, J. D. (1975). Observations upon the role of the peripheral retina in the execution of eye movements. J. Oto-rhino-lar. Borderlands. 37, 65–73.

MacKay, D. M. (1970a). Elevation of visual threshold by displacement of retinal image. Nature, 225, 90–92.

MacKay, D. M. (1970b). Interocular transfer of suppressive effects of retinal image displacement. Nature, 225, 872–873.

Optican, L. M., D. S. Zee, and F. Chu (1985). Adaptive response to ocular muscle weakness in human pursuit and saccadic eye movements. J. Neurophysiol., 54, 110–122.

Robinson, D. A. (1963). A method of measuring eye movement using a scleral search coil in a magnetic field. IEEE Trans. Biomed. Eng., 26, 137–145.

Schultheis, L. W., and D. A. Robinson (1981). Directional plasticity of the vestibulo-ocular reflex in the cat. Ann. N. Y. Acad. Sci., 374, 504–512.

Ter Braak, J. W. G. (1957). "Ambivalent" optokinetic stimulation. Folia Psychiat. Neurol. Neerl. 60, 131–135.

ACKNOWLEDGEMENTS

We thank Dr. Lance M. Optican for numerous helpful discussions.

Short Term Saccadic Adaptation in the Monkey

E. J. Fitzgibbon, M. E. Goldberg and
M. A. Segraves

Laboratory of Sensorimotor Research, National Eye Institute,
Bethesda, Maryland, USA, and Department of Neurology,
Georgetown University School of Medicine,
Washington, DC, USA

INTRODUCTION

Man and monkey can adapt the gain of the saccadic system when their extraocular muscle activity is inappropriate for the accurate foveation of visual stimuli. This gain change is usually conjugate. Thus weakness of an extraocular muscle in one eye results in a gain increase in the normal eye when a subject is forced to view the world exclusively through the weak eye because the neural signal to the weak eye has been augmented to drive the eye properly. (Kommerell, Olivier, and Theopold, 1976; Optican and Robinson, 1980). This inaccurate extraocular muscle activity can be simulated by requiring a subject to make saccades to a target that moves consistently during the saccade (McLaughlin, 1967). The subject behaves as if the resulting under- or overshoot were due to a malfunction of the oculomotor system rather than to a movement of the target, and eventually makes a saccade not to the initial position of the target but to its final position. We have used this paradigm in the rhesus monkey to change the amplitude of the saccadic response to a visual target, and then see if the change were reflected in the saccades evoked by electrical stimulation of the superior colliculus.

METHODS

Under general anesthesia, with aseptic surgical technique, two rhesus monkeys (Macaca mulatta) were fitted with hardware for head holding, a scleral search coil for eye movement recording, and a recording cylinder through which electrodes could be introduced into the superior colliculus. After recovery, the monkeys were trained to look at a spot of light and make saccades from target to target. Eye movements were measured using the magnetic search coil method (Robinson, 1963). A PDP 11 computer was used for eye position sampling and behavioral control.

Each trial began with the monkeys fixating a $.25^o$ spot of light projected on a tangent screen 57cm in front of them. Between 700 and 1200 ms after the initiation of fixation the original fixation point disappeared and a second target appeared on the screen. This target was positioned by a pair of servo-controlled mirror galvanometers that could move it through a distance of 20° in 8 ms. The computer monitored the monkey's eye position at a rate of 1 Khz. When it detected an eye velocity greater than 50°/sec, the computer blanked the target, moved it, and reilluminated it. The entire operation took place while the monkey was performing the saccade, so that at the end of the saccade the monkey had to make a corrective saccade initially to compensate for the intrasaccadic target step. If the stimulus jumped back towards the original fixation point, the effective necessary saccade was shorter (gain-shortening paradigm). If the stimulus jumped further away, the effective necessary saccade was longer (gain-lengthening paradigm).

Electrical stimulation was performed through a fine tungsten wire electrode moved hydraulically through a 18g guide tube. Suprathreshold pulses were delivered by a Grass S-88 stimulator through PSIU6 constant current stimulus isolators. All stimulation was performed while the monkey looked at the central fixation point used in the adaptation studies in order to avoid orbital position effects on saccade amplitude (Segraves and Goldberg, 1984). Pulses were biphasic, no more than 50ua per phase, with a duration of 0.2 per phase, a train length of 70ms and a pulse frequency of 330 Hz. At the start of an experimental day, the unadapted monkey would look at the central fixation point while the superior colliculus was stimulated. The mean amplitude and direction of the resultant saccades provided the baseline from which saccadic gain was increased or decreased in the experiments. The baseline saccade target was located at the point on the screen that would be fixated by the saccade evoked by the electrical stimulation. Baseline saccade amplitudes varied from 8 to 35 degrees depending upon the location of the collicular electrode. Some stimulation sites were marked by passing current through the microelectrode, and the brains were subsequently analysed to verify that the stimulation sites were in the intermediate layers of the superior colliculus.

RESULTS

The dynamics of short term saccadic adaptation: Monkeys could be induced to change the gain of their saccadic eye movements by as much as 40% in both the

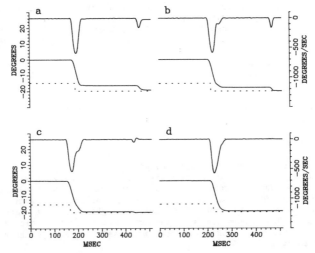

Fig. 1. Performance in the gain-lengthening paradigm. In each trace top line is velocity (scale to right), middle trace horizontal eye position and bottom trace stimulus position (both position scales to left). Since the stimulus makes the original step at time 0, the original fixation point is not shown, but is, in each case, located at 0°.

gain-lengthening and gain-shortening paradigms. Figure 1 shows a typical series of saccades in the gain-lengthening paradigm. At first (Fig. 1a) the monkey made a saccade appropriate to fixate the target at its original position,

followed by a corrective saccade with the usual saccadic latency to acquire the
target at its new position. Within 200 trials the saccade grew larger, but the
presence of two maxima in the velocity waveform indicates that rather than
simply making a longer normal saccade, the monkey produced an extra corrective
saccade close to the time of the initial saccade. Sometimes the second saccade
can be seen only as a shoulder in the velocity waveform of the larger saccade
(Fig. 1c). At times 3 individual velocity maxima could be seen.

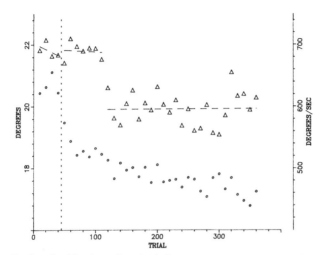

Fig 2. Amplitude and velocities of adapted saccades in the
gain-shortening paradigm. Saccade amplitude (circles) and
velocity (triangle) plotted as a function of trial number.
Each point is the mean of ten consecutive trials. The
vertical dotted line shows the beginning of adaptation
trials. There is a significant transition in velocity
between trials 100 and 130, and thereafter the velocity does
not change. Three regression lines are shown, for the pre-
adaptation trials, the adaptation trials before the velocity
decrement, and the adaptation trials after the velocity
decrement.

Within 400 to 800 trials the monkey made adapted saccades with normal appearing
velocity profiles (Fig. 1d). After the monkey had begun to change the gain of
the saccade it tended to vary strategy from trial to trial. Saccades with
distinct velocity maxima were intermixed with those in which the second maximum
appeared as a shoulder in the velocity curve. Even normal appearing adapted
saccades could be interspersed with abnormal appearing ones. If the monkey had
not aquired the target at the end of the initial saccade, the ensuing corrective
saccade always appeared at the usual latency (Figs. 1b, 1c, 1d). It was
difficult to achieve gain changes larger than 25% if the monkey were not first
adapted to an intermediate target step. More trials were required to achieve
adaptation to larger target steps.

The time course for decreasing saccadic gain in the monkey was much shorter.
Within 25 trials the visually guided saccades would decrease in amplitude and
maximal gain change for a jump from 20° to 15° could be obtained within 200
trials. Here the velocity waveform did not show the multiple maxima seen in the
gain-lengthening paradigm. However, the velocities were not normal: the peak
velocity of the adapted saccades remained equal to that of the unadapted
saccades for a number of trials in which the saccadic amplitude had already
decreased (Fig. 2). In the example shown, the peak velocity began to decrease

after about 70 trials and stabilized at the lower velocity after 100. The final peak velocity of the adapted saccades has an amplitude–velocity relationship beneath the main sequence for saccades performed in the unadapted state earlier the same day (Fig. 3). The time course for returning gain to normal from a gain–shortened state was prolonged and saccades often remained hypometric even after 1000 trials.

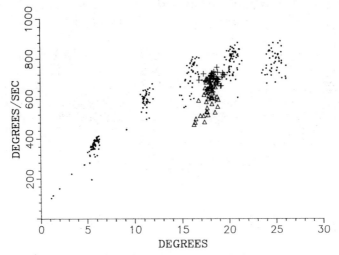

Fig 3. Relationship of adapted velocities in the gain-shortening paradigm to the main sequence. Peak saccadic velocity is plotted as a function of amplitude for pre-adaptation saccades (dots), pre–velocity–decrement saccade (pluses) and post–velocity–decrement saccades (triangles).

The effect of adaptation on saccades evoked by electrical stimulation of the superior colliculus: The superior colliculus was stimulated before, during and after adaptation. The saccades evoked by electrical stimulation were not affected by the adaptation process. Figure 4 shows saccades evoked by electrical stimulation and visual stimuli before and after adaption. The waveforms of the electrically evoked saccades were normal, even at times when the waveforms of the adapting visually guided saccades were abnormal. Electrically evoked saccades always had the amplitude of the unadapted saccades, even for consecutive stimulation and adapted visual saccades.

DISCUSSION AND CONCLUSIONS

These results show that rhesus monkeys can change the gain of their saccadic system in response to a consistent intrasaccadic target displacement. The gain change has the hallmark of an adaptive change in that it occurs gradually and is extinguished gradually. However, the process is not simply an adjustment of low level motor mechanisms. The presence of several velocity maxima during the adapted saccades in the gain-lengthening paradigm, and higher than normal maximum velocities during the gain-shortening paradigm argues that the mechanism involves processes other than changing the gain of a single saccade. In addition, since electrical stimulation of the superior colliculus evokes the unadapted saccade even when the adapted saccades have normal velocity profiles, the process is not simply a change in the response of the brainstem saccadic system to a supranuclear command, but rather must entail the elaboration of a different saccadic strategy by supranuclear centers.

This strategy most likely involves the generation of a corrective saccade predictively, so that the primary saccade and the corrective occur nearly simultaneously, and the corrective saccade is embedded into the waveform of the original saccade. That such a strategy is used is apparent from the velocity waveforms of the gain-lengthened saccades, in which one can easily see two velocity maxima. We can also infer it from the amplitude-velocity relationships

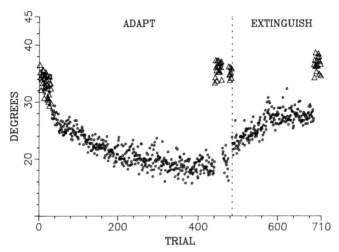

Fig 4. Comparison of saccades evoked by electrical stimulation of the superior colliculus with adapted and unadapted visually guided saccades. For early trials stimulation (triangle) and visually-guided trials (dots) are intermixed. The vertical dotted line signfies the beginning of extinction trials in which the stimulus was not stepped during the saccade.

of the gain-shortened saccades, in which the peak velocity of the adapted saccade begins as that of the unadapted saccade and then falls below the main sequence, as if a saccade in the opposite direction were subtracted from the original saccade.

REFERENCES

Kommerell, G., Olivier, D., and H. Theopold (1976). Adaptive programming of phasic and tonic components in saccadic eye movements. Investigation in patients with abducens palsy. Invest. Ophthal., 15, 657-660.
McLaughlin, S. C. (1967). Parametric adjustment in saccadic eye movements. Percept. & Psychophys., 2, 359-362.
Optican, L. M., and D. A. Robinson (1980). Cerebellar-dependent adaptive control of primate saccadic system. J. Neurophys., 44, 1058-1076
Robinson, D. A. (1963). A method of measuring eye movement using a scleral search coil in a magnetic field. IEEE Trans Biomed Eng 10, 137-145.
Robinson, D. A. (1972). Eye movements evoked by collicular stimulation in the alert monkey. Vision Research, 12, 1795-1808.
Segraves, M. A., and M. E. Goldberg (1984). Initial orbital position affects the trajectories of large saccades evoked by electrical stimulation of the monkey superior colliculus. Soc. Neurosci. Abstr., 10, 59.

Adaptive Responses in Human Smooth Pursuit

J. R. Carl and R. S. Gellman

Laboratory of Sensorimotor Research, National Eye Institute, NIH, Bethesda, Maryland, USA

Studies of adaptation in the pursuit system have been hampered by the lack of a clear description of the stimuli that drive the response. In particular, the role of predictive elements and the effect of target position have remained unclear. The existence of predictive elements is apparent from observations that a target with a repeating waveform may be tracked with a phase lead. In this instance, the system must be responding to some internal model of the target rather than the target motion itself, but it is unclear how long it takes to generate that model or how it is updated.

The relative importance of position as a stimulus for the pursuit system has also remained controversial. In order to study the pursuit response without the usual interspersed saccades, Rashbass (1961) utilized a stimulus in which the target stepped away from fixation and ramped back, creating retinal slip towards the fovea. The eye appeared to move in the direction of the target velocity, away from the target position, leading to the suggestion that target velocity was the pertinent stimulus for the pursuit system. In an early quantitative study of pursuit, Robinson (1965) noted that the response to this step-ramp stimulus was delayed compared to that for a simple ramp stimulus, and suggested that the pursuit system had in fact taken some notice of the target position. More recently Pola and Wyatt (1980) have demonstrated pursuit system responsiveness to position in some conditions. The step-ramp "Rashbass" stimulus has remained a popular technique for studying pursuit responses, most recently by Optican, Zee and Chu (1985) in an analysis of pursuit plasticity in patients with ocular muscle weakness, and by Lisberger and Westbrook (1985) in a study of normal monkeys.

In order to better understand the control of smooth pursuit, we studied the first 500 ms of tracking response after a change in target motion in 7 normal subjects (Gellman and Carl, 1985), and then in 4 of the subjects after a gain adapting period. The significant findings for normal pursuit were: (i) the latency for all subjects was about 100 ms, regardless of whether tracking was already underway or not; (ii) the acceleration for the pre-saccadic period (the first 60–100 ms of response) was low, about $50^{\circ}/s^2$, fairly constant, and essentially independent of target velocity (range 5–40°/sec); (iii) there was a response to position errors that had a latency of 100 ms and a similar acceleration, but only lasted about 50 ms; (iv) predictive mechanisms became apparent at about 200 ms with higher accelerations that were dependent on target velocity.

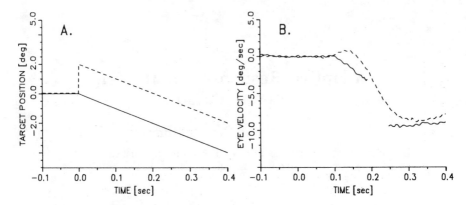

Fig 1. A comparison of responses to ramp and step-ramp stimuli.
A: The target positions for a simple ramp to the left at 10°/s
(solid line) and for a step-ramp with a velocity of 10°/s (dashed
line). B: Typical averaged waveforms (16 trials) of eye velocity
response to ramp and step-ramp stimuli for one subject in the
pre-adapted period. Saccades were cut out of all trials, leaving
a blank region in the ramp response. There were only rare
saccades made in the step-ramp trials. Note that the latency of
response to the ramp stimulus is about 100 ms, and the pre-
saccadic portion is a nearly linear increase in velocity,
indicating a constant acceleration. The post-saccadic portion has
nearly matched the target velocity of 10 °/sec. The step-ramp
response also has a latency of 100 ms, but the initial velocity is
in the direction of the position of the target, and only after
about 50 ms does it reverse to the direction of the target
velocity.

Figure 1 demonstrates some of these findings and illustrates some of the
differences between ramp and step-ramp responses. Since the eyes reach target
velocity at roughly the same time for both stimuli, the effective acceleration
is very similar. In both cases, the effective peak acceleration occurs about
200 ms after ramp onset, which coincides with the time of the catch-up saccade
in the pure ramp case. The response to the step-ramp stimulus is a complex
combination of position and velocity responses, which limits its usefulness in
determining the expected response to non-conflicting stimuli.

These results suggested to us that the pursuit response consists of several
separate components that might have independent adaptive regulation. Although
in some senses a closed loop system, pursuit has a 100 ms delay in the
feedback loop and operates open loop during this brief period after changes in
target velocity. We tested the pursuit response of normal subjects before and
after an adaptation period in which they viewed target ramps with altered
feedback.

Methods. The eye movements of 4 normal human subjects were recorded with the
search coil technique (Robinson, 1963). The target was a 1/10° spot of white
light that was back projected via mirror galvanometers onto a tangent screen 1
meter in front of the subject. The room was otherwise dark, and the target
brightness was at least 2 log units above the perceptual threshold. The eye
velocity signal (analog differentiation, bandpass 0-100 Hz) was digitized at
500 Hz, and eye position and target position at 250 Hz.

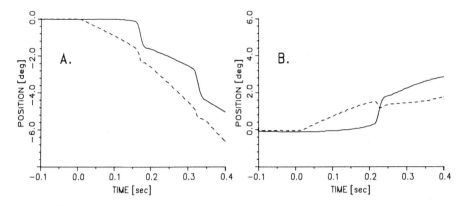

Fig 2. Examples of altered feedback during the adapting period.
The eye position traces are solid, and the mirror position traces
are dashed. A: A 10°/s ramp to the left with positive feedback
(open loop). The eye position is added to the mirror position.
The feedback is turned off during the saccades so that only a
small portion of the saccadic amplitude is present in the mirror
position. B: A trial with negative feedback and a 10°/s ramp to
the right. The eye position is subtracted from the mirror
position, so the velocities will be equal when the eye moves at
5°/s.

The test stimuli were target ramps at 10°/sec and step-ramps where the target
stepped away about 2° and then ramped back at 10°/sec ("Rashbass" stimulus).
The step size of the step-ramp stimulus was adjusted so that the subject did
not make a saccade for 300 ms or more in most trials. Similar stimuli with
2°/sec ramps were used in one subject with comparable results. The timing and
order of the stimuli were pseudo-randomly varied and responses from 16 trials
of each type were averaged after removing saccades. During pre and post
adaptation testing, the target was blanked after 300 ms; during adaptation it
remained visible for 500 to 700 ms. During the 20 minute adaptation period,
10°/sec ramps were used with the eye position added to the target position
(positive feedback), creating an open loop where pursuit responses could not
decrease the retinal slip velocity; this was designed to challenge the system
to increase its gain. The eye position could also be subtracted from the
target position (negative feedback), thereby doubling the effectiveness of the
eye response; this was designed to induce a decreased gain. In both of these
conditions, the altered feedback was turned off during saccades so the changes
would be minimized for saccades. Rightward and leftward ramps were
intermixed, with positive feedback created for one direction and negative
feedback for the other. Figure 2 illustrates the eye and mirror positions for
both of these stimulus alterations.

Results. All subjects showed a similar pattern of adaptation. The responses
to test ramp stimuli before and after the adapting period are shown for two
subjects in Fig. 3. The dotted traces are the pre-adapted responses, and the
solid lines are post-adaptation. The pre-saccadic responses are essentially
identical, while the post-saccadic velocities show changes in the expected
directions in all subjects. Since continued smooth pursuit of the target
would provide information about the velocity errors introduced by adaptation,
the test ramps were kept short (300 ms) in the test periods to limit feedback
that might extinguish the adaptation.

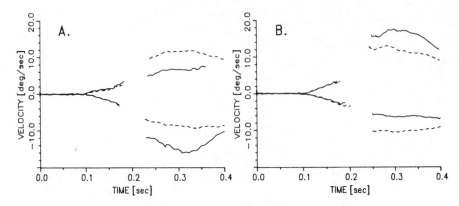

Fig 3.   Eye velocity responses of two subjects before (dashed) and
after (solid) an adapting period.   Note that the pre-saccadic
portion of the response did not change, while the post saccadic
portion has adapted in the expected direction.   A: Positive
feedback to the left and negative feedback to the right.   B:
Positive feedback to the right and negative feedback to the left.

Comparisons of the first few post-adaptation test responses with the last few
showed little difference.   When objectively measured for all subjects, the
pre-saccadic accelerations were on average increased slightly in   both
directions by the adaptation.   The increases in post-saccadic velocities
averaged 62% and the decreases 39%. (Whereas there was no theoretical limit
on the   increase in eye velocity that our paradigm might produce, the maximum
decrease was limited to a 50% reduction.)

Adaptation may occur in saccades and post-saccadic drift (Kommerell, Olivier,
and Theopold, 1976; Optican and Miles, 1985), so we also used step-ramp
stimuli in the test periods to eliminate possible contamination by saccade
related adaptation.   The initial response to the step-ramp stimulus was always
in the direction of the target position (fig. 1), and the effects of the
adaptation paradigm on the initial component were variable, with two of the
subjects showing some change in the position response in one direction only.
The velocity attained by 250 ms, however, showed a consistent change in the
same manner as for the ramp stimuli. Since, for this paradigm, there are no
saccades by 250 ms, it follows that neither saccades nor post-saccadic drift
were accounting for the adaptation.

Discussion. We suggest that smooth pursuit responses consist of several
relatively independent responses.   One is a short latency (100 ms) response
that is independent of target velocity.   The fact that this response was
observed to be independent of target velocity in the unadapted state suggested
that it was unlikely to be subject to adaptive control. This earliest portion
of the response was not consistently or markedly affected by our adaptation
paradigm.

The second response has a latency of about 200 ms, an acceleration that does
depend on target velocity, and was readily affected by our adaptation
paradigm. The eye velocity at 250 ms, whether post-saccadic or part of a
step-ramp response, normally approaches the target velocity and there is
little subsequent overshoot or oscillation. This performance is far better
than that of a simple negative feedback model using a 100 ms delay and
accelerations such as those found in our subjects.

We suggest that the improvement results from an internal estimate of target velocity that has been formed before 200 ms. The saccadic accuracy to moving targets also suggests that by the time of saccadic onset some estimate of target velocity is available. These data lead us to suggest that the system takes about 150 ms to assess target velocity. If the pursuit system were to use an internal "efference" copy of eye velocity to compare to this internal target velocity estimate, the effect of the 100 ms delay in the feedback loop could be eliminated. This could result in higher accelerations without oscillation, apparent by 200 ms in our subjects. The accuracy of the target velocity estimate would be an important parameter of this scheme, and if the estimate were incorrect, an error signal in the form of retinal slip would indicate the direction and magnitude of the error. Adaptation would result from an attempt to match the estimate of target velocity to actual target velocity. By 250 ms into the response the gain of this system can be expressed as the ratio of eye velocity (which has matched target velocity estimate) to actual target velocity. This gain is the part of the tracking response that was altered in our subjects.

REFERENCES

Gellman, R.S. and Carl, J.R. (1985). Human smooth pursuit: Early responses to sudden changes in target velocity. Soc. Neuroscience Abstr., 11, 79.
Kommerell, G., Olivier, D. and Theopold, H. (1976). Adaptive programming of phasic and tonic components in saccadic eye movements. Investigations in patients with abducens palsy. Invest. Ophthalmol., 15, 657-660.
Lisberger, S.G. and Westbrook, L.E. (1985). Properties of visual inputs that initiate horizontal smooth pursuit eye movements in monkeys. J. Neuroscience, 5, 1662-1673.
Optican, L.M. and Miles, F.A. (1985). Visually induced adaptive changes in primate saccadic oculomotor control signals. J. Neurophysiol., in press.
Optican, L.M., Zee, D.S. and Chu, F.C. (1985). Adaptive response to ocular muscle weakness in human pursuit and saccadic eye movements. J. Neurophysiol., 54, 110-122.
Pola, J. and Wyatt, H.J. (1980). Target position and velocity: the stimuli for smooth pursuit eye movements. Vision Res., 20, 523-534.
Rashbass, C. (1961). The relationship between saccadic and smooth tracking eye movements. J. Physiol., 159, 326-338.
Robinson, D.A. (1963). A method of measuring eye movement using a scleral search coil in a magnetic field. IEEE Trans. Biomed. Eng., 26, 137-145.
Robinson, D.A. (1965). The mechanics of human smooth pursuit eye movement. J. Physiol., 180, 569-591.

ACKNOWLEDGEMENT

We thank Dr. Fred Miles for support and advice.

APVOS-L*

Adaptive Compensation to Changes in the Oculomotor Plant

S. Grossberg[†]

Center for Adaptive Systems, Mathematics Department, Boston
University, Boston, MA 02215, USA

1. Introduction: Synthesizing Movement Commands from Multiple Adaptive Circuits

This chapter outlines and applies some real-time neural modelling results from the book which Michael Kuperstein and I have written about the adaptive dynamics of saccadic eye movements (Grossberg and Kuperstein, 1985). Our approach has been to investigate how brain systems are designed to form an adaptive relationship with their environment. Instead of focussing upon a few performance characteristics of a neural system, we consider the types of developmental and learning problems that a brain system *as a whole* must solve before accurate performance can be achieved. Our analysis of saccadic eye movements has identified a set of distinct learning problems that its control system needs to solve in order to achieve accurate performance characteristics. The solutions of these learning problems take the form of real-time circuits that have a natural interpretation as neural networks. We have hereby related an anatomical multiplicity of brain regions to a functional multiplicity of learning problems.

In this chapter, I will focus upon two model neural circuits which control adaptive compensation to changes in the oculomotor plant. In order to fully understand these circuits, it is necessary to also know the functional role that such adaptive compensation plays in the total synthesis of an accurate movement command. In particular, one of these adaptive circuits uses both outflow signals and inflow signals. Other adaptive circuits that we have developed also make use of outflow signals, but in each of these circuits the outflow signals accomplish different functional tasks and are therefore coded and transformed in different ways.

2. Automatic Compensation for Present Position: Movement Vectors from Target Positions and Corollary Discharges

One of these additional adaptive circuits clarifies how target position information is compared with present position information to generate a movement command (Guthrie, Porter, and Sparks, 1983; Mays and Sparks, 1980, 1981; Schiller, True, and Conway, 1979). Target positions are partly derived from visual signals due to lights on the retina. By contrast, present positions of the eye within the head are described in motor coordinates. A fundamental

† Supported in part by the Air Force Office of Scientific Research (AFOSR 85-0149) and the National Science Foundation (NSF IST-8417756).

Acknowledgements: Thanks to Cynthia Suchta for her valuable assistance in the preparation of the manuscript and illustrations.

calibration problem needs to be solved before the network can compare target positions and present positions. A visually-derived target position needs to be transformed into motor coordinates so that it can be compared with present position signals that are also computed in motor coordinates. Obviously this transformation must be learned. This learned transformation replaces one representation of target position (the visually-activated one) with another representation of target position (the motor one). That is why we call this network the *head-muscle interface*, or HMI. Our theory shows how the *same* HMI transformation that learns this coordinate change *also* computes the degree of mismatch between target position and present position. The degree of mismatch between a target position and a present position generates a motor code, in the form of a "vector difference," that can be used to accurately move the eyes.

The HMI uses outflow signals, in the form of corollary discharges, as a basis for its computations of present position. This fact provides a basis for considering a separate adaptive circuit, which we have called the Muscle Linearization Network (MLN). The MLN is one of the circuits which controls adaptive compensation to changes in the oculomotor plant within our theory. The need for an MLN can be seen through the following considerations.

3. Distinguishing Corollary Discharges from Calibrations of Muscle Plant Contractions

In addition to providing a corollary discharge of present position, an outflow signal also moves the eyes by contracting extraocular muscles. However, the laws that govern the muscle plant are not known *a priori* to the outflow source. It is not known *a priori* how much the muscle will contract in response to an outflow signal of prescribed size. Even if the system somehow possessed this information at one time, it might turn out to be the wrong information at a later time, since the muscle characteristics can change through time.

The relationship between the size of an outflow command and the amount of muscle contraction is, in principle, undeterminable without some type of additional information. This additional information must characterize the muscle plant's response to outflow signals. To accomplish this, the system needs to compute a reliable measure of an outflow command as well as a reliable measure of the muscle's response to that command. Corollary discharges provide a reliable measure of outflow commands using signal sizes that the outflow pathway is capable of generating. The muscle responses to these signals may initially be much too large, much too small, or even nonlinear, due to the characteristics of the muscle plant. In order to convert outflow signals into a full range of linear muscle contractions, somehow the brain needs to eventually adjust the responses of the muscle plant to these outflow signals. Such adjustments have the effect of causing the muscle to respond as if it were a different plant, notably a linear plant with a carefully chosen gain.

4. Outflow-Inflow Pattern Matches and Linearization of Muscle Responses: Automatic Gain Control via the Cerebellum

Some type of information about muscle plant characteristics is thus needed to calibrate muscle contractions that veridically respond to outflow signals. We suggest that a brain region exists wherein comparisons between outflow and inflow signals are used for this purpose. We have called this region the *outflow-inflow interface*, or OII.

How does the outflow system determine whether an outflow signal *should* cause a large or a small muscle contraction? How does the outflow system determine whether an outflow signal of a fixed size is large or small from a functional viewpoint? How big is "big"? What are the system's computational units? We suggest that an outflow signal to its agonist muscle is "big" if the outflow signal to the corresponding antagonist muscle is "small." The *relative* sizes of agonist and antagonist outflow signals, not any absolute quantity, determine the desired size scale. Expressed in another way, the *spatial pattern*, or *normalized motor synergy*, of agonist and antagonist outflow signals determines the functional size scale. Due to this fact, disturbing the inflow from one muscle can cause adaptive compensation in the learned gains of all other muscles which are used to compute that muscle's motor synergy.

If outflow signal sizes are computed in muscle coordinates, then the information which expresses the muscle plant's responses to these signals must also be computed in muscle coordinates. The simplest way to accomplish this is to use length-sensitive or tension-sensitive inflow signals from the muscles themselves.

This argument suggests that spatial patterns of outflow signals are matched against spatial patterns of inflow signals at the OII. Good matches imply that the muscles are responding linearly, and with a reasonable gain, to outflow signals. Bad matches must be able to adjust plant gain as well as plant nonlinearities. Mismatches within the OII generate error signals that can change the size of the total outflow signal to the muscle plant (Fig.1). The conditionable part of the total outflow signal adds or subtracts the correct amount of signal to make the muscle react *as if* it is a linear muscle plant with a reasonable gain. The muscle plant does not itself change. Rather, automatic gain control signals compensate for its imperfections through learning. We have developed a model for these automatic gain changes in which the cerebellum (or AG stage in Fig. 1) is the site of learning. If the muscle plant changes due to aging or accidents, mismatches are caused within the OII and trigger new learning. The gain control signals automatically alter the total outflow command until the muscle again reacts linearly. Thus the linearization of the muscle plant is a learning process that takes place on a slower time scale than registration of a corollary discharge.

Figure 1a provides a macrocircuit diagram of the MLN. In Fig. 1a, the source of movement signals is an outflow signal that branches into two parallel pathways. One pathway generates an unconditioned movement signal. It is assumed that tonic (T) cells are the source of the unconditioned outflow pathway to the motoneuron (MN) cells. The total saccade-related signal from the T cells to the MN cells is assumed to derive from a direct unconditioned pathway and an indirect conditioned pathway through the AG stage, or cerebellum. This property enables the output from the total tonic cell population to provide accurate corollary discharges to the HMI despite the existence of nonlinearities of muscle response in the absence of cerebellar compensation. The gain of the conditioned signal is determined by error signals from the OII to the AG stage. This sort of adaptive OII calibration does not guarantee accurate foveation. Separate adaptive circuits which are sensitive to visual-error signals are needed to accomplish this (Grossberg and Kuperstein, 1985). The MLN merely guarantees a linear muscle response to whatever signals happen to activate the T cells.

5. Saccadic Dysmetria and Adaptation to Strabismus Surgery

The existence of a conditioned cerebellar pathway suggests an important role for oculomotor nuclei that occur between tonic cells and eye muscles. A cellular interface is needed at a stage subsequent to the tonic cells but prior to the muscles at which the total outflow signal, both unconditioned and conditioned, to the muscles can be computed. Figure 1b thus suggests the existence of a pathway from the AG stage, or cerebellum, to the MN cells of the oculomotor nuclei.

Ron and Robinson (1973) have reported the existence of saccade-related *direct response cells* in the dentate nucleus of the cerebellum. Direct electrical activation of these cells can elicit saccades with latency of 5–9 msec. These reaction times are consistent with the existence of a direct pathway from the direct response cells to the MN cells of the oculomotor nuclei. The theory suggests that a subset of the direct response cells may be part of the conditioned movement pathway that linearizes muscle responses. If so, selective transection of this pathway should destroy the linearity of muscle responses.

Partial support for this hypothesis follows from the experiments of Vilis, Snow, and Hore (1983) and of Snow, Hore, and Vilis (1985). These authors have shown that lesions of the medial cerebellar nuclei or tenectomy of the medial and lateral recti can cause dysmetria in the affected eye muscles. Such lesions do not, however, distinguish between cerebellar pathways to the oculomotor nuclei and to other saccade-controlling pathways, such as the saccade generator.

The experiments of Steinbach and Smith (1981) have also suggested a role for inflow signals in the eye movement control system. These authors studied the arm-pointing behavior of patients who had been operated upon to correct strabismus. Grossberg and Kuperstein (1985) provide a detailed mechanistic analysis of their data. One point of special interest is noted herein: Cutting all inflow signals obviously generates the largest possible mismatches with outflow signals. Why, then, is the adaptation discussed by Steinbach and Smith (1981) destroyed by this manipulation? An analysis of the microscopic design of the OII suggests that only the inflow signals to the OII are excitatory; outflow signals from the T cells to the OII are inhibitory (Fig. 1a). Thus destroying inflow pathways eliminates the excitatory source of error signals from the OII to the AG stage. This conclusion shows that it is

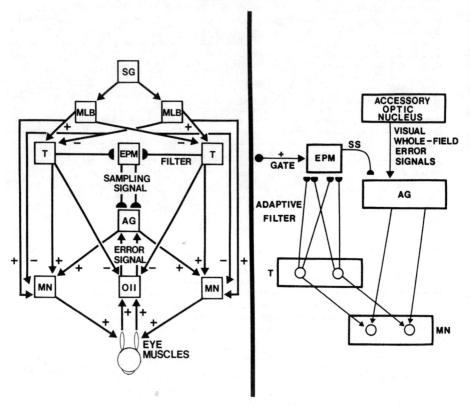

Fig. 1. (a) The muscle linearization network, or MLN: The OII generates error signals to the AG stage which alter the gain of the conditioned pathway to the MN. The sampling signals of these conditioned pathways are generated by an eye position map (EPM) which recodes outputs from the tonic (T) cells of the saccade generator (SG). The medium lead bursters (MLB) of the SG excite their T cells and MN cells while they inhibit antagonist T cells and MN cells. The T cells also excite the corresponding MN cells and generate outflow signals to the OII, where they are matched against inflow signals. (b) Circuit diagram of a tension equalization network (TEN): The network prevents post-saccadic drift from occurring during gaze. It adaptively balances agonist-antagonist tensions even though the agonist-antagonist muscle lengths are unequal. As in the muscle linearization network, an eye position map (EPM) is the source of sampling signals to the adaptive gain (AG) stage.

insufficient to merely use heuristic concepts like "mismatch" to understand a circuit like the OII. A mechanistic analysis is also needed of how the mismatch is computed.

6. Adaptive Sampling during Saccades

Our analysis of the OII also predicts that the cerebellar learning which linearizes eye muscle responses takes place *during* saccades at a fast sampling rate. If the learning circuit is fast enough to deliver sampling and error signals several times during a saccade, say within 15 or 20 msec., then conditioned gains could be learned for components of each saccadic movement in which not too much nonlinearity has accumulated. The saccade is then decomposed into movement "frames," each of whose nonlinear distortions could separately be dealt with as a function of eye position within that frame.

7. Tension Equalization Network: Stable Postures and Post-Saccadic Drift

The MLN is not the only adaptive circuit within our theory that compensates for changes within the oculomotor plant. Unlike the MLN, whose learning goes on during saccades, the Tension Equalization Network (TEN) learns to maintain the postures assumed by the eyes between saccades, and thereby helps to prevent post-saccadic drift (Optican and Robinson, 1980; Optican, Zee, and Chu, 1985). Thus the MLN helps to control the pulse gain of the saccade, whereas the TEN helps to control its step gain. Cutting the pathways subserving these gain control signals can cause saccadic overshoots and post-saccadic drifts (Optican and Robinson, 1980), even if the muscle plant is undamaged.

Figure 1b schematizes the TEN. As in the MLN, learning of the conditioned gain signals takes place in the AG stage, or cerebellum, and both unconditioned and conditioned movement signals converge upon the motoneurons (MN). Unlike the MLN, whose error signals are derived from outflow-inflow mismatches during active movement, the error signals of the TEN are derived from whole-field visual motions during posture. The theory suggests a single microcircuit for the cerebellum that is capable of learning the correct gains in response to the different combinations of sampling signals, error signals, and output signals of these circuits. We also suggest that the TEN is homologous in several respects to the neural circuit for VOR adaptation, with the T cells of the TEN replaced by vestibular signals in the VOR circuit.

REFERENCES

Grossberg, S. and Kuperstein, M. (1985). **Neural Dynamics of Adaptive Sensory-Motor Control: Ballistic Eye Movements.** North-Holland, Amsterdam.

Guthrie, B.L., Porter, J.D., and Sparks, D.L. (1983). Corollary discharge provides accurate eye position information to the oculomotor system. *Science*, **221**, 1193–1195.

Mays, L.E. and Sparks, D.L. (1980). Saccades are spatially, not retinocentrically, coded. *Science*, **208**, 1163–1165.

Mays, L.E. and Sparks, D.L. (1981). The localization of saccade targets using a combination of retinal and eye position information. In A.F. Fuchs and W. Becker (Eds.), **Progress in Oculomotor Research.** Elsevier North-Holland, Amsterdam, pp.39–47.

Optican, L.M. and Robinson, D.A. (1980). Cerebellar-dependent adaptive control of primate saccadic system. *J. Neurophysiol.*, **44**, 1058–1076.

Optican, L.M., Zee, D.S., and Chu, F.C. (1985). Adaptive response to ocular muscle weakness in human pursuit and saccadic eye movements. *J. Neurophysiol.*, **54**, 110–122.

Ron, S. and Robinson, D.A. (1973). Eye movements evoked by cerebellar stimulation in the alert monkey. *J. Neurophysiol.*, **36**, 1004–1021.

Schiller, P.H., True, S.D., and Conway, J.L. (1979). Paired stimulation of the frontal eye fields and the superior colliculus of the rhesus monkey. *Brain Res.*, **179**, 162–164.

Snow, R., Hore, J., and Vilis, T. (1985). Adaptation of saccadic and vestibulo-ocular systems after extraocular muscle tenectomy. *Invest. Ophthal. Visual Sci.*, **26**, 924–931.

Steinbach, M.J. and Smith, D.R. (1981). Spatial localization after strabismus surgery: Evidence for inflow. *Science*, **213**, 1407–1408.

Vilis, T., Snow, R., and Hore, J. (1983). Cerebellar saccadic dysmetria is not equal in the two eyes. *Exp. Brain Res.*, **51**, 343–350.

ADAPTATION TO VESTIBULAR LESIONS

Recovery from Unilateral Peripheral Vestibular Lesions

R. W. Baloh*, V. Honrubia**, R. D. Yee***,
L. Langhofer** and K. Minser**

*Department of Neurology, **Department of Surgery, Division of
Head and Neck, ***Department of Ophthalmology,
University of California, Los Angeles, CA 90024, USA

ABSTRACT

After unilateral peripheral vestibular lesions patients exhibit asymmetric
rotational induced nystagmus and shortening of the dominant VOR time
constant. With compensation symmetry returns but the change in time constant
persists. These findings are discussed within the framework of current
models of the VOR.

INTRODUCTION

Clinicians have long been aware of the remarkable ability of patients to
recover from peripheral vestibular lesions. Within a few weeks of an acute
lesion involving the eighth nerve or labyrinth patients often return to work
with minimal functional deficit. Those who slowly lose the function of one
labyrinth over months to years (e.g. due to an acoustic neuroma) may not have
any symptoms or signs of vestibular loss. Compensation for bilateral
vestibular lesions requires more time and is less complete but young patients
usually return to near normal activity. Over the past several years we have
published a series of reports documenting the dynamics of adaptive changes in
the vestibulo-ocular reflex (VOR) after peripheral vestibular lesions (Baloh,
Honrubia and Konrad 1977; Honrubia and others 1984; Baloh, and others 1984).
In this report we will summarize our findings in patients with unilateral
peripheral vestibular lesions and discuss the findings in light of recent
models of the VOR.

MATERIALS AND METHODS

The patients selected for presentation had complete absence of response to
caloric stimulation (including to iced water) on one side caused by end organ
or vestibular nerve damage. The patients were studied in acute stage when
possible and all were studied in a chronic compensated state (on clinical
grounds). The clinical diagnoses were: surgical eighth nerve section (5
patients), probable labyrinthine infarction (2), post-traumatic (1) and
vestibulopathy of unknown cause (possibly viral) (3). None of the patients
had neurological symptoms or signs. The mean age was 48 ± 10 years (range
31-59).

349

Ten volunteer normal subjects composed the control group. All had normal audiometric testing and a negative history for otological or neurological disorders. Their mean age was 38 ± 9 years (range 30 to 55 years).

Eye movements were recorded with direct current electro-oculography. Detailed descriptions of the recording equipment have been reported (Baloh and others, 1980). Calibration was performed before each subtest to minimize the effect of fluctuation in corneoretinal potential.

Horizontal vestibular nystagmus was induced by rotating the normal subjects and patients in darkness with eyes open. The subjects performed mental arithmetic continuously throughout the testing to maintain a constant state of alertness. The rotatory chair was mounted on a Goerz-Inland Model 800 rotatory table that allowed precise control of the angular acceleration through the use of velocity-error feedback.

All subjects were rotated sinusoidally at 0.0125 Hz, peak velocity 100 degrees per s; 0.05 Hz, peak velocity 60 degrees per s; 0.2 Hz, peak velocity 60 degrees per s, and 0.4 Hz, peak velocity 30 degrees per s, and with impulses of acceleration (approximately 140 degrees per s^2) producing a change in angular velocity of 100 degrees per s (clockwise and counterclockwise).

Complete details of the on-line digital computer analysis techniques are reported elsewhere (Baloh and others, 1980). From plots of slow phase eye velocity, asymmetry was calculated by comparing the peak slow phase velocity with ampullopetal and ampullofugal stimulation of the remaining intact labyrinth by the following formula: (ampullopetal - ampullofugal/ampullopetal + ampullofugal) X 100. Symmetry in the normal subjects was calculated by comparing clockwise and counterclockwise responses in a similar fashion. For sinusoidal frequencies a fast Fourier transform was executed giving the magnitude and phase of the fundamental and first two harmonics. Gain (peak eye velocity/peak head velocity) and phase measurements were then calculated from cycles with minimum harmonic distortion (first 2 harmonics less than 10% of fundamental) by comparing the amplitude and phase of the fundamental with those of the computer-generated head velocity stimulus.

To evaluate the impulse data, a logarithmic plot of nystagmus slow phase velocity versus time after the step change in head velocity was generated on the computer terminal. The gain (peak eye velocity/change in head velocity) was taken directly from these plots by averaging the eye velocity for 1 second at the peak of response. The time constant of the exponential decay in slow phase eye velocity was calculated from the slope of a least square regression line fitted to the eye velocity data.

RESULTS

Acute changes. Rotational testing in patients with acute unilateral peripheral vestibular loss invariably results in gain asymmetries; rotation toward the side of the lesion (ampullopetal stimulation of the remaining intact labyrinth) produces higher gain than rotation away from the lesion side. As demonstrated by the patient data shown in Figure 1 (left side) this asymmetry can be traced to static and dynamic factors. There is a DC shift of the data toward the side of the lesion (best seen in the plots of slow phase eye velocity versus chair velocity) that can in part be explained by the presence of spontaneous nystagmus (slow phase toward the side of the lesion). However, the average slow phase velocity of spontaneous nystagmus is invariably less than the DC bias measured with rotational testing. For example, in the patient data illustrated in Fig. 1 (left side) the average slow phase velocity of the patients spontaneous nystagmus at the time of

rotational testing (recorded with eyes open in darkness) was 4 deg/sec while
the D/C bias measured during rotational testing varied from 5 to 17 deg/sec
for different sinusoidal frequencies. In addition to the DC bias there is a
difference in the slope of eye velocity vs chair velocity in each direction
(best seen for the 0.2 Hz stimulus). With rotation toward the side of the
lesion (in this case to the left) the slope (or gain) is less than with
rotation toward the intact side. This difference in slope results from a
difference in excitation and inhibition of the spontaneous firing rate of the
remaining intact labyrinth (so-called Ewald's second law) (Baloh, Honrubia
and Konrad, 1977). With compensation (Fig. 1 right side) both the static and
dynamic asymmetries diminish and the rotational responses are approximately
symmetrical. In the few patients that have been studied with serial
rotational tests after eighth nerve section, VOR symmetry returns
within 3 months to 1 year after operation.

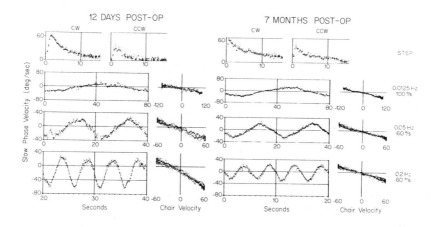

Fig. 1. Rotational responses from a patient 12 days
         after and 7 months after left VIIIth nerve
         section for removal of a small acoustic
         neuroma confined to the internal auditory
         canal. Prior to surgery bithermal caloric
         responses were normal.

Shortening of the dominant VOR time constant is a consistent finding after an
acute unilateral peripheral vestibular lesion. On sinusoidal rotational
testing this results in a decrease in gain and an increase in phase lead of
eye velocity relative to head velocity at low frequencies of rotation. This
change in time constant is present immediately after the lesion and persists
for years after the lesion. We have recorded shortening of the dominant VOR
time constant as early as 1 day after surgical ablation of the labyrinth.
Patients followed serially after eighth nerve section show a stable low
frequency phase shift for as long as 10 years after operation.

Chronic compensated state. Individual patient VOR gain, phase and time
constant measurements in the chronic compensated stage (at least 3 months

post lesion) are shown in Fig. 2. Mean values ± 1 standard deviation for the
normal subjects are given for comparison. At the lowest frequency tested
(0.0125 Hz) all patients gain and phase lead values were at least 1 standard
deviation from the normal mean whereas at and above 0.2 Hz most patient
values fell within 1 standard deviation of the normal mean. Compared to the
normal group the patients mean gain was significantly decreased (p < 0.05)
and mean phase lead significantly increased at 0.0125 and 0.05 Hz.
Furthermore, the patients with the lowest VOR gain at low frequencies tended
to have the shortest time constants whether measured directly from impulse
responses or calculated from phase lead values.

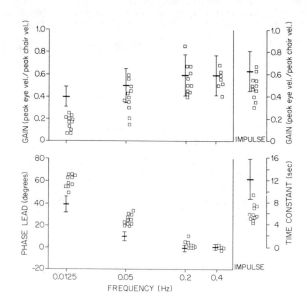

Fig. 2. Gain, phase and time constant measurements
         from sinusoidal and step rotational stimuli
         in patients with chronic compensated uni-
         lateral peripheral vestibular lesions.
         Normal mean values ± 1 standard deviation
         are given by horizontal bars with attached
         vertical bars.

DISCUSSION

Our patients with chronic compensated unilateral peripheral vestibular
lesions showed consistent gain deficits at low frequencies of sinusoidal
rotation (< 0.05 Hz) but had normal gain values at higher frequencies (> 0.2
Hz). Similar changes have been observed in animals who have undergone
unilateral labyrinthectomy or semicircular canal blockage although the degree
of gain recovery after the lesion appears to be species-dependent with the
greatest recovery occurring in primates (Wolf and Kos, 1977; Paige, 1983).
Rabbits and cats show only minimal gain recovery (Zuckerman, 1967; Baarsma
and Collewijn, 1975; Maioli, Precht and Ried, 1983). Shortening of the

dominant VOR time constant (increase in low frequency phase lead) is also a
consistent finding in animals and humans after unilateral peripheral
vestibular lesions. This change in the VOR time constant is present within
hours after the lesion and remains for years. Shortening of the dominant VOR
time constant is not specific for a unilateral peripheral lesion, however, as
it also occurs with bilateral peripheral lesions and with lesions of the
brain stem (Baloh and others, 1984; Blair and Gavin, 1981). It can occur in
normal subjects who have been habituated to continuous vestibular stimulation
(Baloh, Henn and Jager, 1982). In brief, shortening of the dominant VOR time
constant appears to be a nonspecific finding accompanying a decrease in VOR
sensitivity.

The functional implications of the low-frequency VOR gain and phase deficits
in patients with unilateral lesions appears to be minimal. Since all had
normal VOR gain and phase measurements at high frequencies, they could rely
on visual-ocular control (pursuit) to compensate for the low-frequency
deficit.

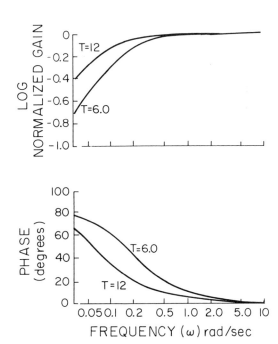

Fig. 3.   Normalized gain and phase lead values
          predicted by a first-order linear model of
          the vestibulo-ocular reflex (equation 1)
          assuming 2 different system time constants
          (T).

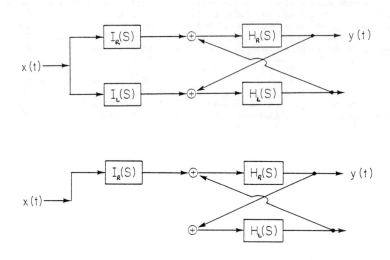

Fig. 4. Simplified cross-coupled model of the
vestibulo-ocular reflex for normal subjects
(upper) and patients with unilateral
peripheral lesions (lower). The input x(t)
is head movement, I and H represent the
semicircular canal and central vestibular
pathways, respectively and the output y(t)
is eye movement.

Models of the VOR and unilateral vestibular lesions. Although somewhat
oversimplified, a traditional first-order linear model of the VOR provides a
useful framework for interpreting the results of rotational testing in
patients with peripheral vestibular lesions. Using the Laplace frequency
domain transformation (s), the VOR gain to stimulation in the frequency range
used in this study (0.0125 to 0.4 Hz) can be approximated by the following
equation:

$$\dot{E}/\dot{H} = sK/(sT + 1) \qquad \text{(Equation 1)}$$

where $\dot{E}$ = eye velocity, $\dot{H}$ = head velocity, K = a sensitivity coefficient in
units of degrees per s per degree per s^2, and T = the time constant of the
system response.

The Bode plots in Fig. 3 illustrate the predicted gain and phase of the VOR
at different frequencies of sinusoidal rotation assuming two different values
of T in Equation 1. Comparing the model predictions with actual data in
normal subjects and patients in Fig. 2 leads to several interesting
observations. In the normal subjects an average time constant of about 12
seconds (measured from impulse responses) nicely predicts the mean gain and
phase lead values measured from sinusoidal responses. Patients with
unilateral peripheral vestibular lesions uniformly exhibit a shortening of
the dominant VOR time constant (about 6 seconds) as measured from the

response to impulse stimuli. As the model predicts, this is associated with an increase in phase lead and a decrease in gain at low frequencies of sinusoidal stimulation. It is not clear whether the decrease in system time constant is a direct result of the peripheral lesion or represents an adaptive change within the central VOR.

To investigate this question further the VOR model can be divided into a peripheral (I) and central component (H) as shown in Fig. 4 (upper half). Within the central nervous system feed back pathways (probably the vestibular commissural connections are most important) result in a prolongation of the VOR time constant beyond that of the peripheral cupular time constant (Buettner, Buttner and Henn, 1978; Honrubia and others, 1982; Galiana and Outerbridge, 1984). Assuming symmetric function the VOR system shown in Fig. 4 can be represented by the following equation:

$$VOR(s) = I(s)H(s)/[1-H(s)] \qquad \text{(Equation 2)}$$

In simple terms the VOR output represents the processing of the inner ear I(s) by the central vestibular pathways H(s) in a positive-feedback configuration (i.e. multiplying I(s) by H(s)/[1-H(s)]. Since we can measure VOR(s) (as in Fig. 2) and estimate I(s) from afferent nerve data in primates (Goldberg and Fernandez, 1971), H(s) can also be estimated.

A unilateral peripheral vestibular lesion is simulated by removing the inner ear processor on one side as shown in the lower half of Fig. 4. The VOR system function in this case is given by the equation:

$$VOR(s) = I_R(s)H_R(s)/[1-H_R(s)H_L(s)] \qquad \text{(Equation 3)}$$

To evaluate this model we caluculated VOR(s) assuming that I(s) and H(s) are the same as in normal subjects (i.e. one labyrinth is removed but the central processor is unchanged). With this assumption equation 3 predicts an approximate 50% drop in gain and minimal change in the system time constant (clearly unlike our patient data). Therefore, changes in the central processor (H) are required if the model is to simulate the patient data. Because of the coupling provided by commissural connections between the two sides, only small changes in (H) are necessary to account for the gain and phase changes seen in patients with chronic compensated unilateral lesions. The reader is referred to a more detailed bilateral model of the VOR central pathways proposed by Galiana and Outerbridge (1984) for further insight into the process involved in compensation after unilateral peripheral vestibular loss.

REFERENCES

Baarsma, E. A. and H. Collewijn (1975). Changes in compensatory eye movements after unilateral labyrinthectomy in rabbit. Arch. Otolaryngol., 211, 219-230.

Baloh, R. W., V. Honrubia and H. R. Konrad (1977). Ewald's second law re-evaluated. Acta Otolaryngol., 83, 475-479.

Baloh, R. W., L. Langhofer, V. Honrubia and R. D. Yee (1980). On-line analysis of eye movements using a digital computer. Aviat. Space Environ. Med., 51, 563-567.

Baloh, R. W., V. Henn and J. Jager (1982). Habituation of the human vestibulo-ocular reflex with low-frequency harmonic acceleration. Am. J. Otolaryngol., 3, 235-241.

Baloh, R. W., V. Honrubia, R. D. Yee and K. Hess (1984). Changes in the human vestibulo-ocular reflex after loss of peripheral sensitivity. Ann. Neurol., 16, 222-228.

Blair, S. M. and M. Gavin (1981). Brainstem commissures and control of time constant of vestibular nystagmus. Acta Otolaryngol., 91, 1-8.

Buettner, U. W., U. Buttner and V. Henn (1978). Transfer characteristics of neurons in vestibular nuclei of the alert monkey. J. Neurophysiol., 41, 1614-1628.

Galiana, H. L. and J. S. Outerbridge (1984). A bilateral model for central neural pathways in vestibulo-ocular reflex. J. Neurophysiol., 51, 210-241.

Goldberg, J. M. and C.sd Fernandez (1971). Physiology of peripheral neurons innervating semicircular canals of the squirrel monkey: I. Resting discharge and response to constant angular acceleration. J. Neurophysiol., 34, 635-660.

Honrubia, V., H. A. Jenkins, R. W. Baloh and C. G. Y. Lau (1982). Evaluation of rotatory vestibular tests in peripheral labyrinthine lesions. In V. Honrubia and M. A. B. Brazier (Eds.), Nystagmus and Vertigo. Clinical approaches to the patient with dizziness. Academic Press, New York. pp. 57-80.

Honrubia V., H. A. Jenkins, R. W. Baloh, R. D. Yee and C. G. Y. Lau (1984). Vestibulo-ocular reflexes in peripheral labyrinthine lesions. I. Unilateral dysfunction. Am. J. Otolaryngol., 5, 15-26.

Maioli, C, W. Precht and S. Ried (1983). Short-and-long-term modifications of vestibulo-ocular response dynamics following unilateral vestibular nerve lesions in the cat. Exp. Brain Res., 50, 259-274.

Paige, G. D. (1983). Vestibulo-ocular reflex and its interaction with visual following mechanisms in the squirrel monkey: II. Response characteristics and plasticity following unilateral inactivation of horizontal canal. J. Neurophysiol., 49, 152-168.

Wolf, J. W. and C. M. Kos (1977). Nystagmic responses of the rhesus monkey to rotational stimulation following unilateral labyrinthectomy: final report. Trans. Am. Acad. Ophthalmol. Otolaryngol., 84, 38-45.

Clinical Aspects of Otolith-Oculomotor Relationships

M. Gresty, H. Barratt, A. Bronstein and N. Page*

Medical Research Council Neuro-Otology Unit, Institute of
Neurology, National Hospital, Queen Square,
London, WC1N 3BG and
*33 Devonshire Place, London, W1

DEFINITIONS:

Horizontal eye movements: unfortunately taken to mean eye movements in the
transverse plane of the head which is confusing if the head is tilted away
from earth-upright. Here termed "lateral".
Vertical eye movements: unfortunately taken to mean eye movements in the
sagittal plane. Here termed "sagittal". Corollaries: downbeat and upbeat
nystagmus become "caudal and rostral beating nystagmus".
Bob: linear motion along the rostro-caudal axis of the human body.
Surge: linear backwards/forwards motion orthogonal to the direction of the bob.
Heave: linear side to side motion along the axis orthogonal to the axis of bob.
Yaw: angular motion about an axis oriented upright with respect to the body
Pitch: angular motion about a left to right axis.
Roll: angular motion about an axis oriented in the direction of surge.

PHYSIOLOGY OF OTOLITH OCULOMOTOR INTERACTIONS

1.   The dynamics of normal head movement and otolith-ocular reflexes.

Geometrical considerations suggest that eye movements compensatory for linear
head movement would be required only for near targets which implies that there
should be an interaction between vergence and otolith-ocular functions. The
theoretical performance requirements for an otolith ocular reflex are
determined by the dynamics of head movement. Thus for example
the peak acceleration of the head in "bob" of an average height/weight male
jogging with an uneven pace with head kept Earth upright is between 0.5 and
0.7 "g" at 2-3 Hz. This gives a peak to peak displacement of about 5 cms. If
this man were attempting to fixate on targets, perhaps foliage, he is trying
to fend off at arms length (say, 70 cm) then a compensatory eye movement of
about 4° would be required. Similarly, if our man is sparring and dodges
then the head has typical accelerations of 0.25 "g" peak at about 0.8 Hz.
This produces a peak to peak displacement of 20 cm which would require a
compensatory eye movement of 17° at arms length.

Fast linear head movements at high frequencies produce oscillopsia. For
bobbing at 2 Hz the oscillopsia is detectable at target distances up to about
5 m so that the threshold retinal slip producing oscillopsia at this frequency
is about 0.5°. Thus previous studies of eye movements induced by linear
sinusoidal motion which is isolated or combined with constant velocity rotation

have shown that otolith-ocular reflex responses to purely linear stimuli are
weak (Reviewed by Barnes, 1979). In contrast a recent finding in our
laboratory is that if a subject is rotated on the turntable with his head off
centre so that there is a significant linear stimulation of the otoliths, eye
movements are produced which compensate for both the linear and angular
components of the head movement. For example, with sinusoidal motion at a
constant angular peak acceleration, adding a linear component of 0.3g at
1.5 Hz produces a slow phase velocity in excess of that induced by angular
motion alone, of 30°/sec peak in the dark for unexpected stimuli. At 0.5 Hz
and 0.1 g the additional eye velocity is of the order of 15°/sec peak. Higher
eye velocities are produced by imaginary fixation on near targets and gains in
the light at frequencies greater than 1 Hz (limit of pursuit) are close to
unity with little oscillopsia. These findings indicate that powerful
compensatory eye movements can be elicited by otolith stimulation which interact
with vergence mechanisms and are "switched" in by combined angular and linear
stimuli. It is possible that these otolith ocular reflexes are mediated by
controlling the gain of the canalicular reflexes rather than by a direct
pathway.

The otoliths respond to a static attitude with respect to gravity in the same
way as if the head were accelerating at 1g in a direction opposite to the pull
of gravity. However, even in the absence of visual fixation, head tilt does
not induce eye movements in the form of spontaneous lateral or sagittal,
positional nystagmus in normal subjects. If such eye movement responses
did exist they would be provoked by almost every head movement and be quite
inappropriate, and this may be one reason for the absence or weakness of
otolith-ocular reflexes in response to purely linear acceleration.

2.   Otolith influences orienting the eyes to Earth-horizon.

Ocular counter-rolling is well established as a possible otolith ocular
reflex and is one aspect of a head and eye response to tilt away from Earth
vertical termed the "ocular tilt reaction" by Westheimer and Blair (1975), in
which the eyes skew and tort towards the direction of Earth-horizon alignment
together with head tilt in roll towards a more Earth-upright position. It is
possible, as in the case of other species, that there are similar reflexes in
the transverse and sagittal planes.

3.   Otolith influences on semicircular canal signals.

If the head is rotated slowly in yaw with the axis of rotation tilted away
from Earth-upright, the changing attitude of the otolith organs with respect
to the gravity vector provide a supplementary signal indicating continuing
rotation although the canal activity decays (Guedry, 1965). Conversely, after
prolonged rotation, the canals provide an inappropriate signal which induces a
sense of rotation and nystagmus. These effects can be curtailed by tilting
the head out of the orientation in which it was rotated (Schrader and
colleagues, 1985). This phenomenon is termed "dumping" post rotatory nystagmus.
It is interesting to note that aeronauts shake their heads about in a similar
fashion to stop dizziness provoked by unusual flight manoeuvres. In other
situations, otolith stimulation can shorten or lengthen the time constant of
canal responses. For examples, caloric responses may be prolonged if the
irrigation is performed under high g levels and the time constant of post
rotatory nystagmus is altered if rotation is performed with the head at different anges of tilt with respect to the g vector (reviewed by Benson, 1974).

Comment: from the above considerations it is clear that otolith stimulation
may generate or influence slow phase eye movements either directly in response
to tangential component of head movement or indirectly by influencing velocity
storage and adaptational mechanisms related to canalicular-ocular reflexes.
Disorders of these mechanisms may play a significant part in generating abnormal
eye movements found in patients with neuro-otological disease.

OTOLITH INFLUENCES ON THE OCULAR TILT REACTIONS

Ocular counter-rolling, torsional nystagmus, skew deviation and skewing
nystagmus and tilt of the head towards upright are all components of the
ocular tilt reaction which realigns the eyes with earth horizontal in response
to displacement of the head in roll from its normal Earth-upright attitude.

Patients with peripheral labyrinthine lesions do not show consistent patterns
of asymmetry of ocular counter-rolling (Kirienko and colleagues, 1984). Bidirectional counter-rolling is preserved with complete unilateral loss of
vestibular function, indicating that a single otolith organ is capable of
generating movements in both directions as well as preserving balance with
respect to the upright direction. These observations are in accordance with
the bidirectional orientation of the hair cells. In patients who show a marked
asymmetry of counter-rolling or who show a head tilt or skew deviation, it is
probable that the peripheral damage is restricted to one part of the otolith
organ leaving the remainder to generate an imbalance in tonus or asymmetry of
dynamic response. The time course of recovery from a partial peripheral
otolith lesion can be long. A patient with head tilt, ocular torsion and skew
deviation caused by an iatrogenic partial utricular lesion who was reported by
Halmagyi and co-workers (1978) took about two years before a reasonable
recovery.

With the exception of Kean's (1975) survey of skew deviation there is little
reported information on the effects of central lesions on the ocular tilt
reaction. In our own limited experience the counter-rolling component may be
affected in lesions involving the medulla or pons or mesencephalon. In general
the response to head movement in roll down to the side of the lesion may be
reduced or absent.

Spontaneous torsional nystagmus is associated with lesions in a variety of sites
throughout the brainstem and may or may not be affected by static head tilt
although the head movement most torsional nystagmus should be modified by
superimposed ocular counter-rolling. As yet we have no information as to the
localising value of torsional nystagmus which is or is not head movement
sensitive.

See-saw nystagmus: This nystagmus is typically reported in mesencephalic
lesions. In one of our patients with a craniopharyngioma the nystagmus
consisted of a slow phase torsion of the eyes to the left side combined with a
synchronous elevation of the right eye and depression of the left eye followed
by torsional and vertical fast phases which reset the eye position. The seesaw was enhanced by head movement in roll and static tilt in the direction of
the fast phase of the nystagmus and reduced by movement and tilt in the
opposite direction. The eye movement sequence resembles a grossly enhanced
ocular counter-rolling.

The characteristics of some torsional nystagmus, including see-saw nystagmus,
and, in particular, their response to head tilt suggest that they are abnormally
elicited ocular counter-rolling. In some patients a complete abnormal ocular
tilt reaction may develop. For example, one of our female patients with
definite multiple sclerosis developed a head tilt in roll down to the left
shoulder, a right/left skew deviation associated with a nystagmus of skew in
which the right eye beat caudally as the left eye beat rostrally and a
torsional nystagmus in which the fast phase beat to the right shoulder. This
picture is probably produced by a vestibular (otolith ?) hypertonus on the
right side relative to a hypotonus on the left. Alternating skews and
alternating hypertropia may also be related to otolith function but have not
been investigated with appropriate techniques (Kean, 1985).

Comment: Kean concluded that skew deviations may represent part of an abnormal ocular tilt reaction and in about 70% of cases the lesion lateralises to the side of the lower eye. Similarly Brain (1926) concluded that in the majority of cases of acquired head tilt the lesion was lateralised to the side of the direction of tilt. It is likely that the other components of the abnormal ocular tilt reaction, torsional and skewing nystagmus, have a similar lateralising value.

OTOLITH INFLUENCES ON SAGITTAL EYE MOVEMENTS

i)   The effects of head tilt and linear acceleration on nystagmus in the sagittal plane (vertical nystagmus with respect to the skull).
Primary position nystagmus in the sagittal plane: rostral beating (upbeat) nystagmus and caudal beating (downbeat) nystagmus.

Spontaneous nystagmus which is present in the primary position of gaze, as opposed to nystagmus which results from failure to maintain eccentric gaze, is frequently related to vestibular mechanisms. The characteristics and neuro-logical significance of primary position sagittal nystagmus have been the subjects of recent extensive reviews (see below). Both caudal and rostral beating nystagmus may be enhanced or suppressed by convergence and frequently are sensitive to head tilt and linear accelerations. Downbeat nystagmus tends to diminish in amplitude with tilt to a supine position whereas upbeat nystagmus tends to be enhanced in this position. In some instances, tilt, inverts the direction of nystagmus relative to the head. Both in the presence and absence of fixation, the canalicular sagittal vestibular ocular reflex is asymmetrical with considerable elevation of gain in the direction of the slow phase of the nystagmus and a reduction of gain in the opposite direction. The nystagmus appears to be more sensitive to modulation by canal signals than by linear acclerations. Pursuit and optokinetic reflexes are absent in the opposite direction to the slow phase of the nystagmus and also probably deranged when in the same direction as the slow phase. In some patients it is possible to place the head in an attitude with respect to the "g" vector in which spontaneous nystagmus is absent. When tested by angular displacements about this position the canalicular vetibular ocular reflex is normal. Similar data is not available for pursuit and optokinetic movements.

The neurological significance of rostral (up)-beating nystagmus is its localising value for lesions of the central tegmentum of the brainstem, probably at the ponto-medullary and ponto-mesencephalic borders (Fisher and colleagues, 1984). Caudal (down)-beating nystagmus is frequently associated with cerebellar ectopia and cerebellar degeneration (about 50% of cases), in about 40% of instances the cause remains unknown and the remaining instances are associated with a variety of conditions including intracranial tumour, as possible side effect of lithium carbonate therapy and in the cherry red spot myoclonus syndrome. The site of lesions provoking caudal beating nystagmus is likely to involve the vestibular cerebellum (Halmagyi and colleagues, 1983).

ii)   The mechanism of spontaneous, primary position, sagittal nystagmus.
The features of the nystagmus which require explanation are the extreme asymmetry of vestibular ocular reflexes which is switched in at certain angles of tilt and the contrasting lack of sensitivity to purely linear acceleration. These observations may be explained on the basis of our finding that linear acceler-ation of the skull induces high velocity eye movements when combined with angular motion as described earlier. The abnormality probably arises in otolithic mechanisms and is switched in when the subject is tilted to certain positions in which the otolith organs have abnormal sensitivity.

iii)   Effects of otolith stimulation on saccadic eye movements in the sagittal plane.
The effects of abnormal otolith influences on saccadic eye movements in the

sagit   ie have not been investigated. However, drawing parallels with
their   ices on lateral eye movements there may be otolithic related
effec   e metrics and didrectional bias of saccades.

ITH INFLUENCES ON LATERAL EYE MOVEMENTS

Abnori   novements may result from lesions or of the peripheral vestibular
end o   rve, the central nervous system and the extra ocular muscles or be
congei   Je have looked for the effects of otolith stimulation, in
partic   :ad tilt with respect to the "g" vector, on spontaneous nystagmus
and sa   ibnormalities in patients with all these types of disorder.
Otolit   cts can be found in about 50% of patients. They occur in both
acquir   ongenital disorders with both peripheral and central lesions. As
yet we   t identified the factors which determine whether the abnormal eye
moveme   influenced by otolith stimulation. Lateral eye movements are
more l   be related to linear acceleration and orientation of the "g"
vector   :ransverse plane along an axis passing through the ears. Accordingly,   lowing observations concentrate on the results of this mode of
stimula   lowever, the eye movements observed in the normal Earth-upright
positio   :hange characteristics when the head is tilted into other
attitud   as pronation and supination in which the "g" vector is not
acting   sely.

1.   fects of head tilt on the nystagmus of peripheral vestibular
            s.

We have   l the effects of tilt of the head from normal Earth-upright on
the spon   dark nystagmus in a patient with a stable right sided loss of
vestibul   .ion presumed to arise from infection and in a patient with
Meniere'   e with predominately right sided involvement. In both patients
near tot   of right sided lateral canal function was demonstrated with
caloric   n. The findings in both patients were similar. In the upright
position   upine and with head horizontal with right ear down there was
dark nyst   i primary gaze and on left gaze. With the head tilted away
from Eart   it, slow phase velocities were higher than in the upright
attitude.   prone and with head horizontal, left ear down, both patients
had right   ; nystagmus in all positions of gaze.

The findi   n to our two patients is that with the head tilted to a
horizonta   ion, so that the "g" vector is oriented along an axis passing
through tl nystagmus whose slow phase becomes directed Earth-downwards
in this al , increases in slow phase velocity. Slow phase in the opposite
direction decreases in velocity and can reverse. For the reason that the
direction of nystagmus is indicated by the fast phase this effect could be
termed geo-fugal enhancement.

2.   The effects of head tilt on central primary position and gaze evoked
      nystagmus (acquired and congenital).

The effects of tilt of the head with respect to the "g" vector are similar for
spontaneous nystagmus in primary gaze or evoked by lateral gaze. The most
common fining is of geofugal enhancement of nystagmus as illustrated in
Figure 1 by recordings taken from a male patient with a left sided cerebellar
tumour. With the head in the Earth-upright position there was gaze evoked
nystagmus to the right and left. With the rostro-caudal axis of the head
tilted to an Earth-horizontal position, left ear down, there was a lateral
nystagmus beating to the right ear in both primary and on right lateral gaze.
With the left ear down there was a nystagmus beating to the left ear in all
positions of gaze. Nystagmus in the supine position was the same as in the
upright position.

Please do not remove. SECONDARY STACKS. This item is tagged for

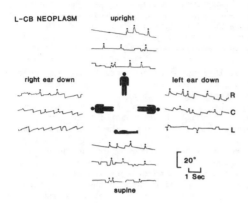

Figure 1.

Nystagmus recorded on right (R), centre (C) and left (L) gaze in various positions of tilt with respect to the gravity vector taken from a patient with a left sided tumour of the cerebellum. The dots indicate blink artifacts.

We have observed enhancement of geofugal nystagmus in some but not all subjects with classic, idiopathic congenital nystagmus.

If one considers that the pull of gravity is equivalent to an acceleration in the opposite direction, then the bias on the slow phase of the nystagmus described in the previous paragraph is in a direction which would be compensatory for the acceleration (i.e., right ear down produces the same stimulation to the otolith as the head accelerating to the left in the absence of gravity. This would require a compensatory eye movement to the right). More rarely one observes the inverse response in which nystagmus slow phase velocity is enhanced in the same direction as the equivalent acceleration: geo-petal enhancement.

The preceeding observations involve two different sorts of effects. One is of a bias acting on slow phase velocity in all positions of gaze. This looks to be the case with the nystagmus recorded with right ear down in Figure 1. The second effect is of a shifting of the null point of the nystagmus. Comparison of the nystagmus in the upright position and with left ear down shows that the null point of the nystagmus appears to have shifted from a centre right position (upright) to a centre left position (left ear down).

3.   The effects of head tilt on acquired periodic alternating
        nystagmus (PAN).

We have had opportunity to study PAN of different varieties. In one patient with acquired idiopathic PAN, the nystagmus was enhanced by accommodative and fusional vergence whereas the nystagmus in the other patient who had Friedreich's ataxia was unaffected. The third patient had congenital PAN.

The vergence-unrelated PAN had a period of 16 seconds. Tilt of the head with respect to the "g" vector modified by exerting a tonic slow phase bias which was always in an Earth-downwards direction. Thus, in the upright, prone and supine positions the PAN had similar periods; with the right ear down and rostro-caudal axis of the head horizontal, the nystagmus became left beating with a waxing and waning modulation of slow phase velocity at the cycle time of the PAN, with left ear down the nystagmus became right beating with similar characteristics.

The characteristics of the PAN which enhanced on vergence were investigated with the eyes fixated on a target at 30 cm. The period was 160 seconds with

the head in the Earth-upright position and with left or right ears down, the
nystagmus became unidirectional, beating to the right and left respectively as
in the case reported above. The most dramatic results were observed in the
prone and supine positions in which the period of the nystagmus reduced to
3 - 7 seconds (Figure 2).

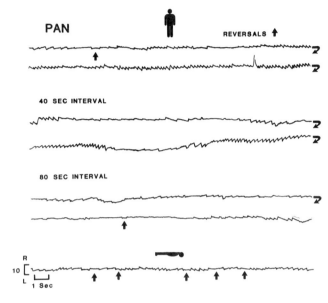

Figure 2.

See text. The intervals indicate that the nystagmus has continued
for the durations shown. The arrows indicate reversal of nystagmus.

The period of the congenital PAN was 120 seconds in the upright position
reducing to 60 seconds when the head was tilted to a supine position.

The hypothesis has been forwarded that PAN arises from an imbalance of the
oculomotor feedback loops responsible for velocity storage and adaptation to
prolonged stimuli. The evidence from normal physiology that otolith stimulation can affect the time constants of both of these suggests that this is how
head tilt can so profoundly affect the period of some types of PAN.

4.   Otolithic influences on saccadic eye movements.

There would appear to have been no reported investigations, in normal subjects
or in patients, of the influence of otolithic stimulation on saccadic eye movements. We have encountered one patient with a predominately left sided medullo-
blastoma who produced short inter-saccadic interval, hypometric saccades to the
left in all positions with the exception of lying horizontally with right ear
down in which his saccades were normal (Figure 3). In addition to this case,
David Zee has anecdotally related to us that one of his patients exhibited
square wave jerks only when his head was tilted at certain angles with respect
to the "g" vector. In a patient such as ours it would seem that the metrics of
space or of the head's motion relative to external space are distorted by an

abnormal otolith signal which is switched in when the otolith has a certain
attitude with respect to gravity.

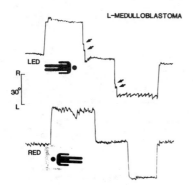

Figure 3.

30° saccades made to right and
left gaze showing hypometria to
the left when the patient is
positioned with the left ear down
and normometric saccades when the
patient is right ear down. The
arrows indicate the corrective
saccades.

5.   Effects of orientations of the "g" vector orthogonal to the
          transverse plane (pronation and supination).

Nystagmus velocity and, in our limited experience, saccade metrics can be
affected by positioning with respect to "g" in directions independent of the
direction of the type of eye movement affected. This observation would suggest
that these effects are related to adaptation and velocity storage mechanisms
affected by orientation in the gravitational field rather than to the direct
influence of otolith-ocular reflexes.

OVERVIEW

Examination of patients with neuro-oto-ophthalmological disease frequently
reveals that they have abnormal eye movements, nystagmus in particular, whose
amplitudes are affected by tilt with respect to "g". With suitable equipment
one can show that the movements are also affected by linear accelerations.
Gross abnormalities in the form of highly asymmetrical vestibular ocular
reflexes are revealed by combinations of linear and angular head movements.
Such effects, related to otolith stimulation, are not a general property of all
oculomotor abnormalities for they do not occur in all patients with pathological nystagmus and other ocular instabilities. They are probably specific to
lesions affecting oculomotor mechanisms related to vestibular function.

REFERENCES

Barnes, G.R. (1979) Vestibular system: Review Article. Clinical Physics and
        Physiological Measurement. 1 : 3 - 40
Benson, A.J. (1974) Modification of the response to angular accelerations by
        linear accelerations. In Vestibular system Part 2. Psychophysics,
        Applied Aspects and General Interpretations. Ed. H.H. Kornhuber
        Chapter IV
Brain, W.R. (1926) On the rotated or 'cerebellar' posture of the head.
        Brain 49 : 61 - 75
Fisher, A., Gresty, M., Chambers, B. and Rudge, P. (1983) Primary position
        upbeating nystagmus. A variety of central positional nystagmus.
        Brain 106 : 949 - 964
Guedry, F.E. Jr. (1965) Orientation of the rotation-axis relative to gravity:
        its influence on nystagmus and the sensation of rotation. Acta
        Otolaryng. (Stockh.) 60 : 80 - 83

Halmagyi, G.M., Rudge, P., Gresty, M.A. and Sanders, D. (1983) Down-
     beating nystagmus. A review of 62 cases. Archives of Neurology
     40 : 777 - 784
Keane, J.R. (1975) Ocular skew deviation. Archives of Neurology 32 :
     185 - 190
Kean, J.R., (1985) Alternating skew deviation: 47 patients.
     Neurology 35 : 725 - 728
Kirienko, N.M., Money, K.E., Landolt, J.P., Graybiel, A. and Johnson, W.H.
     (1984) Clinical testing of the otoliths: a critical assessment
     of ocular counter-rolling. The Journal of Otolaryngology 13 :
     281 - 288
Nylen, C.O. (1950) Positional nystagmus; a review and future prospects.
     Journal of Laryngology and Otology 64 : 295 - 318
Schrader, V., Koenig, E. and Dichgans, J. (1985) The effect of lateral
     head tilt on horizontal prostrotatory nystagmus I and II and the
     Purkinje effect. Acta Otolaryngol. (Stockh.) 100 : 98 - 105
Westheimer, G., Blair, S.M. (1975) Synkinese der Augen und Kopfbewegun-
     gen bei Hirnstammreizungen am wachen Macacus-Affen.
     Experimental Brain Research 24 : 89 - 95

Visual Acuity and Gaze Precision

C. J. Henderson*, G. M. Halmagyi* and I. S. Curthoys**

*Department of Neurology, Royal Prince Alfred Hospital
Camperdown, New South Wales 2050, Australia
**Department of Psychology, University of Sydney,
New South Wales 2006, Australia

INTRODUCTION

It is generally maintained that the principal function of the vestibulo-ocular reflex (VOR) is to preserve clear vision during head movements by stabilising gaze and minimising retinal slip. Until recently it was thought that the normal VOR was fully compensatory and stabilised gaze perfectly. Steinman and others (1980, 1982, 1985) have however shown that this is not so, and that even in normal subjects relatively slow head movements at 1.3 Hz, 30°/s peak velocity, can produce gaze shifts up to 3°/s.

Labyrinthine defective patients complain of blurred, moving vision (oscillopsia) during head movement. We have been investigating this symptom, and in the present study we have sought to answer two questions: 1) is visual acuity during head movements better in normals than in labyrinthine defective and ophthalmoplegic patients and if so to what extent? 2) can the differences in visual acuity among individuals be explained by differences in gaze velocity?

We have sought to answer these questions by measuring, during active horizontal head rotations, gaze velocity using scleral search coils and relating this to visual acuity using high contrast square wave gratings flashed for 25 ms at selected head velocities, measured separately.

METHODS

Horizontal displacement of the head and in some subjects of the right eye was recorded using magnetic search coils (Collewijn, van der Mark & Jansen, 1975; Collewijn, Martins & Steinman, 1981). In this method eye displacement is measured with respect to an earth fixed magnetic field and therefore represents the line of sight in space, that is "gaze". Displacement of the eye with respect to the head was derived by electronically subtracting head displacement from gaze displacement. Head, eye and gaze velocities were derived by electronically differentiating the displacement signals (H, E, G). "Gaze velocity" therefore is a direct measure of retinal slip velocity. Each subject, comfortably seated with his head at the centre of an 8 m³ magnetic field was asked to watch a fixation dot on a screen 1.6 m from his eyes while making active horizontal head movements sufficiently fast to trigger a visual display on the screen. The cue for the subject to make a head movement was that the fixation light would go out. The visual display consisted of a 6° x 7° low average luminance (10 cd/m²) high contrast (0.95) vertical square wave gratings from 21 to 1.5 cycles/degree on photographic slides (one spatial frequency per slide) illuminated by a 64 LED array through a standard slide projector. When head velocity, which was available to a computer-controlled window–comparator, reached one of five levels selected from 60°/s to 220°/s, velocities within the natural range of head movements (Barnes, 1979), the LED array was triggered and illuminated one grating slide for 25 ms. If the grating bars were distinctly visible during the head movement, the subject would indicate this by pushing a "yes" button, and if they were not, by pushing a "no" button. After each response the computer selected the spatial frequency of the next stimulus by controlling the projector magazine. An adaptive psychophysical procedure (single staircase) was used, so that if the subject responded that he could see the bars the next target had a higher spatial frequency. Stimuli were presented until 4 response reversals were obtained and the average of those 4 reversals was the visual acuity for that head velocity. The computer then reset the head velocity trigger level for the next head velocity series. Head velocities were tested in random order. To improve the precision of measurement this whole sequence was usually repeated 3 times and the final acuity measurement at each head velocity was the average of the three acuities. Each sequence took about 7 minutes so the entire test occupied about 20 minutes. Testing was conducted using low ambient illumination (<0.2 cd/m^2) so other objects were clearly visible in the room. A low fixation-target luminance was used. Both of these experimental conditions were chosen to prevent the target producing an after-image.

We tested the grating acuity of a number of normal subjects and patients and for some of these individuals, measured gaze velocity in another session. In a few individuals we verified the adequacy of this testing procedure by simultaneously measuring acuity and gaze velocity.

SUBJECTS AND PATIENTS

Twenty-nine normal subjects, 6 labyrinthine defective patients and 2 patients with external ophthalmoplegia were studied. With the head still, each had vision that was at least 21 cycles/degree or better on the test used here. None of the normal subjects had a history or evidence of significant eye, ear or brain disease and none complained of oscillopsia or blurred vision in daily life or when their heads were vigorously shaken in the laboratory. At the time of the test none of the labyrinthine defective or ophthalmoplegic patients admitted to oscillopsia or blurred vision during normal daily activities but did so during head shaking in the laboratory. When asked what they saw when their heads were shaken they would look surprised and remark: "It's bouncing up and down of course, because my head's shaking – isn't that normal". The labyrinthine defective patients all had absent or nearly absent caloric and rotational nystagmus. One patient had bilateral acoustic neuromas totally removed and has been reported in detail (Halmagyi and Curthoys, 1985). One ophthalmoplegic patient had an incomplete chronic progressive external ophthalmoplegia affecting both eyes and another had a nearly complete unilateral external ophthalmoplegia due to an intracavernous meningioma.

RESULTS

Grating acuity decreased in all normal subjects as head velocity increased from 60° to 220°/s (Fig. 1); however there was a large range of acuities between normal subjects at each velocity tested. At 60°/s head velocity there was a twofold variation in grating acuity from 10 to 20 cycles/degree and at 220°/s a threefold variation from 5 to 15 cycles/degree. The decrease in acuity in normal subjects from 60° to 220°/s head velocity was 2 to 10 cycles/degree with a mean of 4 cycles/degree.

At 60°/s head velocity best visual acuity in labyrinthine defective and ophthalmoplegic patients was 10 cycles/degree which is about the same as the worst visual acuity in normals at that head velocity (Fig. 1). With increasing

head velocity, visual acuity in labyrinthine defective and ophthalmoplegic
patients declined at about the same slope as in normals to be as low as 2
cycles/degree at 220°/s head velocity. At most head velocities there is a
fairly clear separation between normals and labyrinthine defective patients.

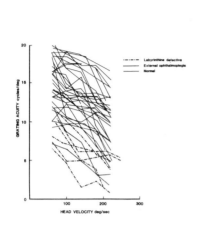

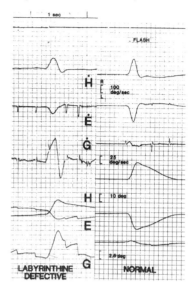

Fig. 1. Acuity for high contrast
vertical square wave gratings as a
function of peak head velocity during
head rotations in 29 normals, 6
labyrinthine defectives and 2
external ophthalmoplegics. Grating
acuity decreases as head velocity
increases from 60°/s to 220°/s. Some
normals' grating acuity approaches
that of labyrinthine defectives.

Fig. 2. Horizontal head, eye and
gaze displacement (H, E, G) and
velocity (H, E, G) in a labyrinthine
defective patient (left) and in a
normal subject (right) during an
active rightward head rotation
recorded with magnetic search coils.
Gaze velocity reaches 70°/s in the
labyrinthine defective patient. (G
and G = x4 gain)

In those individuals whose gaze velocity was measured with eye coils the
increase in gaze velocity was closely correlated with head velocity. Figure 2
(right) shows gaze velocity in a normal subject making an active rightward head
rotation with a peak velocity of about 200°/s. Peak gaze velocity during head
movement reaches 10°/s. The figure also shows the visual display being
triggered for 25 ms ("flash") at a level of 60°/s head velocity. Figure 2
(left) shows an active rightward head rotation at a peak velocity of 180°/s
during which gaze velocity reaches 75°/s in a labyrinthine defective patient.
In 3 normal subjects and 2 labyrinthine defective patients we measured peak gaze
velocity as a function of peak head velocity. To obtain these measurements,
gaze velocity traces were carefully checked to exclude those movements where
there was a saccade, quick phase or blink about the time of peak head velocity.
Some normal subjects routinely had smooth gaze shifts free of these factors even
at very high head velocities whereas other normals produce a saccade, or more
usually a quick phase in the direction of head movement on almost every trial,
particularly at high velocities. Consequently to obtain the data shown in
Figure 3, many high velocity head movement records had to be examined to obtain
those with only smooth gaze shifts. Labyrinthine defective patients usually had
smooth gaze shifts uninterrupted by quick phases. In normal subjects at a head
velocity of 60°/s gaze velocity varied between 2°/s and 5°/s. With increasing

head velocity, gaze velocity remained constant in one subject but in others it
gradually rose to 20°/s at 180°/s head velocity and 40°/s at 250°/s head
velocity. Gaze velocity in labyrinthine defective patients increased steeply
from 20°/s at 50°/s head velocity to 80°/s at 180°/s head velocity (Fig. 3).
These direct measurements of gaze can be used to interpret the grating acuity
measurements. Grating acuity is plotted as a function of gaze velocity for one
normal subject in Figure 4. At low gaze velocities (5°/s) acuity was about 20
cycles/degree; when gaze velocity had increased to 20°/s acuity had decreased
steeply to 6 cycles/degree. Further increases in gaze velocity produced only
slight decreases in visual acuity so that doubling gaze velocity to 40°/s
dropped visual acuity by only one more cycle/degree to 5 cycles/degree.

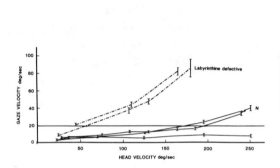
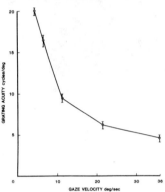

Fig. 3. Gaze velocity as a function of
head velocity in 2 labyrinthine
defective patients and 3 normals (N)
during active horizontal head rotation.
A gaze velocity of 20°/s is produced by
180°/s head velocity in normals but by
only 50°/s head velocity in labyrinthine
defectives. Vertical bars indicate ±2
SD.

Fig. 4. Acuity for high contrast
vertical square wave gratings as
a function of gaze velocity
during active horizontal head
rotations in a normal subject.
Most of the decrease in visual
acuity occurs at gaze velocities
between 5°/s and 20°/s.

DISCUSSION

These results show that visual acuity as measured by high contrast square wave
gratings falls in some normal subjects by up to 75% during natural velocity head
movements. This decrease in visual acuity can be due to factors such as blinks,
quick phases and saccades, but one major factor in some normal subjects is
inadequate control of gaze velocity which may reach up to 20°/s at a head
velocity as low as 180°/s. Twenty degrees/second appears to be one of two
critical gaze velocities, as visual acuity in normals hardly decreases any more
with increases in gaze velocity above this level. The other critical gaze
velocity is about 5°/s, below which we, like Steinman and others (Steinman &
Collewijn, 1970; Steinman, Cushman & Martins, 1982; Steinman and others, 1985),
found only a small decrease in visual acuity. Therefore most of the visual
degradation due to retinal smear appears at retinal slip velocities from 5°/s to
20°/s.

The relative disadvantage of labyrinthinine defective and ophthalmoplegic
patients during head movements is shown by the head velocity required to cause a
retinal slip or gaze velocity of 20°/s. Figure 3 shows that in a normal subject
a head velocity of at least 180°/s is needed to induce a gaze or retinal slip
velocity of 20°/s, whereas in a labyrinthine defective patient a mere 50°/s head

velocity will suffice. This indicates that during head movements a labyrinthine defective subject will experience the same visual degradation as a normal subject but at head velocities that are only one third as high. The VOR is not perfect but it does dampen gaze velocity enough to allow normal subjects to move their heads faster than labyrinthine defectives and still see well. There are unexpected variations between normal individuals in their visual acuity during natural head movements. Some seem as poor as labyrinthine defectives or ophthalmoplegics on our test yet are completely free of symptoms in natural situations. The reason for this is uncertain but it may be that during natural head movements they restrict their head velocities, blink, make saccades or quick phases, or take advantage of forward or backward visual masking (Campbell & Wurtz, 1978) and sample their visual worlds during times of low retinal image smear.

CONCLUSIONS

During active horizontal head rotations we have measured gaze velocity and visual acuity using high contrast square wave gratings triggered on for 25 ms by selected head velocities from 60° to 220°/s. We found:

1) that in some normal subjects visual acuity during head movements is not much better than in labyrinthine defective o in ophthalmoplegic patients;

2) that the below 5°/s gaze velocity visual acuity is hardly impaired;

3) that from 5 to 20°/s gaze velocity visual acuity decreased steeply;   and

4) that above 20°/s gaze velocity visual acuity does not deteriorate much more.

From this we conclude that the VOR in normal subjects attenuates gaze shifts during head movements but generally allows normals to retain good vision and still move their heads 3 or 4 times as fast as without VOR.

ACKNOWLEDGEMENTS

Dr Henderson was supported by a National Health and Medical Research Council Postgraduate Scholarship. Dr Halmagyi and Dr Curthoys were supported by a National Health and Medical Research Council Project Grant. We thank Dr Christopher Game and Mr Michael Todd for their help with the theoretical, computing and electronic aspects of this project.

REFERENCES

Barnes, G.R. (1979). The role of the vestibular system in head-eye co-ordination. J. Physiol. Lond. 287, 127–147
Campbell, F.W. and R.H. Wurtz (1978). Saccadic omission: why we do not see a grey-out during a saccadic eye movement. Vision Res., 18, 1297–1303
Collewijn, H., F. van der Mark, and T.C. Jansen (1975). Precise recording of human eye movements. Vision Res. 15, 447–450
Collewijn, H., A.M. Martins, and R.M. Steinman (1981). Natural retinal image motion: origin and change. Ann. N.Y. Acad. Sci., 374, 312–329
Halmagyi, G.M. and I.S. Curthoys (1985). Compensatory eye movements in the absence of vestibular function. Proc. Barany Society (in press)
Steinman, R.M. and H. Collewijn (1970). Binocular retinal image motion during active head rotation. Vision Res., 20, 415–429
Steinman, R.M., W.B. Cushman, and A.J. Martins (1982). The precision of gaze. A review. Human Neurobiol., 1, 97–109
Steinman, R.M., J.Z. Levinson, H. Collewijn, and J. van der Steen (1985). Vision in the presence of known retinal image motion. J. Opt. Soc. Am. 2, 226–223

Neuronal Mechanisms Underlying Compensation of Otolith Function after Vestibular Lesion

O. Pompeiano

Istituto di Fisiologia Umana, Cattedra I, Università di Pisa,
56100 Pisa, Italy

INTRODUCTION

Unilateral vestibular deafferentation causes not only oculomotor deficits but also a postural asymmetry, characterized by head and body tilt towards the side of the lesion, flexion of the ipsilateral limbs and extension of the contralateral ones. These changes in posture observed under static conditions are also associated with changes in phasic postural adjustments during movement,and it is the combination of disturbances occurring during both static and dynamic conditions that impairs locomotion in the acute stage. However, powerful adaptive mechanisms quickly come into play, so that the control of equilibrium at rest and during motion is progressively reestablished (cf. Flohr and Precht, 1981). The vestibular nuclei represent one of the main structures involved not only in the development of the postural and motor deficits described above, but also in the complete recovery after unilateral vestibular deafferentation (Igarashi and others, 1978). Since most of the vestibular units so far tested (cf. Xerri and others, 1983) belonged to the medial (MVN) and superior vestibular nuclei (SVN), which are particularly driven by the canal input and project to motoneurons innervating the extraocular and axial musculature (cf. Wilson and Melvill Jones,1979), experiments were performed to study the effects of unilateral acute (aVN) or chronic vestibular neurectomy (cVN) on the static and dynamic behavior of units located in the lateral vestibular nuclei of Deiters, LVN (Lacour and others,1985; Pompeiano and others,1984; Xerri and others,1983), that are particularly driven by the macular input (cf. Boyle and Pompeiano,1980) and project to the spinal cord (Pompeiano and Brodal, 1957). These lateral vestibulospinal (VS) neurons actually excite ipsilateral neck and limb extensors, thus controlling posture (Pompeiano, 1975) and locomotion (Orlovsky,1972). The results of these experiments will allow to better understand the neuronal basis for the lesion-induced postural deficits and the compensatory changes leading to the restoration of normal behavior.

EXPERIMENTAL PROCEDURES

The experiments were performed in cats decerebrated either before (aVN) or 2-4 months after unilateral neurectomy (cVN), i.e. when compensation of the postural and locomotor deficits had occurred. The results of these experiments were then compared with those obtained in control experiments performed in decerebrate cats with both vestibular nerves intact.

After decerebration, the animal's head was placed in a stereotaxic frame and pitched 20° nose down, while stimulating electrodes were inserted in the spinal cord

between T12 and L1 for antidromic activation of VS neurons. Activity of individual
LVN neurons was recorded in the animal at rest as well as during sinusoidal tilt
around the longitudinal axis of the animal leading to stimulation of labyrinth
receptors. For each unit, in addition to the resting discharge rate (imp./s), we
determined the base frequency (mean discharge rate in imp./s evaluated during tilt),
the gain (absolute change of firing rate per degree of tilt, imp./s/deg), the sensitivity (percentage change of the mean discharge rate per degree, %/deg) and the
phase angle of the fundamental component of response (evaluated as the phase difference in arc degrees between the peak of the side-down displacement of the animal,
indicated by $0°$, and the peak of the unit response). At the end of the experiments
the recorded units were identified histologically as being located either in the
rostroventral (rvLVN) or in the dorsocaudal part (dcLVN) of Deiters'nucleus, which
project mainly, but not exclusively, to the cervical and the lumbosacral segments
of the spinal cord, respectively (Pompeiano and Brodal, 1957).

RESULTS

Resting Discharge and Response Characteristics of LVN Neurons to Standard Parameters of Tilt after Unilateral Acute Vestibular Deafferentation
The activity of 350 LVN neurons was recorded in control experiments (Boyle and
Pompeiano, 1980), as well as after ipsilateral (Pompeiano and others,1984; Xerri
and others,1983) or contralateral aVN (Lacour and others,1985).
The base frequency of the vestibular units responsive to standard parameters of
tilt ($0.026Hz,+10°$), which closely corresponded to the mean discharge rate evaluated at rest, significantly decreased on average from 43.6+54.4,SD imp./s in control
experiments to 23.4+20.7,SD imp./s after ipsilateral aVN, a reduction which affected both the rvLVN and dcLVN neurons. On the other hand on the intact side the base
frequency corresponded to 34.6+19.5,SD imp./s, due to a decrease in firing rate of
the rvLVN neurons. In control experiments,the faster the conduction velocity of
VS axon, the lower was the unit discharge rate at rest (Manzoni and others, unpublished observations; cf. also Boyle and Pompeiano,1981). However, this negative
correlation between unit resting discharge and axonal conduction velocity was lost
bilaterally after aVN, due to a selective decrease in firing rate of the slow
units on both the lesioned and the intact side, not associated with changes of fast
units.
The units responding to standard parameters of tilt were almost equally distributed
in the rvLVN (72.2%) and the dcLVN (69.9%) on the deafferented side. However, the
proportion of units responding to tilt was significantly higher in the former than
in the latter part of Deiters'nucleus, both in control experiments (91.2% rvLVN
and 67.6% dcLVN), as well as on the intact side (100% rvLVN and 75.4% dcLVN).
The response gain and sensitivity of the LVN neurons to standard parameters of
tilt corresponded on average to 0.61+0.52,SD imp./s/deg and 3.50+2.87,SD %/deg,
respectively, after ipsilateral aVN. These values were significantly higher than
those obtained in control experiments (0.48+0.44,SD imp./s/deg and 2.54+2.71,SD
%/deg) as well as on the intact side (0.47+0.33,SD imp./s/deg and 1.88+1.75,SD
%/deg). Moreover, while in control experiments the gain and sensitivity of the
rvLVN neurons were on average significantly higher than those of the dcLVN units,
these values became comparable after unilateral aVN: in particular, the gain and
sensitivity increased in the dcLVN of the lesioned side, but decreased in the
rvLVN of the intact side. No significant correlation was found in all preparations

between gain and conduction velocity of the VS neurons, which explains why in control experiments the faster the axonal conduction velocity the higher was the response sensitivity to tilt, due to their lower resting discharge. This positive
correlation between sensitivity and conduction velocity , however, was lost bilaterally after aVN, due to a decrease in firing rate of the slow units on both the
lesioned and the intact side.

As to the response pattern of LVN neurons to standard parameters of tilt, we found
that after ipsilateral aVN 48.8% of the units were excited during side-down tilt
(α -responses), while 37.2% were excited during side-up tilt (β -responses), the
remaining units showing intermediate phase angle of responses. In control experiments
48.0% of the units showed α-responses, but only 26.0% showed β -responses. These
findings contrast with those obtained on the intact side, where most units (54.7%)
exhibited β -responses, but only 28.1% showed α -responses. The significant decrease in α- and increase in β -responses on the intact side with respect to the
controls and to the lesioned side involved particularly the dcLVN. Finally,in control experiments the units showing an α-or β -pattern displayed an average phase
lead of +12.3+28.6°,SD with respect to the extreme side-down or side-up animal displacements, thus being attributed to stimulation of macular, utricular receptors.
This value decreased significantly to +3.3+23.1°,SD on the lesioned side, but remained almost unmodified on the intact side (+9.4+30.8°,SD).

Resting Discharge and Response Characteristics of LVN Neurons to Standard Parameters
of Tilt after Unilateral Chronic Vestibular Deafferentation
The activity of 189 LVN neurons recorded after ipsilateral cVN, i.e. when compensation of the postural and motor deficits had occurred, was compared with that of
170 LVN neurons tested after ipsilateral aVN (Pompeiano and others,1984; Xerri and
others,1983).

In chronic preparations the base frequency of the responsive units corresponded on
average to 20.9+17.1,SD imp./s. Surprisingly, this value was similar to that obtained after ipsilateral aVN and significantly lower than that obtained in control
experiments. However, the negative correlation found in control experiments between
unit resting discharge rate and conduction velocity of the corresponding VS axon
(Manzoni and others, unpublished observations; cf. also Boyle and Pompeiano, 1981)
that was lost after ipsilateral aVN, reappeared after cVN, where the faster the
conduction velocity of the axon the lower was the unit discharge rate at rest.
This finding was due to partial recovery of firing rate of the slow units,whereas
that of the fast units decreased significantly with respect to the value obtained
after ipsilateral aVN.

In contrast to the results obtained in acute experiments, where the proportion of
units affected by tilt was comparable in both divisions of LVN, in chronic preparations the proportion of rvLVN units responsive to tilt (76.7%) became significantly higher than that of the dcLVN units affected by the same input (61.6%),thus
approaching the control values.

The average response gain of the LVN units ipsilateral to the side of the chronic
vestibular deafferentation (0.40+0.40,SD imp./s/deg) was lower than that obtained
in acutely deafferented preparations,thus becoming comparable to the control values.
Moreover, a slight positive correlation was found between gain and conduction velocity of the corresponding VS axon. The average response sensitivity of the LVN
neurons after cVN (3.29+3.11,SD %/deg) was also comparable to that obtained in control experiments. Moreover,the mean value obtained for the rvLVN neurons became
significantly higher than that of the dcLVN neurons, as shown in preparations with
the vestibular nerves intact. Obviously, the positive correlation between response
sensitivity and axonal conduction velocity,that was lost after ipsilateral ·aVN,
reappeared in chronic preparations due to a recovery in resting discharge rate of

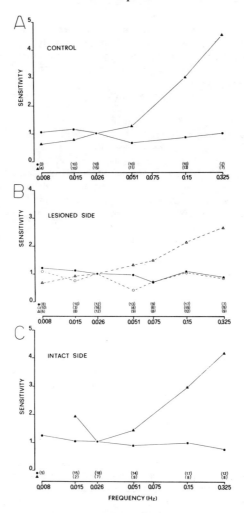

Fig.1. Sensitivity of responses of LVN neurons to increasing frequencies of sinusoidal tilt in control experiments (A) and after ipsilateral (B) or contralateral
vestibular neurectomy (C).
The sensitivity of the first harmonic responses of LVN neurons has been evaluated
in decerebrate cats during sinusoidal tilt at the peak amplitude of 10° for increasing frequencies of animal displacement (from 0.008 to 0.325Hz). Mean values of responses, normalized at 0.026Hz, have been plotted; in parentheses are numbers of
units tested for each parameter of stimulation. A: the activity of 10 static (filled circles) and 15 dynamic neurons (filled triangles) was recorded in control experiments (Boyle and Pompeiano,1980). B: filled circles indicate the response sensitivity of 17 neurons, which did not show any change over the whole frequency range
after ipsilateral aVN. Open symbols indicate the response sensitivity of 19 static
(open circles) and 12 dynamic neurons (open triangles) after ipsilateral cVN (Xerri
and others,1983). C: as in control experiments, two populations of 18 static (filled circles) and 9 dynamic units (filled triangles) were observed after contralateral
aVN (Lacour and others, 1985).

the slow VS units.

After   ipsilateral cVN, the distribution of the response patterns of LVN neurons
to standard parameters of tilt (50.8%α-responses,44.0% β-responses, and 5.2%
intermediate responses) was comparable to that obtained after ipsilateral aVN.How-
ever, the average phase lead of the responses with respect to the extreme animal
displacements, that was significantly reduced after ipsilateral aVN, increased up
to +16.2+25.5°,SD after cVN, thus returning to the control values.

Dynamics of Response of LVN Neurons to Changing Frequency of Tilt after Unilateral
Acute and Chronic Vestibular Deafferentation

In control experiments two populations of LVN neurons were characterized on the
basis of their sensitivity changes by increasing frequency of tilt from 0.008 to
0.32Hz,+10°(Boyle and Pompeiano,1980).The first population of static units (n=10)
showed a stable or a reduced gain and sensitivity, while the phase angle of responses remained positional despite the increase in angular acceleration from 0.02
to 38.5°/sec². The second population of dynamic units (n=15), however, showed a
progressive increase in gain and sensitivity as well as in phase lag of responses
by increasing the frequency of tilt above 0.026Hz; this last finding was responsible
for the average changes in phase angle of responses of all the recorded units(n=25),
which progressively increased from a lag of -10.1° at 0.008Hz to a lag of -67.2° at
0.32Hz.Both slow- and fast-conducting VS units contributed to the dynamic responses
(cf. Boyle and Pompeiano,1981)(Fig.1A).

After aVN, all the LVN units tested on the lesioned side (n=17) showed a great stability in the average gain,sensitivity and phase angle of responses to increasing
frequency of tilt (Xerri and others,1983). On the other hand on the intact side
(Lacour and others,1985) both static (n=18) and dynamic units(n=9), whose VS axons
covered the whole range of conduction velocities, were observed, as shown in control experiments; however, the phase lag of all the responses obtained in these
experiments at 0.32Hz(-17.4+29.8°,SD) was on average smaller than that obtained in
control experiments(-67.7+21.3°,SD) (Fig. 1B).

After cVN(Xerri and others,1983), not only static(n=19) but also dynamic units
(n=12) were recorded ipsilaterally to the side of the vestibular deafferentation.
These two populations of neurons, which included both slow- and fast-conducting
units, closely resembled those obtained in control experiments; however, the increase in response gain and sensitivity only partially recovered after cVN, while
the progressive increase in phase lag of responses to increasing frequency of tilt
seen in control experiments was substituted by an average phase lead of about +10°
which remained constant over the frequency range, as shown after ipsilateral aVN
(Fig. 1C).

DISCUSSION

Effects of Acute Vestibular Deafferentation

In the present experiments performed after ipsilateral aVN, the mean discharge
rate of the vestibular neurons located in both the rvLVN and the dcLVN significantly decreased on the lesioned side(Xerri and others,1983) with respect to the con-
trols(Boyle and Pompeiano,1980); moreover, a slight decrease of the mean discharge
rate affected the rvLVN neurons on the intact side (Lacour and others,1985).The
units whose firing rate was depressed by the ipsilateral(Pompeiano and others,
1984) or contralateral vestibular deafferentation(Lacour and others,1985) were the
slow-conducting (small) VS neurons, whereas the fast-conducting (large) VS neurons
were not particularly affected. It appears, therefore, that the labyrinth input of

one side keeps under its tonic excitatory control not only the small-size LVN neurons of the ipsilateral side, but also to a lesser extent those of the contralateral side, possibly by utilizing crossed excitatory pathways passing through the
medullary reticular formation (cf. Shimazu,1972) and the cerebellar fastigial nu-
cleus(Erway and others,1978). This finding is in agreement with the "size principle" which states that for a given excitatory input impinging on a homogeneous
population of neurons, the smaller the size of the neurons, the higher is the input
resistance, so that the more effective is the corresponding input in exciting them
(cf. Henneman and Mendell,1981).
All the effects described above led to a relative imbalance (50%) between the LVN
of both sides, which accounts for the postural and locomotor deficits after labyrinthectomy. This imbalance would obviously be more prominent if the resting discharge of the LVN neurons on the intact side increased as a result of the contralateral labyrinth deafferentation, as shown for the MVN and the SVN neurons(cf.
Xerri and others,1983). This finding, although not fully confirmed in the literature, has been attributed to imbalance of the intervestibular commissural connec-
tions(cf.Pompeiano,Mergner and Corvaja,1978), which are inhibitory in function and
driven by the canal input (cf.Shimazu,1972;Galiana and others,1984).However, ana-
tomical(Pompeiano,Mergner and Corvaja,1978) and physiological data(cf.Shimazu,1972)
exclude that the LVN of both sides, driven by the macular input, are interconnected
by commissural pathways. The absence of inhibitory commissural connections between
the LVN of both sides may account for the prominent contraction of limb extensors
which can be elicited bilaterally following symmetric changes in head position or
during landing or jumping.
After unilateral aVN, the proportion on the intact side of units responding to
standard parameters of tilt was greater in the rvLVN than in the dcLVN(Lacour and
others,1985), as shown in control experiments(Boyle and Pompeiano,1980); however
on the lesioned side this proportion decreased in the rvLVN but remained unchanged in the dcLVN(Xerri and others,1983). This finding can be attributed to the fact
that the primary vestibular afferents originating from macular utricular receptors
terminate mainly in the ipsilateral rvLVN(cf.Siegborn and Grant,1983), where they
monosynaptically excite the corresponding target neurons(cf.Wilson and Melvill Jones,
1979).
It is of interest that in control experiments the average gain and sensitivity of
the unit responses to standard parameters of tilt were higher in the rvLVN than in
the dcLVN(Boyle and Pompeiano,1980). These values, however, became comparable
after unilateral aVN, due to a decrease in gain and sensitivity of the rvLVN neurons on the intact side(Lacour and others,1985) and an increase of the dcLVN neurons on the lesioned side with respect to the controls(Xerri and others,1983).The
former effects can in part be due to a reduced activity of the crossed excitatory
pathways originating from the deafferented side, and leading to a selective decrease in mean discharge rate of the rvLVN neurons on the intact side. On the
other hand, the increase in response gain and sensitivity of the dcLVN neurons on
the lesioned side, despite the loss of excitatory drive from the corresponding
labyrinth, can in part be attributed to some imbalance in the activity of the crossed inhibitory pathways made by the VS neurons of one side acting on neurons of the
crossed spino-reticulocerebellar pathway and then, through the Purkinje cells of
the contralateral cerebellar vermis, on the dorsocaudal part of the corresponding
LVN(cf.Pompeiano,1979). The decreased amplitude of modulation of LVN neurons on
the hypertonic side, coupled with an increased amplitude on the hypotonic side,
may in part counteract the postural asymmetry produced by the unilateral vestibular deafferentation, thus leading to more balanced postural adjustments during
head movements.

In decerebrate cats, tilt around the longitudinal axis of the animal produces contraction of both the ipsilateral limb extensors during side-down tilt (α-responses)
and the ipsilateral neck extensors during side-up tilt (β-responses)(cf.Schor and
Miller,1981).These effects are apparently related to the discharge of LVN neurons
showing different patterns of response to tilt; there are in fact VS neurons which
may activate either ipsilateral limb extensors during side-down tilt (α-responses)
or ipsilateral neck extensors during side-up tilt (β-responses)(cf.Pompeiano,1984).In
preparations with the vestibular nerves intact, the proportion of LVN neurons showing α-responses was about twice that of the units showing β-responses, both in the
rvLVN and the dcLVN (Boyle and Pompeiano,1980). This finding apparently agrees with
the observation that the primary afferents that are excited during side-down or
side-up tilt originate from the medial and the lateral part of the utriculus, respectively, due to different morphological polarization of the receptors. However,
after unilateral aVN, the predominant population of LVN neurons located on the lesioned side still showed α-responses, in spite of the interruption of the corresponding primary afferents (Xerri and others,1983), whereas on the intact side the
proportion of units showing α-responses decreased to about half that displaying
β-responses despite the integrity of the corresponding vestibular nerve(Lacour and
others,1985). This last finding, which affected particularly the dcLVN, probably
depends on suppression of the vectorial interaction which may normally occur
between the excitatory volleys originating from the ipsilateral labyrinth and the
inhibitory volleys driven by the contralateral vestibular system and acting
through the corticocerebellar loop on the dcLVN. The persistence of lateral vestibular units showing α-responses on the lesioned side, coupled with the prominent
increase in units showing β-responses on the intact side is essential to produce
the appropriate contraction of limb extensors on the deafferented side during lateral tilting in that direction; in fact,the increase in the extensor tonus of the
limbs made hypotonic by the vestibular deafferentation during side-down tilt would
be determined not only by LVN neurons showing α-responses on the deafferented side,
but also by LVN neurons showing β-responses on the intact side(cf. also Schor and
Miller,1982).

Effects of Chronic Vestibular Deafferentation
The proportion of units responsive to standard parameters of tilt, which was selectively reduced in the rvLVN after ipsilateral aVN, recovered in chronic preparations; however, the mean discharge rate of the responsive LVN neurons did not change
with respect to the value obtained soon after the lesion(Xerri and others,1983).
This finding was at first surprising in view of the full compensation of the postural and locomotor deficits produced by the vestibular deafferentation, but it
can be understood if we assume that compensation of the vestibular syndrome depends
on a redistribution of the excitatory labyrinth drive within different populations
of LVN neurons. In fact, the negative correlation found in control experiments
between resting discharge rate and conduction velocity of the VS axons, which was
lost after ipsilateral aVN,reappeared after cVN due to a partial recovery in firing rate of the small neurons, while that of the large neurons tended to decrease
(Pompeiano and others,1984).It seems, therefore, that the postural atonia produced
by ipsilateral aVN depends mainly on disfacilitation of the small VS neurons, while
its compensation after cVN is related to partial recovery in the background discharge of these neurons.
As expected, the response gain and sensitivity of the LVN neurons to standard parameters of tilt, which increased after ipsilateral aVN, returned to the control
values after cVN; however, in the latter preparations the distribution of the re-

sponse patterns remained similar to that obtained after ipsilateral aVN, due to persistent loss of the normal interaction between the outputs of the two labyrinths
(Xerri and others,1983). It is of interest that in these chronic preparations the
average phase lead of the responses relative to the extreme animal displacements,
which decreased after ipsilateral aVN with respect to the controls(Xerri and others,
1983), returned to the control value(Boyle and Pompeiano,1980). This anticipation
of the phase angle of responses of VS neurons in chronically deafferented animals
represents an important factor that intervenes in the compensation of the dynamic
motor deficits following unilateral vestibular deafferentation.

Dynamics of the Responses
Two main populations of LVN neurons were observed in control experiments by increasing frequency of tilt(Boyle and Pompeiano,1980). The first population of neurons
showed a stability in gain, sensitivity and phase angle of the responses, while the
second population showed a progressive increase in gain and sensitivity as well as
in phase lag of the responses by increasing frequency of tilt. These responses were
still observed after bilateral canal plugging, thus being attributed to stimulation
of macular receptors(Schor and Miller,1982). After unilateral vestibular deafferentation, both static and dynamic units were found on the intact side(Lacour and
others,1985). On the deafferented side,however, the population of dynamic units
disappeared in acute experiments but reappeared in chronic experiments; yet, the
phase angle of the responses remained positional over the frequency range, due to
suppression of the normal interaction of afferent volleys originating from the ipsilateral and contralateral macular receptors within the LVN(Xerri and others,1983).
A stability in the phase angle of motor-unit responses of the triceps brachii to
increasing frequencies of tilt was also observed after ipsilateral labyrinthectomy
(Berthoz and Anderson,1972).
In summary, it appears that the LVN units displaying a dynamic sensitivity on the
intact side were unable to provide this dynamic information to the LVN neurons
acutely deprived of their ipsilateral vestibular input, which thus displayed only
static responses. The same neurons, however, play a crucial role in the recovery
of the dynamic sensitivity of the chronically deafferented LVN neurons. Therefore,
the persistence of a dynamic sensitivity on the intact side is apparently unable
to prevent the occurrence of the deficits in phasic postural reactions and the locomotor disorders described in the first stage after unilateral vestibular deafferentation. But this population of dynamic LVN neurons, which contributes to the
partial recovery of the dynamic sensitivity to tilt of the chronically deafferented neurons, probably intervenes in the recovery of the dynamic equilibrium function.
This is supported by behavioral data on bilaterally vestibular-neurectomized preparations (Lacour,1981).

A theoretical model for the neuronal processes responsible for compensation of the
static and dynamic ocular motor and postural responses following unilateral vestibular deafferentation postulates that vestibular compensation is brought about by
gain changes in the commissural system between the vestibular nuclei(cf.Galiana
and others,1984). The anatomical finding that in the cat direct intervestibular
connections originate, in part, from the MVN and SVN which project mainly to extraocular motoneurons, but not from the LVN which projects to the axial and limb extensor motoneurons(Pompeiano and others,1978), supports the hypothesis that these commissures play a critical role in the recovery of ocular motor function, but excludes that in mammals their fibers are required to produce plastic changes in the vestibular system leading to compensation of postural and locomotor deficits. It is
likely, therefore, that other crossed excitatory or inhibitory pathways, some of

which involving the cerebellar loop, are responsible not only for the changes in
static and dynamic properties of the LVN neurons after unilateral vestibular deafferentation (as proposed in the present report), but also for the compensation
of the vestibulospinal functions.

SUMMARY

In decerebrate cats, the spontaneous discharge as well as the dynamic characteristics of response of LVN neurons to sinusoidal stimulation of macular labyrinth receptors were investigated after unilateral acute (aVN) or chronic vestibular neurectomy (cVN). LVN neurons were also antidromically activated from the spinal cord
and their cell size characterized indirectly on the basis of the conduction velocity of the corresponding vestibulospinal axons.
The spontaneous discharge as well as the responses of individual LVN neurons to roll
tilt of the animal were first recorded after unilateral aVN, both on the deafferented and the intact side, and the results compared with those obtained in control
experiments with the vestibular nerves intact. Asymmetric changes in static and
dynamic postural and motor responses, after unilateral aVN, were found to be associated with parallel changes in static and dynamic properties of the corresponding LVN neurons. In addition, the neuronal processes underlying the recovery of
postural and motor deficits after unilateral vestibular deafferentation were investigated by recording and comparing on the deafferented side the resting discharge as well as the response characteristics of LVN neurons to tilt after aVN
and cVN.
The possible contribution of small and large vestibulospinal neurons in the development and compensation of static and dynamic postural and motor deficits, respectively, was discussed in relation to the crossed pathways involved by the
labyrinth volleys. The absence of direct commissural connections between the LVN of
both sides excludes that their fibers intervene in the vestibular compensation of
postural and motor asymmetries.

REFERENCES

Berthoz,A., and J.Anderson(1972).Frequency of vestibular influence on extensor
    motoneurons.III.Neck and forelimb motor unit activity after hemilabyrinthec-
    tomy. Brain Res.,45, 236-240.
Boyle,R., and O.Pompeiano(1980). Reciprocal responses to sinusoidal tilt of neu-
    rons in Deiters'nucleus and their dynamic characteristics. Arch.ital.Biol.,
    118, 1-32.
Boyle,R., and O.Pompeiano(1981). Relation between cell size and response character-
    istics of vestibulospinal neurons to labyrinth and neck inputs.
    J.Neuroscience,1, 1052-1066.
Erway,L.C., B.Ghelarducci,O.Pompeiano, and M. Stanojević (1978). Responses of cer-
    ebellar fastigial neurons to stimulation of contralateral macular labyrinthine
    receptors. Arch.ital.Biol.,116,205-224.
Flohr,H., and W.Precht(1981). Lesion-induced Neuronal Plasticity in Sensorimotor
    Systems, Springer, Heidelberg.
Galiana,H.L., H.Flohr, and G.Melvill-Jones(1984). A reevaluation of intervestibul-
    ar nuclear coupling:its role in vestibular compensation. J.Neurophysiol.,51,
    242-259.

Henneman,E., and L.M. Mendell(1981). Functional organization of motoneuron pool and
    its inputs. In J.M.Brookhart and V.B.Mountcastle(Eds.),Handbook of Physiology.
    Sect.1.The Nervous System.Vol.II.Motor Control.Am.Physiol.Soc.,Bethesda,MD.
    Part.1,pp.423-507.
Igarashi,M.,J.K.Levy,M.F.Reschke,T.Kubo,and T.Watson(1978).Locomotor dysfunction
    after surgical lesions in the unilateral vestibular nuclei region in squirrel
    monkeys. Arch.Oto-Rhino-Laryng.,221,89-95.
Lacour,M.(1981).Contribution à l'Étude de la Restauration des Fonctions Posturo-
    cinétiques après Labyrinthectomie chez le Singe et le Chat.(Ph.D. thesis).
    Université d'Aix-Marseille I, Marseille.
Lacour,M.,D.Manzoni,O.Pompeiano,and C.Xerri(1985). Central compensation of vesti-
    bular deficits.III.Response characteristics of lateral vestibular neurons to
    roll tilt after contralateral labyrinth deafferentation.J.Neurophysiol.,54,
    120-137.
Orlovsky,G.N.(1972).Activity of vestibulospinal neurons during locomotion. Brain
    Res.,46,85-98.
Pompeiano,O.(1975).Vestibulo-spinal relationships.In R.F.Naunton(Ed.), The Vesti-
    bular System, Academic Press, New York,pp.147-180.
Pompeiano,O.(1979).Neck and macular labyrinthine influences in the cervical spino-
    reticulocerebellar pathway.Progr.Brain Res.,50, 501-514.
Pompeiano,O.(1984).A comparison of the response characteristics of vestibulospinal
    and medullary reticulospinal neurons to labyrinth and neck inputs. In C.D.
    Barnes (Ed.),Brainstem Control of Spinal Cord Function. Academic Press, New
    York,pp.87-140.
Pompeiano,O., and A.Brodal(1957).The origin of vestibulospinal fibers in the cat.
    An experimental-anatomical study, with comments on the descending medial lon-
    gitudinal fasciculus.Arch.ital.Biol.,95,166-195.
Pompeiano,O.,T.Mergner,and N.Corvaja(1978).Commissural, perihypoglossal and reticu-
    lar afferent projection to the vestibular nuclei in the cat. An experimental
    anatomical study with the method of the retrograde transport of horseradish
    peroxidase.Arch.ital.Biol.,116,130-172.
Pompeiano,O.,C.Xerri,S.Gianni,and D.Manzoni(1984). Central compensation of vesti-
    bular deficits.II.Influences of roll tilt on different-size lateral vestibular
    neurons after ipsilateral labyrinth deafferentation.J.Neurophysiol.,52,18-38.
Schor,R.H.,and A.D.Miller(1981). Vestibular reflexes in neck and forelimb muscles
    evoked by roll tilt.J.Neurophysiol.,46,167-178.
Schor,R.H.,and A.D.Miller(1982).Relationship of cat vestibular neurons to otolith-
    spinal reflexes.Exp.Brain Res.,47,137-144.
Shimazu,M.(1972). Organization of the commissural connections: physiology.Progr.
    Brain Res.,37,177-190.
Siegborn,J., and G.Grant(1983). Brainstem projections of different branches of the
    vestibular nerve.An experimental study by transganglionic transport of horse-
    radish peroxidase in the cat.I. The horizontal ampullar and utricular nerves.
    Arch.ital.Biol.,121,237-248.
Wilson,V.J., and G.Melvill Jones(1979). Mammalian Vestibular Physiology. Plenum
    Press, New York.
Xerri,C.,S.Gianni,D.Manzoni,and O.Pompeiano(1983). Central compensation of vesti-
    bular deficits.I.Response characteristics of lateral vestibular neurons to roll
    tilt after ipsilateral labyrinth deafferentation. J.Neurophysiol.,50,428-448.

Functional Recovery Following Peripheral Vestibular Lesions: Due to — in Spite of — in Parallel with — or without Synaptic Reorganization?

N. Dieringer and W. Precht

Institut für Hirnforschung, Universität Zürich, August-Forelstr. 1,
CH-8029 Zürich, Switzerland

Hemilabyrinthectomy (HL) results in a 'vestibular lesion syndrome'. In most species, the symptoms include severe postural asymmetries of head, trunk and limbs, a strong ocular nystagmus and asymmetries in the gains of dynamic reflexes. Since the removed receptor cells do not regenerate and surviving cells of the VIIIth nerve in Scarpa's ganglion do not redevelop normal resting rates (Jensen, 1983; Sirkin, Precht and Courjon, 1984), recovery of function must be generated by the central nervous system. Central adjustments have to cope with two major groups of motor deficits. Firstly, a new balance in the innervation of those motor systems has to be reestablished which control posture. Secondly, the gain of dynamic vestibular reflexes has to be recalibrated to reduce the lesion-induced asymmetry in their compensatory action during locomotion. In the following the results from recent behavioral, anatomical and neurophysiological studies in cat and frog are summarized. For more extensive reviews see Schaefer and Meyer, 1974 and Precht and Dieringer, 1985.

'Compensation' - A Common Recovery Process for all Deficits?

Recovery for different symptoms progresses at different rates and to different extents even in individuals of the same species and age. Head tilt and tonic vertical eye deviation persist permanently in guinea pig (Schaefer and Meyer, 1974), rabbit (Baarsma and Collewijn, 1975) and probably in rat (Sirkin, Precht and Courjon, 1984). Eye nystagmus, however, is considerably reduced or even absent one week after HL in these as in other mammalian species. Likewise, postural recovery in monkey (Wolfe and Kos, 1977), cat (Maioli, Precht and Ried, 1983) and frog (Dieringer and Precht, 1981; Agosti, Dieringer and Precht, 1986) is not necessarily paralleled by a similar improvement in the performance of dynamic vestibular reflexes.

In posturally well-adapted cats Maioli, Precht and Ried (1983) found severe deficits in the gain and phase values of the vestibulo-ocular reflex (VOR) even 22 months after HL (Fig. 1). Reduction of response asymmetry started about 10 days after the lesion and developed only slowly over many months, except for a few cats with an abrupt gain increase between days 5 and 10 after HL.

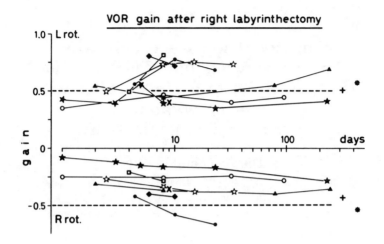

Fig. 1. Time course of VOR gain changes in ten adult cats following
vestibular nerve section on the right side. Gains for rotations to
the intact (left; L rot.) and to the lesioned (right; R rot.) side
were computed after the responses were corrected for the velocity
of the slow phase of a spontaneous nystagmus (from Maioli, Precht
and Ried, 1983).

Frogs recover posturally reasonably well within 2-3 months after HL
(Kolb, 1955; Flohr, and co-workers, 1981). However, only about 25%
of them exhibit symmetrical vestibulo-collic reflexes (VCR; Dieringer and Precht, 1981). Improvement in the responses of abducens
nerves to velocity steps to the lesioned side varies between zero
up to a return to normal control values in posturally recovered HL
frogs (Agosti, Dieringer and Precht, 1986).

These results show that some vestibular functions such as maintenance of ocular, head and body balance at rest are restored reasonably well, while dynamic vestibular reflexes such as VOR and VCR
recover less readily or not at all. Such differences are not too
surprising, for the lesion symptoms arise from loss of input from
two different sense organs – the otolith organs and the canals –
the signals of which are differently processed centrally. Selective
lesions of utricular and canal nerves in frogs show that particular
deficits after HL can be attributed to the loss of information from
particular receptor organs (see Precht and Dieringer, 1985). Likewise, in posturally and dynamically recovered HL frogs no postural
decompensation occurs, if the remaining horizontal canal on the intact side is plugged or its nerve is cut, even though VOR and VCR
in the horizontal plane are totally abolished (Dieringer, unpubl.
data). These results in acute and chronic frogs indicate that horizontal canal-dependent and otolith-dependent control systems are,
and remain, rather well seperated and that recovery after HL occurs
independently for the different systems.

Adaptation, Substitution or Restitution?

The poor spontaneous recovery of the VOR gain in a large percentage
of cats and their well-known capabilities to use visual information

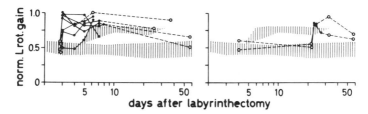

days after labyrinthectomy

Fig. 2. Time course of VOR gain changes in two groups of hemilabyrinthectomized cats in response to a 0.1 Hz sinusoidal oscillation
before, during and after periods of forced oscillation in the
light. Circles indicate data obtained before or several days after
forced oscillation. Dots refer to values measured after forced oscillation. Shaded areas represent the range of spontaneous recovery
of the VOR gain over time (see Fig. 1). VOR gains were normalized
relative to the control values before the lesion (from Maioli and
Precht, 1985).

to modify this gain prompted Maioli and Precht (1985) to assess
whether this adaptive plasticity of the VOR is affected by labyrinthectomy. Two groups of cats were allowed to recover spontaneously
for 2 and 23 days after HL, respectively. Thereupon cats were oscillated in front of a patterned surround 3-5 h daily for 2-6 consecutive days. When tested again in the dark, VOR gain was increased already after a few hours of oscillation (Fig. 2). The induced gain increase was in both groups of animals larger than the
spontaneously occurring gain increase, but when training was discontinued it slowly decreased again over time. Thus the gain of the
VOR can still be adaptively modified acutely after HL, however,
this mechanism is obviously not used to its fullest possible extent
in most spontaneously recovering cats. Since in all cats of a
chronic stage a considerable recovery from overall behavioral motor
deficits was observed, persisting VOR deficits may be compensated
by sensory substitution processes, e.g. by optokinetic, neck proprioceptive and other somatosensory inputs and/or by a change in
the motor control strategies (see contributions by Peterson and by
Bles in this volume).

As in cats only in a small percentage of chronic HL frogs VCR responses are recovered to some extent. Conspicuously in all HL animals gaze movements (eye in space) in the light are saccadic whenever the animal is rotated towards the lesioned (right) side (Fig.
3A,C). In dynamically improved HL frogs, gaze movements in the dark
are saccadic as well during a rotation of the animal towards the
lesioned side (Fig. 3D). In the remaining (only posturally recovered) chronic HL animals, gaze movements in the dark are as asymmetric as in posturally normal frogs in which the right horizontal
canal nerve was sectioned (Fig. 3B). Compensatory movements in the
light are saccadic to either side about 1-2 days after both horizontal canal nerves are sectioned (Dieringer and Precht, 1985). In
these animals horizontal VOR and VCR responses are totally abolished. Since optokinetic 'catch up' saccades, interactions between
the bilateral vestibular nuclei or between eye and head movements
and a slow recovery process can be excluded (Dieringer and Precht,
1985), these saccades are most likely triggered by proprioceptive
inputs which are disinhibited after a vestibular lesion. Functionally these head saccades can substitute for part of the missing

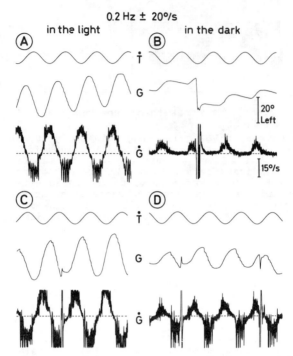

Fig. 3. Compensatory gaze movements of frogs with vestibular
lesions. A,B: Gaze movements of a frog one day after sectioning of
the right horizontal canal nerve. Note saccadic movements to the
left in the light (A) and asymmetry of movements in the dark (B).
C,D: Gaze movements of a frog 620 days after hemilabyrinthectomy on
the right side. Note saccadic movements to the left in the light
(C) and in the dark (D). T indicates table velocity, G gaze position, G gaze velocity and dashed lines indicate zero gaze velocity
(from Dieringer and Precht, unpublished).

slow phase VCR component (see Fig. 3A and D). For an analogous substitution of slow phase VOR components by eye saccades in monkey
and man see Dichgans and co-workers, 1973; Kasai and Zee, 1978;
Berthoz, 1985. To trigger these saccades in the dark the VCR gain
of HL frogs has to increase sufficiently to activate proprioceptive
inputs.

Recovery of dynamic vestibular reflex responses in the absence of
sensory cues other than vestibular was studied by Agosti, Dieringer
and Precht (1986). Bilateral abducens nerve responses evoked by
velocity steps in the dark were recorded from paralysed control and
HL frogs in the acute and chronic stage. Acutely after HL responses
in the bilateral abducens nerves were asymmetrically reduced with
respect to those in controls. Practically identical results were
obtained from animals in which only the horizontal canal nerve was
sectioned. In HL animals of a chronic stage abducens nerve responses evoked by steps to the lesioned side differed between individuals, even though all animals tested had posturally recovered to a
similar degree. In two animals abducens nerve responses were as de-

ficient as in HL animals of an acute stage. In three animals responses were improved but still smaller than in controls and in one animal responses were as large as in controls. This large variability indicates a range in potential improvement from zero up to normal control values. Since in this preparation substitution from other sensory systems was excluded, the observed improvement represents a partial restitution of function. The improved responses resulted from an increase in activity that was released by disinhibition. This inhibition in turn is controlled by horizontal canal-dependent input from the intact side, since plugging of this canal abolished all direction-specific responses in the horizontal plane. Otolithic and vertical canal signals were not found to be relevant for the observed responses. From these results it appears that the observed partial restitution of function of horizontal reflex performance depends exclusively on signals derived from receptors of the intact horizontal canal.

Synaptic Reorganization - Well-or Mal-Adaptive?

In the cat Korte and Friedrich (1979) found a number of morphological changes in the partially deafferented superior vestibular nucleus 5 to 6 days after HL. Most interestingly, on the lesioned side a new group of synaptic boutons with flattened vesicles appeared that was not present on the control side. These observations suggest lesion-induced plastic changes in the organization of yet unidentified inputs on the partially deafferented side. Such a reactive synaptic reorganization might involve not only one but potentially all unlesioned, converging pathways. In the frog suggestive evidence for lesion-induced changes in several pathways converging on central vestibular neurons was obtained in anatomical, electrophysiological and pharmacological experiments.

Taking advantage of the well-described major ascending projections of dorsal root fibers to the brainstem and the cerebellum in intact frogs (Antal, Tornai and Székely, 1980; Székely, Antal and Görcs, 1980), the projections from brachial, ascending dorsal root fibers were studied autoradiographically in control and chronic HL frogs by Dieringer, Künzle and Precht (1984). Comparison showed that projections into the partially denervated vestibular nuclear complex of HL animals were far more dense than in control animals. However, in the cerebellar granular layer, no obvious difference was observed in the extent of dorsal root projections between both groups of animals. These results suggest an increase in the number of ascending dorsal root terminals within the partially deafferented vestibular nuclei of HL frogs. As far as functional aspects are concerned, recent results obtained by Amat, Matus-Amat and Vanegas (1984) are of interest. Acutely after a bilateral labyrinthectomy these authors observed an expansion of the area in which cerebellar units responded to passive neck oscillations. A similar acute disinhibition of spinal inputs after a vestibular lesion was assumed above to explain the occurrance of saccadic head movements. In addition to the early changes in the responses of cerebellar units, in chronic frogs an even larger number of neurons was found to be responsive to spinal inputs. This additional increase in chronic frogs might be mediated in part by the increased dorsal root-vestibular input as described above.

These anatomical findings appear to corroborate assumed structural changes such as reactive synaptogenesis as a likely explanation for electrophysiological results obtained in chronic HL cats (Precht, Shimazu and Markham, 1966) and frogs (Dieringer and Precht, 1979a,

b). In both cases evidence was found for an increased control of
the vestibular commissural system over partially deafferented vestibular neurons. In the cat, the thresholds of electric stimulation
of the intact vestibular nerve for producing inhibition of type I
neurons in the chronically deafferented vestibular nuclei were
lower than those in controls. However, such a change in the thresholds was not observed by Ried, Maioli and Precht (1984). In the
frog, an increase in the synaptic efficacy of excitatory commissural projections was observed and in addition, crossed inhibition,
which is only poorly developed in intact frogs, had increased in
chronic HL animals as well. Recent results obtained by Kasik and
colleagues (1986) demonstrate that changes in the efficacy of these
and of other brainstem connections are present even in the excised,
in vitro medulla.

An increase in the commissural control over partially deafferented
vestibular neurons might be expected to produce different results
in cat and frog, due to the differences in the organization of the
commissural systems in both species. The response patterns of horizontal canal-dependent central vestibular neurons were studied in
chronic HL frogs and cats by Dieringer and Precht (1981) and Ried,
Maioli and Precht (1984). For a review see Precht and Dieringer
(1985). In essence, the numbers of horizontal canal driven neurons
with type I responses were found to be normal with respect to controls on the intact side, but drastically reduced on the lesioned
side of both species. Neurons with type II responses were almost
absent on the intact side of chronic HL frogs and cats. However, on
the lesioned side the number of neurons with type II responses, was
strongly increased in frogs but normal in cats.

The large increase in the number of neurons exhibiting type II responses on the lesioned side of chronic frogs, associated with an
almost complete absence of type I responses in most individuals on
that side, may be explained by the increase in the efficacy of the
frog's excitatory commissural system. Some of these type II responses on the lesioned side could have arisen from former type I
neurons. Functionally, these former type I neurons with type II
responses would no longer assist but oppose dynamic responses
evoked by rotation to the intact side. Such a mal-adaptive process
could in fact explain why the response magnitude in the abducens
nerve was reduced for larger velocity steps towards the intact side
in chronic with respect to acute HL frogs (Agosti, Dieringer and
Precht, 1986). That in some chronic HL frogs dynamic responses are
restituted to some degree in spite of an increase in the efficacy
of the excitatory commissural system could be related with a concomitant increase in the efficacy of crossed inhibitory brainstem
and trans-cerebellar pathways (Dieringer and Precht, 1979b). This
possibility has to be tested in chronic animals with well-defined
dynamic reflex characteristics.

In chronic HL cats the large reduction of the number of neurons
with type I responses on the lesioned side, associated with a normal number of type II neurons on the same side, could be explained
by the strong (and eventually even increased) inhibition of type I
by type II neurons. Many of these type I neurons, deprived of their
major excitatory input, could thereby be simply kept below threshold. Such an interpretation is strengthened by the fact that no
evidence was found for a transneuronal degeneration by Ried, Maioli
and Precht (1984) and that no functional cell loss occurs in uni-
laterally canal-plugged animals (Abend, 1977), in which a tonic excitatory input from vestibular afferents is still present.

CONCLUSIONS

Anatomical and electrophysiological evidences suggest that synaptic reorganization takes place postoperatively in the partially deafferented vestibular nuclei of cats and frogs. These changes involve excitatory and inhibitory inputs from different sensory systems and may underlie processes such as restitution and substitution of function. Single unit studies in both species indicate, however, that not all changes in the synaptic organization between the bilateral vestibular nuclei are necessarily beneficial for the recovery of dynamic vestibular reflexes. In the absence of sensory cues other than vestibular, a partial restitution of dynamic vestibular reflex performance is present only in some but not in other individuals. Behavioral studies in both species indicate that remaining dynamic vestibular reflex deficits are substituted by inputs from other sensory systems. Even though HL does not impair the cat's ability to rapidly adapt the gain of its vestibulo-ocular reflex in the case of a visual-vestibular conflict, this mechanism is apparently not used to a large extent to improve functional recovery.

REFERENCES

Abend, W.K. (1977). Functional organization of the superior vestibular nucleus of the squirrel monkey. Brain Res., 132, 65-84.
Agosti, R., N. Dieringer, and W. Precht (1986). Partial restitution of lesion-induced deficits in the horizontal vestibulo-ocular reflex performance measured from the bilateral abducens motor output in frogs. Exp. Brain Res., in press.
Amat, J., P. Matus-Amat, and H. Vanegas (1984). Visual (optokinetic) and somesthetic inputs to the cerebellum of bilateral labyrinthectomized frogs. Neurosci., 11, 885-891.
Antal, M., I. Tornai, and G. Székely (1980). Longitudinal extent of dorsal root fibers in the spinal cord and brain stem of the frog. Neurosci., 5, 1311-1322.
Baarsma, E.A., and H. Collewijn (1975). Changes in compensatory eye movements after unilateral labyrinthectomy in the rabbit. Arch. Oto-Rhino-Laryngol., 211, 219-230.
Berthoz, A. (1985). In A. Berthoz and G. Melvill Jones (Eds.), Adaptive mechanisms in gaze control, Elsevier, Amsterdam, New York, Oxford. Chap. 12, pp. 177-208.
Dichgans, J., E. Bizzi, P. Morasso, and V. Tagliasco (1973). Mechanisms underlying recovery of eye-head coordination following bilateral labyrinthectomy in monkeys. Exp. Brain Res., 18, 548-562.
Dieringer, N., and W. Precht (1979a). Mechanism of compensation for vestibular deficits in the frog. I. Modification of the excitatory commissural system. Exp. Brain Res., 36, 311-328.
Dieringer, N., and W. Precht (1979b). Mechanism of compensation for vestibular deficits in the frog. II. Modifications of the inhibitory pathways. Exp. Brain Res., 36, 329-341.
Dieringer, N., and W. Precht (1981). In H. Flohr and W. Precht (Eds.), Lesion-induced neuronal plasticity in sensorymotor systems, Springer Verlag, Berlin, Heidelberg, New York. pp. 184-196.
Dieringer, N., and W. Precht (1985). Coordination of fast phases of head and eye in intact and vestibularly lesioned unrestrained frogs. Neurosci. Lett., in press.

Dieringer, N., H. Künzle, and W. Precht (1984). Increased projection of ascending dorsal root fibers to vestibular nuclei after hemilabyrinthectomy in the frog. Exp. Brain Res., 55, 574-578.

Flohr, H., H. Bienhold, W. Abeln, and I. Macskovics (1981). In H. Flohr and W. Precht (Eds.), Lesion-induced neuronal plasticity in sensorymotor systems, Springer Verlag, Berlin, Heidelberg, New York. pp. 153-172.

Jensen, D.W. (1983). Survival of function in the deafferented vestibular nerve. Brain Res., 273, 175-178.

Kasai, T., and D.S. Zee (1978). Eye-head coordination in labyrinthine-defective human beings. Brain Res., 144, 123-141.

Kasik, P., S.L. Cochran, N. Dieringer, and W. Precht (1986). Evidence for an alteration in brainstem cholinergic pathways following unilateral labyrinthectomy in the frog. Brain Res., in press.

Kolb, E. (1955). Untersuchungen über zentrale Kompensation und Kompensationsbewegungen einseitig entstateter Frösche. Z. vergl. Physiol., 37, 136-160.

Korte, G.E., and V.L. Friedrich (1979). The fine structure of the feline superior vestibular nucleus: Identification and synaptology of the primary vestibular afferents. Brain Res., 176, 3-32.

Maioli, C., and W. Precht (1985). On the role of vestibulo-ocular reflex plasticity in recovery after unilateral peripheral vestibular lesions. Exp. Brain Res., 59, 267-272.

Maioli, C., W. Precht, and S. Ried (1983). Short- and long-term modifications of vestibulo-ocular response dynamics following unilateral vestibular nerve lesions in the cat. Exp. Brain Res., 50, 259-274.

Precht, W., and N. Dieringer (1985). In A. Berthoz and G. Melvill Jones (Eds.), Adaptive mechanisms in gaze control, Elsevier, Amsterdam, New York, Oxford. Chap. 17, pp. 251-268.

Precht, W., H. Shimazu, and C.M. Markham (1966). A mechanism of central compensation of vestibular function following hemilabyrinthectomy. J. Neurophysiol., 29, 996-1010.

Ried, S., C. Maioli, and W. Precht (1984). Vestibular nuclear neuron activity in chronically hemilabyrinthectomized cats. Acta Oto-Laryngol., 98, 1-13.

Schaefer, K.P., and D.L. Meyer (1974). In H.H. Kornhuber (Ed.), Handbook of sensory physiology, Vol. VI/2. Springer Verlag, Berlin, Heidelberg, New York. Chap. XI, pp. 463-490.

Sirkin, D.W., W. Precht, and J.H. Courjon (1984). Initial, rapid phase of recovery from unilateral vestibular lesion in rat not dependent on survivial of central portion of vestibular nerve. Brain Res., 302, 245-256.

Székely, G., M. Antal, and Th. Görcs (1980). Direct dorsal root projection onto the cerebellum in the frog. Neurosci. Lett., 19, 161-165.

Wolfe, J.W., and C.M. Kos (1977). Nystagmic responses of the rhesus monkey to rotational stimulation following unilateral labyrinthectomy: Final report. Trans. Am. Acad. Ophthalmol. Otolaryngol., 84, 38-45.

Adaptation of the Vestibulo-ocular Response after Short Periods of Optokinetic Stimulation in Man

R. D. Yee* and R. Baloh**

*Department of Ophthalmology, Jules Stein Eye Institute
**Department of Neurology, Reed Neurological Research Institute
UCLA School of Medicine, Los Angeles, CA 90024, USA

INTRODUCTION

Most studies of adaptation of the vestibulo-ocular response (VOR) by visual stimuli in animals and in man have used simultaneous activations of the visual and vestibular systems of long duration. Lisberger and his colleagues (1984) placed magnifying and minifying goggles on monkeys and subjected them to sinusoidally moving optokinetic patterns for 33 hours, while their heads were stationary. Effects on the VOR were much smaller than those when the monkeys were rotated passively within a stationary optokinetic drum, producing simultaneous optokinetic and vestibular stimulations. Collewijn and his colleagues (1983) fitted normal human subjects with magnifying and minifying spectacles, and rotated their heads actively and passively as they viewed an optokinetic stimulus. They found that most of the adaptation of the VOR occurred within 30 minutes after the onset of head rotations. Yagi and his co-workers (1981) reported that normal human subjects, who wore image-reversal prisms and fixated a stationary light while being rotated sinusoidally, showed adaptive changes of the VOR gain after only 15 minutes of stimulation. Westall and Schor (in press) presented normal human subjects with an optokinetic pattern moving in one direction, while they rotated the subjects sinusoidally. After only two minutes of stimulation a directional asymmetry in the VOR gain was found.

The goal of the present study was to determine if unidirectional optokinetic stimulation for short periods of time without simultaneous vestibular stimulation can produce adaptive changes in the VOR in normal human subjects and in patients with cerebellar disorders. The effect on smooth pursuit was also studied.

METHODS

Six normal human subjects, who did not have significant ophthalmic, neurologic or otologic abnormalities, and three patients with cerebellar disorders, that were identified by neurologic examination and neuroradiologic tests, were studied after their informed consents were obtained. Two patients had idiopathic cerebellar atrophy syndromes and one patient had a Chiari malformation (type 2) with onset of symptoms in adult life.

Horizontal eye movements were recorded by DC electro-oculography (EOG). Eye movements were displayed by a curvilinear polygraph and were analyzed by an

on-line, microcomputer system (Baloh and colleagues, 1980a). In analyses of
the VOR and pursuit saccades were removed and the eye movement gains were calculated as peak eye velocity/peak stimulus velocity. Phase relationships were
measured by comparing the timing of the peak eye velocity and peak stimulus
velocity.

Subjects were seated on a motorized chair within a 2 meter diameter, cloth,
optokinetic drum. The interior of the drum consisted of 3 deg, white, vertical
stripes placed every 15 deg against a black background. The VOR gain during
sinusoidal rotation of the chair (0.4 Hz, 60 deg/sec peak velocity) was measured, while the subjects performed mental arithematic. The chair was stationary and the drum was rotated to the right and to the left for periods of 5, 30
and 60 minutes. The subjects were instructed to look straight ahead and to
focus on each stripe, as it passed in front of them. They were asked not to
follow stripes throughout the visual field. The lights were turned off at the
end of the periods of optokinetic stimulation. Sinusoidal chair rotation was
begun immediately after the lights were turned off or after optokinetic after-
nystagmus (OKAN) and optokinetic after-after-nystagmus (OKAAN) had ceased.

The smooth pursuit target was a small, helium-neon laser dot that was reflected from a mirror galvonometer attached to the chair onto the drum surface
in the dark. The target moved sinusoidally at frequencies of 0.2 to 0.8 Hz and
with peak velocities of 22.6 to 90 deg/sec. Pursuit was measured before optokinetic stimulation and after OKAN and OKAAN had ceased.

CHAIR .4 HZ, 60 °/SEC

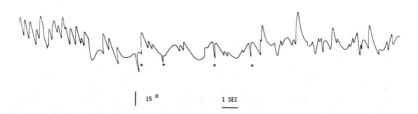

15 °   1 SEC

Fig. 1. VOR after 5 min optokinetic stimulation to left in
normal subject. Top line - chair velocity (rotation
began when lights turned off. Bottom line - eye
position. Deflections up were to right. *'s mark
eyelid blink artifacts.

RESULTS

Unidirectional optokinetic stimulation produced an asymmetry in the VOR, in
which the slow component velocity (SCV) in the direction of the previous drum

rotation was increased and the SCV in the opposite direction was decreased. The VOR of a normal subject after 5 minutes of OKN stimulation to the left is shown in Fig. 1. The subject had had nearly equal VOR gains to the right and left before optokinetic stimulation. Immediately after the lights were turned off SCV's to the left were increased and SCV's to the right were decreased, and the eyes deviated toward the left side of the orbit. These effects gradually decreased over the next 30 sec. OKAN can persist for periods up to 2 min, and its contribution is difficult to separate from that of adaptive changes in the VOR after short periods of optokinetic stimulation. Figure 2 presents the VOR SCV's in this subject before and after 60 min of optokinetic stimulation. The baseline gains to the right and left were nearly equal. Immediately after optokinetic stimulation a velocity bias of about 30 deg/sec to the left was present, which decreased the gain to the right and increased the gain to the left. These effects decreased gradually, but were still present 10 minutes after optokinetic stimulation was stopped when OKAN was unlikely to have been present.

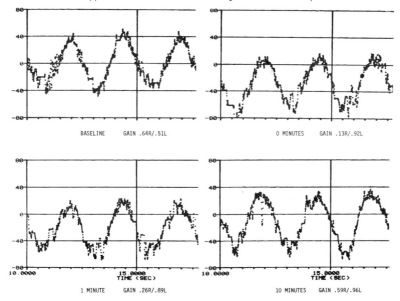

Fig. 2. VOR SCV's after 60 min optokinetic stimulation to left in same subject. + SCV's were to right. - SCV's were to left. VOR gains to right and left are shown. 0 min lights turned off.

The peak SCV's of the VOR in another normal subject after 60 minutes of optokinetic stimulation to the left are shown in Fig. 3. The mean peak SCV's +/- 1 S.D. before optokinetic stimulation and 25 to 30 minutes after stimulation are shown at the left and right margins of the graphs, respectively. At time 0 min the lights were turned off. The large amplitude, abrupt changes in SCV's were probably primarily due to OKAN. The effects at 1 min probably reflected adaptation of the VOR. The ratio of VOR gain to the right/VOR gain to the left was calculated and reflected the directional symmetry during a cycle of VOR. The VOR ratios (mean +/- 1 S.D.) of the same subject are present in Fig. 4. The VOR ratio was approximately 1 before optokinetic stimulation (left margin) and after 25 to 30 min (left margin). Figure 5 demonstrates the VOR ratios in the same subject for a period of about 20 minutes after the optokinetic stimulation. The VOR ratio returned gradually to baseline levels after about 18 minutes.

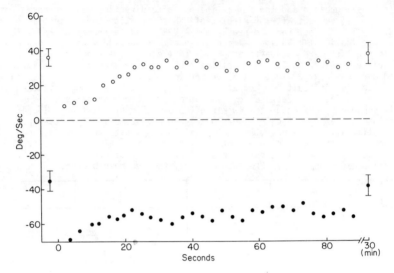

Fig. 3. Peak SCV's of each VOR cycle after 60 min optokinetic
stimulation to left in another normal subject. 0 min
lights turned off.   SCV's right (top), left (bottom).

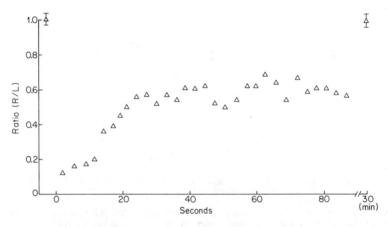

Fig. 4. Ratios of VOR gain right/VOR gain left after 60 min
optokinetic stimulation to left in same subject, as
in Fig. 3.

In another set of experiments chair rotation in the dark was not begun until
after OKAN and OKAAN had ceased. The difference in VOR gain ratio before optokinetic stimulation and the ratio of the maximum adaptive change (baseline gain
right/gain left)-(maximum change gain right/gain left) was calculated. Data
from rightward and leftward optokinetic stimulations were combined. The mean
difference in ratios +/- 1 S.D. of the normal subjects after 5, 30 and 60 minutes of stimulation were 0.26 +/- 0.16, 0.39 +/- 0.13 and 0.61 +/- 0.11, respectively. The large standard deviations reflected the variability of the

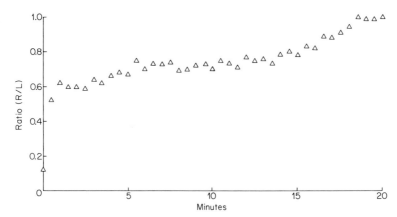

Fig. 5. Ratios of VOR gain right/VOR gain left after 60 min
optokinetic stimulation to left in same patient, as
in Fig. 3.

degree of adaptive changes in the VOR among the subjects. The percent difference in VOR gain ratios was calculated as (difference in ratios/baseline ratio)
X 100. The percent differences after 5, 30 and 60 minutes of optokinetic stimulation were 27 +/- 18%, 46 +/- 20% and 57 +/- 15%, respectively. Optokinetic
stimulations did not significantly affect VOR phase relationships in any of the
normal subjects.

The two patients with idiopathic cerebellar atrophy syndromes had severely impaired pursuit, optokinetic nystagmus (OKN) and synergistic visual-vestibular
interactions, and could not suppress their VOR with fixation (Baloh and colleagues, 1981). No OKAN was present. Their VOR gains were within the normal
range for our laboratory. As expected, optokinetic stimulations did not produce adaptation of the VOR.

The patient with a Chiari malformation had downbeat nystagmus and moderately
impaired pursuit and sinusoidal OKN. The pursuit gains to the right and left
were 0.51 and 0.49, respectively (0.4 Hz, 45 deg/sec). OKN gains to the right
and left were 0.18 and 0.07, respectively (0.05 Hz, 60 deg/sec). The VOR gain
during sinusoidal rotations (0.05 to 0.4 Hz, 22.6 to 60 deg/sec) was unusually
high (nearly 1). The gains during synergistic visual-vestibular interactions
(rotation within a lighted, stationary optokinetic drum) and attempts to suppress the VOR by fixation of a light attached to the chair were the same as the
VOR gain in the dark. Constant velocity, optokinetic stimulation produced a
gradual build-up of OKN over many seconds. The final, maximum levels of OKN
SCV were normal or nearly normal. We have described this phenomenon in other
patients with disorders affecting the midline structures of the cerebellum with
and without downbeat nystagmus (Yee and colleagues, 1979; Yee and colleagues,
1985). The slow build-up of OKN SCV is demonstrated in Fig. 6. Optokinetic
stimulations produced adaptive changes in the VOR, that were similar to those
observed in the normal subjects.

Smooth pursuit was not modified by prior optokinetic stimulation in the normal
subjects. The closed-loop pursuit system was apparently able to compensate for
any eye velocity bias that was produced by the optokinetic stimulation. The
pursuit system was impaired in the patients with cerebellar disorders, and might
not be expected to be able to compensate for a bias. However, no modification
of pursuit was found.

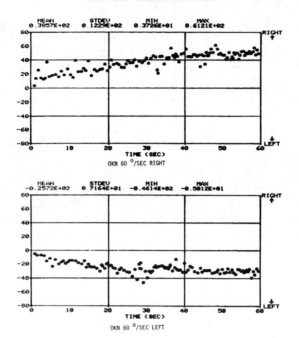

Fig. 6. OKN SCV's of each nystagmus beat in patient with
        Chiari malformation. Optokinetic drum constant
        velocity 60 deg/sec right (top) and left (bottom).

DISCUSSION

Unidirectional optokinetic stimulation for short periods of time can produce
transient, adaptive modification of the VOR in normal human subjects. The
adaptive changes in the VOR are distinct from an algebraic summation of the
OKAN and the VOR, since the adaptive changes clearly persist longer than does
OKAN after 30-60 minutes of optokinetic stimulation. The range of OKAN duration was 20 sec to 3 minutes; whereas, the duration of changes in VOR gain persisted from 10 to 25 minutes. The durations of OKAN and adaptive changes in
the VOR were more similar after only 5 minutes of optokinetic stimulation, and
would be more difficult to separate if testing of the VOR were not delayed until after the OKAN ceased. Westall and Schor (in press) presented simultaneous
sinusoidal chair rotation and unidirectional optokinetic stimulation to normal
subjects for two minutes, and continued the chair rotation after the visual
stimulation was terminated by turning off the lights. The VOR was recorded for
60 sec after the termination of visual stimulation. Data from the last 30 seconds were used to measure VOR adaptation to avoid effects of OKAN. However,
since the OKAN could not be monitored directly, it is possible that OKAN contributed to the adaptive changes. Schor and Westall have observed VOR adaptation in normal subjects after very short periods of optokinetic stimulation
without simultaneous vestibular stimulation (personal communication).

The adaptive changes found in this study were similar in magnitude to those reported by Yagi and his colleagues (1981) and Westall and Schor (in press). The
previous studies used simultaneous vestibular and visual stimulations. In the
former study the mean decrease in VOR gain in normal subjects was 0.33 after

1 hour of stimulation. In our study optokinetic stimulation increased the gain in the direction of drum rotation and decreased the gain in the opposite direction. If the optokinetic stimulation is assumed to produce a velocity bias in the direction of drum rotation, the mean change in VOR gain was 0.29 after 1 hour of stimulation. Westall and Schor (in press) did not present VOR gains in their report. The difference in VOR gain ratios, as defined in our study, had a mean of 0.28 in normal subjects after 2 minutes of stimulation. In our study the mean difference in gain ratios after 5 minutes of optokinetic stimulation was 0.26.

The vestibulocerebellum is important in adaptation of the VOR. Lesions of the flocculus in non-primate animals (Robinson, 1976; Nagao, 1983) and in the monkey (Lisberger and colleagues, 1984) abolished adaptive changes in the VOR. However, it is not clear if the cerebellum is the structure in which motor learning takes place. Learned information might be stored elsewhere, and the cerebellum might simply be part of the pathway that mediates the adaptive changes (Demer and Robinson, 1982; Miles and colleagues, 1980). Yagi and coworkers (1981) fitted patients with cerebellar disorders with image-reversal prisms, and rotated them sinusoidally for 1 hour while they viewed a stationary light. VOR adaptation was produced in some patients, but was absent in others. They suggested that adaptation occurred in patients with less severe damage to the cerebellum.

Our two patients with cerebellar atrophy syndromes had markedly impaired pursuit, OKN and visual-vestibular interactions, that were consistent with severe damage to the vestibulocerebellum. VOR adaptation was absent. The patient who had the Chiari malformation and preservation of VOR adaptation had moderately severe ataxia and moderate impairment of sinusoidal pursuit and sinusoidal OKN. A gradual build-up of OKN to constant velocity stimulation was found. Normal humans demonstrate an immediate increase in OKN amplitude and SCV when exposed to the constant velocity drum rotations used in this study.

We have described other patients who have had build-up of OKN. These patients have had lesions of the midline cerebellum (Yee and colleagues, 1979; Yee and colleagues, 1985), lesions of the parietal lobe (Baloh and colleagues, 1980b) and maldevelopment of retinal cone photoreceptors (Baloh and colleagues, 1980c; Yee and colleagues, 1981). We suggested that these patients had defects in the smooth pursuit pathways, such that the contributions of smooth pursuit to OKN, including rapid acceleration, were absent. A subcortical optokinetic system that is similar to that in animals with poorly-developed foveas was intact. The subcortical system produced the build-up of OKN. The finding of preserved VOR adaptation in the patient in this study suggests that elements within the subcortical system participate in the process of adaptation.

BIBLIOGRAPHY

Baloh, R. W., L. Langhofer, V. Honrubia, and R. D. Yee (1980a). On-line analysis of eye movements using a digital computer. Aviat. Space Environ. Med., 51, 563-567.
Baloh, R. W., R. D. Yee, and V. Honrubia (1980b). Optokinetic nystagmus and parietal lobe lesions. Ann. Neurol., 7, 269-276.
Baloh, R. W., R. D. Yee, and V. Honrubia (1980c). Optokinetic asymmetry in patients with maldeveloped foveas. Brain. Res., 186, 211-216.
Baloh, R. W., R. D. Yee, J. Kimm, and V. Honrubia (1981). Vestibular-ocular reflex in patients with lesions involving the vestibulocerebellum. Exp. Neurol., 72, 141-152.
Collewijn, H., A. J. Martins, and R. M. Steinman (1983). Compensatory eye movements during active and passive head movements: fast adaptation to changes in visual magnification. J. Physiol., 340, 259-286.

Demer, J. L., and D. A. Robinson (1982). Effects of reversible lesions and
    stimulation of olivocerebellar system on vestibuloocular reflex plasticity.
    J. Neurophysiol., 47, 1084-1106.
Lisberger, S. G., F. A. Miles, and D. S. Zee (1984). Signals used to compute
    errors in monkey vestibuloocular reflex: possible role of flocculus. J.
    Neurophysiol., 52, 1140-1153.
Miles, F. A., D. J. Braitman, and B. M. Dow (1980). Long-term adaptive changes
    in primate vestibuloocular reflex. IV. electrophysiological observations
    in flocculus of adapted monkeys. J. Neurophysiol., 43, 1477-1493.
Nagao, S. (1983). Effects of vestibulocerebellar lesions upon dynamic charac-
    teristics and adaptation of vestibulo-ocular and optokinetic responses in
    pigmented rabbits. Exp. Brain. Res., 53, 36-46.
Robinson, D. A. (1976). Adaptive gain control of vestibuloocular reflex by the
    cerebellum. J. Neurophysiol., 39, 954-969.
Westall, C. A., and C. M. Schor (in press). Adaptation of the vestibulo-ocular
    reflex in amblyopia. Invest. Ophthalmol. Vis. Sci.
Yagi, T., M. Shimizu, S. Sekine, T. Kamio, and J. Suzuki (1981). A new neur-
    otological test for detecting cerebellar dysfunction. Ann. NY. Acad. Sci.,
    374, 526-531.
Yee, R. D., R. W. Baloh, V. Honrubia, and C. G. Y. Lau (1979). Slow build-up
    of optokinetic nystagmus associated with downbeat nystagmus. Invest.
    Ophthalmol. Vis. Sci., 18, 622-629.
Yee, R. D., R. W. Baloh, and V. Honrubia (1981). Eye movement abnormalities in
    rod monochromacy. Ophthalmology, 88, 1010-1017.
Yee, R. D., E. Stein, R. W. Baloh, and V. Honrubia (1985). Eye movement pat-
    terns in downbeat nystagmus. Invest. Ophthalmol. Vis. Sci. Suppl., 26, 47.

Plastic Changes in Cervicoocular and Vestibuloocular Reflexes Elicited by Labyrinthine Lesions or Altered Visual Feedback

B. W. Peterson, J. F. Baker and C. Wickland

Northwestern University Medical School, Chicago,
IL 60611, USA

In normal animals, the vestibuloocular reflex (VOR) plays a crucial role in stabilizing gaze. When the VOR is impaired by labyrinthine lesions, animals initially must rely on slowly responding visual tracking and optokinetic mechanisms to stabilize gaze (Raphan and Cohen, 1978). Over time, however, plastic adaptive mechanisms act to improve gaze stability by bringing into play oculomotor reflexes elicited by alternative sensory systems such as neck proprioceptors or altering vestibuloocular reflexes elicited by the surviving labyrinthine receptors. This paper will examine the properties of two such adaptively generated oculomotor reflexes: the cervicoocular reflex (COR) and the cross-coupled vestibuloocular reflex (X-VOR).

I. PROPERTIES OF THE CERVICOOCULAR REFLEX

In normal animals, the smooth phase eye movements (as opposed to eye position changes produced by saccadic movements) produced by rotating the neck with the head held fixed in space are very small except at frequencies less than 0.05 Hz, where the VOR no longer adequately stabilizes gaze (Baker and colleagues, 1982; Barmack, Nastos, and Pettorossi, 1981; Fuller, 1980). After labyrinthine lesions, however, the COR increases dramatically and reaches gains (ratio of eye movement to neck rotation) of 0.2-0.4 (Baker and colleagues, 1982; Dichgans and colleagues, 1973; Kasai and Zee, 1978;).

In collaboration with J. Goldberg and R. Schor, we have studied both the dynamic properties and time course of development of the COR in alert cats after inactivation of the semicircular canals by plugging. To quantify COR dynamics, we placed animals in a totally dark room and recorded their horizontal eye movements in response to sinusoidal rotation of the body about an earth fixed head at frequencies of 0.1-2.5 Hz. Rotation amplitudes were scaled so that the stimulus had the same velocity at all frequencies. Typical records during stimulation at 0.1 and 1.0 Hz are shown in Fig. 1A for a cat 8-10 months after plugging of the horizontal semicircular canals. At both frequencies, slow phase eye movements to the right occurred during rightward rotation of the body, which is equivalent to leftward rotation of the head on the trunk. The COR therefore acts in a compensatory fashion, indicated by a phase of approximately 0. The phase curve in Fig. 1B indicates that such compensatory behavior is observed across the entire 0.1-2.5 Hz frequency range. Gain is also approximately constant at all frequencies tested. This simple dynamic behavior is interesting since it indicates that neuronal pathways responsible for the COR are able to transform neck sensory signals into motor commands with the appropriate dynamic properties to compensate for the low pass filter characteristic of the oculomotor plant (Skavenski and Robinson, 1973).

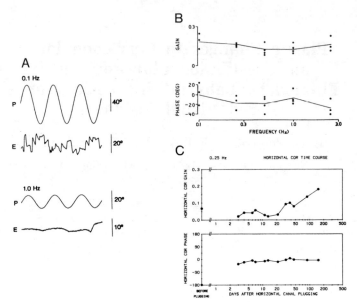

FIGURE 1. Properties of cervicoocular reflex (COR) in canal-plugged cats.   A.
Eye movements evoked by horizontal neck rotation in dark in a cat 8   to   10
months after plugging of horizontal canals.   Upward deflections indicate
rightward body or eye rotation. Frequencies of stimulation were 0.1, 1.0 Hz.
B.   Frequency response of COR in same cat. Gains and phases of reflex eye
movements measured in several experiments more than 8 months after plugging are
plotted against stimulus frequency.   C. Time course of development of COR.
Reflex gains and phases are plotted at various times from 3-170 days after
horizontal semicircular canal plugging.

Another interesting property of the COR is the slow time course of its
development following semicircular canal plugging. As illustrated in Fig. 1C,
the reflex remains at a barely detectable gain of 0.04 for the first 20 days
following plugging, and then rises slowly over the next 150 days to reach a
final value of about 0.2. This behavior contrasts sharply of that of the VOR,
where plastic changes have time constants measured in minutes or hours
(Collewijn, Martins and Steinman, 1983; Miles and Eighmy, 1980; Schultheis
and Robinson, 1981). Both the slow development of the COR and its low gain in
normal animals are difficult to reconcile with electrophysiological evidence
that neck receptors exert short latency excitatory actions upon vestibuloocular
relay neurons in anesthetized cats with normal labyrinthine function (Hikosaka
and Maeda, 1973). Our working hypothesis is that in alert animals this short
latency excitation is counterbalanced by the action of less direct pathways.
We cannot explain, however, why this balance is so slow to shift in response to
gaze error signals that occur after semicircular canal plugging.

II.   VESTIBULOOCULAR REFLEXES AFTER SEMICIRCULAR CANAL PLUGGING

In   collaboration   with   J.   Goldberg and R.   Schor, we have examined
vestibuloocular reflexes after plugging of all six semicircular canals, or the
four vertical canals or the two horizontal canals. Cats with all six canals
plugged retain a VOR when rotated in earth-vertical planes due to otolith

function.   The otolith-mediated VOR is strong during low-frequency rotations
(gain is 0.6 or better at 0.05 Hz), but at 1.0 Hz and above it becomes quite
weak and has lagging phase.   Reflex eye movements are virtually absent,
however, when cats with all canals plugged are rotated in earth-horizontal
planes in the dark. When large, high-frequency rotations are applied, a small
residual VOR can be observed which has a 90 degree phase lead and a gain that
increases linearly with stimulus frequency (Baker and colleagues, 1982). We
attribute this residual VOR to impulsive movements of the cupula and endolymph
in the plugged canals.

After plugging the four vertical canals, rotations in earth-horizontal planes
reveal simple vestibuloocular behavior.   VOR gain is approximately 1 when
rotation is in the plane of the intact horizontal semicircular canals (at a
pitch of 21 degrees nose down from the stereotaxic horizontal plane). When the
animal is tilted so that the horizontal semicircular canals are at an angle
with respect to the plane of rotation, gain decreases as the cosine of the
angle.   No   vertical   eye   movements are produced by rotation in any
earth-horizontal plane.

More complex behavior is observed in cats in which only the horizontal canals
are plugged. When rotated horizontally in the null plane, where no vertical
canal activation occurs (approximately 28 degrees nose down from horizontal
sterotaxic plane), these animals exhibit no VOR other than the residual
response seen after all canals are plugged. As illustrated in Fig. 2A,
however, rotations with the nose elevated above the null plane elicit a
vigorous, compensatory horizontal VOR. As shown in Fig. 2B for two different
animals, the horizontal VOR gain increases sinusoidally with the angle of
elevation of the head above the null plane and reaches an maximum value of
0.3-0.4.

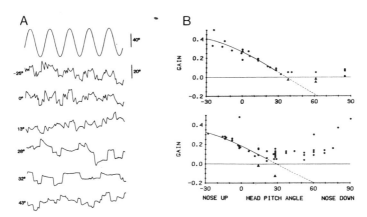

FIGURE 2.   Horizontal VOR in cats with plugged horizontal canals. Traces at
left show horizontal eye movements evoked by horizontal whole body rotations
indicated by top trace. Each trace was recorded with animal's head tilted at
different angles nose up (negative angles) or nose down (positive angles) with
respect to the stereotaxic horizontal plane. Gains and phases of smooth
horizontal vestibuloocular eye movements for this cat are plotted against head
tilt angle at the upper right. Plot at lower right is equivalent data from
another animal.

The properties of the horizontal VOR as illustrated in Fig. 2 indicate that it is evoked by stimulation of vertical semicircular canals. An explanation of the coupling between vertical canals and horizontal eye movements must be sought in a kinematic analysis of the neuronal processes that couple the six semicircular canals to the six extraocular muscles. Robinson (1982) has suggested that this analysis can be greatly simplified by assuming that the canals and muscles act as three push-pull pairs. We have tested the validity of this assumption by recording EMG activity of the six extraocular muscles in decerebrate cats during rotations in a large number of planes. The optimal axes for activating antagonistic muscles within each pair (shown in Fig. 3) are nearly opposite. Thus, the optimal planes are nearly the same and the assumption of pairing holds at least for the decerebrate cat.

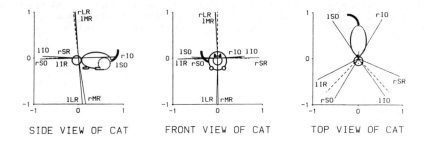

SIDE VIEW OF CAT   FRONT VIEW OF CAT   TOP VIEW OF CAT

FIGURE 3. Axes of maximal response of ten extraocular muscles recorded in a decerebrate cat, seen from three views. Use the right-hand rule to determine direction of rotation corresponding to an axis. r = right, l = left. SO = superior oblique, IO = inferior oblique, SR = superior rectus, IR = inferior rectus, LR = lateral rectus, MR = medial rectus.

Our EMG records from extraocular muscles also allow us to compute the normal coupling between afferent input from each pair of canals and motor output to each pair of extraocular muscles. These are given in Table 1A below. Ezure and Graf (1984) derived a similar matrix from measurements of the geometry of canals and extraocular muscles. The important terms for our present analysis are the left and middle coefficients in the bottom row, which specify the coupling between vertical canals and horizontal rectus muscles. The very small values of these terms indicate that in the cat, vertical canals normally produce very little horizontal eye movement (peak gain approximately 0.03). To produce a typical peak gain of 0.30 observed in our three horizontal canal-plugged cats, these terms, which presumably represent activation of vestibuloocular pathways, must increase to 0.247 and -0.209. To explore more fully the properties of the adaptive system responsible for this change, we undertook the experiments described in the next section.

TABLE 1

A. Normal	CANAL PAIR INPUT			B. Adapted	CANAL PAIR INPUT		
EYE MUSCLE PAIR OUTPUT	rP1A	rA1P	rH1H	EYE MUSCLE PAIR OUTPUT	rP1A	rA1P	rH1H
rSOIO	.978	.170	.006	rSOIO	.978	.170	-.128
rSRIR	-.425	.915	-.015	rSRIR	-.425	.915	.208
rLRMR	.021	-.001	-.993	rLRMR	.021	-.001	-.997

TABLE 1. A. Connections between semicircular canal pairs and eye muscle pairs revealed by EMG recordings in 5 decerebrate cats. Each number indicates strength and sign of coupling between the indicated canal pair and a pair of muscles in the right eye. B. Canal to eye muscle connections after four hours of adaptation to horizontal rotation coupled with synchronous vertical optokinetic rotation.

Before leaving the canal plugging experiments, however, we must consider what occurs when the horizontal canal-plugged cat is rotated with its head tilted below the null plane. In this case, activity of the vertical canals reverses in sign and thus horizontal eye movements produced by the vertical canals should become anticompensatory as indicated by the dashed lines in Fig. 2B. The behavior of the two cats shown in the figure is more complex. The first animal suppresses all vestibuloocular eye movements during such nose down rotations, while the second manages to produce a compensatory VOR. The data thus suggest that adaptive changes in the VOR can be specific to a particular postural position of the head.

III. CROSS-AXIS VOR PLASTICITY IN NORMAL CATS

In 1981, Schultheis and Robinson reported that pairing horizontal optokinetic stimulus with pitch rotation led to development of horizontal vestibuloocular eye movements during pitch rotations in the dark. In collaboration with R. Harrison and N. Isu, we have adopted their paradigm as a convenient way of exploring the time course and dynamics of cross-axis plasticity. We began our analysis with the simple situation in which 28 degree/s sinusoidal vertical (pitch) optokinetic stimulation was paired with 18 degree/s sinusoidal horizontal rotation. The animal was positioned with its head 28 degrees down from the horizontal stereotaxic plane so that the rotation activated primarily horizontal semicircular canals. Figure 4A shows vertical eye movements produced by 0.25 Hz horizontal rotation before and after 2 hours of paired optokinetic vestibular training at 0.25 Hz. The adaptively generated X-VOR is clear in the smooth phase eye velocity records shown below each eye position trace.

APVOS-N*

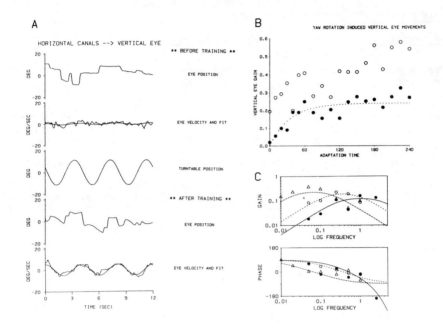

FIGURE 4. Vertical eye movements evoked by horizontal rotation before and after cross-axis training. A. Records of vertical eye position and velocity during 0.25 Hz horizontal rotation shown at center before (upper traces) and after (lower traces) exposing cat to 2 Hr of 0.25 Hz horizontal rotation paired with vertical optokinetic stimulation. B. Time course of development of cross-axis vertical VOR in same 0.25 Hz training paradigm. Filled circles indicate gain of VOR in dark, open circles, eye movements produced by combined visuo-vestibular stimulation during training. Dashed line is exponential curve with 37 min time constant fitted to the data. C. Frequency response of vertical eye movements elicited by horizontal rotation after cross-axis visuo-vestibular training at 0.05 Hz (triangles), 0.25 Hz (open circles) and 1.0 Hz (filled circles). Band pass filters fitted to data are plotted by dashed (0.05 Hz), dotted (0.25 Hz) and solid (1.0 Hz) lines (see text).

Figure 4B shows the time course of development of the X-VOR. Over the 4 hour period of our observations, the time course is well-approximated by a single exponential with a 37 minute time constant, as indicated by the dashed line. Cross-coupling was maintained for at least 12 hours in the dark, but declined rapidly with a typically less than 10 minute time constant when animals were rotated in the presence of a stationary visual pattern. We also monitored the gain of the vertical VOR in the dark during the adaptive process and found it to be unchanged. Assuming that the torsional VOR is also unchanged, the brainstem interconnection matrix of the adapted VOR at 4 hours would be as shown in Table 1B. Note that the major changes occur in two terms in the right-hand column, which specifies coupling of horizontal canals to vertical eye movers. We have also performed an equivalent experiment in which an animal lying on its side experiences the same visual and vestibular stimuli. In this case, adaptive training causes vertical canal stimulation to generate horizontal eye movements, while eye movements produced by the horizontal canals are unchanged. The time course of this process is similar to that shown in Fig. 4B.

The dynamic properties of vertical eye movements induced by horizontal rotation were the same in all four animals tested. As illustrated in Fig. 4C, both gain and phase characteristics could be closely approximated by the behavior a band-pass filter centered on the frequency at which training occurred. Thus, when training was at 0.05 Hz, adaptive eye movements had the maximum gain and approximately 0 degrees (compensatory) phase at approximately 0.05 Hz. When training was at 0.25 Hz, the maximum gain and 0 degrees phase occurred at that frequency.

Published information concerning the dynamics and time course of plastic adaptive changes in the horizontal VOR induced by magnifying or reducing lenses indicates that such changes resemble those described here. Godaux, Halleux and Gobert (1983) and Lisberger, Miles, and Optican (1983) have measured changes in the horizontal VOR gain and phase when animals wearing such lenses were oscillated sinusoidally at a fixed frequency. Their data appear to be well-approximated by the behavior of a band-pass filter as we observed for the X-VOR. The time courses often described for onset and extinction of changes in horizontal VOR gain produced by magnifying or reducing lenses are longer than those we report here for the X-VOR (Gonshor and Melvill-Jones, 1976; Miles and Eighmy, 1980). However, initial gain changes produced by such lenses can occur quite rapidly (Collewijn, Martins, and Steinman, 1983; Miles and Eighmy, 1980) which suggests that VOR plasticity may involve processes with two time constants. A longer training period will be required to see whether cross-axis VOR plasticity also exhibits two time constants. If so, this will support our hypothesis that cross-axis adaptive changes are merely a spatial extension of the familiar one-dimensional adaptive process.

As indicated above, we also investigated adaptive changes when animals lying on their sides were rotated in an earth-horizontal plane while viewing an optokinetic pattern that rotated in an earth-vertical plane. Dynamics of the adaptive horizontal eye movements produced by the pitch-like stimulus in this case had the characteristics of a band-pass filter as did the vertical eye movements illustrated in Fig. 4. We were therefore surprised when we studied adaptation produced by pairing pitch rotation in a vertical plane with horizontal optokinetic stimulation as described by Schultheis and Robinson. The dynamic properties of horizontal eye movements produced by pitch rotation in the dark after 2 hours of such training at 0.25 Hz are shown in Fig. 5. Rather than peaking at the training frequency, gain was largest at the lowest frequency tested and fell continuously over the frequency range. The combination of falling gain and phase advance at lower frequencies indicates that this behavior cannot be modeled by a band-pass filter or any other combination of filters in series. Instead, a parallel network like that shown in Fig. 5 (right) is required. Here, two signals converge at the input of a band-pass filter. One, which enters the filter unchanged, could be the head velocity signal from semicircular canals. The other, which passes through an integrator (1/S), could represent a head position signal from otolith organs. For the model to work, the latter signal must act in an inhibitory fashion. The dashed line shows the good fit to the data obtained with such a model.

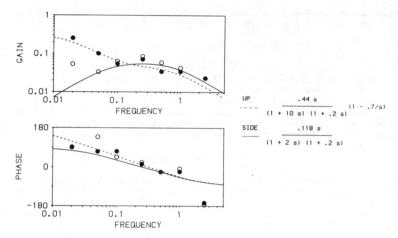

FIGURE 5.   Gains and phases of horizontal eye movements evoked by rotation of animal in its sagittal plane. Rotations were either about horizontal axis (pitch: filled   circles,   dashed   line   transfer   function) or about the earth-vertical axis (lying on side:open circles, solid line transfer function). Transfer   functions   used   to   fit   the   two types of data are given in Laplace nomenclature.

The form of the model in Fig. 5 suggested that the plasticity mechanism might be coupling both vertical canal and otolith signals to horizontal extraocular nuclei. To test the system's ability to couple otolith signals in this way, we performed the pitch rotation-horizontal optokinetic testing on an animal with plugged vertical canals and found that adaptively generated horizontal eye movements could indeed be produced in the absence of canal input.   When observed in this way, the dynamics of the presumed otolith-induced horizontal eye movements resembled the simple band-pass filter behavior illustrated in Fig. 4C.   Apparently, the subtractive interaction required by the model in Fig. 5 occurs only when both canals and otoliths are activated together during the training. Alternatively, the band-pass filter behavior of the X-VOR might be due to a stable adaptation of otolith function in vertical VOR developed over several months after canal plugging and before testing.

In attempting to analyze the responses to pitch rotation further, we encountered another situation in which motor learning appears to depend upon posture.   When animals trained in the vertical plane pitch paradigm described above were tested with horizontal plane rotation while lying on their sides to observe vertical canal coupling to horizontal eye movers, virtually no horizontal eye movement occurred at the training frequency. Similarly, animals trained in the side-lying position and then tested with pitch rotation in the dark exhibited weaker adaptive horizontal eye movements than   expected. Apparently, position cues from otolith organs or other receptors act to gate the eye movements produced by the X-VOR so that they are maximal in the posture in which the original training occurred. This postural dependency of canal-ocular reflexes is not entirely surprising, since even in the normal animal   these   reflexes must vary for rotations in earth-horizontal and earth-vertical planes to compensate for the presence of simultaneously acting otolith-ocular reflexes.

The overall picture of the VOR plasticity process which emerges from these studies indicates that it is remarkably flexible. With appropriate visual-vestibular pairing, either canal or otolith signals generated by rotations in any plane can be coupled to any set of extraocular muscles. Dynamics of the coupling can be adjusted to maximize image stability at the frequency at which training occurs. More remarkably, the system appears able to adjust coupling independently for different postures of the head so that the VOR performs optimally regardless of the orientation of the animal in space. These intriguing properties will provide challenges for those seeking to decipher the neuronal substrates of the plasticity process.

ACKNOWLEDGEMENTS: This work was supported by NIH Grants EY 04058 and EY 05289.

REFERENCES

Baker, J., Goldberg, J. Peterson, B., and Schor, R. (1982). Oculomotor reflexes after semicircular canal plugging in cats. Brain Res. 252, 151-155.

Barmack, N.H., Nastos, M.A., and Pettorossi, V.E. (1981). The horizontal and vertical cervico-ocular reflexes of the rabbit. Brain Res., 224, 261-278.

Collewijn, H., Martins, A.J., and Steinman, R.M. (1983). Compensatory eye movements during active and passive head movements: fast adaptation to changes in visual magnification. J. Physiol. (Lond) 340, 259-286.

Dichgans, J., Bizzi, E., Morasso, P., and Tagliasco, V. (1973). Mechanisms underlying recovery of eye-head coordination following bilateral labyrinthectomy in monkeys. Exp. Brain Res. 18., 548-562.

Ezure, K., and Graf, W. (1984a). A quantitative analysis of the spatial organization of the vestibulo-ocular reflexes in lateral- and frontal-eyed animals. I. Orientation of semicircular canals and extraocular muscles. Neurosci. 12, 85-93.

Ezure, K., and Graf, W. (1984b). A quantitative analysis of the spatial organization of the vestibulo-ocular reflexes in lateral- and frontal-eyed animals. II. Neuronal networks underlying vestibulo-oculomotor coordination. Neurosci. 12, 95-109.

Fuller, J. F. (1980). The dynamic neck-eye reflex in mammals. Exp. Brain Res. 41, 29-35.

Godaux, E., Halleux, J., and Gobert, C. (1983). Adaptive changes of the vestibulo-ocular reflex in the cat: the effects of a long-term frequency-selective procedure. Exp. Brain Res. 49, 28-34.

Gonshor, A., and Melvill-Jones, G. (1976). Extreme vestibulo-ocular adaptation induced by prolonged optical reversal of vision. J. Physiol (Lond) 256, 381-414.

Hikosaka, O., and Maeda, M. (1973). Cervical effects on abducens motoneurons and impulses and their interaction with vestibulo-ocular reflex. Exp. Brain

Res. 18, 512-530.

Kasai, T., and Zee, D.S. (1978). Eye-head coordination in labyrinth-defective human beings. Brain Res. 144, 123-141.

Lisberger, S.G., Miles, F.A., and Optican, L.M. (1983). Frequency-selective adaptation: evidence for channels in the vestibulo-ocular reflex? J. Neurosci. 3, 1234-1244.

Miles, F.A., and Eighmy, B.B. (1980) Long term adaptive changes in primate vetibuloocular reflex. I. Behavioral observations. J. Neurophysiol. 43, 1406-1425.

Paige, G.D. (1983). Vestibuloocular reflex and its interactions with visual following mechanisms in the squirrel monkey. II. Response characteristics and plasticity following unilateral inactivation of horizontal canal. J. Neurophysiol. 49, 152-168.

Raphan, T., and Cohen, B. (1978). Brainstem mechanisms for rapid and slow eye movements. Ann. Rev. Physiol. 40, 527.552.

Robinson, D.A. (1982). The use of matrices in analyzing the three-dimensional behavior of the vestibuloocular reflex. Biol. Cybern. 46, 53-56.

Schultheis, L.W., and Robinson, D.A. (1981). Directional plasticity of the vestibulo-ocular reflex in the cat. Ann. N.Y. Acad. Sci. 374, 504-512.

Skavenski, A.A., and Robinson, D.A. (1973). Role of abducens neurons in vestibulo-ocular reflexes. J. Neurophysiol. 36, 724-738.

ACTH/MSH-like Neuropeptides and Lesion-induced Plastic Processes

H. Flohr, U. Lüneburg and C. Richter-Landsberg

Department of Neurobiology, University of Bremen,
D-2800 Bremen 33, FRG

Over the last decade, an increasing number of studies have suggested that the pituitary and hypothalamic peptides ACTH, α-MSH and β-MSH may play an important role in the behavioral adaption of an organism to its environment. Evidence in support of this concept has so far been obtained from two experimental approaches:

1. The acquisition and retention of learned behavior can be enhanced pharmacologically by administration of ACTH/MSH-like neuropeptides. This finding has been confirmed for a range of behavioral tasks, such as classical and instrumental conditioning, habituation and imprinting and for a variety of species, such as mammals (including man), birds, reptiles, amphibians and fish. The effects are independent of the classical endocrine actions of the respective hormones; apparently, the behaviorally active part of these peptides is a common sequence of four amino acids in position 4-7 of the ACTH-molecule.

2. Learning in a number of tasks can be inhibited by interventions in endogenous peptidergic systems, e.g., by hypophysectomy, antisera to ACTH or MSH, or by means of the heptapeptide [D-Phe^7] ACTH$_{4-10}$. For recent reviews see De Wied and Jolles (1982), Dunn (1984), Gispen and Zwiers (1985).

Recent observations using the paradigm of vestibular compensation (Flohr and Lüneburg, 1982) indicate that these peptides may also play a role in lesion-induced plastic processes, i.e., those processes in which damage to the nervous system or to the sensory or motor interface is followed by recovery of the initially disrupted function.

In the following a summary is given of experimental results dealing with three questions:

1. Do ACTH/MSH-like peptides exert pharmacological effects on the recovery of function following peripheral vestibular lesions comparable to those observed in other learning paradigms?

2. Can a physiological role of these peptides in lesion-induced plastic processes be established by the same interventive approach employed in other learning paradigms?

3. Which cellular mechanisms might underly both the pharmacological
    effects and the assumed physiological role of these peptides?

The experiments to be described were conducted on Rana temporaria.
Unilateral labyrinthectomy was carried out in the anesthetized
(MS 222) animal using an extracranial approach as described by
Ewald (1892). The main postural symptom, head deviation to the side
of the lesion, was used to quantify the extent of the functional
deficit and the course of its recovery.

Pharmacological Effects of ACTH$_{4-10}$, ACTH$_{1-10}$, α-MSH and ORG 2766.

Figure 1 gives a survey of the peptides studied so far. As shown in
Fig. 2a, the acquisition of the compensated state can be significantly accelerated by ACTH$_{4-10}$. The peptide is effective in doses of
5-1000 µg/kg per day. In the initial phase of compensation the improvement is independent of dose, but at a later stage, when the
functional deficit is low (i.e., with a head tilt of less than 10°),
only a high dose appears to exert an effect. The pharmacological
effects would thus seem to be related in some way to the degree of
the functional deficit. ACTH$_{1-10}$ (Fig. 2b) and α-MSH (Fig. 2c) in
comparable doses also increase the rate of compensation. The ACTH
analogue, ORG 2766, has been shown to be the most effective ACTH-
like peptide in other learning paradigms (De Wied and Jolles, 1982).
The same is true in vestibular compensation, the peptide being active in nanogram amounts (Fig. 2d).

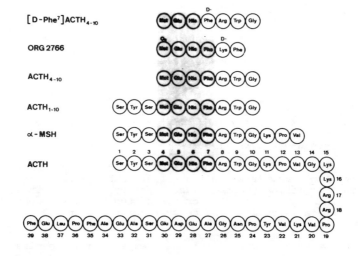

Fig. 1

Structure of ACTH/MSH analogues tested in the present
investigation.

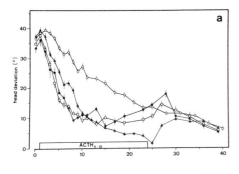

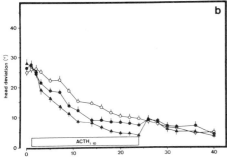

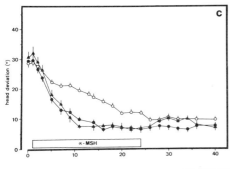

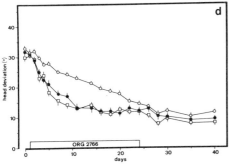

Fig. 2 a-d

Effects of $ACTH_{4-10}$ (a), $ACTH_{1-10}$ (b), α-MSH (c) and ORG 2766 (d) on compensation following unilateral labyrinthectomy in Rana temporaria. The peptides were administered daily i.l. from the 1st to the 24th postoperative day.
Ordinates: head deviation in degrees, mean value $\pm$ S.E.; abscissas: time in days.

(a) $ACTH_{4-10}$ was tested in three different doses:
●   5 µg/kg per day (n=20);
□   35 µg/kg per day (n=20);
▲ 250 µg/kg per day (n=35);
○ NaCl-treated control (n=50).

(b) $ACTH_{1-10}$ was tested in two doses:
●   50 µg/kg per day (n=16);
▲ 350 µg/kg per day (n=16);
○ NaCl-treated control (n=16).

(c) α-MSH was tested in two doses:
●   5 µg/kg per day (n=16);
▲ 500 µg/kg per day (n=16);
○ NaCl-treated control (n=28).

(d) ORG 2766 was tested in two doses:
● 250 ng/kg per day (n=32);
□ 1000 ng/kg per day (n=32);
○ NaCl-treated control (n=32).

Effects of Hypophysectomy and [D-Phe⁷]ACTH₄₋₁₀.

The effects of hypophysectomy 8-12 days prior to hemilabyrinthectomy on vestibular compensation are shown in Fig. 3: the compensation
process is markedly slowed down relative to sham-operated controls.
By daily administration of 250 µg/kg ACTH₄₋₁₀ from the first postoperative day onwards, a normal or even enhanced rate of compensation can be restored in hypophysectomized animals (Fig. 3). When
this treatment is discontinued on day 17 of the experiment, a gradual decline to the low levels of compensation manifested by the
untreated hypophysectomized animals is observed.

These effects are remarkably similar to those observed in other
learning paradigms, e.g., active and passive avoidance in the rat.
In this case, hypophysectomy results in an impaired learning performance but this deficit can be reversed by chronic treatment with
ACTH₄₋₁₀ (Bohus and others, 1973). As in the present study, this
protective effect was of short-term nature.

[D-Phe⁷]ACTH₄₋₁₀ is an analogue of the ACTH₄₋₁₀ molecule, whereby
the phenylalanine in position 7, which plays a key role in the me-
diation of the behavioral effects, has been replaced by its D-en-
antiomer. In certain behavioral tasks this agent has been shown to
exert effects antagonistic to ACTH₄₋₁₀ (De Wied and Jolles, 1982).
As can be seen from Fig. 4a, it inhibits the compensation process.
Furthermore, if given in the fully or partially compensated state
(Fig. 4b) it induces a partial decompensation, i.e., a temporal re-
appearance of the postural deficits.

Taken together, these findings are consistent with the assumption
that ACTH/MSH-like neuropeptides might play a physiological role
in the compensation phenomenon.

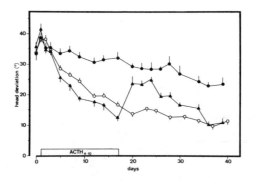

Fig. 3

Time course of vestibular compensation in Rana temporaria
following hypophysectomy with and without ACTH₄₋₁₀ treatment. Hypophysectomy was carried out 8-12 days prior to labyrinthectomy. ● hypophysectomy only (n=10); ▲ hypophysectomy plus ACTH₄₋₁₀ administration from the 1st to the 17th
day after hemilabyrinthectomy, 250 µg/kg per day (n=14);
  o NaCl-treated control (n=30). Ordinate: head deviation
in degrees, mean value ± S.E.; abscissa: time in days.

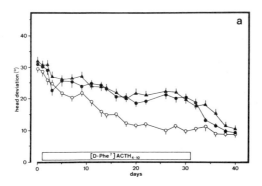

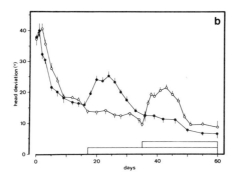

Fig. 4 a-b

Effects of [D-Phe⁷]ACTH₄₋₁₀ on vestibular compensation.
(a) [D-Phe⁷]ACTH₄₋₁₀ was given from the 1st to the 31st
day following hemilabyrinthectomy. Two different doses
were tested : ● 1000 µg/kg per day (n=16); ▲ 4000 µg/kg
per day (n=16); ○ NaCl-treated control (n=16).
(b) Effect of [D-Phe⁷]ACTH₄₋₁₀ on partially compensated
animals. The peptide was administered in a dose of
250 µg/kg per day beginning with a) the 17th (●) or b)
the 35th (○) postoperative day (n=15 for both groups).
Ordinates: head deviation in degrees, mean value ± S.E.;
abscissas: time in days.

Cellular Mechanisms: The Possible Involvement of Brain
Phosphoproteins.

A currently favored mechanism by which ACTH-like neuropeptides could
exert their action is the phosphorylation-dephosphorylation reaction
of proteins present in the cytoplasm or in synaptic membranes (De
Wied and Jolles, 1982; Gispen and Zwiers, 1985; Mahler and others,
1982; Rodnight, 1982). Such a post-translational modification of
proteins could provide a basis for their role in the modification
of neuronal contacts. The state of phosphorylation of one or more
proteins could

a)   modulate voltage independent membrane channels, thereby altering
     the gain of conventional synapses;

b)   modulate voltage dependent membrane channels that control ion
     fluxes underlying impulse generation or, in the case of the pre-
     synaptic terminal, transmitter release;

c)   affect the catalytic or regulatory potency of membrane consti-
     tuents and thus alter their capacity to interact with neuroac-
     tive ligands such as transmitters, hormones or modulators;

d)   influence the degree of phosphorylation of cytoplasmic proteins,
     which, in turn, could lead to multiple changes in cellular phy-
     siology such as enzyme activation or protein synthesis.

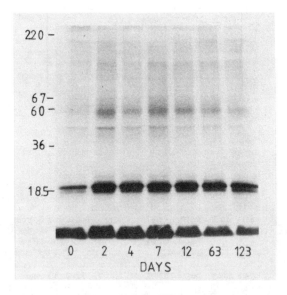

Fig. 5

Stimulation of a 21 KD phosphoprotein. Animals were labyrinthectomized and sacrificed at the indicated time. Brains
were homogenized. Aliquots were phosphorylated in the presence of [γ-^{32}P]ATP as described by Sloboda and others
(1975). The reaction was carried out for 3 minutes at 20°C.
Phosphoproteins were analyzed by SDS-polyamide gel electrophoresis followed by autoradiography.

We have recently found (Richter-Landsberg and Flohr, unpublished)
that the phosphorylation pattern of the frog brain changes during
the course of vestibular compensation. Within one day following hemilabyrinthectomy the appearance of a 21 KD phosphoprotein is greatly stimulated. Maximal stimulation is observed 2-4 days following
hemilabyrinthectomy and an increased level is maintained throughout
the course of compensation (Fig. 5).

Protein phosphorylation in the nervous system is regulated by a
number of extracellular signals such as neuromodulators, the response often being mediated by intracellular second messengers, e.g.,
cAMP, cGMP or Ca^{++}. The phosphorylation reaction of the 21 KD phosphoprotein stimulated by vestibular lesion is independent of cAMP
and cGMP but is regulated by Ca^{++} and $ACTH_{1-24}$. High concentrations
of Ca^{++} (5-10 mM) result in an inhibition or dephosphorylation,
whereas low Ca^{++} concentrations (<1 mM) stimulate phosphorylation
(Fig. 6a). $ACTH_{1-24}$ added to the incubation medium at concentrations
of $10^{-7}-10^{-9}$ M has a stimulating effect, whilst an inhibition is observed at 10^{-4} M (Fig. 6b).

Though the functional significance of the appearance of a specific
phosphoprotein is far from clear, the possibility exists that a
calcium- and ACTH-regulated protein kinase is involved in the compensation process. Exogenously administered peptides could exert
their action by interacting with this intrinsic mechanism.

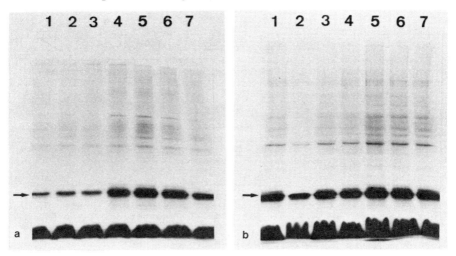

Fig. 6 a-b

Effects of Ca^{++} and $ACTH_{1-24}$ on endogenous phosphorylation
of frog brain proteins. In vitro phosphorylation in the presence of either Ca^{++} (a) or $ACTH_{1-24}$ (b) was carried out as
described in Fig. 5. The autoradiographic images of 7.5-15%
slab gels are shown.
(a) Ca^{++} was added in the following concentrations: (1) 10 mM;
(2) 5 mM; (3) 1 mM; (4) 0.1 mM; (5) 0.01 mM; (6) 0.001mM and
no Ca^{++} was added in (7).
(b) (1) control sample without $ACTH_{1-24}$; (2-7) $ACTH_{1-24}$ was
added to the incubation medium at a final concentration of
10^{-4} M; 10^{-5} M; 10^{-6} M; 10^{-7} M; 10^{-8} M; 10^{-9} M respectively.
Arrow: 21 KD phosphoprotein.

The existence of a phosphorylation-dephosphorylation system regulated synergistically by Ca^{++} and neuromodulator agents is of particular interest in the light of speculations on the possible mechanism of adaptive control of modifiable neuronal networks (Flohr, 1983). With Ca^{++} as a concomittant of ongoing or shortly terminated electrical activity such a system, in principle, would show activity dependent neuromodulation. Activity dependent neuromodulation exhibits features of fundamental importance for all concepts of adaptive control, allowing a diffuse modulator signal to be addressed selectively to functionally active targets. If the release of the neuromodulator agent were, as it appears, a consequence of the positively or negatively reinforcing characteristics of an experience, it would then, in the long term, act as a specific reinforcer of those parts of a neuronal circuitry generating the associated behavior. By means of trial and error the modulatory action could positively reinforce functionally adequate processes and/or inhibit inadequate processes and thus exert continuous control over the adaptive state of a given network.

Generally speaking, activity dependent neuromodulation would seem an ideally suited cellular mechanism for bringing about concerted and goal-directed changes in distributed neural networks.

References

Bohus, B., W.H. Gispen and D. De Wied (1982). Effects of lysine vasopressin and $ACTH_{4-10}$ on conditioned avoidance behavior of hypophysectomized rats. Neuroendocrinology, 11, 137-142.

De Wied, D. and J. Jolles (1982). Neuropeptides derived from proopiocortin: behavioral, physiological and neurochemical effects. Physiol. Rev., 62, 976-1059.

Dunn, A.J. (1984). Effects of ACTH, β-lipotropin and related peptides on the central nervous system. In C.B. Nemeroff and A.J. Dunn (Eds.), Peptides, Hormones and Behavior, MIT Press, Falcon House, Lancaster, pp. 273-348.

Ewald, J.R. (1892). Physiologische Untersuchungen über das Endorgan des Nervus octavus. Bergmann, Wiesbaden.

Flohr, H. and U. Lüneburg (1982). Effects of $ACTH_{4-10}$ on vestibular compensation. Brain Res., 248, 169-173.

Flohr, H. (1983). Control of plastic processes. In E. Basar, H. Flohr, H. Haken and A.J. Mandell (Eds.), Synergetics of the Brain, Springer, Berlin, Heidelberg, pp. 60-74.

Gispen, W.H. and H. Zwiers (1985). Behavioral and neurochemical effects of ACTH. In A. Lajtha (Ed.), Handbook of Neurochemistry, Vol. 8, 2nd ed. Plenum Press, New York, London, pp. 375-412.

Mahler, H.R., L.P. Kleine, N. Ratner and R.G. Sorensen (1982). Identification and topography of synaptic phosphoproteins. In W.H. Gispen and A. Routtenberg (Eds.), Progress in Brain Research, Vol. 56, Elsevier, Amsterdam, pp. 27-48.

Rodnight, R. (1982). Aspects of protein phosphorylation in the nervous system with particular reference to synaptic transmission. In W.H. Gispen and A. Routtenberg (Eds.), Progress in Brain Research, Vol. 56, Elsevier, Amsterdam, pp. 1-25.

Sloboda, R.D., S.A. Rudolph, J.L. Rosenbaum and P. Greengard (1975). Cyclic AMP-dependent endogenous phosphorylation of a microtubule-associated protein. Proc. Natl. Acad. Sci. (USA), 72, 177-181.

NEURONAL MECHANISMS
OF ADAPTATION

Neuronal Mechanisms of Adaptation: a Viewpoint

R. Baker

Department of Physiology and Biophysics, New York University
Medical Center, 550 First Avenue, New York, NY 10016, USA

INTRODUCTION

The brain has the capacity to use its molecular machinery to convert information into a form that can be stored as short or long term memory. Many investigators have searched the CNS for macromolecules that fulfill criteria for
encoding such lengthy stability. To date, two things appear certain. First
there is no direct evidence that DNA can be modified to encode learning. Yet,
on the other hand, other molecules from proteins and carbohydrates to RNA are
capable of rapid turnover. Thus, one may conclude that the only neuronal feature of sufficient stability to sustain long term memory must be embedded in
the patterns of connectivity intrinsic to the adult CNS. Structurally, this
hypothesis is envisioned to include malleability of synaptic contacts but
draws the line at any higher level synaptic reorganization. As largely exemplified by work in invertebrates (Kandel and Schwartz, 1982; Quinn, 1984) and
more recently, vertebrates (Kasamatsu; Aoki, this volume) it is clear that alterations in specific molecules (i.e., biochemical mechanisms) are the molecular events that ultimately precede the realization of physiological alteration
in neural circuits.

But exactly what comprises an alteration in a neural circuit? My colleagues
in the oculomotor field have been provincial, maybe more careful, in their arguments about the molecular and neural events accompanying learning. One
might expect this from their vantage of disciplinary secularization. In the
preface to Adaptive Mechanisms in Gaze Control, Berthoz and Melvill Jones
(1985) claim their title to be an unanswered question, but they argue that
present knowledge in the field is so large that possibilities for future de-
velopments are immense. Does this observation adequately describe the iceberg
of plasticity? Or as concluded in the viewpoint that follows, does it only
touch the tip?

GENERAL OBSERVATIONS

Plasticity is present not only in motor systems, but also in every behavior
that can be conceived for any CNS. Adaptive mechanisms in the oculomotor system be they of open (e.g. VOR) or closed (saccades or pursuit) loop control
(Optican, this volume) are not easily categorized into the associative or
non-associative classical experimental paradigm. For example, the VOR is certainly not a "sensitization" and neither can one specify a "conditioned" or
"unconditioned" stimulus (cf. Galiana; Miyashita, this volume). In the
terminology of Gould and Marler (1984), the VOR might be distinguished as

associative 'trial and error' motor learning (with the added advantage that it becomes analagous to deductive reasoning). Nonetheless the search for the central correlates to adaptive control is not substantively different for the VOR, saccades or pursuit, than those efforts surrounding classical condition-ing in another part of the oculomotor system such as the rabbit nictitating membrane (Thompson and others, 1976). At issue, is insight into the underly-ing adaptive mechanisms and especially a detailed study of the structural ele-ments involved in isolated innate (unlearned and genetically inherited) behav-ioral patterns (usage of innate follows Bateson, 1984). When, not if, contro-versy arises in terminology then write it off as semantic confusion stemming from our fields limitations in choosing appropriate words to characterize our restricted view of behavior and its ensuing neuronal correlates. Assuming this status to be largely true the best alternative is to retain the generally stated opinions "learning is the exclusive function of the brain" and as such "learning is the permanent change in behavior resulting from experience". Adaptation, plasticity, associative learning or whatever aside, the bottom line on the inventory sheet is that neurons and their associated circuitry in the CNS are there to learn, but how? This brings to mind several rather di-verse issues that may be relevant to our 'secular' oculomotor position, nam-ely - neural specificity, ontogeny, ethology and of course, true adaptation. However, generally the focus throughout the paper remains on the issue of 'normal' physiology and its relationship to learning.

In view of the varied temporal nature of plasticity acquisition (both short and long term) as well as the processes associated with reversal (habituation and extinction), it is almost certain that many of our long held concepts of oculomotor system organization must be altered considerably if we are to ever understand the physiological mode of brain operation. Yet, insight into func-tion will not necessarily tell anyone how a learning process works. Before some common principle (and it likely will be common) is postulated for a par-ticular oculomotor adaptation, we first must integrate the wealth of knowledge available at both the molecular and neural signal level in other systems, largely invertebrate (not a trivial task).

Learning must be considered from an ethological perspective. We must discard our arbitrary, and incorrect, separation of these adaptive phenomena from the realm of 'normal' physiological processess. This change should begin at the level of the innate (genetically inherited) properties of the extant circuitry and extend up to re-evaluating the meaning of our private terms such as gain, bias, etc that are presently used to define limits of 'normal' oculomotor op-eration. Another issue to examine is how plasticity following neuronal in-jury, ablation and subsequent regeneration are related to compensation, be it by the process of substitution, restitution etc (Zee and others; Deng and others; Dieringer and Precht, this volume). Largely it is held that following nerve cell trauma and/or loss there can be molecular and neural events that lead to recovery or respecification of physiological responses with reinnerva-tion beneficial in the sense of an 'adaptive plasticity' that restores func-tional operation of the system. As expressed later, this view is a capri-cious, if not outright mistaken, assumption.

Arising from these disparate views is the larger theme that adaptation and plasticity in the adult animal reproduce the ontogenetic development of the brain in terms of molecular and neural components. This hypothesis suggests synaptic connections can be re-established in a neurospecific (i.e. trophic factors) and activity-dependent (i.e. phosphorylation of some sort) fashion according to the way they occurred during development (Schmidt and others, this volume). Mechanistically, the sequela is that neurons following an in-jury may de-differentiate to a point where they can once again use so-called DNA guided mechanisms to reassemble structurally with purposeful physiological endpoints. It is particularly this latter argument (maybe the only) that is commented on herein with evidence to the contrary, because the features of target recognition accompanying reinnervation of the extraocular neuromuscular junction can all be tested (Fig. 1 legend to be read now). By contrast central synaptic reorganization following vestibular (Dieringer and Precht, this volume) or cortical lesion (Newsome and others, this volume) are truly more elusive. In fact, they are unbelievably more complex situations because adaptation (learning again) is superimposed on an indeterminate extent of restorative neurospecifity in synaptic re-organization. Yes it is true, even the most abberant pattern of re-innervation learns and if by chance it provides for maladaptive behavior, then an older, basic phylogenetic design intervenes,

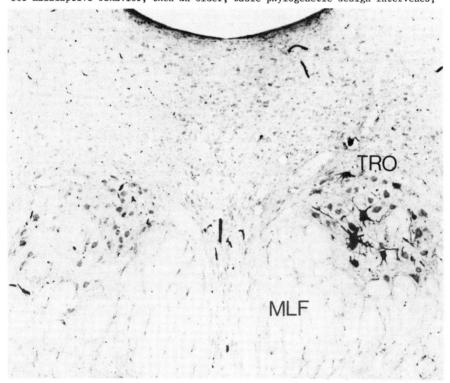

Fig. 1. Ever since Sperry's classic work in the early 40's of crossing hind limb nerves in the rat up to and including his own attempts of rewiring the teleost and amphibian oculomotor system , it has been clear that the extent of normal co-ordinated movement restored following regeneration is variable (Sperry, 1947; Sperry and Arora, 1965). Claims that peripheral extraocular nerves in antecedent vertebrates could recognize the right muscle and even if they didn't, respecify their activity (i.e. learn a new response) were seriously questioned by Scott (1977) who showed the previous behavioral observations to be inadequate. Although the issue of myotypic respecification in the sense of plasticity did not lose appeal, our recent work is also contrary to Sperry's view. The above photomicrograph of the cat trochlear nuclei was obtained 2 years after complete denervation of all extraocular muscles by central cuts of the IIIrd, IVth and VIth nerves. The presence of labeled motoneurons in the right trochlear nucleus following selective injection of HRP into the left inferior rectus muscle demonstrates that reinnervation of mammalian extraocular muscles was not specific. Furthermore, foreign innervation was maintained even though motoneuronal behavior did not respecify as tested physiologically (Baker et al, 1985).

namely - natural selection.   However, from the ethological perspective, inappropriate behaviors can still be illuminating for understanding adaptive mechanisms (Gould and Marler, 1984).

At the outset I excused the oculomotor field from studying adaptive mechanisms because to date the experimental approaches have been so predictably superficial.   Efforts have been largely predicated on establishing a site for correlating the neural event to the postulated plasticity.   There are interesting aspects of this pretense, the most obvious being the profuse satisfaction expressed for having not only described the plasticity (generally at the behavioral level) but also pointing out an area of the brain participating in the learning (with the latter conclusion largely based on its absence).   Is anyone concerned that these studies are superimposed on a putative structure-function appreciation of circuit organization that doesn't exist yet, not even for the VOR?   The answer is no.   But, if true, then how can one ever hope to ascertain causality (where, when and how something changes)?   This causality sequence is actually the simplest one to address!   If the paradox has a solution, then in my mind it largely relates to exercising fully the caveat stated initially - namely the adult central nervous system must be considered in its entirety as plastic because this is its fundamental raison d'etre.   Whatever happens in the CNS is generated by a normal physiological repertoire of innate (phylogenetically adapted) programmable events.   A more specific definition would be that the biochemical machinery at the molecular level as well as at the physiological is already specified as being necessary and sufficient (maybe even appropriate, but that contention is specious due to evolutionary considerations) to permit alterations in behavior.   Why bring this conundrum up in the context of this book?   Because such a viewpoint produces significant overtones (obviously) in at least two directions, one clinically related.

First, if adaptation is simply viewed as an expression of normal physiological range and mode of oculomotor operation, then pathology largely reflects a disadvantageous time dependent relationship between the two processes.   How is it possible to tell when plasticity is truly finished?   Symptoms are not expressed at the moment pathology begins, but are seen when the system can no longer effectively adapt.   Plasticity has been initiated much earlier and in the absolute sense from ontogenetic maturity.   In fact, this paradox always exists. Frequently, many adaptive processes are really maladaptive in the sense that the behavior produced has no innate way (i.e. no resort to DNA encoding) of compensating for a particular performance or a function that has been lost. If the innumerable number of lesion studies (this volume) have contributed anything to our understanding of brain function, then it is to largely confirm the above argument.   Namely, it has given us the quantitative estimate of neuronal machinery with accompanying molecular mechanisms that can be sacrificed at any particular moment without being noticed (by us).   In effect, natural plasticity is that in which no behavioral modification becomes recognizable at all.   The strength of oculomotor experimental sophistication fortunately lies on the side of sensory and motor deception (the latter used with scientific definition).   Thus normalcy of physiological responses can be adequately assessed before pathology becomes complete (Gresty; Kommerell and others, this volume).   Note also that normal physiological response reads just as well as plasticity in the previous sentence (and all others).

Is there any reason to pursue further understanding of oculomotor plasticity other than the incentive for studying the innate (phylogenetically adapted) cellular and molecular mechanisms?   The simple answer is no; however, the question asked is whether there is any residual clinical relevance?   My suspicion is that the answer is the same as that to the question's relationship to neurological diagnosis.   Understanding these basic phenomena might be of assistance in establishing predictive tests, but they certainly would not alter therapeutic rationale (Dell'Osso and Daroff, this volume).   Will pharmacological manipulation in the oculomotor system be a fruitful endeavor to pursue

(McElligott and Freedman; Cohen and others, this volume)? More to the point, will it be possible to effectively alter the time course of learning without concomittant understanding of mechanism? Unlikely. Naturally, the issue really addressed is why so much time is spent on trying to understand the etiology of certain processes when the hope they offer is so little. The ethological point of view encouraged in this article avoids that question, because it argues that we should strive to understand the balance between neural plasticity and the genetically pre-ordained synaptic connections. True adaptation aside, oculomotor plasticity is nothing other than oculomotor physiology.

This brings the story around to what one probably would have guessed to be the major focus of this meeting. Namely – how does one go about looking for, and at, the mechanisms underlying normal physiological changes? In this regard, my convictions lead to the expression of two points, not necessarily that closely related, and unfortunately substantiating a long-held curse for this audience (so I will not underline anything), specifically – to give a semblance of rationality and reason to work done in invertebrates and to suggest a more ubiquitous experimental use of particular vertebrates.

The first topic is phylogeny. There are many interesting points to pursue, but the first is to agree that learning is specified within an organisms natural history and that manifestation alone gives the functional significance to what is learned. Nonetheless, all behaviors commonly studied in the oculomotor system for their adaptive plasticity are ones equally well developed in species that have been extant for more than three hundred million years. A conservative hypothesis in 'evolution of learning' states that there is no good evidence for either a qualitative or quantitative difference in learning among any of the vertebrates (invertebrates ?) except for man's linguistic ability (Macphail, 1982). The main point is that particular neural solutions, including their molecular mechanisms, are not new to mammals, but have been obtained from antecedent genomes. In the beginning (not my expression) there were a finite number of neurons and circuits and they could do it!

Frequently it is argued that antecedent vertebrates with their inherent regenerative capacity and higher degree of neural specificity exhibit little adaptive plasticity. Of course this is not true as illustrated by visual and vestibular control of goldfish eye movement (Schairer and Bennett, 1985). Also, reinnervation of extraocular muscle is just as random in fish as mammals (Fig. 1). The lack of neural specificity suggests regenerative processes might be considered the same in all species and, unfortunately, not adaptive at all. Given the precedent for common neuronal and molecular mechanisms in antecedent species, how could efficaciousness of the extensive machinery evolved in the mammalian brain ever be questioned? It can't, but on the other hand given present knowledge and expertise, one might seriously doubt whether understanding of these processes may occur earlier in mammals than in antecedent species. This concern is expressed with a note of optimism because of Macphail's belief that revealing the details of the normal physiological expression of a particular plasticity in one species can lead to a general understanding of all such behaviors. In other words, explanation can originate anywhere.

The adaptive role of selective learning is a concept originating from early ethological studies (Gould and Marler, 1984). A particularly good example is the VOR (Yee and Baloh, this volume) operating over its normal range of -1.0 to +2.0 (gain) but requiring a little time for changing from one setting to another (historically there are few oculomotor events that aren't called 'adaptive' and thus my exaggeration is within limits). One might have hoped, but to no avail, that events surrounding a 'plastic' acquistion (computational or molecular) would have been discussed. What sign stimuli (i.e. cues) initiate and sustain the physiological change and at what level(s)? What are the morphological alterations required?. Is it in the dimensions or simply dynamics of a synaptic bouton, or dendritic spine or can it be a smaller molecular

event such as the number, or kinetics, of ionic channels? Can it be predicated upon cell recognition of the flow of neural information in two circuits
like Miyashita proposed (but Lisberger discounted) for the cerebellum (cf. also Leonard and Simpson; all in this volume). The simple spike responsiveness
to vestibular signals was postulated by Miyashita to be under the influence of
retinal error signals conveyed by visual climbing fibers and a molecular modification was, at least, inferred at this meeting. Certainly everyone can see
(not agree on) parts of the scenario just proposed and few would disagree that
any of this lies outside conventional physiological boundaries. In fact,
hardly anyone would disagree to a simple definition of plasticity as physiology with a time course called learning. The temporal nature of such physiological processes is perhaps why we infer structural alteration more than specific molecular mechanisms. Certainly, epigenetic mechanisms associated with
outside world interactions are required for full developement of the adult
brain and its connectivities (Changeux, 1983). However, the biological constraint in all adult species studied is the same - namely the CNS must learn
largely by means that do not require any, even small scale, structural reorganization (i.e. no rewiring).

There are many puzzling aspects of motor learning that, in part, relate to the
above temporal factors, but there are others more dependent on response direction (not considering the consequence of positive or negative reinforcing
characteristics of the sign stimuli). There is good evidence that oppositely
directed processes are not continuations of the same cellular, molecular or
neuronal mechanisms in there entirety (Hawkins, 1984; Quinn, 1984; Miles and
Eighmy, 1980). The widespread 'frequency selective' adaptation in the vertebrate VOR (Lisberger and others, 1983; Schairer and Bennett, 1985) argues for
common synaptic and molecular mechanisms across species with the learning phenomena capable of being distributed (parcelled out) in homogenous populations
of neurons. This intriguing observation supports the contention that plasticity is not a uniform event in particular neural behaviors and thus learning
may not be an obligatory feature of all neurons. If so, then it raises the
question of how it got that way? Where is it determined? And the conditions
that specify the sites where it appears in neural circuits? Learning obviously comes in simple, and then successively more complex, packages all cascaded
together to explain one single behavioral event. I would argue that the a-
mount and/or site of learning actually need not be a constant phylogenetic
feature (fairly safe given no site has yet been specified). Actually pursuing
sites in which there is little, or no, learning is logical (everyone looks for
the 'plastic' site so there will be less competition).

It is highly probable that the neuronal composition of circuits has been consistently altered during phylogeny by placing more adaptive pressure on particular neurons at a critical time. Is the extent of plasticity an emergent
feature of neurons that pre- or postdates interaction with the environment?
Either way, both processes could contribute to the development of the adult
connectivity (Changeux, 1983). Appropriateness of eye movements throughout
phylogeny are sustained by structural and functional changes in VOR neurons
including peripheral adaptive modifications in extraocular muscle-globe relationships (Graf and others, 1983). Are the phylogenetically altered pattern
and mode of vestibular axonal collateralizations sufficient for producing the
different extraocular and other motor behaviors or is learning a necessary
parallel? When the behavioral specification becomes larger than the range of
the neuronal circuitry's plasticity then a new generation of neurons may be introduced. If new neurons learn then obviously, some types of learning could
not have appeared previously in a presumed antecedent species (at least in
that morphological form). The collection of pathways over time is presumably
based on conservative molecular and cellular mechanisms, but nonetheless
learning is likely transformed into a very complex mosaic by the time it
reaches the mammalian brain (it is not written that this interpretation is the
case). My suspicion is, as expressed earlier, that the adaptive mechansim may

be a terribly simple solution especially if one can pinpoint the behavioral (neuronal) repetoire of reasonably homologous circuits between species. Finally, these arguments do not consider genesis of new neurons as a means of plasticity since from the viewpoint of speciation a new neuron is certainly not a plastic response. It is a true adaptation. Evolutionary chance, not insufficiency of the existing machinery, begets a new morphological entity. Here the circle becomes complete since this is the point where DNA finally learns. The latter mechanism is the true mark of speciation, even though from the behavioral viewpoint there may have been no apparent advantage for the particular adaptation under scrutiny.

How much truth lies in the contemporary contention that cellular lability underlying adaptive mechanisms extends into adulthood? At the outset, I suggested that neurons, in their lifetime, could not learn any new tricks from DNA. Often that is interpreted as a restrictive viewpoint relegating the status of individual neurons to static, configured, unalterable parts of a neural circuit. On the surface this is probably true; however, in recent years, action has been intense in the much larger arena promoting chemical potentiality. This enterprise is especially pursued by those who do not fundamentally view the CNS in its reductionist mechanism of action as being simply electrical. Of course, all agree that synaptic transmission is neurohumoral, that is given, but what roles should we envision for the nearly 100 recognized peptides in the CNS (Flohr and others, this volume). Or the equally expansive monoaminergic system (McElligott and Freedman, this volume)? We can already conclude that the view "one neuron, one transmitter" is certainly the exception. The new rule appears to be that one neuron can actually modulate the expression of its genetic material so as to generate and secrete a number of chemical molecules. The complexity of relationships existing between identified, released and incorporated substances is just becoming apparent in the vertebrate CNS (Lynch and Baudry, 1984).

There is a continual dynamic interaction between neurons at their specialized zones of synaptic contact with a turnover of membrane bound proteins at the molecular level leading up to, and including, demonstrable alterations in synaptic connectivity and efficacy between established elements (Hawkins, 1984). This finding alone suggests that during the lifetime of any hard wired circuit there is change. The key to understanding adaptation is the ability to measure the correct property distributed throughout several (probably more) populations of neurons. There is little written about the amount, distribution and effectiveness of changes at particular sites within the oculomotor system (cf however, Berthoz and Melvill Jones, 1985). Yet, with all its infinitely interactive subsystems of eye movement, the mammalian oculomotor playground remains a spectacular place to play. Logically speaking, the stronger arguements will be those clearly showing sites where no molecular or neuronal change occurs during learning. Together with the earlier assertion that, for all practical purposes, we have not yet specified any site at which an alteration occurs (including time course) leads to the conclusion that determining the neuronal correlate will not be as effortless as envisioned (and this task is just the prelude to the next assignment).

In the future, few will confuse locating the site of a plasticity with establishing a mechanism. Neurons can only vary in frequency and so do target cells. Changing the number of action potentials per unit time (independent of their duration) describes a neuronal correlate to plasticity at only an intermediate level. It begs the next question (largest part), which is specifying the mechanism. There is reasonable biochemical and physiological data obtained in the invertebrate that not only specifies the particular site at which a modification occurs, but in part the molecular mechanism(s) accompanying such changes (Hawkins, 1984). The causality in such arguments is good, but will we ever be able to get close in a mammalian motor system, like the oculomotor, to establishing these mechanisms? The answer to date is

definitely no, but there is a clear direction. These behaviors must be ex-
tracted from the in vivo, and set in the more favorable in vitro, surroundings. Somehow the learning must be impervious to this transition between the
two extreme environments. This particular goal may not be as impossible as it
appears because of recent advances in isolated tissue technology (Llinas,
1984). Given its nature, the molecular basis must arise from the more aces-
sible in vitro physical conditions. So, therefore, the most salient message
that one can possibly extract from contemporary in vivo oculomotor work is
demarcation of the site for the next stage of investigation. However, chasing
an explicit problem for the wrong reason is justifiable if the next answer
provides enlightenment. Perhaps, this might be a fitting place to end this
commentary because one could argue this to be true for the study of all physiological processes including those referred to as learning. The study of
adaptive mechanisms in the oculomotor system has not yet really begun, even
though in our minds, it was the topic of this meeting.

At this point, why not leave an allusion (or illusion) of creative, and certainly entangled, ideas about adaptation from the viewpoint of phylogenetic
pressures within oculomotor system evolution. It has been argued that the initial designs of the semicircular canal coordinate system, extraocular muscle
arrangment and intrinsic coordinate system (i.e. vestibular neurons which produce the eye movement) were necessary, sufficient and appropriate for realizing beautiful rotations of the globe around optic axes enabling a constant
stream of uninterrupted visual images for any displacement of that body in
space (Graf and Simpson, 1981). The lengthy introductory statement means that
the neuronal and plant design effecting eye movement in the earliest vertebrate was spectacular (all things considered). Notably, physiological mechanisms were specified that permitted the system to change its range when either
an intrinsic perturbation (neurons even die in fish) or an extrinsic one (other fish) appeared. This being the case, can it be argued that greater adaptive pressure was placed on movement (i.e. oculomotor) as opposed to vision?
Throughout phylogeny a co-operative selection process enhanced performance of
both. Certainly, the transition from lateral to frontal-eyed mammal had a major impact on use of vision (disparity being what it is). Evolution acts on
performance, not an associative process directly. One system may be conservative and the other not. Thus, although some argue that epigenetic causality
resides on the motor side, this obviously can not be true. A finely wired
circuit, but connected differently, suddenly appeared in the course of phylogeny, and there may have been survival value. Phrased as such this particular
viewpoint avoids the erroneous caveat that an ontogenetic gene event within
either the visual or oculomotor system provided the impetus for a wiring
change. Such assertion would be entirely false because, for better or worse,
it was the conjoint, but chance, improvement in the performance of both systems that allowed for enhanced visual capacity maintaining a species existence. It became more fit for a particular environment, so it survived.
Given the peculiar ecological niches available throughout evolution, this line
of argumentation raises the intriguing possibility that not all (the majority?) changes in circuitry can be viewed as optimizing neural performance. In
fact, it could be argued that some antecedent (as long ago as you can think)
patterns of synaptic organization exhibited more optimum solutions than those
now found in mammals. This does not necessarily mean that we have a degener-
ate oculomotor system, but it certainly does suggest an accumulation of neuronal modifications that are neither selected for, or against, in successive
generations of certain species. Given this scenario, it might be questioned
whether or not the adaptive mechanisms specified earlier will ever be understood in any more explicit detail in the immediate future than afforded by the
explanations presently available. One hopes, at least, our biases will not
belittle the choice of neural representations for the evolutionary sequence.
In closing, I can not resist quoting Cuppy (1941) whose unintentional, but
clear, reference to the issue of 'adaptation or extinction' pointed out that:
"It was very clever of the Pterodactyls to think of flying, but that's all you

can say for them. They were doomed from the start because they had no feathers and wishbone, or furcula, as flying vertebrates should have. Pretty soon the Archaeopteryx, a genuine bird, came along, and the Pterodactyls faded away. They didn't belong in the picture and public opinion was against them.[1]

[1]If you're booked for extinction, there's nothing much you can do about it."

REFERENCES

Baker, R., C. Peck, R.F. Spencer, J. Delgado-Garcia and J. Winterkorn (1985). Structural and functional assessment of the reinnervation pattern of cat extraocular muscle following central cut of the IIIrd, IVth and VIth cranial nerves. Soc. Neurosci. Abst. 11: 973, 1985.

Bateson, P.P.G. (1984). Genes, evolution, and learning. In The Biology of Learning. P. Marler and H.S. Terrace. (Eds), Springer Verlag, Heidelberg, pp. 75-88.

Berthoz, A. and G. Melvill Jones (1985). Adaptive Mechanisms in Gaze Control. Elsevier Science Publishers, Amsterdam.

Changeux, J.P. (1983). L'homme neuronal. Fayard. Paris.

Cuppy, W. (1941). How to Become Extinct. The University of Chicago Press.

Gould, J.L. and P. Marler (1984). Ethology and the natural history of learning. In The Biology of Learning. P. Marler and H.S. Terrace. (Eds), Springer Verlag, Heidelberg, pp. 47-74.

Graf, W., R.A. McCrea and R. Baker (1983). Morphology of posterior canal-related secondary vestibular neurons in rabbit and cat. Exp. Brain Res. 52: 125-138.

Graf, W. and J.I. Simpson (1981). The relations between the semicircular canals, the optic axis and the extraocular muscles in lateral-eyed and frontal-eyed animals. In Progress in Oculomotor Research. A. F. Fuchs and W. Becker. (Eds), Elsevier, New York, pp. 409-417.

Hawkins, R.D. (1984). A cellular mechanism of classical conditioning in Aplysia. J. Exp. Biol. 112: 113-128.

Kandel, E.R. and J.H. Schwartz (1982). Molecular biology of learning: Modulation of transmitter release. Science. 218: 433-442.

Llinas, R.R. (1984). Comparative electrobiology of mammalian central neurons. In Brain Slices. R. Dingledine (Ed), Plenum Publishing pp. 7-24.

Lisberger, S.G., F.A. Miles and L.M. Optican (1983). Frequency-selective adaptation: evidence for channels in the vestibulo-ocular reflex? J. Neurosci. 3: 1234-1244, 1983.

Lynch, G. and M. Baudry (1984). The biochemistry of memory: A new and specific hypothesis. Science. 224: 1057-1063.

Macphail, E. (1982). Brain and Intelligence in Vertebrates. Clarendon Press. Oxford.

Miles, F.A. and B.B. Eighmy (1980). Long-term adaptive changes in primate vestibulo-ocular reflex. I. Behavioral observations. J. Neurophysiol. 43: 1046-1425.

Quinn, W.G. (1984) Work in invertebrates on the mechanisms underlying learning. In The Biology of Learning. P. Marler and H.S. Terrace. (Eds), Springer Verlag, Heidelberg, pp.197-246.

Schairer, J.O. and M.V.L. Bennett (1985). Changes in the gain of the vestibulo-ocular reflex induced by combined visual and vestibular stimulation in goldfish. Brain Res. (in press).

Scott, S.A. (1977). Maintained function of foreign and appropriate junctions on reinnervated goldfish extraocular muscles. J. Physiol. 268: 87-109.

Sperry, R.W. (1947). Nature of functional recovery following regeneration of the oculomotor nerve in amphibians. Anat. Rec. 97: 293-316.

Sperry, R.W. and H.L. Arora (1965). Selectivity in regeneration of the oculomotor nerve in the cichlid fish, Astronotus ocellatus. J. Embryol. Exp. Morph. 14: 307-317.

Thompson, R.F., T.W. Berger, C.F. Cegavshe, M.M. Patterson, R.A. Roemer, T.J. Teyler and R.A. Young (1976). The search for the engram. Am. Psychol. 31: 309-227.

Simple Spike Modulation of Floccular Purkinje Cells During the Reversible Blockade of Their Climbing Fiber Afferents

C. S. Leonard and J. I. Simpson

Department of Physiology and Biophysics, New York University
Medical Center, 550 First Avenue, New York, NY 10016, USA

INTRODUCTION

The functions of the two distinctly different afferent systems to the
cerebellar cortex continue to be sought through an understanding of the
relations between the simple spike (SS) and complex spike (CS) activity of
Purkinje cells. Recording, stimulating and lesioning have all been used to
probe these systems for possible interactions. The tack that we report here
falls in the category of lesioning.

Inactivation of the inferior olive, either permanently by means of
3-acetylpyridine or coagulation, or reversibly by means of cooling or local
anesthetics, results in a rapid, pronounced increase in the spontaneous SS
rate of Purkinje cells (Benedetti, Montarolo and Rabacchi, 1984; Colin, Manil
and Desclin, 1980; Echelman, Demer and Robinson, 1983; Leonard and Simpson,
1982; Montarolo, Palestini and Strata, 1982; Savio and Tempia, 1985; Strata,
1985). This observation has renewed interest in the possibility that the
reciprocal relation between the SS and CS firing rates often seen during
natural stimulation may be due to a suppressive action of CS activity.
Indeed, Colin, Manil and Desclin (1980) have suggested that following the loss
of CS activity the Purkinje cell rapidly enters into a 'non-computing' mode.
This general notion was cast into two specific forms by Demer and Robinson
(1982) to offer speculative explanations of the prompt increase in the gain of
the vestibuloocular reflex that they observed in the alert cat following
lidocaine anesthesia of the climbing fiber system. One proposal was that a
multiplicative relation exists between the firing rate of a climbing fiber and
the SS modulation of its Purkinje cell. Thus, blocking the climbing fiber
would be equivalent to multiplying the SS modulation by zero. The second
proposal was that loss of the climbing fiber input results in an increase of
SS activity to a saturation rate preventing, or at least substantially
reducing (Demer, Echelman and Robinson, personal communication), response
modulation.

Our studies were undertaken to examine directly what happens to the SS
modulation when a Purkinje cell's climbing fiber input is inactivated (Leonard
and Simpson, 1982). Those findings are further documented in this report, and
show that, in the short term, lidocaine blockade of the climbing fiber input
to the rabbit flocculus results in an increase in the spontaneous SS rate, but
that the SS modulation in response to natural visual and vestibular stimulation remains unchanged.

METHODS

At least three days prior to each experiment, a pigmented rabbit was anesthetized with either a mixture of Nembutal (10 mg/kg) and alpha-chloralose (60 mg/kg) or a mixture of ketamine (30 mg/kg), acepromazine (0.3 mg/kg) and xylazine (5 mg/kg), and was implanted with a head holder and a recording chamber located over the paramedian lobule of the cerebellum. On the day of the experiment, the rabbit was reanesthetized with the ketamine mixture. A tracheostomy was performed and the surrounding area was infiltrated with a long-lasting local anesthetic (Marcaine, 0.75% with epinephrine). The caudal portion of the fourth ventricle was exposed, permitting a dorsoventral approach to the inferior olive. The surgical field was infiltrated with Marcaine and 5 % lidocaine paste was applied to all exposed surfaces. The animals were then artificially respirated and paralyzed with Flaxedil.

The lidocaine injecting pipettes had tip diameters between 5 and 15 microns and were filled with 2% or 4% lidocaine HCl in pH adjusted physiological saline. They were positioned in the caudal half of the dorsal cap of Kooy by recording the multi-unit response of olive cells to moving visual stimuli. The principal source of floccular climbing fibers is the dorsal cap and the cells of its caudal half respond preferentially to horizontal image motion on the contralateral retina (Alley, Baker and Simpson,1975; Barmack and Hess, 1980). Since dorsal cap cells with similar visual receptive field properties are grouped together (Simpson, Graf and Leonard, 1981), the modulation of the multi-unit activity is a reliable indicator of tip location within the dorsal cap. Lidocaine was ejected by compressed air pulses. The volumes injected into the brain were estimated by measuring the diameter of the fluid bead that formed at the tip of the pipette when pressure pulses were applied prior to entering the brain.

Extracellular recordings were made from single floccular Purkinje cells using glass micropipettes filled with 2M NaCl solution (3-8 Mohm dc resistance). Purkinje cells were identified by the presence of spontaneous climbing fiber responses (complex spikes) followed by pauses in the SS activity. SS activity was discriminated from CS activity and separate peristimulus histograms were compiled using standard techniques. The Purkinje cells studied were those with CS activity preferentially modulated by horizontally moving visual stimuli, as were the inferior olivary cells located near the tip of the lidocaine pipette.

The visual stimulus was a 70° square textured, random pattern rear-projected onto a tangent screen positioned 57cm from the rabbit's eye and centered on the optic axis. The direction and speed of the pattern were controlled using two mirror galvanometers in the projection path. Vestibular stimulation was generated by sinusoidally rotating the entire animal about the earth vertical axis using a servo-controlled turntable. The rabbits were positioned so that their vertical semicircular canals were minimally stimulated by this rotation.

RESULTS

The consequences of localized injections of lidocaine into the dorsal cap will be presented first with regard to the spontaneous SS rate and then with regard to the SS modulation induced by visual and vestibular stimuli.

Lidocaine was delivered as a series of individual 1-10 nanoliter pulses while monitoring the CS activity of the recorded Purkinje cell. The amount of lidocaine necessary to silence the CS was typically less than 10 nanoliters, delivered over the course of about a minute. In several instances, a single injection of 5 nanoliters or less blocked the CS within a few seconds, which

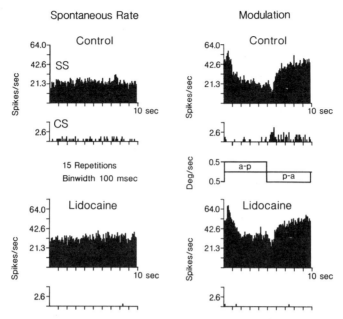

Fig. 1 Effect of lidocaine blockade of CS activity
on spontaneous SS activity and on the SS modulation
induced by <u>visual</u> stimulation. The velocity profile
of the stimulus is shown in the right column (a–p,
anterior to posterior movement). The SS modulation
histograms differed only by an offset representing
the 52% increase in the spontaneous SS rate; the
envelope of the modulation remained virtually
unchanged. This Purkinje cell's SS modulation to visual
stimulation was unusual in that its response polarity
was the same as that of the CS modulation.

is the shortest latency that can be readily resolved given the low frequency
of spontaneous CSs. In these cases, spontaneous CSs could resume within one
minute. The first sign of recovery from the blockade was the occasional
spontaneous CS which gave way to the gradual re-establishment of the original
spontaneous CS rate over the next three to five minutes. To prolong the time
during which the CS was silenced, additional injections were periodically made.

Subsequent to the cessation of spontaneous CSs, a Purkinje cell's SS rate
typically increased to a new steady-state value within 1–2 minutes (Figures 1
and 2). In 24 Purkinje cells whose pre-lidocaine spontaneous SS rates ranged
from 24sp/s to 100sp/s (mean = 48.3sp/s), the absolute increase in firing rate
after CS blockade ranged from 6sp/s to 52sp/s (mean = 16.4sp/s). Expressed in
percent, the increases ranged from 7.6% to 100% (mean = 35.7%). In 5 other
Purkinje cells, CS blockade produced no change in SS rate. Following the
onset of recovery of the CS activity, the SS rate declined gradually to the
pre-injection level. These observations on spontaneous SS activity are
qualitatively in agreement with those of others who have blocked spontaneous
CSs using methods that compromised more of the inferior olive (Colin, Manil
and Desclin, 1980; Echelman, Demer and Robinson, 1983; Montarolo, Palestini
and Strata, 1982; Savio and Tempia, 1985). Only a small fraction of the

increase in spontaneous SS rate could be attributed to the removal of the pause in SS discharge associated with the CS, as was also found by Montarolo, Palestini and Strata.(1982).

The SS activity of floccular Purkinje cells is modulated by visual and vestibular stimuli, and in the case of visual stimultion, the SSs and CSs are typically reciprocally modulated (Ghelarducci, Ito and Yagi, 1975; Leonard and Simpson, 1983; Simpson and Hess, 1977). In 24 P-cells, SS modulation to visual or vestibular stimuli was examined before and during CS blockade. In contrast to the readily seen difference between the spontaneous SS rate histograms obtained before and during lidocaine blockade, no differences in the envelope of SS modulation could be detected by visually comparing the response histograms (Figures 1 and 2). That is, apart from a constant offset due to the increase in spontaneous rate, the SS response histograms obtained before and during CS blockade were virtually superimposable. Even those portions of the histogram corresponding to the part of the periodic stimuli where the CS activity had been the most intense prior to lidocaine injection were unchanged. Small variations in the bin-to-bin comparisons were no greater than those seen when pairs of control histograms obtained before lidocaine injection were visually compared.

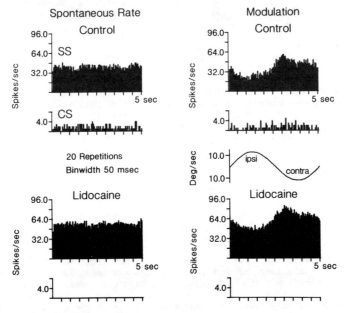

Fig. 2 Effect of lidocaine blockade of CS activity on spontaneous SS activity and on the SS modulation induced by <u>vestibular</u> stimulation. The velocity profile of the stimulus is shown in the right column. While the spontaneous SS rate increased, the absolute depth of SS modulation remained unchanged.
For this particular Purkinje cell the vestibular stim- ulation in the dark resulted in a modest CS modulation; such modulation occured in a small minority of Purkinje cells whose CS activity was well modulated by rotation of the visual world about the earth vertical axis.

Preservation of the modulation pattern about the elevated spontaneous rate was found independent of the level of the initial spontaneous SS rate or of the percent increase in the spontaneous rate. The modulation pattern remained unchanged following lidocaine injections of up to 0.3 microliters (34% increase in spontaneous rate) made in the span of one minute. Furthermore, preservation of modulation was found for constant speed visual stimuli as well as for sinusoidal vestibular stimuli and therefore it is not likely to be peculiar to a particular sensory modality or stimulus waveform.

DISCUSSION

The short term effects of silencing the CS activity of floccular Purkinje cells on their SS activity can be succinctly stated: the spontaneous rate increased, but the modulation in response to the visual or vestibular stimuli did not change. When expressed as a percent of spontaneous rate, the modulation, of course, decreased because of the increased spontaneous rate, but the absolute amount by which the firing rate was modulated above and below the elevated spontaneous level remained the same. These two findings may seem paradoxical because an increase in spontaneous activity is often referred to as an increase in the level of 'excitability', suggesting that the modulation depth would also be altered. For example, if one supposes that the increased spontaneous SS rate is produced by an increased sensitivity of the Purkinje cell to excitatory synaptic input, then an increased depth of SS modulation should result. Clearly, our results are inconsistent with this simple supposition. Rather, the observations made on SS activity after silencing the CS activity can be described as a change in bias without a change in sensitivity.

Our findings have a direct bearing on three issues. First, they show that the more extreme propositions (see Introduction) on the short term interaction between SS and CS activity can be ruled out. That is, the Purkinje cell does not enter into a 'non-computing' mode following cessation of CS activity, and blocking of the climbing fiber input is not equivalent to multiplying the SS modulation by zero. Second, since the modulation pattern of the SS activity was essentially unchanged by blocking a modulated climbing fiber input, climbing fiber activity does not necessarily underlie SS-CS reciprocity, at least in the short term. While the pause in SS activity associated with the CS must contribute a small amount to the reciprocity, its contribution was below the level of resolution of our histograms. This is in part due to a short period of increased probability of SS discharge that often occurs after the pause (McDevitt, Ebner and Bloedel, 1982). The third issue upon which our findings bear is the proposition (Demer and Robinson, 1982; Demer, Echelman and Robinson, personal communication) that removal of the climbing fiber input may, within minutes, result in either a complete or partial saturation of the SS modulation. Our data do not support this suggestion, and we note that even though the spontaneous SS rate often increased by a substantial percent, the peak SS firing frequency during modulation was typically still less than the upper limit of the close-to-linear portion of Purkinje cell frequency-current curves (Llinas and Sugimori, 1980). In view of our findings, and those of Benedetti and colleagues (1983) showing complete suppression of the spontaneous firing of many cerebellar and vestibular nuclei neurons during inactivation of the inferior olive, an explanation of the behavioral outcome of Demer and Robinson's experiments requires a clearer understanding of the relations between Purkinje cells and their target neurons.

Supported in part by NIH Grant NS-13742.

REFERENCES

Alley, K., Baker, R., and Simpson, J.I., (1975). Afferents to the vestibulocerebellum and the origin of the visual climbing fibers in the rabbit. Brain Res., 98, 582-589.

Barmack, N.H., and Hess, D.T. (1980). Multiple-unit activity evoked in the dorsal cap of inferior olive in the rabbit. J. Neurophysiol., 43, 151-163.

Benedetti, F., Montarolo, P.G., Strata, P., and Tempia, F. (1983). Inferior olive inactivation decreases the excitability of the intracerebellar and lateral vestibular nuclei in the rat. J. Physiol., 340, 195-208.

Benedetti, F., Montarolo, P.G., and Rabacchi, S. (1984). Inferior olive lesion induces long-lasting functional modifications in the Purkinje cells. Exp. Brain Res., 55, 368-371.

Colin, F., Manil, J., and Desclin, J.C. (1980). The olivocerebellar system. Delayed and slow inhibitory effects: an overlooked salient feature of the cerebellar climbing fibers. Brain Res., 187, 3-27.

Demer, J.L., and Robinson, D.A. (1982). Effects of reversible lesions and stimulation of olivocerebellar system on vestibuloocular reflex plasticity. J. Neurophysiol., 45, 1084-1107.

Echelman, D.A., Demer, J.L., Robinson, D.A. (1983). Effects of reversible lesions and stimulation of the inferior olive on floccular Purkinje cell activity in the cat. Soc. Neurosci. Abst., 9, 608

Ghelarducci, B., Ito, M., and Yagi, N., (1975). Impulse discharges from flocculus Purkinje cells of alert rabbit during visual stimulation combined with horizontal head rotation. Brain Res., 87, 66-72.

Leonard, C.S., and Simpson, J.I., (1982). Effects of suspending climbing fiber activity on the discharge patterns of floccular Purkinje cells. Soc. Neurosci. Abst., 8, 830.

Leonard, C.S., and Simpson, J.I. (1983) Rotational polarity of Purkinje cell activity in the rabbit flocculus. Soc. Neurosci. Abs., 9, 608.

Llinas, R., and Sugimori, M., (1980). Electrophysiological properties of in vitro Purkinje cell somata in mammalian cerebellar slices. J. Physiol., 305, 171-195.

McDevitt, C.J., Ebner, T.J., and Bloedel, J.R. (1982). The changes in Purkinje cell simple spike activity following spontaneous climbing fiber inputs. Brain Res., 237, 484-491.

Montarolo, P.G., Palestini,. M., and Strata, P., (1982). The inhibitory effect of the olivocerebellar input on the cerebellar Purkinje cells in the rat. J. Physiol., 332, 187-202.

Savio, T. and Tempia, F. (1985). On the Purkinje cell activity increase induced by suppression of inferior olive activity. Exp. Brain Res.. 57, 456-463.

Simpson, J.I., Graf, W. and Leonard,. C.S. (1981). The coordinate system of visual climbing fibers to the flocculus. In A. Fuchs and W.S. Becker (Eds.), Progress in Oculomotor Research, Elsevier-North Holland, Amsterdam. pp. 475-484.

Simpson, J.I., and Hess, R. (1977). Complex and simple visual messages in the flocculus. In R. Baker and A. Berthoz (Eds.), Control of Gaze by Brain Stem Neurons, Elsevier, Amsterdam. pp. 351-360.

Strata, P. (1985). Inferior olive: Functional aspects. (1985). In J.R. Bloedel, J. Dichgans, and W. Precht (Eds.), Cerebellar Functions, Springer-Verlag, Heidelberg. pp. 230-246.

Neuronal Circuit Modifications Underlying Adaptation of the Vestibuloocular Reflex

Y. Miyashita

Department of Physiology, University of Tokyo, Tokyo 113, Japan

A lot of efforts have been devoted to identify the neuronal circuit responsible for adaptation of the vestibuloocular reflex (VOR) and to build a model for the VOR control system. However, a controversy still exists in evaluating the crucial roles of the cerebellum in the VOR adaptation, and it seems urgent to solve the controversy on a sound experimental basis. One clue for solution may be obtained from examination of involvment of the inferior olive in the VOR adaptation, as the inferior olive has been assumed to play a key role in learning mechanisms of the cerebellar cortex. This article attempts such an examination through data collected in studies on adaptive modification of the horizontal VOR (HVOR) under combined visual-vestibular stimulations in rabbits, cats and monkeys. These data are further viewed in the light of recent studies of the effect of olivo-cerebellar impulses which induce long-term modification of synaptic transmission in the cerebellar cortex.

Lesion and Stimulation Experiments on the Inferior Olive

Lesion experiments of the cerebellar flocculus have been shown to abolish the VOR adaptation in rabbits (Ito et al., 1974), in cats (Robinson, 1976) and in monkeys (Lisberger, Miles & Zee, 1984). Lesion experiments so far carried out in the brainstem have disclosed that the inferior olive is the only site whose chronic lesion abolished adaptation of the HVOR without affecting the dynamic characteristics of either VOR or optokinetic eye movement (OKR) (Ito & Miyashita, 1975). Severance of visual pathway to the dorsal cap of the inferior olive at a preolivary level (hatch in Fig. 1) causes this effect. This rostral olivary lesion eliminated the visual response of the dorsal cap neurons, but did not affect their tonic activity (Miyashita & Nagao, 1984). Lesion of the dorsal cap itself abolished HVOR adaptability in rabbits, although it also impaired dynamic characteristic of the VOR (Ito & Miyashita, 1975) and OKR (Barmack & Simpson, 1980) as lesion of the flocculus did (Hassul Daniels and Kim, 1976; Keller & Precht, 1979; Ito, Jastreboff and Miyashita, 1982; but also see Robinson, 1976; Zee et al., 1981). This implies a possible complication which would occur when we affect tonic activity of the olivary neurons. Haddad et al, (1980) also demonstrated that dorsal cap lesion abolished VOR adaptability in cats. In monkeys, no data have yet been available as to effects of interruption of the visual climbing fiber pathway on the VOR adaptability.

Reversible paralysis of olivary neurons in cats by local injection of narcotics induced a transient increase in VOR gain (Demer & Robinson, 1982). Stimulation

of climbing fibers induced a VOR gain decrease in alert cats when the stimulus
frequency was increased up to 40-60 Hz. Climbing fibers were thus claimed to
code "a gain-modulating signal", which would have an action to multiply the
head velocity signal coded on parallel fiber discharges. This theory predicts
a change of tonic climbing fiber activity in parallel with adaptive changes of
the VOR gain. However, this prediction failed to be confirmed by flocculus
single unit recordings in VOR adaptation (Watanabe, 1985). The cause of these
acute disturbances upon VOR dynamics is not clear at the present; but the
effect of climbing fiber paralysis might be related to the withdrawal of tonic
climbing fiber activity (see later). The effects of climbing fiber stimulation
at 40-60 Hz (Demer & Robinson, 1982) are more difficult to interpret because
the natural firing frequency of climbing fibers during VOR adaptation is around
1-2 Hz and hardly exceeds 10 Hz (see Fig. 2A).

Neuronal Connections around Dorsal Cap

The visual pathway to the dorsal cap has been analyzed well in cats and rabbits
(Fig. 1). Hoffman et al. (1976) suggested the Nucleus of Optic Tract (NOT) to
be a relay nucleus from the retina to the dorsal cap in cats. Maekawa & Takeda
(1977) found labeled neurons in the Dorsal Terminal Nucleus (DTN) as well as in
the NOT after injection of HRP into the dorsal cap in rabbits.
However, it should be noted that climbing fibers from the dorsal cap terminate
only at a part of the flocculus (Hoddevik & Brodal, 1977; Yamamoto, 1979). In
cats, ventrolateral outgrowth of the principal olive, rostral areas of the
principal and medial accessory olive, also send olivo-floccular fibers which
terminate in 8 separate longitudinal bands (Gerrits & Voogd, 1982).   At the
present stage of investigation, no experimental data are available to suggest
what kind of information is conveyed by these 'extra-dorsal cap' floccular
afferents.

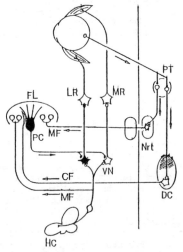

Fig. 1 Simplified schematic neuronal connections for adaptation of horizontal
VOR. FL, cerebellar flocculus.   PT, pretectal area. DC, dorsal cap of the
inferior olive. Nrt, nucleus reticularis tegmenti pontis.   VN, vestibular
nucleus. MR & LR, medial and lateral rectus motoneurons. HC, horizontal
canal. CF, climbing fiber. MF, mossy fiber. PC, Purkinje cell. Interruption
of visual climbing fiber pathway at rostral inferior olive (hatch) eliminated
VOR adaptation.

On the other hand, from HRP studies, floccular Purkinje cells which project to
different brainstem nuclei (medial and superior vestibular nuclei, nucleus
prepositus hypogrossi, cerebellar lateral nucleus etc) were also found to be
localized differentially in rabbits (Yamamoto, 1979; Balaban, 1984), in cats
(Bigare, 1980) and in monkeys (Balaban et al., 1981). Ito, Orlov & Yamamoto
(1982) demonstrated in rabbits that single-pulse microstimulation of the
flocculus (5-30 μA) inhibited a vestibuloocular reflex from the horizontal
canal to the medial and lateral rectus muscle. The effective stimulation sites
were shown to receive climbing fiber signals from the ipsilateral retina.
Thus, floccular Purkinje cells which receive visual climbing fiber afferents
are intimately connected to the horizontal vestibuloocular reflex, and other
Purkinje cells may be related to different control functions.

Climbing Fiber Responses of Floccular Purkinje Cells

In the monkey flocculus, it has recently been shown that <u>complex</u> spike
discharges are modulated effectively during combined visual-vestibular
stimulation (Watanabe, 1984). In this experiment, vestibular stimulation was
applied by sinusoidally rotating a turntable on which a monkey chair was
installed, and visual stimulation by rotating a cylindrical screen with a
checkerboard pattern around the turntable. Either one of the following two
types of combined visual-vestibular stimulation was applied to induce an
adaptive gain change of the HVOR: 1) 20° turntable rotation combined 180°
out of phase with 20° screen rotation (outphase combination); 2) 50°
turntable rotation combined in phase with 50° screen rotation (inphase
combination).
In examining climbing fiber responses of Purkinje cells, it was important to
distinguish areas of the flocculus according to effects of local stimulation
through the recording microelectrode. In one area (H-zone), the
microstimulation (300Hz, 1sec, less than 40 μA) induced abduction of the
ipsilateral (to the flocculus) eye, indicating intimate relationship with the
HVOR (see above). In other areas (non-H-zone), the stimulation induced
vertical or no eye movements.

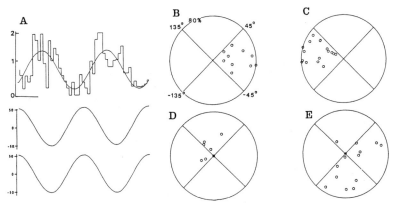

<u>Fig. 2</u> Modulation of <u>complex</u> spikes during combined visual-vestibular
stimulation. Upper trace in A represents spike density histogram (pulse/sec)
for <u>complex</u> spikes in a H-zone Purkinje cell during inphase combination.
Middle and lower traces, screen velocity (o/sec) and head velocity (o/sec).
Calibration, 1 second. B, C, <u>complex</u> spike modulation in H-zone Purkinje
cells. D, E, simular to B, C, but for modulation in non-H-zone Purkinje cells.
B, D, under outphase combination. C, E, under inphase combination (Watanabe,
1985).

In 48 Purkinje cells thus tested, the response pattern of the <u>complex</u> spike was very different between the H-zone and non-H-zone. When Purkinje cells were sampled in the H-zone, modulation of the <u>complex</u> spike was regularly inphase with head rotation (mean ± S.E. for phase shift 5.4+22.3°, for amplitude 62 9+22.2%; n=10) under the outphase combination (Fig. 2B), whereas under the inphase combination (C) it was regularly out-of-phase (phase shift 172+15.3°, amplitude 62.9+24.1%; n=17). In non-H-zone Purkinje cells, the modulation of <u>complex</u> spike discharge was very weak. And, if it ever occurred, its phase shift was very different from that of H-zone Purkinje cells (Fig. 2D,E).
In the dark, no modulation of <u>complex</u> spikes was observed during vestibular stimulation. Thus, the modulation elicited during visual-vestibular adaptive stimulation was presumed to represent optokinetic responsiveness. The <u>complex</u> spike discharge in the H-zone is then, enhanced during contralateral and depressed during ipsilateral movement of the visual environment. This H-zone specific responsiveness of <u>complex</u> spikes is same in its direction selectivity as that of rabbits' Purkinje cells (Ghelarducci, Ito & Yagi. 1975; Simpson & Hess, 1977 Miyashita & Nagao, 1984). It is also the same as that of NOT neurons (Collewijn, 1975) and dorsal cap neurons (Barmack & Hess. 1980) in rabbits. It is reasonable to conclude that in monkeys, as well as in rabbits and cats, H-zone Purkinje cells receive visual climbing fiber afferents through the neuronal circuit shown in Fig. 1. although we should wait for experimental anatomical evidence to confirm the connections in monkeys.

Adaptive Change of Simple Spike Responses in VOR

H-zone Purkinje cells in monkeys consistently changed their <u>simple</u> spike responses to head rotation in parallel with adaptive VOR gain changes and in a direction opposite the <u>complex</u> spike modulation (Watanabe. 1984). In this experiment, each session of experiments began when a Purkinje cell activity was recorded stably. Then, the HVOR gain and spike discharge of the Purkinje cell was sampled during sinusoidal rotation in the dark (50, 0.3Hz) (Fig. 3A).

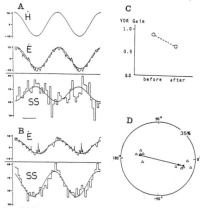

<u>Fig. 3</u> Changes in <u>simple</u> spike modulation of a Purkinje cell correlated to adaptation of the horizontal VOR. A, B, head velocity (Ḣ), eye velocity (Ė) in degree/sec, and <u>simple</u> spike discharge (SS) in pulse/sec recorded in the dark before (A) and after (B) one hour adaptation of the VOR. Time calibration. 1 sec. C, gain change in the adaptation of the horizontal VOR. D, polar diagram for modulation of <u>simple</u> spike discharge of Purkinje cells induced by head rotation in the dark. Values for modulation estimated in five successive measurements are indicated by open triangles (before) and closed (after the adaptation). Arrow connects mean values (Watanabe. 1985).

After combined visual-vestibular stimulation (outphase or inphase combination, see above) for one hour, the HVOR and spike discharge of the same Purkinje cell were again tested (Fig. 3B). If the Purkinje cell had been lost in the course of the combined adaptive stimulation, the session was terminated. Fig. 3 illustrates for an H-zone Purkinje cell. When inphase combination of visual-vestibular adaptive stimulation effectively decreased the HVOR gain in one hour, simple spike responses to head rotation in the dark, which was originally out of phase with head velocity, was converted to inphase with head velocity (Fig. 3A,B,C). Similarly, 20 H-zone cells tested under inphase visual-vestibular combination shifted their simple spike discharge to augment inphase modulation. By contrast, for 15 H-zone cells tested under outphase visual-vestibular combination, the shift of simple spike modulation was in the opposite direction. However, in non-H-zone Purkinje cells, these systematic changes of simple spike modulation were not observed.

This result differs from previous neuronal recording in monkeys (Miles et al., 1980a) where no systematic shift to outphase direction was detected for simple spike modulation in the dark during adaptation to high VOR gain. However, in their experiment climbing fiber response was reported to be 'extremely weak' and only 12 out of 128 tested Purkinje cells modulated (phase shift not described) their complex spike discharge (Miles et al., 1980b). These features resemble those of our non-H-zone Purkinje cell responses.

Miles et al. (1980a) also claimed that a simple spike modulation shift, if it ever occurred, might be a secondary effect of VOR gain change because simple spike response to head rotation contains a component proportional to eye velocity. However in rabbits' H-zone Purkinje cells the eye-velocity sensitive component accounts for only about one-fourth of the Purkinje cell responses to head rotation (Miyashita, 1984). In monkeys' H-zone cells, elimination of the eye velocity component by lesion of the vestibular nuclei preserved the modulation shift of simple spikes in VOR adaptation (Watanabe, 1984). Thus, the modulation shift of simple spikes in VOR adaptation at least contains primary plastic events in the cerebellar cortex, which contribute to control brainstem reflex pathways from the vestibular canal to ocular motoneurons (Fig. 1).

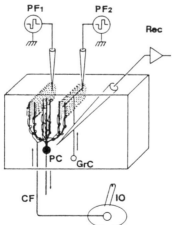

Fig. 4 A method to test the interaction between climbing fiber and parallel fiber activation in the cerebellar cortex. PF1, PF2, microelectrodes for stimulating two beams of parallel fibers in the molecular layer. IO, another electrode for stimulating climbing fibers (CF) in the inferior olive (Ekerot & Kano, 1985).

Taken together with the <u>complex</u> spike responses discussed in the previous
section (Fig. 2), these results imply that when <u>complex</u> spikes modulate
outphase during visual-vestibular adaptive stimulation, the <u>simple</u> spike
response to head rotation in darkness becomes more inphase, and that when
<u>complex</u> spikes modulate inphase, the <u>simple</u> spike response becomes more
outphase. These reciprocal patterns of <u>complex</u> spike modulation and <u>simple</u>
spike modulation shift are consistent with the assumption that the synaptic
transmission from the vestibular mossy fibers through parallel fibers to
Purkinje cells (represented by <u>simple</u> spikes) is depressed by conjoint
activation of climbing fibers through visual pathways (Ito, 1984). Next, we
will discuss the direct evidence at the cellular level for the assumption.

Effects of Climbing Fiber Activation on Simple Spikes

The climbing fiber impulses produce both a powerful EPSP and a prolonged
plateau-like potential in dendritic branches of Purkinje cells. In addition to
this primary effect, climbing fiber impulses produce depressant or facilitatory
after-effects on the <u>simple</u> spike activity of Purkinje cells (McDevitt, Ebner &
Bloedel, 1982). A sustained inhibitory after-effect is represented by a
release excitation, which occurs subsequent to destruction (Colin, Manil &
Desclin, 1980) or cooling of the inferior olive (Montarolo, Palestini & Strata,
1982). The spontaneous discharge rate of <u>simple</u> spikes doubles, and the
typical irregular <u>simple</u> spike discharge changes to a regular steady firing
pattern. These drastic effects may provide a cellular basis of the difficulty
in eye movement study which attempts to evaluate the functional role of the
olivo-cerebellar system by lesion of the inferior olive itself, as already
pointed out in the first section.
More important from the view point of VOR adaptation is the interaction of
climbing fiber impulses with parallel fiber-Purkinje cell transmission, which

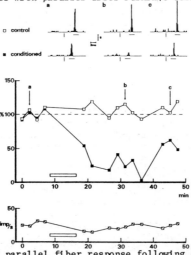

Fig. 5 Depression of parallel fiber response following conjunctive stimulation
with climbing fibers. A, peristimulus time histograms of Purkinje cells for
control and test parallel fiber beams. Time of stimulation indicated by
arrowheads. B Purkinje cell responsiveness to stimulation of control (open
circle) and test (closed circle) parallel fiber beams, plotted as a percent of
the mean firing index prior to conjunctive stimulation. The horizontal open
bar indicates conjunctive stimulation. a-c, responses shown in the histograms
in A (Ekerot & Kano, 1985).

may provide a synaptic basis for the cerebellar motor learning in general. Ito, Sakurai & Tongroach (1982) first tackled this challenge by electrically stimulating a vestibular nerve (20 Hz), which projects to the flocculus as mossy fibers, conjointly with climbing fibers (4 Hz), and they found that conjunctive stimulation depressed the Purkinje cell responsiveness to vestibular nerve stimulation for more than one hour. As the conjunctive stimulation did not affect the responsiveness of putative basket cells it was concluded that signal transmission at parallel fiber-Purkinje cell synapses undergoes a long-term depression after conjunctive activation of the climbing fiber on the Purkinje cell.

Then, this conclusion was more directly tested by stimulating parallel fibers through microelectrodes placed in the molecular layer (Ito & Kano 1982; Ekerot & Kano, 1985). Two separate parallel fiber beams impinged dendritic arborization of a single Purkinje cell (Fig. 4). The firing index of the Purkinje cell from each beam was used as an index of parallel fiber-Purkinje cell synaptic transmission. When one of the two beams was stimulated in conjunction with the inferior olive, the transmission from that parallel fiber beam was specifically depressed; the transmission from the other beam remained unchanged (Fig. 5). This specificity suggests that the effect of a conjunctive stimulation is not due to general depression in Purkinje cells, which occurs after the repetitive stimulation of climbing fibers (8-10 Hz; Rawson & Tilokskulchai, 1981), but that the effect is localized to a site in the parallel fiber-Purkinje cell synapses involved in conjunctive stimulation. It should be noted that this long-term depression did not occur when either parallel fibers or climbing fibers were stimulated without conjunction.

Recently, putative neurotransmitters of the parallel fiber were applied electrophoretically through a micropipette to see whether their applications in conjunction with climbing fiber stimulation could be substituted for the electrical stimulation of parallel fibers in conjunction with climbing fiber stimulation (Kano & Kato, 1985). Glutamate and, more effectively, quisqualate application could succesfully induce the long-term depression of the parallel fiber-Purkinje cell synaptic transmission, while neither aspartate nor kainate did. This indicates that quisqualate-sensitive glutamate receptors on the Purkinje cell dendrites are responsible for the molecular processes underlying the long-term depression.

Conclusions

The importance of the olivo-floccular system in the VOR adaptation was first demonstrated by lesion experiments in rabbits and cats. Multiple olivo-floccular projections which terminate differentially in longitudinal bands were also revealed in cats and rabbits. Corresponding experimental data in monkeys are not yet available. However. the complex spike discharge of a single Purkinje cell recorded in the monkey flocculus revealed specific optokinetic responsiveness and functional localization similar to those in rabbit flocculus. Simple spike responses to head rotation in darkness were found to undergo a systematic modulation shift during adaptive gain change of the HVOR in the Purkinje cells which were selected according to the visual climbing fiber input and the inhibitory effect upon horizontal VOR pathways. This observation in monkeys accords with those in rabbits (Dufossé et al., 1978; Nagao, in preparation).

Climbing fiber activation of a Purkinje cell results in short and long-term after-effects on the Purkinje cell activity. Among them, conjunctive stimulation of climbing fibers and parallel fibers was shown to produce a long-term depression of parallel fiber-Purkinje cell synapses which does not occur by parallel fiber stimulation alone. These results are consistent with the hypothesis that the flocculus Purkinje cells adaptively control the HVOR through modification of their simple spike responsiveness to vestibular signals under influences of retinal error signals conveyed by visual climbing fiber pathways.

R E F E R E N C E S

Balaban C. D., Ito M and Watanabe E. (1981). Demonstration of zonal projections from the cerebellar flocculus to vestibular nuclei in monkeys (Macaca fuscata). Neurosci. Lett.. 27, 101-105.

Barmack, N. H. and Hess, D T. (1980). Multiple-unit activity evoked in dorsal cap of inferior olive of the rabbit by visual stimulation. J. Neurophysiol., 43, 151-164.

Barmack, N. H. and Simpson J. I. (1980). Effects of microlesions of dorsal cap of inferior olive of rabbits on optokinetic and vestibuloocular reflexes. J. Neurophysiol.. 43 182-206.

Demer, J L. and Robinson. D A. (1982) Effects of reversible lesions and stimulation of olivocerebellar system on vestibuloocular plasticity. J. Neurophysiol., 47 1084-1107.

Ekerot, C. F. and Kano, M. (1985). Long-term depression of parallel fibre synapses following stimulation of climbing fibres. Brain Res. in press.

Gerrits, N. M. and Voogd, J. (1982). The climbing fiber projection to the flocculus and adjacent paraflocculus in the cat Neuroscience. 7, 2971-2991.

Haddad, G. M , Demer J. L. and Robinson, D. A. (1980). The effect of lesions of the dorsal cap of the inferior olive and the vestibuloocular and optokinetic systems of the cat. Brain Res. 185, 265-275.

Hoffman, K. P. Behrend, K. and Schoppmann A. (1976). A direct afferent visual pathway from the nucleus of the optic tract to the inferior olive in the cat. Brain Res. 115. 150-153.

Ito, M, and Miyashita, Y. (1975). The effects of chronic destruction of the inferior olive upon visual modification of the horizontal vestibulo-ocular reflex of rabbits. Proc. Jpn. Acad.. 51, 716-720.

Ito, M , Orlov, I. and Yamamoto. M (1982). Topographical representation of vestibuloocular reflexes in rabbit cerebellar flocculus. Neuroscience. 7, 1657-1664.

Ito, M. Sakurai, M. and Tongroach, P. (1982). Climbing fiber induced depression of both mossy fibre responsiveness and glutamate sensitivity of cerebellar Purkinje cells. J. Physiol. 324, 113-134.

Lisberger, S. G. Miles, F. A. and Zee D·S. (1984). Signals used to compute errors in monkey vestibuloocular reflex: Possible role of flocculus. J. Neurophysiol., 52. 1140-1153.

Miles, F. A Braitman, D J and Dow B M. (1980a). Long-term adaptive changes in primate vestibuloocular reflex. IV. Electrophysiological observations in flocculus of adapted monkeys. J. Neurophysiol. 43 1477-1493.

Miles, F. A. Fuller J H. Braitman. D. J. and Dow B. M (1980b). Long-term adaptive changes in primate vestibuloocular reflex. III. Electrophysiological observations in flocculus of normal monkeys. J. Neurophysiol., 43 1437-1476.

Miyashita, Y. (1984). Eye velocity responsiveness and its proprioceptive component in the floccular Purkinje cells of the alert pigmented rabbit. Exp. Brain Res., 55, 81-90.

Miyashita, Y and Nagao, S. (1984). Analysis of signal content of Purkinje cell responses to optokinetic stimuli in the rabbit cerebellar flocculus by selective lesions of brainstem pathways. Neuroscience Res.. 1 223-241.

Robinson, D. A. (1976). Adaptive gain control of vestibuloocular reflex by the cerebellum. J. Neurophysiol., 39, 954-969.

Simpson, J. I. and Hess. R. (1977). Complex and simple visual messages in the flocculus. In Baker. R. and Berthoz. A.(eds), Control of Gaze by Brain Stem Neurons, Elsevier Amsterdam. 351-360.

Watanabe E. (1984). Neuronal events correlated with long-term adaptation of the horizontal vestibulo-ocular reflex in the primate flocculus. Brain Res., 297, 169-174.

Watanabe. E. (1985). Role of the primate flocculus in adaptation of the vestibulo-ocular reflex. Neuroscience Res.. in the press.

Pharmacological Manipulation of Vestibular Plasticity

J. G. McElligott* and W. Freedman**

*Department of Pharmacology, Temple University School of
Medicine, Philadelphia, PA 19140, USA
**Bioengineering Program, National Science Foundation,
Washington, D.C. 20550, USA

INTRODUCTION

Adaptation via gain changes in the horizontal vestibulo-ocular reflex (VOR) results from prolonged mismatching of visual and vestibular inputs. This adaptative gain control mechanism has been shown to compensate for the effects of wearing reversing prisms or telescopic lenses. Many studies have emphasized the importance of the cerebellum in modification of the VOR. Vestibular afferents convey information from receptors in the labyrinth, informing the cerebellum of acceleration and position of the head. These afferent fibers terminate in the fastigial nuclei and the flocculo-nodular lobe of the cerebellum. The flocculus also receives visual inputs, while projecting its output via Purkinje cell axons to cells of the vestibulo-ocular reflex in the brain stem. Even though the gain of the VOR is no longer subject to modification following destruction of the flocculo-nodular lobe, questions have been raised about the actual "seat" of this adaptation being in the cerebellum (Miles and Lisberger, 1981). In fact, the exact mechanism by which the adaptation takes place is unknown. Thus, while no definitive experiment has been carried out to pinpoint the exact nature and location of the modifiability, it appears to be intimately related with the cerebellar circuitry.

Perhaps a look at another related system which has been implicated in neuroplasticity may help to provide some of the answers regarding this matter. Up until the present there have been few studies that have attempted to relate adaptation and motor learning with the noradrenergic system even though norepinephrine (NE) has long been thought to be involved in the learning process (Kety, 1972). In the cerebellum, NE has a profound effect. It selectively improves the signal to noise ratio of evoked versus spontaneous activity, enhancing the sensitivity of cerebellar neurons to both excitatory and inhibitory afferent inputs (Freedman and colleagues, 1977; Woodward and colleagues, 1980). Cerebellar NE is not directly involved with specific or detailed information transfer, but rather serves as a neuromodulator altering postsynaptic responsiveness of conventional neurotransmitters.

443

Recent studies in our own lab on locomotor behavior, show that acquisition of, but not motor performance per se, correlates directly with cerebellar NE levels (Watson and McElligott, 1984). Another study (Keller and Smith,1983) has shown that intra-cisternal injection of 6-OHDA which severely depleted stores of cerebellar NE prevented the modification of the VOR gain (decreases). Since a seeming decrease in gain can occur due to a reduction in the level of alertness, and since high doses of 6-OHDA can produce motor disturbances and changes in arousal levels, the intention of this study was to investigate this same phenomenon but to use instead gain increases in the VOR. Careful attention was also paid to the animals' state of alertness during both the modification and the testing stages.

METHODS

Female cats were implanted with pre-formed eye coils and head blocks constructed of dental acrylic. A cannula which allowed a liquid reward to be introduced directly into the animals' mouth was incorporated into each implant. After initial testing and modification of the VOR, the neurotoxin 6-OHDA (1.2 -2.4 mg) in a saline-ascorbic acid (0.1 mg/ml) solution was injected intra-cisternally in small multiple doses. After a post-infusion recovery period of 2 weeks, testing and modification again took place.

Head restrained animals were placed on a hydraulically driven, servo-controlled vestibular platform located in a light-proof room. Electromagnetic field generating coils used to measure the animal's eye movements were also mounted on the platform (Fig. 1A). An optokinetic drum was attached to a ceiling mounted servo-controlled electrical motor. Control of the platform, drum, sequencing of events and collection of data, were under computer control. The vestibular platform and optokinetic drum were calibrated to produce equal but opposite angular rotations. Before and after each experiment, the field generating coils were rotated (+/-10 degrees) with respect to the animal held in an earth fixed position. This calibration provided a measure of system repeatability and a method to adjust the data for any possible drift in the equipment.

In order to increase the gain of the VOR, the optokinetic drum was oscillated 180 degrees out-of-phase with the platform. Both the platform and the drum movements during modification periods were pseudo-random, i.e., a linear combination of several frequencies (0.07 to 0.4 Hz @ ±12.5 degree; Figure 1B). Each modification period lasted for 15 minutes. As a measure of the animal's level of alertness, the number of saccades made by the animal was counted during each modification period. The animal received a small milk reward for producing saccadic eye movements. In addition to the milk reward, auditory and tactile stimulation were provided to assure high levels of alertness. Measurement of the VOR in the dark (0.25 Hz @ +/-10 degrees) took place following each 15 minute modification period. Modification followed by a VOR measurement was repeated over a 4 hour period. In addition, the animals were tested for their ability to fixate on an object of visual interest before and after this 4 hour period,

Horizontal eye position and velocity as well as table position were recorded throughout the experiment on a chart recorder (Fig. 2) and also stored on a

A.

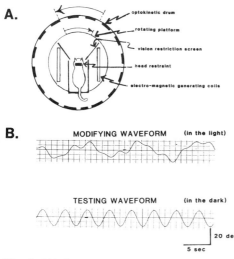

A. PRE-MODIFICATION

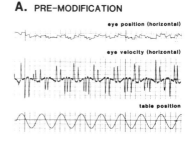

B. POST-MODIFICATION (4 hour)

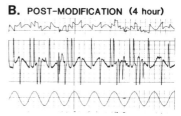

Fig. 1 (A) Overhead view of the apparatus; (B) modifying and test waveforms.

Fig. 2 Sample of chart recording before (A) and after (B) modification.

computer disk. Reconstruction of the slow phase horizontal eye position signal was carried out later by removing the fast phases (saccades) via a computer program (Fig. 3). The gain and phase angle of the remaining slow phase of the horizontal eye position signal with respect to the platform position output signal were computed for each test. The computer program chose the "best" 40% of data in each test period where "best" is defined as the section of the reconstructed data in which the peak-to-peak value of the horizontal eye signal is the largest (Fig. 3). Fast Fourier Transforms (FFT) of reconstructed eye and platform position signal were computed. The ratio (FFT-eye/FFT-table) at the test frequency was computed for each test period. Immediately, at the conclusion of behavioral testing, neurochemical analysis was carried out in order to verify the extent of catecholamine depletion. Tissue samples from the cerebellum, visual cortex and brainstem were collected. Quantitative determinations of NE and dopamine (DA) were made using high performance liquid chromatography with electrochemical detection (HPLC-EC).

RESULTS

Ten female cats were attached by their head block implant to the restraining apparatus which was secured to the hydraulically driven vestibular platform. After a calibration of the system, the animals were tested in the light for their ability to fixate on an object of visual interest (animated experimenter's face, jangling keys or a rat restricted to a small cage) while they were rotated (0.25 Hz @ +/-10 degrees) about the horizontal axis on the platform. At the completion of these tasks, the cats were tested in the dark to determine the gain of the VOR compared to the value obtained during visual fixation. The average gain of the VOR in the dark relative

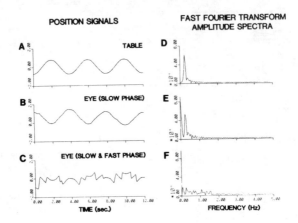

Fig. 3 Computer generated waveforms of position signals (A, B, C) with their associated amplitude spectra (D, E, F).

to that obtained during the visual fixation in the light for these cats was 0.91.

The animals were then subjected to a four hour modification procedure which was directed at increasing the gain of the VOR. While these animals were oscillated in a pseudo-random fashion (0.07 - 0.4 Hz) on the platform, an optokinetic drum was oscillated in the same manner but 180 degrees out of phase with the table.   During and at the end of the modification period, the animals were tested in the dark at a single frequency (0.25 Hz @ ± 10 deg) for changes in the gain of the VOR   The average VOR gain at the end of the period for all the animals was 1.15 (when compared to the visual fixation). This represents a gain increase of 31% for the group of the ten cats.   The VOR gain before and after the modification period is shown for 1 animal in Fig. 2.

After a period of not less than one week, the animals were injected intra-cisternally with 6-OHDA. The animals were tested again at the end of a two week period for modification of the VOR using the same procedure previously employed. During this period the change in VOR gain went from 0.93 to 0.98.   This is considerably reduced and represents only a 5% increase in gain after 4 hours of modification.

Even though the group of ten animals as a whole increased their VOR gain by 31% prior to injection, there appeared to be two separate subgroups, namely, those animals which changed their gain substantially (high gain modifiers; n = 6) and those who did not manifest significant changes in gain (low gain modifiers; n = 4). A high gain modifier was defined to be any animal which changed its gain over the four hour period by an amount ≥ 25%. When the animals were divided into these two groups, the average gain increase for the high gain modifiers was 48% (range 26% to122%) when tested prior to injection with 6-OHDA.   After the intra-cisternal injections, the percent gain change manifested by these animals fell to

2%. For the low gain modifiers, the increase in gain prior to injection was 6% (range -3% to 18%), and this changed to 8% after administration of the neurotoxin 6-OHDA. This data is presented graphically in Fig. 4.

Two of the animals received control intra-cisternal injections of saline-ascorbic acid (0.1mg/ml) prior to initial testing and modification. Subsequently both of these animals produced substantial VOR gain increases (≥ 25%) and thus were included in the high gain group that later received 6-OHDA injections.

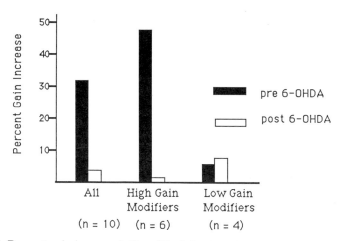

Fig. 4 Percent gain increase before (black bars) and after (white bars) 6-OHDA injection for all the animals. Also presented separately are percentages for high and low gain modifiers.

The state of alertness or arousal level of the animal is one of the critical parameters that can vary during both the modification and the testing period. It is possible to have a lack of change or to record a low value for the VOR as a result of a low level of arousal. In order to ensure that the animals were well aroused and fully alert, we presented the animals with a variety of auditory, tactile and gustatory stimulation during the testing and the modification procedures. In order to obtain an independent measure of the animals' state of alertness, we decided to count the number of saccades made during the modification period. This helped to assure us that a relatively constant level of arousal was maintained over the entire four hour modification period. Furthermore, it also helped in assessing if this level was maintained during the modification period after the administration of 6-OHDA. For all the animals, the average rate of saccade production was 29.7 saccades/min or about 1 saccade every 2 seconds during the modification period prior to 6-OHDA injection (Fig. 5). Gradually, over the four hour period the rate dropped slightly from a rate of 32.7 (1st hour) to 26.8 saccades/min (4th hour). After 6-OHDA injection, the overall average rate was 28.8 saccades/min. There was also a similar slight reduction in the rate of saccades from 31.8 saccades/min (1st hour) to 28.4 saccades/min (4th hour). There was no evidence of differences in saccade

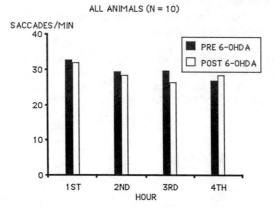

Fig. 5 Average number of saccades/min generated during each of the 4 hours before (black bars) and after (white bars) 6-OHDA injection.

production when the data for the high gain modifiers were compared to that of the low gain modifiers both during the modification period or when the pre-injection period was compared to that of the post-injection period.

At the completion of the experiment, samples from brain tissue (cerebellum, brain stem, and visual cortex) were taken from each animal. Using High Pressue Liquid Chromatography with Electro-chemical Detection (HPLC-EC), assays for catecholamine content (NE and DA) were measured. The most significant depletion was observed in the cerebellar norepinephrine content (23.9% of control animals). The minimal cerebellar depletion of the high gain animals was 32% of control values. The brain stem (59.1% of control) and the visual cortex (45.5% of control) for all the animals manifested less NE depletion. The dopamine content of the cerebellum is only a fraction (5%) of the norepinephrine content and manifested only a slight reduction (77.1%). In general, there was less dopamine depletion in the other regions. This was expected since small multiple injections of 6-OHDA tend to deplete the NE while preserving the DA systems (Hoffer and colleagues, 1973).

DISCUSSION

Cats which normally increased their VOR gain after 4 hours of modification were not able to modify this gain to the same extent after intra-cisternal injections of 6-OHDA. Six of these cats which were classified as high gain modifiers manifested the greatest reduction in their ability to modify gain. The average gain increase of 48% before injection, was reduced to an increase of only 2% after 6-OHDA injection. The other 4 animals in this study (low gain modifiers) had a pre-injection gain increase of only 6%. After the injection, the gain change for these cats was virtually unchanged at 8%.

An independent estimate of the level of alertness was obtained by counting the number of saccades made during the modification both before and after the 6-OHDA injection. Since there was no change in the number of saccades during this period, it was concluded that the levels of arousal was also unchanged. Thus, the lack of VOR gain increase after injection of 6-OHDA could not be attributed to a decrease in the level of alertness.

Six-hydroxydopamine when injected intra-cisternally can produce depletions of both NE and DA in the regions around the ventricles. However, the method of injection that we employed (i.e., small multiple injections) minimized DA depletion. Several regions were assayed for changes in catecholamine levels. These areas, namely, the cerebellum, brain stem, and visual cortex, are the regions where the most significant depletion of NE takes place and where the structures responsible for the maintainance or modification of the VOR are presumably located. Interestingly enough, the cerebellum which appears to be intimately involved in the modification of the VOR, was the structure that had the greatest depletion of NE.

There is considerable anatomical and physiological evidence that NE has a profound and significance influence in the cerebellum (Hokfelt and Fuxe, 1969; Woodward and colleagues, 1979). Furthermore, recent studies (McElligott, Ebner and Bloedel, 1984) have shown that intra-cisternal injection of 6-OHDA alters climbing fiber enhancement of evoked mossy fiber responses recorded in the Purkinje cells of normal animals (Ebner, Yu and Bloedel, 1983). This is especially significant since visual input involved in the VOR comes into the cerebellum via the climbing fibers whereas the vestibular information to these same Purkinje cells enters via the mossy fiber system. Furthermore, Ito, Sakurai and Tongroach (1982) have shown that there is a specific change in vestibular afferent mossy fiber input to Purkinje cells when stimulation of this input was coupled with activation of climbing fibers.

Gilbert (1975) has proposed a schema for cerebellar learning. He postulated that increased discharge of locus coeruleus cells would release larger quantities of NE at Purkinje cell synapses to signal a favorable outcome worthy of consolidation. Thus, the enhanced short term changes of mossy fiber input to the Purkinje cells (via the parallel fibers), affected by the climbing fibers, could be turned into long term synaptic changes and could be mediated by NE release.

However, this emphasis on cerebellar-noradrenergic mechanisms may be premature, since the intra-cisternal injection of 6-OHDA reduced NE in several other equally important areas. The influence of the NE system in this phenomenon may lie external to the cerebellum and more careful examination of extra-cerebellar sources in the brain stem and elsewhere may reveal its presence.

Acknowledgements: It is a pleasure to acknowledge the technical assistance of Troy Carter during the course of these experiments. This work was supported by a grant from the National Science Foundation(BNS-8410231) and from NIH (SO7-RR05417).

REFERENCES

Ebner, T. J., Q. X. Yu, and J. R. Bloedel, (1983). Increase in Purkinje cell gain associated with naturally activated climbing fiber input. J. Neurophysiol., 50, 205-219.

Freedman, R., B. J. Hoffer, D. J. Woodward, and D. Puro, (1977). Interaction of norepinephrine with cerebellar activity evoked by mossy and climbing fibers. Exper. Neurol., 55, 269-288.

Gilbert, P. F. C., (1975). How the cerebellum could memorize movements. Nature (London), 254, 688-689.

Hoffer, B.J., G. R. Siggins, D. J. Woodward, and Bloom, F.E., (1973). Spontaneous discharge of Purkinje neurons after destruction of catecholamine-containing afferents by 6-hydroxydopamine. Brain Res., 30, 425-430.

Hokfelt, T., and K. Fuxe, (1969). Cerebellar monoamine nerve terminals, a new type of afferent fibers to the cortex cerebelli. Exp. Brain Res., 9, 63-72.

Ito, M., M. Sakurai, and P. Tongroach, (1982). Climbing fiber induced depression of both mossy fiber responsiveness and glutamate sensitivity of cerebellar Purkinje cells. J. Physiol., 324, 113-134.

Keller, E. L., and M. Smith, (1983). Suppressed visual adaptation of the vestibuloocular reflex in catecholamine-depleted cats. Brain Res., 258, 323-327.

Kety, S. S., (1972). The possible role of the adrenergic systems of the cortex in learning. Res. Publ. Ass. Nerv. Ment. Dis., 50, 376-389.

McElligott, J. G., T. J. Ebner, and J. R. Bloedel, (1984). Reduction of cerebellar norepinephrine alters climbing fiber enhancement of mossy-parallel fiber input to the Purkinje cell. Soc. Neurosci., 10, #217.12 752.

Miles, F. A., and S. G. Lisberger, (1981). Plasticity in the vestibulo-ocular reflex: a new hypothesis. Ann. Rev. Neurosci., 4, 273-299.

Watson, M. and J. G. McElligott, (1984). Cerebellar norepinephrine depletion and impaired acquisition of specific locomotor tasks of rats. Brain Res., 296, 129-138.

Woodward, D. J., H. C. Moises, B. D. Waterhouse, B. J. Hoffer, and R. Freeman, (1979). Modulatory actions of norepinephrine in the central nervous system. Fed. Proc., 38, 2109-2116.

Reconciling Observations on Putative Sites for Adaptive Plasticity of the Vestibulo-ocular Reflex

H. L. Galiana

Aerospace Medical Research and Biomedical Engineering Unit,
Faculty of Medicine, McGill University, 3775 University St.,
Montreal, Quebec, Canada H3A2B4

CEREBELLAR-BRAINSTEM INTERACTIONS IN THE VOR

The discussion below will refer to a schematic model of pathways in the vestibulo-ocular reflex (VOR), providing for strong interactions between ocular premotor signals in the vestibular brainstem, and vestibular signals on Purkinje cells (PJ) in the cerebellum. The example here refers to the horizontal VOR, and is illustrated in Fig. 1. Details on the anatomical and physiological bases for this model structure are given elsewhere (Galiana, in press).

The model in Fig. 1 provides for second-order cells in the vestibular nuclei (VN), which are modulated by vestibular primary signals, and by an efference copy of eye position (E*), via feedback of premotor signals through the filter H. In other words, these 2° cells represent so-called eye-movement vestibular cells in the VN (Tomlinson and Robinson, 1984), projecting to the cerebellum and receiving themselves an inhibitory influence from the cerebellum. As such, the model resembles an extended version of the VOR schematic presented by Miles and Lisberger (1981), with the addition of extended coupling between cerebellar and brainstem pathways, and the provision for the influence of cross-midline signals on VN responses, through effective self-feedback with loop gain 'g'. All blocks in Fig. 1 represent pure gains, except for the block H, which represents a

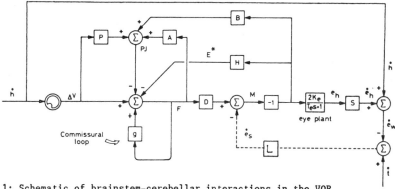

Fig. 1: Schematic of brainstem-cerebellar interactions in the VOR

low-pass filter with a single time constant. Visual-vestibular interactions are restricted to the contribution of image slip velocity ($\dot{e}_s$), again in the manner of Miles-Lisberger, as might occur during target pursuit. Thus the dashed pathways are only active in the light.

Now one might ask of what use is such a model. The answer of course is that assuming it represents reasonably well the actual anatomy, a model can be used as a kind of "dry experiment", to determine the optimal protocol for distinguishing between potential sites for the adaptation of the VOR, in the normal behaving animal. This is equivalent to determining the sensitivity of various responses to parametric changes in the figure.

One result is immediately obvious: regardless of the site of VOR plasticity, beit cerebellar (through parameters P, A or B) or in the brainstem (in parameters g, D or filter H), premotor VN responses during head rotation in the dark should always reflect any changes in VOR gain level, with a parallel though not necessarily equal change in sensitivity (e.g. increased sensitivity to head rotation after raising the VOR gain). Hence observations on VN responses are not useful in deducing possible sites for VOR adaptation, and will not be discussed here further. Cerebellar responses are a completely different matter; observations at this level do offer the possibility of distinguishing between sites, and evaluating potential transferal of the adaptive load to alternate sites during long-term adaptation of the VOR. This is detailed below in discussing this session's presentations.

The VOR in the Dark

In Fig. 1, the VOR in the dark, during head rotation in the canal passband, can be shown to be proportional to

$$\dot{e}_h/\dot{h} \propto - (1-P) \, D \, K_e \, / \, [T \, (1+A-BD-g) \,] \qquad (1)$$

while PJ responses will be proportional to

$$PJ/\dot{h} \propto P \, + \, [\, (1-P) \, (A-BD) \, / \, (1+A-BD-g) \,] \qquad (2)$$

Thus, increasing g and/or the absolute value of negative (A-BD) could theoretically increase the VOR, as expressed in Equ. 1. In either case, PJ modulation during VOR in the dark will decrease, according to Equ. 2. Therefore putative sites for VOR plasticity in cerebellar or brainstem (here commissural) pathways cannot be differentiated during VOR in the dark.

VOR Suppression

During VOR suppression in Fig. 1, $\dot{t}=\dot{h}$, and ocular responses are given by

$$\dot{e}_h/\dot{h} \propto - (1-P) \, D \, / \, [\, L \, (1+A-g) \,] \qquad (3)$$

which is greatly reduced from Equ. 1 because of the combined effect of a large visual loop gain (L), and loss of -BD in the denominator. On the other hand, PJ responses are now approximated by

$$PJ/\dot{h} \propto P \, + \, [\, A \, (1-P) \, / \, (1+A-g) \,] \qquad (4)$$

for large L.

In this protocol, ocular responses are much less sensitive to any parametric changes that led to a VOR gain change in the dark. However, whatever small change may be observed, the sensitivity of ocular responses during suppression will necessarily change in the same direction as the forced change in VOR (e.g. slight increase after important increase in VOR gain in the dark), and this regardless of the site of plasticity (cerebellar or brainstem).

However, if we now consider the PJ responses, we find that the two potential sites for adaptation will have very different effects: in fact, the predicted changes in PJ modulation are in opposite directions, depending on the site used for parametric changes. For example, if VOR gain were increased with parametric changes in A and/or BD, PJ responses during VOR suppression would be reduced from those in the preadapted state. On the other hand, increasing VOR gain by increasing commissural gain, g, would result in larger modulations on PJ firing rates during VOR suppression. Therefore, simply observing the direction of change in cerebellar responses, during normal visual-vestibular interactions, might be sufficient to localize the site of parametric adaptation.

DISCUSSION

Simpson (this book) observed in rabbit that removal of climbing fibre activity did not alter the depth of modulation on PJ responses during head rotation in the dark. Only PJ resting rate seemed significantly affected. Two points should be raised here. First, if one considers that models, such as that in Fig. 1, represent the average behaviour of populations of cells at different levels, then even a change in the resting rate of PJ cells might be sufficient to cause a change in VOR gain indirectly: a change in the background level of cerebellar inhibition on VN cells could change the resting activity of VN cells, and with it the level of cell recruitment indirectly affecting loop gains and with them VOR gain. Thus, cerebellar control of VOR gain need not be restricted to changes in the modulation depth of PJ responses. Second, Simpson stated that the PJ cells he observed had firing rates sensitive to not only head velocity or eye velocity, but also often to eye position. Firing rates could exhibit pauses or bursts during quick phases of nystagmus. It has been argued before that interactions between the slow- and fast-phase components of nystagmus, on a cell responding to both, could lead to underestimating the true sensitivity to head velocity (Galiana, 1984). This factor may be worth evaluating in Simpson's data.

Miyashita (this book) provides evidence to support the potential plasticity of cerebellar synaptic efficacy, with climbing fibre activity, and shows that the effect can last at least one hour, at least in rabbit. He also concludes from Watanabe's (1984) study that cerebellar responses in monkey during VOR in the dark are also compatible with a cerebellar site for adaptation of the VOR. However, the theoretical results above indicate that the same observations would also be compatible with a brainstem site for VOR plasticity, so long as recordings are restricted to the VOR in the dark. We also need to see cerebellar studies during VOR suppression; then it should be possible to confirm whether cerebellar plasticity supports all of the VOR gain change, only in the acute stages of adaptation (first few minutes) or also in those cases of short-term modifications lasting a few hours.

Lisberger (this book) presents additional evidence in support of his previous studies with Miles (Miles and Lisberger, 1981), arguing that the delays in the responses of the adapted VOR preclude the possible involvement of cerebellar pathways, and in fact point to a brainstem site. Since Lisberger's experiments in monkey involve weeks of progressive adaptation, the time factor may be an important element in determining the site used to support adapted behaviour. As he has argued before, the adaptive load may be progressively transferred from a cerebellar site to a brainstem site, allowing for more rapid reflex operation in the new gain level, once a change has been sensed as being "permanently" required.

In the theoretical analysis above, it is shown that commissural cross-midline coupling would be a powerful putative site for plastic adaptation of the VOR, compatible with previous observations after long-term adaptation of the VOR (Galiana, in press; Galiana, 1985). (Here, long-term is considered to be forced adaptation lasting several days.) This could also explain observations that there are apparently two parallel pathways in the VOR, one of short-delay (14ms) and unmodifyable, and another which contributes to the modified VOR approximately 5ms later (Lisberger and Pavelko, in press; Lisberger, this book). Both of these pathways are presumed to be located in the brainstem since their contributions are too early to allow participation of cerebellar pathways. In Fig. 1, one could visualize that signal transmission through a 2° VN cell would at first reflect only the direct sensitivity to primary afferents, and that the premotor signal would change as cell recruitment and feedback through commissural (or other) loops finally contributed to the total sensitivity to head velocity. This would imply that the modified VOR signal, in the long-term, should be found in the VN, on those very 2° cells which exhibit the most complex patterns in firing rate, modulated by all eye movements and sensory inputs.

REFERENCES

Galiana, H.L. (1984). On evaluating dynamics of central and ocular responses in the VOR. Soc. Neurosci. Abstr., Vol. 10, Part II, p. 1154.
Galiana, H.L. (1985). Commissural vestibular nuclear coupling: A powerful putative site for producing adaptive change. In A. Berthoz and G. Melvill Jones (Eds.), Adaptive Mechanisms in Gaze Control: Facts and Theories, Vol. 1, Reviews of Oculomotor Research, Elsevier Biomedical Press, Amsterdam. pp. 327-344.
Galiana, H.L. (in press). A new approach to understanding adaptive visual-vestibular interactions in the CNS. J. Neurophysiol.
Lisberger, S.G., and T.A. Pavelko (in press). Vestibular signals carried by the pathways subserving plasticity of the vestibulo-ocular reflex in monkeys. J. Neurosci.
Miles, F.A. and S.G. Lisberger (1981). Plasticity in the vestibulo-ocular reflex: A new hypothesis. Ann. Rev. Neurosci., 4, 273-299.
Tomlinson, R.D. and D.A. Robinson (1984). Signals in vestibular nucleus mediating vertical eye movements in the monkey. J. Neurophysiol., 51, 1121-1136.
Watanabe, E. (1984). Neuronal events correlated with long-term adaptation of the horizontal vestibulo-ocular reflex in the primate flocculus. Brain res., 297, 169-174.

OSCILLOPSIA AND
CONGENITAL NYSTAGMUS

Peripheral Ocular Motor Palsy Impairs Motion Perception

Th. Brandt and M. Dieterich

Neurological Clinic, University of Munich, FRG

INTRODUCTION

Oscillopsia versus retinal slip: Involuntary ocular oscillations, secondary to supranuclear disorders override fixation and cause oscillopsia, the illusory movement of a viewed stationary scene. Angular displacement of apparent motion, however, does not quantitatively match the net retinal slip (Brandt, 1982; Wist et al., 1983). Thus, in downbeat nystagmus the illusory motion is smaller than that which would be expected from the amplitude of the nystagmus (Büchele et al., 1983). Nystagmus, and the consequent oscillopsia, increase in amplitude as gaze is directed toward the periphery; the mean ratio between nystagmus and oscillopsia is 0.37. This partial suppression of visual motion perception due to the retinal slip of involuntary oscillations also applies to single objects moving within the visual scene. In the latter circumstance, thresholds for egocentric detection of object motion are significantly raised. Thresholds also increase with increasing nystagmus amplitude. Furthermore, perception of retinal slip is largely suppressed in patients with acquired infranuclear eye movement defects (which cause an inappropriate gain of the vestibulo-ocular reflex) during head oscillation and fixation of a stationary target. This 'adaptive suppression' is beneficial to the extent that it alleviates the distressing oscillopsia with the additional disadvantageous 'side effect' of simultaneously impaired perception of object motion in general.

We will demonstrate that the dissociation between net retinal slip and perceived motion may be due to two separate mechanisms:

1) a physiological inhibitory interaction between self-motion and object-motion perception,

2) a binocular pathological (adaptive?) elevation of thresholds for object-motion perception in acquired monocular extra-ocular muscle paresis.

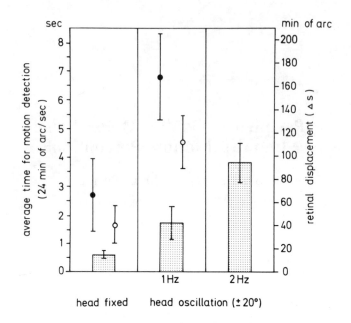

Fig. 1. Thresholds for detection of object-motion (means and
standard deviations) in 12 normal subjects (columns as
compared to 8 patients suffering from acquired peripheral
ocular motor palsies (●: paretic eye; o: unaffected eye).
During the measurements the moving target (24 min of arc/
sec; left or right) was fixated by the subject and the head
was either fixed by a bite board or voluntarily oscillated
about the vertical Z-axis at 1 or 2 Hz with an amplitude
of + 20 degrees (motion perception during vestibulo-ocular
reflex).
Physiologically thresholds for object motion detection
significantly increase in normal subjects with increasing
frequency of head oscillation (columns). With peripheral
ocular-motor palsies a further pathological elevation of
thresholds can be obtained for both the head-fixed condition and head oscillation in both eyes, and is obviously
more pronounced in the affected eye.

Self-motion perception or moving eyes physiologically impair
concurrent object-motion perception

The incidental observation that one has considerable difficulty in
seeing the treetops moving in the wind while driving a vehicle led
us to a systematic study of egocentric object-motion perception
during concurrent self-motion. In a series of laboratory experiments
we found significantly increased thresholds of object motion perception during simultaneous self-motion under various stimulus

conditions. These were vestibular, visual, or cervico-propriocep-
tive stimulations (Probst et al., 1984). Subjects were exposed to
the target which randomly moved either to the right or to the left
at a constant angular velocity of 24 min of arc/sec with a step-
wise increase in exposure times from 0.25 to 10 sec (twenty re-
petitions of each stimulus condition). Conservative determination
of threshold was based on 18 out of 20 possible correct perceptions
of movement as well as direction. Sinusoidal active head oscillation
at 1 Hz about the vertical Z-axis (amplitude ± 20 deg) raised the
detection threshold for object motion of a fixated target (1 deg in
diameter) by a factor up to 3 times that measured when the head was
stationary (Fig. 1). This effect is not simply due to a retinal
slip of the fixated target, because stabilization of the retinal
image was shown to be complete for ± 20 deg head oscillations in
yaw up to a frequency of 1 Hz (Wist et al., 1983).

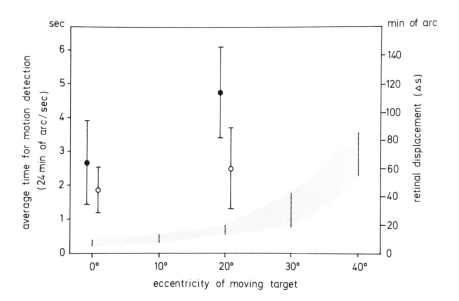

Fig. 2. Thresholds for detection of object motion (means and stand-
         ard deviations) as a function of the horizontal eccentrici-
         ty of the moving target on the retina (0 to 40 degrees) in
         12 normal subjects (shaded area) and 8 patients with
         acquired ocular motor palsies (●: paretic eye;
         o: unaffected eye).
         Average time to detect motion increases with increasing
         eccentricity of the retinal area stimulated in healthy
         subjects. Thresholds of patients are significantly higher
         for both eyes with foveal as well as with parafoveal motion
         stimulation as compared to normal subjects. Thus acquired
         extraocular muscle paresis seems to impair object motion
         perception within the entire visual field.

That real motion of eyes or the head is not the essential stimulus
to suppress object-motion perception was demonstrated by trunk
oscillations relative to head fixed by a bite board (cervical
stimulation), and by circularvection studies with apparent self-
motion induced by movement of a large visual scene (optokinetic
stimulation).
This new phenomenon of a 'physiological inhibitory interaction'
between object- and self-motion perception may reflect lack of
specificness (or a side effect) of the space constancy mechanism,
which provides us with a stable picture of the world during
locomotion.
There may be a somatosensory analogue to this visual phenomenon
since elevated threshold for the perception of electrical stimuli
applied to a fingertip as well as partially suppressed somatosensory
evoked potentials have been found with simultaneous movement of the
stimulated finger in man (Coquery, 1978). The suppression of response activity in the medial lemniscus to contralateral electric
stimulation 100 ms before the onset of active movement in the cat
(Ghez and Pisa, 1972; Coulter, 1973) seems to support the view of
an efferent inhibition of sensory inflow. Since suppression also
occurs with passive movements 'afferent inhibition' must be possible
too (Angel and Malenka, 1982).

Pathological (adaptive?) impairment of motion perception caused by
peripheral ocular motor disorders

It was the amount of net retinal slip tolerated by the patients
without causing oscillopsia as well as the interindividual differences with respect to the degree and the acuity of the paresis which
led us to suspect an additional pathological impairment of motion
perception dependent on the particular disease and distinct from the
phenomenon above described.
Motion perception was investigated separately for the affected and
unaffected eye while fixating a horizontally moving target 1 deg
in diameter, with a constant velocity of 24 min of arc/sec in a
total of 24 patients suffering from abducens (n=14), oculomotor
(n=6), trochlear palsy (n=2), or monocular myasthenic weakness
(n=2).
Thresholds for the detection of object motion (8 patients) with the
head fixed were significantly raised up to a factor of 5 for the
paretic eye and a factor of 3.3 for the normal eye (Fig. 1). With
sinusoidal head oscillations at 1 Hz (which physiologically elevates thresholds) the ratio between thresholds in patients and normals is about 4 for the paretic eye and 2.7 for the unaffected eye
(Fig. 1). This clearly suggests that in patients with acquired
peripheral ocular motor palsies both, the physiological and the
pathological impairment of motion perception summate when the moving
target is fixated during voluntary head motion. These effects are
not restricted to the fovea but also apply to perception of motion
within the peripheral retina (Fig. 2). In normal subjects thresholds
increase with increasing eccentric exposure of the target on the
retina (factor of 1.2 for 20 deg eccentricity); accordingly pathological thresholds in patients are further elevated when a moving
stimulus is viewed from the peripheral retina (factor of 1.7 for
20 deg eccentricity in paretic eye). A central mechanism must be
assumed which affects motion perception since perception of both
eyes is involved even though the paretic eye tends to perform more
poorly.

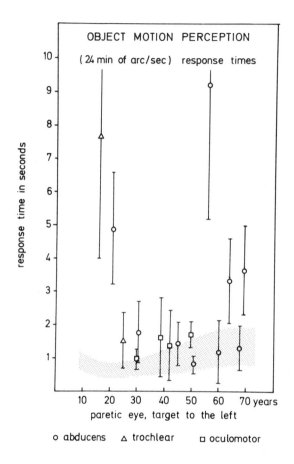

Fig. 3. Response times (means and standard deviations) to detect horizontal object motion at constant angular velocity of 24 min of arc/sec. The shaded area represents a control group of 60 neurological patients without ocular motor disturbances (n=10 for each decade from 10 to 70 years). Response times are shortest at about 20 years of age with increasing mean values and standard deviations in the elderly. Most of the patients with acquired peripheral ocular motor disorders have higher response times for monocular vision of the affected eye. 3 patients (1 with a congenital abducens palsy) between 52 to 70 years appeared normal with respect to motion perception.

OBJECT MOTION PERCEPTION

(24 min of arc/sec) response time

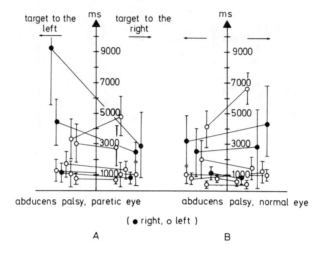

A   B

Fig. 4. Response times (means and standard deviations) to detect
horizontal motion to the left or to the right at a constant
angular velocity of 24 min of arc/sec for 9 patients
suffering from acute or chronic abducens palsy of the right
(●) or left (o) eye. Prolongation of response times shows
no significant directional right/left preponderance of
motion perception suppression in relation to the directional
deficit of eye movement.

In a second series of experiments (16 patients) mean response times
(n=20) to the detection of motion of a projected target (24 min of
arc/sec) were determined instead of conventional threshold measurements which require trying attention of the patient for two hours.
Response times were determined as a function of age (n=10 for each
decade from 10 to 70 years) in a control group of 60 neurological
patients without ocular motor disturbances. Again, response times
of most patients with acquired ocular muscle paresis were longer
and exhibited larger standard deviations compared with the range of
patients of the same age without ocular motor dysfunction (Fig. 3).
3 patients, however, did not show abnormal prolongation of response
times; one of them was the only patient with a congenital abducens
palsy. Prolongation of response times to motion stimuli in patients
was not simply due to a 'retarded reaction' since mean net reaction
times to suprathreshold stimuli were the same for the ocular motor
and the control group (266+ 79 ms and 265+ 58 ms, respectively).
Differences between affected and unaffected eyes were not significant, as there was no direction specific suppression of motion perception (right versus left) with respect to the direction of eye
movement dysfunction in right or ·left abducens palsies (Fig. 4).

Thus, there is a central binocular impairment of motion perception
in patients with acquired peripheral ocular motor palsies which
lasts as long as the palsy lasts, the underlying mechanism of which
is unknown. A similar effect was seen in patients with internuclear
ophthalmoplegia (n=2). The amount of suppression of motion perception seems for the most part to be independent of the degree
of the individual palsy, but the time course in particular the
improvement of motion perception along with the recovery of the
palsy has yet to be studied more thoroughly.

REFERENCES

Angel, R.W. and R.C. Malenka (1982) Velocity dependent suppression of cutaneous sensitivity during movement.
   Exp. Neurology, 77, 266-274

Brandt, Th. (1982) The relationship between retinal image slip,
   oscillopsia and postural imbalance, In G. Lennerstrand et
   al. (eds.), Functional Basis of Ocular Motility Disorders,
   Pergamon Press, Oxford and New York, pp 379-385

Büchele, W., Th. Brandt and D. Degner (1983) Ataxia and oscillopsia in downbeat-nystagmus vertigo syndrome.
   Adv. Oto-Rhino-Laryng., 30, 291-297

Coquery, J.-M. (1978) Role of active movement in control of
   afferent input from skin in cat and man. In G. Gordon (Ed),
   Active Touch - The Mechanism of Reco gnition of Objects by
   Manipulation, Elmsford, New York, pp 161-169

Coulter, J.D. (1973) Sensory transmission through lemniscal
   pathway during voluntary movement in the cat.
   J. Neurophysiol., 37, 831-845

Ghez, G. and M. Pisa (1972) Inhibition of afferent transmission
   in cuneate nucleus during voluntary movement in the cat.
   Brain Res., 40, 145-151

Probst, Th., S. Krafczyk, Th. Brandt and E.R. Wist (1984)
   Interaction between perceived self-motion and object-
   motion impairs vehicle guidance.
   Science, 225, 536-538

Wist, E.R., Th. Brandt and S. Krafczyk (1983)
   Oscillopsia and retinal slip; Evidence supporting a clinical test. Brain, 106, 153-168

Stepping Around: Nystagmus, Self-motion Perception and Coriolis Effects

W. Bles*,** and S. Kotaka***

*Free University Hospital, Amsterdam, The Netherlands
**TNO Institute for Perception, Soesterberg, The Netherlands
***Tokyo Medical and Dental University, Tokyo, Japan

Feedback of the extent of limb movements is provided by somatosensory signals from joint and musculotendinuous receptors. The somatosensory information contributes to the perception of self-motion during active locomotion. Together with vestibular and visual afferences the somatosensory afferences converge upon multimodal neurons in the vestibular nuclei and thalamus which project to cortical sensory areas in the anterior parietal lobe. It could be demonstrated in man that movements of the limbs alone induced self-motion sensation and nystagmus, even in the absence of concurrent vestibular or optokinetic stimulation. Head tilt was found to evoke Coriolis-like sensations.

These effects were demonstrated in objectively stationary subjects seated in darkness inside a rotating cylinder, when they are tracking the rotation of the cylinder by placing their hands on its inner wall (Brandt, Büchele and Arnold, 1977) and in spatially stationary subjects stepping on a small circular treadmill in darkness (Bles, 1981).

From neuro-anatomical data we know that there are several receptors of the somatosensory system which may be involved like Merkel's cells, Meissner's and Ruffini's corpuscles and hair follicles for touch and pressure, Pacinian corpuscles for vibration, and receptors in joints, tendons and muscles for position sense. Several ascending pathways like the dorsal column medial lemniscus pathway, the spinal cervical thalamic pathway and perhaps also the spinal thalamic pathway, are known to convey information from these receptors to the brain. Of importance in the central neural circuits are the relay stations like the lateral reticular nucleus, the inferior olive and especially the vermis and fastigial nucleus because of the coupling to the vestibular nuclei, where the velocity storage mechanism should be located.

This paper will focus on the effects of somatosensory stimulation during stepping in circles on nystagmus, self-motion perception and Coriolis effects.

METHODS

The equipment consisted of a horizontal bar and platform, attached to a rotating vertical pivot situated in the centre of a rotating drum. The drum (Tönnies, Freiburg i.Br.) had a diameter of 1.5 m and was of cylindrical shape. The wall was painted with 52 vertical black and white stripes. For vestibular stimulation the subjects were sitting in darkness on the rotating platform

with their hands resting on the bar. For optokinetic stimulation the subjects
were also sitting but the platform was stationary, the light switched on and
the drum rotating. For somatosensory stimulation the subjects stepped in darkness behind the stationary bar on the floor of the rotating drum.
We used stimuli with a trapezoidal velocity profile for vestibular and somatosensory stimulation (acc. $5°/s^2$ up to a velocity of $50°/s$ which was maintained
for 60 s after which a deceleration of $5°/s^2$ took place to a stop). For optokinetic stimulation the light in the drum was switched on for 60 s during
constant velocity rotation at $50°/s$. Stimuli were applied in both directions;
subjects were standing or sitting in such a way that they really or apparently
moved forward during stimulation.

Horizontal and vertical eye movements were recorded by means of electronystagmography. These signals were recorded together with light indication, position
and velocity of the bar and the drum on a strip chart recorder (Siemens EM
81.80). From these recordings the nystagmus slow phase velocity (SPV) was
calculated and the parameters of the extended mathematical model of Raphan
and Cohen (Raphan, Matsuo and Cohen, 1979; Bles and others, 1985) were opti-
mized by simulation on a digital computer in order to obtain the best fit
to these nystagmus SPV values. Patients verbally reported their self-motion
sensation after each run.

NYSTAGMUS

Apparent Stepping Around (ASA) behind the stationary bar on the floor of the
rotating drum in darkness evokes nystagmus. This ASA nystagmus has a latency
of up to several seconds after stimulus onset and shows a build up of nystagmus
Slow Phase Velocity (SPV). The mean eye position ("Schlagfeld") deviates in
the direction of the fast phase and, following the end of stimulation positive
after nystagmus can be seen similar to optokinetic after nystagmus (OKAN).

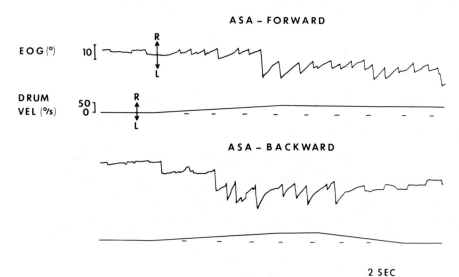

Fig. 1. Apparent Stepping Around nystagmus recorded during
forward and during backward stepping from a patient
with bilateral loss of vestibular function.

The SPV of ASA nystagmus is low in most normals (mean SPV about 4-5°/s with large interindividual variability). All patients devoid of vestibular function, however, showed without exception a clear ASA nystagmus with a mean SPV of about 10°/s (Bles, de Jong and de Wit, 1984). An increased gain is seen also in patients with a unilateral loss of function. We have the impression that, in general, an increased gain of ASA nystagmus can be observed in patients with a vestibular imbalance.

The characteristics of patients without vestibular function are different from normals in that there is no latency in the appearance of nystagmus after stimulus onset (see e.g. Fig. 1) and also a direct decrease during stimulus termination, so without any after nystagmus, similar to the lack of OKAN observed in these patients.

One of our patients was incidently examined during stepping backward (for a short stimulus duration) which resulted in a nice compensatory nystagmus as well (Fig. 1). In between stimulus conditions her position behind the bar was changed but not the turning direction of the drum. Although this patient managed the backward stepping quite well, we prefer forward stepping during routine examination for safety reasons.

The characteristics of the somatosensory nystagmus obtained in healthy subjects and in patients with a bilateral loss of vestibular function suggested somatosensory-vestibular interactions very similar to the visual-vestibular interactions (Bles, de Jong and de Wit, 1984) resulting in an extension of the Raphan-Cohen model for visual-vestibular interaction (Raphan, Matsuo and Cohen, 1979) with a direct somatosensory pathway and an indirect somatosensory pathway with access to the common vestibular and visual velocity storage mechanism (Bles and others, 1985). By these pathways we could account for the slow build up of the somatosensory nystagmus during stimulation and the positive somatosensory after nystagmus in normals. In this way we could also account for the lack of somatosensory after nystagmus as well as for the lack of optokinetic after nystagmus in the patients with loss of vestibular function.

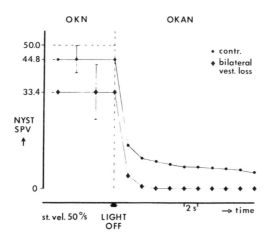

Fig. 2. Mean OKN and OKAN from 10 patients with bilateral loss of vestibular function and from 16 controls.

An interesting observation was that the mean optokinetic nystagmus SPV from the patients with bilateral loss of vestibular function was lower compared

to controls (Fig. 2). The difference accounts for the contribution of the
indirect visual pathway via the velocity storage mechanism (Raphan, Matsuo
and Cohen, 1979) since the integrator of that mechanism is responsible for
the OKAN: The immediate jump in SPV level after stimulus termination is the
same both for controls and these patients (see Fig. 2).

We had the opportunity to examine a patient with a vermis agenesia with a
Dandy Walkers cyste (Kotaka, Watanabe and Bles, 1984). As was to be expected
from neuro-anatomical data, we did not observe ASA nystagmus. Vestibular
stimulation resulted in normal vestibular nystagmus.
We also examined patients with a sensory polyneuropathia of the lower limbs
due to cisplatinum treatment for malignancies. Only a few patients could
sustain the final stimulus velocity of 50°/s for all stimulus conditions.
The ASA nystagmus SPV was lower or at the level of the controls but not absent. This examination was of theoretical interest because of the question
whether tactile or proprioceptive information is more important for the generation of somatosensory nystagmus. Apparently the contact of the hands with
the wall or of the feet with the floor is important since mimicking the movements of hands or feet without that contact does not evoke nystagmus or induce
an illusion of self-motion.

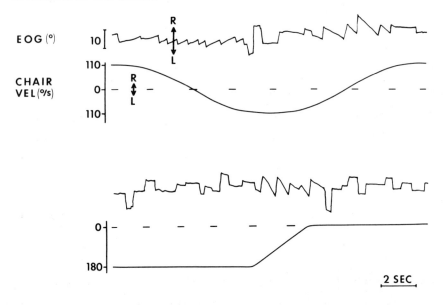

Fig. 3. Nystagmus recordings of a patient with bilateral
        loss of vestibular function during chair rotation
        in darkness.

Hemilabyrinthless patients were found to have a higher gain of the direct
somatosensory path than controls whereas bilateral labyrinthless patients
do have the highest gain (Bles, de Jong and de Wit, 1984). The hemilabyrinthless subjects were found to have a diminished vestibular gain. These findings
suggest that the sensory weighting given to somatic afferent information
is increased, which means compensation for the vestibular deficiency by substitution of other sensory information. Such an increase of the gain of the
direct somatosensory pathway may lead to the misdiagnosis of residual vestibular function if nystagmus or self-motion perception arise during chair

rotation of a labyrinthless patient. Figure 3 shows an example of the nystagmus evoked during sinusoidal stimulation and during rapid deceleration of the chair; these phenomena are observed in almost our patients and that they were labyrinthless indeed was proved by the absence of Coriolis effects during head tilt at high speed velocity rotation.

The increase in gain of the direct somatosensory pathway is not coupled to the functioning of the velocity storage mechanism. One of our healthy controls had no velocity storage mechanism: the best fit to the experimental data was obtained by neglecting the central integrator. He had intact labyrinthine function; The gain of his ASA nystagmus was low. Interestingly this young man could perform head movements during high speed velocity chair rotation for a longer period without getting sick although he reported tumbling sensations adequately. His history revealed immunity to motion sickness.

In combined sensory stimulation as is the case during stepping behind the rotating bar on the stationay floor in darkness, the resulting nystagmus SPV is higher than expected on the base of stimulation of the sensory systems apart (Bles, de Jong and de Wit, 1984). This may be due to pitching head movements which are known to enhance horizontal nystagmus (Raphan and others, 1983). Pitching head movements during ASA do not enhance the ASA nystagmus SPV.

SELF-MOTION PERCEPTION

Similar to the optokinetic Circular Vection (Dichgans and Brandt, 1978) apparent stepping around leads to a sensation of self-motion (Bles, 1981). There seems to be no relationship between the occurence of self-motion sensation and the appearance of nystagmus. We have seen impressive nystagmus recordings from a patient who reported that the bar was stationary and the floor rotating (which was the case indeed) as well as the opposite: saturated self-motion sensation without concurrent nystagmus.

The stimulus patterns as described in the methods section, resulted in negative after sensations following vestibular stimulation, positive after sensation following optokinetic stimulation and no after effects following apparent or real stepping around.
The last finding suggests cancelling of the vestibular negative after sensation by a latent positive somatosensory after sensation. Following rapid stops positive after sensations have been reported (Guedry and others, 1978).

In a study on somatosensory and vestibular interaction in self-motion perception we had the two systems played off against each other. Subjects were stepping behind the bar which was rotating at 50°/s. After 60 s of constant velocity rotation the bar was decelerated maintaining constant stepping velocity by accelerating the drum into the opposite direction. Deceleration and accelaration levels were varied according to the verbal reports of the subjects. They had to indicate changes in direction (from forward to backward) or a complete stop (apparent stepping around). It was found that the median deceleration necessary to stop or reverse the sensation of bar rotation was 9°/s². Similar interactions are known for the visual and vestibular system (Probst, Straube and Bles, 1985).

CORIOLIS EFFECTS

An important aspect of vestibular stimulation is the intra-vestibular mismatch between the otolith and canal information due to Coriolis forces, the so-called vestibular Coriolis effect. Experimentally it has been verified that congruent visual information attenuates the vestibular Coriolis effect whereas

the effect is enhanced by incongruent visual information; it has been shown
too that head movements during pure optokinetic stimulation are leading to
qualitatively the same phenomena (Pseudo-Coriolis effect, Dichgans and Brandt,
1978).

One of us (Bles, 1981) demonstrated that it is possible to induce Coriolis-
like effects by tilting the head during apparent stepping around, very similar
to the optokinetic Pseudo-Coriolis effect (Bles, 1981).

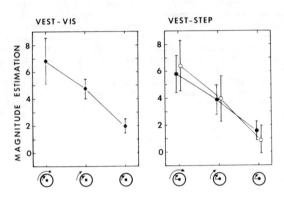

Fig. 4. Magnitude estimation of the Coriolis effects
during visual-vestibular interaction (left side)
and during somatosensory-vestibular interaction
(right side). The open circles refer to estimates
obtained with additional visual information.

The effects of vestibular-somatosensory interactions on the Coriolis effect
have been studied with the following arrangement. The subject stood or was
stepping on the floor of the drum behind the bar with both hands on the
bar. The experimental conditions (see Fig. 4, right side) were chosen in
such a way that vestibular stimulation was held constant and modified by
congruent or incongruent information from the sensory channels. For instance,
the vestibular stimulus was held constant (CCW rotation of the bar) with
modification of the somatosensory information; in one condition (1), the
subject stepped forward on the stationary floor of the drum behind the
CCW rotating bar; in another condition (2), the subject simply stood behind
the CCW rotating bar on the floor of the drum, which also rotated CCW with
the same velocity; in the last condition (3), the subject stepped backward
behind the CCW rotating bar, because the floor of the drum was also rotated
CCW, but with twice the velocity of the bar. The last condition involves
incongruent somatosensory and vestibular motion information. These conditions
were performed in total darkness and with additional visual information.
The accelerations chosen were $3°/s^2$ for a terminal velocity of $60°/s$ and
$6°/s^2$ for a terminal velocity of $120°/s$. Consequently, the stepping acceleration forward or backward was always $3°/s^2$. The subject was instructed
to stay behind the bar, which meant that he was required to step forward
or backward when there was motion of the bar relative to the floor of the
drum.
Under each condition, the subject started with his head tilted toward the
left shoulder. On command, after rotating for 60 s at constant velocity,
he returned his head toward the normal upright position within about 1 second.
Subsequently, he was asked to scale his subjective sensation in relation
to the purely vestibular Coriolis effect, which served as a standard with
an arbitrary value of 5. The absence of any sensation was given the value
0.

The results are shown in Fig. 4 (right side). Modification of the vestibular Coriolis effect (condition 2) by the presence of congruent (condition 1) or incongruent (condition 3) somatosensory motion information can be seen. The magnitude of the Coriolis effect in condition 1 is significantly lower than in condition 2 (p < .01; Wilconxson Signed-Ranks test) and in condition 2 the effect is significantly less than in condition 3 (p < .01). When vision supplements the somatosensory information, the effects are similar and even more impressive.

The somatosensory-vestibular interactions in the Coriolis-effects as shown in Fig. 4, right side, show exactly the same behavior as was found by Brandt, Wist and Dichgans (1971) with visual modulation of the vestibular Coriolis effect (Fig. 4, left side). When vision accords with the somatosensory cues of stepping around, the incongruity with the vestibular stimulus may lead to a very strong reaction and some subjects even have serious difficulties in maintaining equilibrium. However, the Coriolis effect is reduced remarkably when the three systems produce congruent information, which is the normal daily-life situation.

REFERENCES

Bles, W. (1981). Stepping around: Circular vection and Coriolis effects. In J. Long, A. Baddeley (Eds.), Attention and Performance, Vol. IX, Lawrence Erlbaum Associates, Hillsdale, pp. 47-61.
Bles, W., G. R. v.d. Heyde, S. Kotaka and J. P. H. Reulen (1985). Some modelling aspects of nystagmus due to somatosensory-visual-vestibular interactions in stepping around. In M. Igarashi, F. O. Black (Eds.), Vestibular and visual control on posture and locomotor equilibrium. Karger, Basel, pp. 38-42.
Bles, W., J. M. B. V. de Jong and G. de Wit (1984). Somatosensory compensation for loss of labyrinthine function. Acta Otolaryngol. (Stockholm) 97, 213-221.
Brandt, Th., W. Büchele and F. Arnold (1971). Arthrokinetic nystagmus and ego-motion sensation. Exp. Brain Res. 30, 331-338.
Brandt, Th., E. Wist and J. Dichgans (1971). Optisch induzierte Pseudocoriolis Effekten und Circularvektion. Arch. Psychiat. Nervenkr. 214, 365-389.
Dichgans, J. and Th. Brandt (1978). Visual-vestibular interaction: Effects on self-motion perception and postural control. In R. Held, H.W. Leibowitz and H.L. Teuber (Eds.), Handbook of Sensory Physiology, Vol. VIII: Perception. Springer, Berlin, pp. 755-804. ·
Guedry, F. E., L. E. Mortensen, J. B. Nelson and M. J. Correia (1978). A comparison of nystagmus and turning sensations generated by active and passive turning. In J. D. Hood (Ed.), Vestibular mechanisms in health and disease. Academic Press, London.
Kotaka, S., I. Watanabe and W. Bles (1984). Somatosensory-visual-vestibular interaction in case of vermis agenesia. Brain and Nerve, 36 (11), 1083-1088 (in Jap.).
Probst, Th., A. Straube and W. Bles (1985). Differential effects of ambivalent visual-vestibular-somatosensory stimulation on the perception of self-motion. Beh. Brain Res. 16, 71-79.
Raphan, T., B. Cohen, J. Suzuki and V. Henn (1983). Nystagmus generated by sinusoidal pitch while rotating. Brain Res. 276, 165-172.
Raphan, T., V. Matsuo and B. Cohen (1979). Velocity storage in the vestibulo-ocular reflex arc. Exp. Brain Res. 35, 229-248.

Abnormal Head Position and Head Motion Associated with Nystagmus

L. F. Dell'Osso*,*** and R. B. Daroff*,**,***

Ocular Motor Neurophysiology Laboratory* and Neurology
Service**, Veterans Administration Medical Center; and the
Departments of Neurology***, Case Western Reserve University
and University Hospitals; Cleveland, Ohio, USA

INTRODUCTION

Over the 40 different types of nystagmus presently identified (Dell'Osso, 1984), only a few are associated with oscillations of the head or specific head positions. We will discuss those which occur in congenital nystagmus (CN) latent/manifest latent nystagmus (LMLN), the nystagmus blockage syndrome (NBS), spasmus nutans (SN), periodic alternating nystagmus/periodic alternating gaze deviation (PAN/PAGD), and acquired downbeat nystagmus. We will also discuss descriptions of spontaneous and induced "head nystagmus." Vestibular nystagmus induced by head positions (positional nystagmus) or rapid head movements (positioning nystagmus) will not be discussed.

Whereas abnormal head positions are probably always adaptive and compensatory, head oscillations need not be. In each instance we will attempt to identify what affect the oscillation has upon perception (visual acuity.)

CONGENITAL NYSTAGMUS

Patients with CN may exhibit either head oscillations, a head position preference or both. The head oscillations seen in CN were originally thought to be compensatory in nature (Cogan, 1967). The patient was said to be moving his head equally and oppositely to the CN and was thereby stabilizing the eyes in space. In the absence of good eye movement recordings, this became an attractive hypothesis. Metz, and colleagues (1972) provided support for the compensatory hypothesis by simultaneously recording eye and head movements. However, examination of their data reveals a jerky head movement of approximately 30 degrees supposedly compensating for a pendular CN of about 7 degrees. Patients with CN rarely complain of oscillopsia during either steady fixation or while moving (actively or passively). Based on clinical observations and personal experience in sports, we concluded that the vestibulo-ocular response (VOR) of the CN patient functions normally. Recent studies have confirmed the normal functioning of the VOR in CN patients (Carl, and colleagues, 1985; Gresty, and colleagues, 1985). We further reasoned that for the head oscillation to be completely compensatory, the patient had to simultaneously turn off his VOR (i.e., gain reduced to zero) and duplicate exactly the CN waveform (180 degrees out-of-phase) (Daroff, and colleagues, 1978). Our earliest recordings revealed the extreme complexity and high bandwidth of these waveforms and we concluded that the above-described total compensation was impossible. Moreover, the foveation periods of each waveform precluded the necessity for totally

473

stabilizing the eyes in space since for most of each cycle the fovea was off-target and visual information suppressed (this inferred from the lack of oscillopsia) (Dell'Osso, 1973; Dell'Osso and Daroff, 1975). Compensation could be realized during relatively stable (as opposed to motionless) foveation periods with head oscillations and VOR suppression.

Gresty, and colleagues (1978), in a study of a single case, showed by accurate eye and head movement recordings that the head oscillation is merely an extension of the CN and that the normal VOR keeps the eyes stable in space during the foveation periods of the CN waveform. The head oscillations in some patients, under certain conditions, emerge as a manifestation of their ocular motor instability (damped by the mass of the head) and do not result in any acuity improvement or decrement. We concluded, as did Gresty and Halmagyi (1981) and, more recently, Carl, and colleagues (1985), that this is the operable mechanism for head oscillation in <u>most</u> CN patients. The observations that head oscillations appear only <u>during</u> intense fixaton attempts and the accompanying increase in the nystagmus, (i.e., while trying to see targets at the limits of the patient's acuity) and are more prevalent in children who are unconcerned about appearance, support this hypothesis.

There have been recent reports of rare CN patients in which the head oscillation was said to be either truly compensatory or to cancel the eye oscillation (Gresty and Halmagyi, 1981; Gresty, and colleagues, 1984; Taylor, 1980). Here, the word "compensatory" is taken to mean a deliberate <u>head</u> movement that is equal and opposite to an ongoing eye movement with the VOR <u>gain</u> decreased to zero (this usage is opposite to the compensatory <u>eye</u> movement produced by a head movement and the normal VOR gain of one). Unfortunately, no recordings were shown in two of these papers and in the third, the patient identified as having CN with head movements that canceled the nystagmus had convergence (180 degrees out-of-phase) nystagmus that was probably spasmus nutans (see below). Furthermore, the example given for compensatory head oscillation was not convincing; it corresponded exactly to what one would record from a CN patient with a normal VOR operating to negate the effects of his spontaneous head oscillation. We have never observed cancellation of CN by active head shaking.

The only way to differentiate true compensatory head movements from spontaneous head movements would be to compare the foveation periods of the CN waveform when the head is still with the same foveation periods measured during head oscillation. If foveation periods are flat (i.e., eyes motionless) when the head is still, the eye-in-head oscillations seen during head motion are VOR movements added to the CN and the resulting gaze (eye-in-space) tracings will also show flat foveation periods. If foveation periods show the same waveform when the head is still as when it is moving, the head oscillation is truly "compensatory" and only the gaze tracings will show flat foveation periods. Thus, recordings of the CN waveforms under both conditions are necessary to prove the existance of compensatory head movement. To date, we have only observed true compensation of CN by head movements in the data from one CN patient (Carl, and colleagues, 1985). As we had originally predicted, this patient suppressed his VOR gain and

improvement occurred <u>only</u> during foveation periods. With the head still, the foveation periods were not flat and when head movement occurred, the gaze tracing showed flat foveation periods. Patients who have achieved flat foveation periods without head movement can gain nothing by head shaking and any head motion should be presumed to be due to the CN. Those whose foveation periods are not flat may improve them with head motion and their head shaking might be suspected to be compensatory.

Patients with CN often adopt head turns that place their eyes at a preferred gaze angle where the nystagmus is minimal and the acuity maximal. The nulling of CN occurs when the eyes are deviated to the null angle or the head is turned in the opposite direction; this is the basis for both prism and surgical therapies. Up to about 15 degrees, the head turn equals the null angle but beyond that, the amount of head turn is less than that required to balance out the null angle (Fujiyama, and colleagues, 1983). While the exact mechanism of CN nulling is unknown, we hypothesize that the unstable ocular motor system has an equilibrium position (the null angle) that divides two regions of instability, each producing runaway eye movements in opposite directions. The push-pull nature of brainstem neural integrator circuitry is consistent with this conceptualization.

The mechanism underlying abnormal head postures in CN patients that are not simple rotations in the horizontal plane is more obscure. Head tilts toward one shoulder or chin-up and chin-down postures raise the possibility that, for non-strabismic patients, a vestibular input is being used since these postures cause a change in static vestibular firing due to the effects of gravity on the otoliths. Such head postures must be tested under the effects of different gravity vectors (e.g., while the body is in different orientations) before this hypothesis can be evaluated against the alternative; that is, the position of ocular motor equilibrium in such patients requires innervation of muscles in other than the horizontal plane.

LATENT/MANIFEST LATENT NYSTAGMUS

Another congenital type of nystagmus, that is not CN, is latent/manifest latent nystagmus (LMLN) (Dell'Osso, and colleagues, 1979). LMLN is a jerk nystagmus with a decreasing-velocity slow phase that beats in the direction of the fixating eye, the other eye being covered (LN) or open but cortically suppressed (MLN). In many cases of LMLN, the amplitude of the oscillation varies monotonically with gaze angle such that as gaze is directed toward the fast phase, the amplitude increases (Alexander's law). Because of this, and the fact that the ocular motor system seems to be unable to prolong foveation when the slow phases are of decreasing velocity, patients may adopt a head turn to increase their acuity. By turning the head toward the fast phase the fixating eye is placed in adduction where the amplitude of the LMLN is minimal. In cases where the patient has alternate fixation, the head turn will depend on the fixating eye, which will be placed in the adducted position. In patients whose LMLN does not vary in accordance with Alexander's law, a head turn that places the fixating eye in abduction may be preferred. In either case, the head turn will minimize the LMLN and maximize the visual acuity by the resulting increase in foveation time. There may be other factors in some LMLN patients (e.g., an angle kappa) that can result in paradoxical head turns that increase the nystagmus amplitude (Dell'Osso, and colleagues, 1979).

The observation that for the LMLN waveform, the initial rapid movement of the fovea off target precludes plastic adaptation of the ocular motor system deserves comment. In CN waveforms, the slow phases start slowly and increase in velocity as the fovea is driven off target. This low-velocity initial movement is apparently countered by a strong fixation reflex that maintains target foveation and we see the results in the long foveation periods of many CN waveforms. The inability of the LMLN patient to similarly distort the slow phases of LMLN suggests that fixation reflexes are ineffective in the presence of high retinal slip velocities.

NYSTAGMUS BLOCKAGE SYNDROME

The nystagmus blockage syndrome (NBS) is the reduction of a CN or conversion of a CN to a low-amplitude MLN by a purposive esotropia (Dell'Osso, and colleagues, 1983). In either instance acuity is improved. As the esotropia increases, the nystagmus decreases and as the fixating eye follows a target moving laterally towards primary position and then into abduction, the esostropia decreases and the nystagmus increases. The fixating adducted eye necessitates a head turn toward that eye for targets that are in primary position. Often an alternating head turn accompanies alternating fixation in these patients such that the adducted eye is fixating primary-position targets. A head turn is not present when the fixating eye is in primary position and the other (suppressed) eye is esotropic. These head positions mimic those of LMLN patients whose waveforms follow Alexander's law and who are esotropic; this has caused many such patients to be mis-diagnosed as NBS patients. The head turn in the NBS is adopted by the patient to allow fixation of a primary-position target by the adducted eye.

SPASMUS NUTANS

Spasmus nutans (SN) (a condition that has been described by many names: nutatio capitis spastica; gyrospasm; nodding spasm; rotatory spasm; head nodding; and salaam tic) is a benign, self-limiting condition of infants and children that consists of pendular nystagmus (often asymmetric and/or disconjugate) usually associated with head nodding or anomalous head position. Since the characteristics of the nystagmus are described in this volume by Weissman and colleagues, we will confine ourselves to the head movements. They may be inconstant and irregular and may be absent in some patients.

In the first quantitative recording of both the eye and head oscillations in SN, Gresty, and colleagues (1976) showed that the head oscillation canceled the nystagmus, leaving only the normal VOR movements. This cancellation of the nystagmus in SN by head shaking has since been confirmed in other patients (Gresty and Ell, 1981; Gresty and Halmagyi, 1981; Gresty, and colleagues, 1984); in addition we cite the above-mentioned example of cancellation of "CN" by head shaking (Taylor, 1980). The operative mechanism appears to be one of total cancellation of the ongoing nystagmus by intentional head shaking accompanied by the normal VOR. This differs from the head oscillations of CN which are either produced by the instability itself or are compensatory (i.e., used with a suppressed VOR to stabilize the eyes in space only during the foveation periods). Head shaking improves acuity for SN patients and those few CN patients with compensatory head movements; it is unaffected in most CN cases because of the normal VOR.   The cancellation effect explains earlier reports of head nodding without nystagmus in SN (Norton and Cogan, 1954). Nothing is known about the relationship between head posturing and either the nystagmus of SN or visual acuity in SN.

PERIODIC ALTERNATING NYSTAGMUS/PERIODIC ALTERNATING GAZE DEVIATION

Periodic alternating nystagmus (PAN) is a jerk nystagmus that may be either acquired or congenital. It changes direction periodically (or aperiodically if CN) and may include neutral periods during which either no nystagmus or pendular nystagmus is present. Periodic alternating gaze deviation (PAGD) is a condition in which the eyes alternately and conjugately deviate to either side.   PAGD has been observed in a patient who previously had PAN with the same periodicity; they are assumed to be related (Kennard, and colleagues, 1981).

The mechanism of PAN has been linked to a periodic shifting of the nystagmus neutral region and to the optokinetic-vestibular system (Daroff and Dell'Osso, 1974; Leigh, and colleagues, 1981). In both PAN and PAGD cases, there may be a periodic head turning that is in counterphase with the eye oscillations or deviations. It appears that the purpose of this deliberate slow head turning is to keep the region of minimal PAN straight ahead or, in the case of PAGD, to facilitate fixation of targets in primary position.

ACQUIRED DOWNBEAT NYSTAGMUS

Acquired downbeat nystagmus is a jerk nystagmus with slow phases that may be linear, accelerating or decelerating (Abel, and colleagues, 1983). As is the case in horizontal nystagmus, downbeat nystagmus may vary in intensity with vertical gaze.   This can result in the adoption of a chin-up or chin-down head posture by the patient. By minimizing the nystagmus with such a head posture, oscillopsia is reduced and acuity improved. Prisms (bases up or down) can be used to accomplish the desired vertical gaze angle and increased acuity without the head posture.

Downbeat nystagmus may be induced or enhanced by static tilts in the planes of pitch and roll or the supine position (Baloh and Spooner, 1981; Chambers, and colleagues, 1983; Halmagyi, and colleagues, 1983).

ACQUIRED HEAD OSCILLATIONS

In addition to head oscillations associated with nystagmus, there exist conditions that produce such oscillations in the absence of ocular motor instability. Whereas a non-saccadic oscillation of the eyes is designated nystagmus, a similar oscillation of the head is usually called "tremor." The latter are quite commonly encountered with the most common etiologies being parkinsonism, cerebellar disease, and idiopathic movement disorder designated "benign essential tremor." In the past, many types of head tremor have been called head-nystagmus (Kopfnystagmus) (Klestadt, 1936). When head-nystagmus was a commonly used term, labyrinthine fistula was among the most common etiologies (Stscheglow, 1929) and if the term is to retain any contemporary use, it probably should be limited to the rare head oscillation, accompanying ocular nystagmus, secondary to fistula symptomatology.

The concept of head-nystagmus was said to derive from experiments of pigeons where vestibular stimulation provoked rhythimic movements of the head and only minimal ocular nystagmus (Mygind, 1921). With phylogenetic advancement, the head movements became less and the eye movements predominated. Ontogeny seems to be in parallel since rotational stimulation is much more likely to produce post-rotational head movements in human infants than in children or adults (Mygind, 1921). Nevertheless, pendular movements of the head are observed following both rotation and intense optokinetic stimulation in adults (Schmidt and Schmidt, 1978). Indeed, these authors demonstrated regular electromyographic activity in neck muscles, despite the absence of gross head movement, during routine optokinetic stimulation. This "secondary" nuchal activity associated with ocular nystagmus undoubtedly involves pathways and mechanisms that underlie the spontaneous head oscillations in CN.

ACKNOWLEDGEMENTS

This work was supported in part by the Veterans Administration. The authors are grateful for the editorial assistance of Ms. Lorna Westbrook.

REFERENCES

Abel, L.A., S. Traccis, L.F. Dell'Osso, and C.F. Ansevin (1983). Variable waveforms in downbeat nystagmus imply short-term gain changes. Ann Neurol, 13, 616-620.

Baloh, R.W., and J.W. Spooner (1981). Downbeat nystagmus: a type of central vestibular nystagmus. Neurology, 31, 304-310.

Carl, J.R., L.M. Optican, F.C. Chu, and D.S. Zee (1985). Head shaking and vestibulo-ocular reflex in congenital nystagmus. Invest Ophthalmol Vis Sci, 26, 1043-1050.

Chambers, B.R., J.J. Ell, and M.A. Gresty (1983). Case of downbeat nystagmus influenced by otolith stimulation. Ann Neurol, 13, 204-207.

Cogan, D.G. (1967). Congenital nystagmus. Can J Ophthalmol, 2, 4-10.

Daroff, R.B., and L.F. Dell'Osso (1974). Periodic alternating nystagmus and the shifting null. Canad J Otolaryngol, 3, 367-371.

Daroff, R.B., B.T. Troost, and L.F. Dell'Osso Nystagmus and related oscillations. In T. Duane (Ed.), Clinical Ophthalmology, Vol. II.. Harper and Row, Hagerstown Maryland, 1-25, 1978.

Dell'Osso, L.F. (1973). Fixation characteristics in hereditary congenital nystagmus. Amer J Optom Arch Amer Acad Optom, 50, 85-90.

Dell'Osso, L.F. (1984). Nystagmus and other ocular motor oscillations and intrusions. In S. Lessell and J.T.W. Van Dalen (Eds.), Neuro-Ophthalmology - 1984 Vol. III. Excerpta Medica, Amsterdam, 157-204.

Dell'Osso, L.F., and R.B. Daroff (1975). Congenital nystagmus waveforms and
    foveation strategy. Doc Ophthalmol, 39, 155–182.
Dell'Osso, L.F., C. Ellenberger Jr, L.A. Abel, and J.T. Flynn (1983). The
    nystagmus blockage syndrome: congenital nystagmus, manifest latent
    nystagmus or both?. Invest Ophthalmol Vis Sci, 24, 1580–1587.
Dell'Osso, L.F., D. Schmidt, and R.B. Daroff (1979). Latent, manifest latent and
    congenital nystagmus. Arch Ophthalmol, 97, 1877–1885.
Fujiyama, Y., H. Ozawa, and S. Ishikawa (1983). Study on abnormal head position
    in patients with congenital nystagmus. Agressologie, 24, 231–232.
Gresty, M.A., H.J. Barratt, N.G. Page, and J.J. Ell (1985). Assessment of
    vestibulo-ocular reflexes in congenital nystagmus. Ann Neurol, 17, 129–136.
Gresty, M.A., and J.J. Ell (1981). Spasmus nutans or congenital nystagmus?
    Classification according to objective criteria. Brit J Ophthalmol, 65,
    510–511.
Gresty, M.A., and G.M. Halmagyi (1981). Head nodding associated with idiopathic
    childhood nystagmus. In B. Cohen (Ed.), Vestibular and Oculomotor
    Physiology: International Meeting of the Bárány Society. New York Academy
    of Sciences, New York, 614–618.
Gresty, M.A., G.M. Halmagyi, and J. Leech (1978). The relationship between head
    and eye movement in congenital nystagmus with head shaking: objective
    recordings of a single case. Brit J Ophthalmol, 62, 533–535.
Gresty, M.A., J. Leech, M.D. Sanders, and H. Eggars (1976). A study of head and
    eye movement in spasmus nutans. Brit J Ophthalmol, 160, 652–654.
Gresty, M.A., N.G. Page, and H.J. Barratt (1984). The differential diagnosis of
    congenital nystagmus. J Neurol Neurosurg Psychiat, 47, 936–942.
Halmagyi, G.M., P. Rudge, M.A. Gresty, and M.D. Sanders (1983). Downbeating
    nystagmus: A review of 62 cases. Arch Neurol, 40, 777–784.
Kennard, C., G. Barger, and W.F. Hoyt (1981). The association of periodic
    alternating nystagmus with periodic alternating gaze. J Clin Neuro-
    ophthalmol, 1, 191–193.
Klestadt, W. (1936). Nystagmen und Deviationen des Kopfes. In O. Bumke and O.
    Foerster (Eds.), Handbuch der Neurologie, Vol. 4, Allgemeine Neurologie IV.
    Verlag von Julius Springer, Berlin, 608–610.
Leigh, R.J., D.A. Robinson, and D.S. Zee (1981). A hypothetical explanation for
    periodic alternating nystagmus: instability in the optokinetic-vestibular
    system . Ann NY Acad Sci, 374, 619–635.
Metz, H.S., A. Jampolsky, and D.M. O'Meara (1972). Congenital ocular nystagmus
    and nystagmoid head movements. Amer J Ophthalmol, 74, 1131–1133.
Mygind, S.H. (1921). Head-nystagmus in human beings. J Laryngol Otol, 36, 72–
    78.
Norton, E.W.D., and D.G. Cogan (1954). Spasmus nutans: A clinical study of
    twenty cases followed two years or more since onset. Arch Ophthalmol, 52,
    442–446.
Schmidt, D., and C.L. Schmidt (1978). Optokinetischer und vestibulärer
    Kopfnystagmus: Untersuchungem von Normalpersonen und Patienten mit
    angeborenen und erworbenen Augenbewegungsstörungen. In G. Kommerell (Ed.),
    Augenbevegungsstörungen Neurophysiologie und Klinik, Symposion der Deutschen
    Ophthalmologischen Gesellschaft. Bergmann-Verlag, Munchen W. Germany, 301–
    305.
Stscheglow, F. (1929). Ein Beitrag zur Frage über den Kopfnystagmus. Arch
    Ohren- Nasen- Kehlkopfheilk, 121, 291–298.
Taylor, D. (1980). Disorders of head and eye movements in children. Trans
    Ophthal Soc UK, 100, 489–494.

Spasmus Nutans: A Quantitative, Prospective Study

B. M. Weissman*,****, L. F. Dell'Osso*,***,
L. A. Abel*,*** and R. J. Leigh*,**,***

Ocular Motor Neurophysiology Laboratory* and Neurology
Service**, Veterans Administration Medical Center; and the
Departments of Neurology*** and Pediatrics****, Case Western
Reserve University and University Hospitals, Cleveland,
Ohio, USA

INTRODUCTION

Nystagmus in infancy may be due to a variety of disorders. The differential diagnosis includes congenital nystagmus (CN), latent/manifest latent nystagmus (LMLN), nystagmus in association with optic nerve glioma and spasmus nutans. Once optic glioma is excluded, SN may be suspected from anomalous head movement and disconjugte oscillations, but, at present, only follow-up will confirm whether a child has CN or SN.

We have prospectively conducted a study of the ocular oscillations in infants with the presumptive diagnosis of spasmus nutans with the objective of identifying features characteristic of SN early in its course.

METHODS

None of the infants in the study group showed signs of neurologic deficit, diminished visual acuity, strabismus, optic nerve abnormality or ocular pathology. When possible, the infants and children were videotaped before the oculographic recording session. Movements of both eyes were recorded using infrared or DC, electro-oculographic (EOG) techniques. The total system bandwidth (position and velocity) was 0-100 Hz. Although absolute amplitude calibration was not possible, these methodologies allowed accurate measurement of ocular oscillation waveforms. In addition, by equalizing records during saccades, it was possible to judge the relative waveform amplitude in each eye. For most of the recording sessions, eye velocity was also obtained for more accurate delineation of the waveforms.

RESULTS

The mean age of onset was four months with a range of birth to fourteen months. Four of the five exhibited head nodding or tilting in addition to the ocular oscillations. One of the children demonstrated a resolution of his ocular oscillations ten months after their onset, thereby confirming the diagnosis of spasmus nutans. He had no definite history of abnormal head movement. One infant showed no ocular oscillations on the video record although there was occasional head nodding. However, persistence of her nystagmus was evident in the eye movement records.

Table 1 summarizes the nystagmus characteristics. All infants demonstated a pendular waveform both in the initial and follow-up records. The frequency of the ocular oscillations ranged from 3 to 9 Hz. Most patients showed a range of frequencies within one recording session. All of the patients exhibited an asymmetry of the amplitudes of the oscillations in the two eyes. Two patients showed periods of asymmetry and symmetry during a single recording session. Three patients exhibited phase differences ranging between 0 and 180 degrees. In two, the phase difference variablity was in a narrower range, remaining between 120 and 180 degrees. A mean and standard deviation analysis of approximately ten measured cycles from each record underscore this variablity. One infant, R.W., first showed only in-phase oscillations; at a subsequent recording session seven months later, the phase relationships between the waveforms in each eye varied from 0 through 180 degrees.

TABLE 1   Characteristics of Spasmus Nutans

name date	wave- form	frequency	relative amplitude	phase relations	conjugacy
M.L. 1/83	P	3 Hz	R>L =	range: 0 - 180 m: 135.5 sd: 52.9	-1 0,-2
5/85	P	3 - 5 Hz	R>L =	range: 0 - 180 m: 78.7 sd: 61	+1 0,-1 -2,+2
J.H. 1/84	P	4 - 6 Hz	R>L,=	range: 0 - 180 m: 129.7 sd: 73.4	-1,-2 +1,+2 0
5/85			(No ocular oscillations present)		
R.W. 10/84	P	7 - 9 Hz	R>L	range: 0	+1
6/85	P	6 - 7 Hz	L>R	range: 0 - 180 m: 89.6 sd: 70.5	+1,-1
S.T. 2/85	P	6 Hz	L>R	range: 120 - 180 m: 142.1 sd: 22.2	-1
C.D. 4/85	P	5 - 6 Hz	L>R	range: 0 - 180 m: 104.3 sd: 63.7	-1 +1

P - pendular, R - right, L - left, m - mean, sd - standard deviation. Conjugacy scale: +2 - equal amplitudes, in phase; +1 - unequal amplitudes, in phase; 0 - uniocular; -1 - unequal amplitudes, out of phase; -2 - equal amplitudes, out of phase. Amplitudes and conjugacies listed in order of descending incidence.

The conjugacy scale facillates comparison between patients since it indicates both relative amplitudes and phase difference of the oscillation of the two eyes. The terms "in phase" and "out of phase" indicate phase differences of 0 - 90 and 90 - 180 degrees, respectively. Thus, the predominant conjugacy number (shown on the first line of each recording session) corresponds to the mean value of that patient's phase relationship and most common relative amplitude.

Eye movement recordings documented the transient nature of the phase relationship
between the ocsillations of the two eyes. Figure 1 shows both eyes at three
closely spaced·times in a single recording session for one patient. The SN
varied from in phase to 180 degrees out of phase within 2 seconds; the uniocular
portion preceded this by 90 seconds. True uniocular oscillation was recorded in
only three of the seven patients.

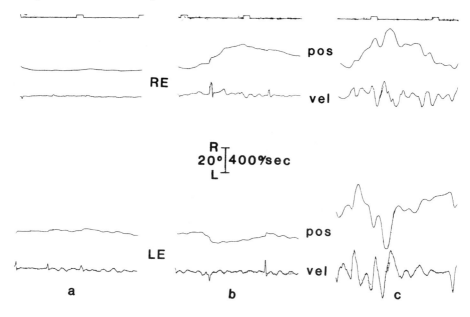

Fig. 1. Examples of spasmus nutans with the following
relative amplitudes: a) uniocular oscillation of the LE; b)
binocular oscillation with no phase difference; and c)
binocular oscillation with 180 degree phase difference. R –
right, L – left, RE – right eye, LE – left eye, pos –
position, vel – velocity and, the timing marks represent 1
second intervals.

In one patient, the vestibulo-ocular reflex was stimulated by quasi-sinusoidal
passive movement of the infant's head in the horizontal plane. This manipulation
did not suppress his ocular oscillations. Active head movement in relation to the
ocular oscillations was not evaluated.

DISCUSSION

Spasmus nutans is a benign, self-limiting condition which should be
differentiated from other diseases of infancy that have significant morbidity and
potential mortality. Several reports describe cases in which infants presented
with pendular and often asymmetric nystagmus initially diagnosed as spasmus
nutans (Albright, and colleagues, 1984; Antony, and colleagues, 1980; Kelly,
1970; Koenig, and colleagues, 1982; Lavery, and colleagues, 1984). These infants
were later found to have optic nerve and intracranial gliomas. An important
clinical feature in all of these patients was the presence of optic nerve
atrophy. Some of the patients exhibited other associated clinical findings such
as diencephalic syndrome and evidence of increased intracranial pressure. This
is the first study, to date, which both clinically and oculographically evaluates

infants carrying the SN diagnosis and quantitatively documents eye movement recordings in a patient whose acquired pendular nystagmus subsequently resolved.

Congenital nystagmus is an ocular oscillation which may be first noted during infancy. The diagnostic distinction between CN, LMLN and spasmus nutans is important. Congenital nystagmus and LMLN are associated with life-long impairment of visual acuity; the CN patient's siblings and children may be similarly affected. Thus, it is important to differentiate congenital nystagmus from spasmus nutans as early as possible.

Gresty, and colleagues (1976) and Gresty and Ell (1981) described three patients who exhibited a distinct pattern of eye/head coordination. All carried a tentative diagnosis of spasmus nutans; head shaking modified their nystagmus so that vision improved. However, all were older children (> three years of age) and follow-up was not obtained. Suppression of nystagmus occurred with both active and passive head shaking. Gresty and colleagues interpreted this adaptive suppression of nystagmus as due to vestibular stimulation. In one of our patients, J.H., we passively horizontally rotated the infant's head and observed no modification of the nystagmus. Our patient had no clear history of anomalous head movement whereas all of Gresty's patients did. This patient's nystagmus subsequently resolved.

Analysis of the waveforms revealed that within a single recording session, both the frequency of the oscillations and the interocular phase relationships may vary considerably, even from second to second. In two patients, variablity in the relative amplitude and waveform characteristics was noted not only during one recording session, but also in different sessions. We were unable to detect abnormal eye or head movements in a video-tape record of the one infant whose SN had clinically resolved; the eye movement recordings clearly showed ocular oscillations.

The etiology of this transient condition of infancy and early childhood still remains to be determined. Earlier reports considered the pathogenesis of this disorder related to diverse causes which included light deprivation, dietary factors, season, epilepsy, and poor socio-economic conditions (Kalyanaraman, and colleagues, 1973; Østerberg, 1937). However, the report of SN in twins points to the importance of genetic factors (Hoyt and Aicardi, 1979; Katzman, and colleagues, 1981).

Quantitative oculography has made analysis of the dynamic characteristics of eye movements possible. For acquired pendular nystagmus in adults, Gresty, and colleagues (1982) suggested a defect with yoking between vertical, horizontal and torsional ocular motor systems. The disconjugate nature of the nystagmus suggests a yoking abnormality. In infants with SN, the abnormality may not represent a static anatomic lesion of the yoking system but, instead, an aberrant development of the connections associated with it; subsequent modification of these may account for the transient nature of the nystagmus and its variability.

One ocular motor system we considered as possibly contributing to development of spasmus nutans is the vergence system. The vergence system, in adults, can be made to oscillate at a mean of 2.5 Hz (Zuber and Stark, 1968). It would be difficult for such a system to account for the rapid (e.g., 11 Hz) ocular oscillations observed with spasmus nutans, but could account for the low frequency oscillations. Moreover, none of the infants we examined showed signs of a strabismus that might indicate an abnormality of the vergence mechanism.

The saccadic system is another ocular motor control system that may account for the development of SN. Zee and Robinson (1979) previously described and modelled saccadic oscillations. Both their patient and model simulation showed high frequency oscillations. A similar instability of this system may result in the observed rapid ocular oscillations seen in SN. However, all of the SN patients we examined made normal saccades.

The pursuit system can also exhibit oscillatory behavior. Recent work by Optican, and colleagues (1985) evaluated the adaptation of the pursuit system in adult patients with monocular ocular motor palsies. They observed 3 Hz ocular oscillations associated with pursuit under conditions causing high pursuit gain. However, this low-frequency oscillation cannot account for the higher frequency waveforms seen in SN.

Spasmus nutans is a still perplexing self-limiting affliction of infancy and early childhood. Future studies should help elucidate the neural substrate of this disorder. This knowledge will help us use recording for early discrimination between spasmus nutans and other ocular oscillations.

ACKNOWLEDGEMENTS

This work was supported in part by the Veterans Administration.

REFERENCES

Albright, A.L., R.J. Sclabassi, T.L. Slamovits, and I. Bergman (1984). Spasmus nutans associated with optic gliomas in infants. J. Pediat., 105, 778-780.
Antony, J.H., R.A. Ouvrier, and G. Wise (1980). Spasmus nutans. A mistaken identity. Arch. Neurol., 37, 373-375.
Gresty, M.A., and J.J. Ell (1981). Spasmus nutans or congenital nystagmus? Classification according to objective criteria. Brit. J. Ophthalmol., 65, 510-511.
Gresty, M.A., J.J. Ell, and L.J. Findley (1982). Acquired pendular nystagmus: its characteristics, localising value and pathophysiology. J. Neurol. Neurosurg. Psychiat., 45, 431-439.
Gresty, M.A., J. Leech, M.D. Sanders, and H. Eggars (1976). A study of head and eye movement in spasmus nutans. Brit. J. Ophthalmol., 160, 652-654.
Hoyt, C.S., and E. Aicardi (1979). Acquired monocular nystagmous in monozygous twins. J. Pediat. Ophthalmol. Strab., 16, 115-118.
Kalyanaraman, K., K. Jagannathan, R.A. Ramanujam, and B. Ramamurthi (1973). Congenital head nodding and nystagmus with cerebrocerebellar degeneration. J. Pediat., 83, 1023-1026.
Katzman, B., L.W. Lu, and R.P. Tiwari (1981). Spasmus nutans in identical twins. Ann. Ophthalmol., 13, 1193-1195.
Kelly, T.W. (1970). Optic glioma presenting as spasmus nutans. Pediat., 45, 295-296.
Koenig, S.B., T.P. Naidid, and Z. Zaparackas (1982). Optic glioma masquarading as spasmus nutans. J. Pediat. Ophthamol. Strab., 19, 20-24.
Lavery, M.A., J.F. O'Neill, F.C. Chu, and L.J. Martyn (1984). Acquired nystagmus in early childhood: a presenting sign of intracranial tumor. Ophthalmol., 91, 425-435.
Østerberg, G. (1937). On spasmus nutans. Acta Ophthalmol., 15, 457-467.
Optican, L.M., D.S. Zee, and F.C. Chu (1985). Adaptive response to ocular muscle weakness in human pursuit and saccadic eye movements. J. Neurophysiol., 54, 110-122.
Zee, D.S., and D.A. Robinson (1979). A hypothetical explanation of saccadic oscillations. Ann. Neurol., 5, 405-414.
Zuber, B.L., and L. Stark (1968). Dynamical characteristics of the fusional vergence eye-movement system. IEEE Trans. Sys. Sci. Cybernet., SCC-4, 72-79.

Motion Perception in Congenital Nystagmus

G. Kommerell, R. Horn, and M. Bach

University Eye Hospital, D 7800 Freiburg, FRG

ABSTRACT

Ten patients with congenital nystagmus (CN) were asked to estimate velocities of a horizontally moving full-field striped pattern. At first, a standard stimulus ("modulus") of 40°/s was given; then, velocities between 15 and 100°/s, presented in random order, had to be estimated relative to the modulus. With stimulus durations of 0.5, 0.2, or 0.1 s, patients were clearly able to distinguish velocities in the range between 15 and 100°/s, although less precisely than normal controls.- The results indicate that the lack of optokinetic responses typically encountered in patients with CN is not due to a sensory defect in the retino-striate pathway.

INTRODUCTION

It is well-known that patients with CN, stimulated by moving contours, do not respond with an optokinetic nystagmus (OKN) (Abadi et al., 1982; Abadi and Dickinson, 1985; Halmagyi et al., 1980; Jung and Kornhuber, 1964; Yee et al., 1980). This implies a defect of the feedback system that controls shift of the image across the retina. According to a recently advanced hypothesis (Kommerell and Mehdorn, 1982), this lack of shift control might be the basic abnormality underlying the development of CN. The question arises if the lack of shift control might be due to a sensory defect. As patients with CN do not usually complain of difficulties in motion perception, we regarded a sensory defect to be unlikely, but quantitative data were lacking. We wanted to know how well patients with CN can estimate velocities of moving contours that would elicit OKN in a normal subject. To investigate this question, we used Stevens' (1957) magnitude estimation technique. This method has already been employed for the investigation of motion perception in normal subjects (Körner and Dichgans, 1967; Dichgans et al., 1969).

METHODS

Subjects were seated in the center of a rotating drum (diameter 1.5 m). Seven degree wide black and white stripes were painted vertically inside the drum. The stripes were illuminated only for fractions of a second by opening a shutter that occluded an electric light source in a box. In the intervals, subjects were in complete darkness. The light source and a ventilator that cooled the box were operated from an auto battery. The light coming out of the box was diffused by reflection on a white sheet of paper so that the subjects' entire visual field was illuminated (Fig. 1). The luminance of the white stripes was 1.9 cd/m^2, and of the black stripes 0.15 cd/m^2. Some of the subjects wore their glasses to get a clear image of the stimulus. Spectacle frames appeared to be of no influence on the velocity estimates, as indicated by a test performed in one of the normal control subjects. There were no other stable contours in the stimulus field that could have provided a clue about relative velocity of the stripes (shearing phenomenon), apart from the egocentric velocity.

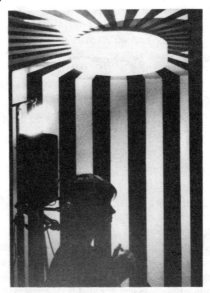

Fig. 1. Experimental set-up photographed with the same light source that was used for the experiments.

Sessions with stimulus durations of 0.5, 0.2, and 0.1 s were performed. Before each session, a standard stimulus ("modulus") of 40°/s was applied three times, and subjects were instructed to call this stimulus "40". Afterwards, stimulus velocities of 15, 20, 25, 30, 40, 50, 60, 70, 80, 90, and 100°/s were presented in a pseudo-random order, so that each velocity appeared once.

Subjects were asked to rate each velocity in relation to the modulus on a linear scale. The modulus was repeated after the first five stimulus presentations. About every 10 s, subjects were given a signal (by briefly switching on a dim diode inside the drum) to release the shutter by pushing a button as soon as they felt ready for the next stimulus. The direction in which the stripes were moved was either right to left or left to right, but was kept constant in each individual subject.

To avoid acoustic clues from the rotating drum, subjects wore earphones that transmitted classic or pop music, according to their preference. Cushions were placed on the chair and under the subjects' feet to shield them from the slight vibrations produced by the drum motor. These measures ensured that subjects could use only visual information to estimate drum velocity.

Eye movements were recorded by electro-oculography (frequency range 0 to 20 Hz). The duration of the stimulus exposure was recorded by an electrical signal derived from the shutter.

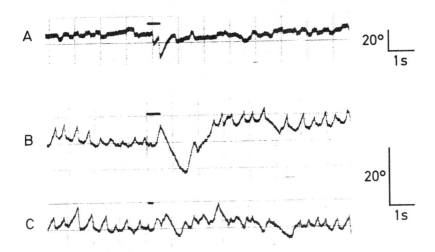

Fig. 2. Electro-oculograms obtained during test sessions.
The periods of stimulation are indicated as horizontal bars. Stripes were moved to the right in all
three examples. (A): normal subject, 0.5 s, 50°/s.
(B): CN patient, 0.5 s, 90°/s. Immediately after the
rightward stimulus, the eyes drifted to the left in
an extended slow phase ("Inversion"); this occurred
repeatedly when the patient was stimulated over
0.5 s. (C): same CN patient as in (B), 0.2 s, 50°/s.

Ten cooperative patients with typical CN were used. Three patients had strabismus, in one of them being associated with oculocutaneous albinism. The other seven patients had binocular stereopsis and no other eye abnormality except horizontal CN. Visual acuities ranged from 0.2 to 1.2, with an average of 0.4. On electro-oculography, patients showed one or several of the CN waveforms as defined by Dell'Osso and Daroff (1975). Optokinetic nystagmus was absent or inverted on horizontal, but present on vertical stimulation.- Six normal subjects were used as controls.

RESULTS

Fig. 2 shows the eye movement records of a normal subject and of a patient with CN when stimulated for periods of 0.5 s and 0.2 s. Normal subjects responded with optokinetic nystagmus and afternystagmus. Even if stimulus durations shorter than the latency period of the OKN were applied, an afternystagmus appeared quite frequently, as described earlier (Kommerell and Thiele, 1970). In patients with CN, the nystagmus waveform that had been present before releasing the shutter usually prevailed during and after stimulation, but occasionally, extended slow phases in the direction opposite to the preceding stimulus ensued (Fig. 2 B).

The velocity estimates of all normal subjects and CN patients are summarized in Fig. 3. The individual estimates contained in Fig. 3 were scattered over a wide range, as indicated by the standard deviation, but the grand averages clearly show that normal subjects and CN patients could differentiate velocities in the range between 15 and 100°/s. However, the coefficient of determination (r^2) between stimulus and estimated velocity, as shown in the individual panels of Fig. 3, was lower in CN patients than in normal subjects. With a stimulus duration of 0.1 s, for instance, the coefficient of determination was only 0.36 in CN patients; this means that only 36% of the response variance was accounted for by the stimulus variance. The U-test of Wilcoxon, Mann and Whitney (Sachs, 1984) confirmed, for all three exposure times, a significant difference between patients and normal subjects at the 5% level.

DISCUSSION

We have demonstrated that patients with CN can differentiate velocities in the range between 15 and 100 °/s. This indicates that the lack of optokinetic responses typically encountered in patients with CN cannot be due to a defect in their sensory, retino-striate pathway; rather, the defect must be sought somewhere between the sensory and the motor apparatus.

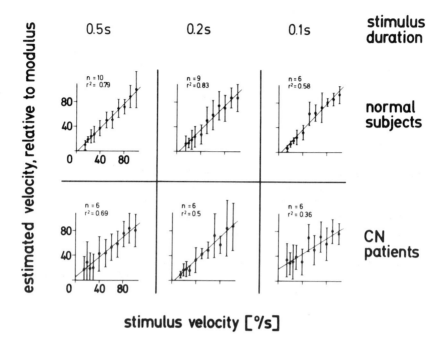

Fig. 3. Compound diagram of velocity estimates obtained from normal subjects (top) and CN patients (bottom). Stimulus durations decrease from the left to the right panel. The responses of all subjects belonging to the respective group were averaged. The vertical lines show the standard deviations, the oblique lines represent the regressions. The coefficient of determination (r^2) between estimated velocity (relative to the modulus) and stimulus velocity (before averaging) is indicated in each panel.

The way in which CN patients manage to estimate object velocities in the presence of oscillating eyes is not yet clear. There are at least two alternatives. Firstly, CN patients could be taking account of eye position at all times during their nystagmus cycle, for instance by an efference copy. Secondly, they could estimate object velocity on the basis of the average eye velocity over a certain period of time. It appears tenable that some CN patients use average eye and retinal slip velocities during one nystagmus cycle as the minimum reference for estimating object velocity. However, some of our patients with cycles as long as 0.5 s were still able to give a good estimate when stimuli were presented for only 0.2 s, i.e., during a fraction of their cycle.

If one wanted to find out whether the precision of velocity estimation depends on the time window in which the stimulus is presented relative to the nystagmus cycle it might be useful to synchronize the stimulus with certain parts of the waveform by using eye velocity as a trigger.

Movement perception is closely related to the localization of stationary visual objects. Patients with CN do not usually see illusionary movements. How do they prevent oscillopsia? If CN patients took account of their eye position at any moment during the nystagmus cycle, and subtracted it from the position of the retinal image, they should see an afterimage oscillate, exactly corresponding to their nystagmus. However, we recently confirmed vom Hofe's (1941) finding that this is not the case. In our series of seven CN patients, two did not see any oscillation of the afterimage in darkness, and the other five reported an oscillation of the afterimage of only about half the nystagmus amplitude (Kommerell, in press). Even more surprising is the report of Goddé-Jolly and Larmande (1973) about three exceptional CN patients who, when looking simultaneously at an afterimage and a real fixation object, saw neither of them oscillate.

These observations suggest that CN patients may be adapted to their impediment by a reduced sensitivity against shift of the retinal image (as also observed in acquired downbeat nystagmus; Büchele et al., 1983). This assumption would also explain the reduced precision in velocity estimation, as found in our investigation. Nevertheless, at least some CN patients appear to be able to use the difference between eye velocity and shift velocity of the retinal image very effectively to estimate object velocity.

REFERENCES

Abadi, R.V., C.M. Dickinson, and M.S. Lomas (1982). Inverted and asymmetrical optokinetic nystagmus. In Lennerstrand, G., D.S. Zee, and E.L. Keller (Eds.), Functional Basis of Ocular Motility Disorders, Pergamon Press, Oxford. pp. 143-146.
Abadi, R.V., and C.M. Dickinson (1985). The influence of preexisting oscillations on the binocular optokinetic response. Ann. Neurol., 17, 578-586.
Büchele, W., T. Brandt, and D. Degner (1983). Ataxia and oscillopsia in downbeat-nystagmus vertigo syndrome. Adv. Oto-Rhino-Laryng., 30, 291-297.

Dell'Osso, L.F., and R.B. Daroff (1975). Congenital nystagmus. Waveforms and foveation strategy. Doc. Ophthalmol., 39, 155-182.

Dichgans, J., F. Körner, and K. Voigt (1969). Vergleichende Skalierung des afferenten und efferenten Bewegungssehens beim Menschen: Lineare Funktionen mit verschiedener Anstiegssteilheit. Psychol. Forsch., 32, 277-295.

Goddé-Jolly, D., and A. Larmande (1973). Les Nystagmus. Masson, Paris, p. 363.

Halmagyi, G.M., M.A. Gresty, and J. Leech (1980). Reversed optokinetic nystagmus (OKN), mechanism and clinical significance. Ann. Neurol., 7, 429-435.

vom Hofe, K. (1941). Untersuchungen über das Verhalten eines zentralen optischen Nachbildes bei und nach unwillkürlichen Bewegungen sowie mechanischen Verlagerungen des Auges. Graefes Arch. Ophthalmol., 144, 164-169.

Jung, R., and H.H. Kornhuber (1964). Results of electronystagmography in man: The value of optokinetic, vestibular, and spontaneous nystagmus for neurologic diagnosis and research. In M.B. Bender (Ed.), The Oculomotor System, Harper and Row, New York, pp. 428-482.

Kommerell, G., and H. Thiele (1970). Der optokinetische Kurzreiznystagmus. Albrecht v. Graefes Arch. klin. exp. Ophthalmol., 179, 220-234.

Kommerell, G., and E. Mehdorn (1982). Is an optokinetic defect the cause of congenital nystagmus? In G. Lennerstrand, D.S. Zee, and E.L. Keller (Eds.), Functional Basis of Ocular Motility Disorders, Pergamon Press, Oxford. pp. 159-167.

Kommerell, G. (in press). Congenital nystagmus: Control of slow tracking movements by target offset from the fovea. Albrecht v. Graefe's Arch. klin. exp. Ophthalmol.

Körner, F., and J. Dichgans (1967). Bewegungswahrnehmung, optokinetischer Nystagmus und retinale Bildwanderung. Albrecht v. Graefes Arch. klin. exp. Ophthalmol., 174, 34-48.

Sachs, L. (1984). Angewandte Statistik, 6. Auflage. Springer, Berlin.

Stevens, S.S. (1957). On the psychophysical law. Psychol. Rev., 64, 153-184.

Yee, R.D., R.W. Baloh, and V. Honrubia (1980). Study of congenital nystagmus: Optokinetic nystagmus. Brit. J. Ophthalmol., 64, 926-932.

ACKNOWLEDGEMENT

This investigation was supported by the Deutsche Forschungsgemeinschaft, SFB 70, B4.

Index